THE BOOK

Volvo 400 Series
Service and Repair Manual

AK Legg LAE MIMI

Models covered

(1691 - 312 - 9AC4)

Volvo 440, 460 and 480 models, including Turbo and special/limited editions
1.6 litre (1596 cc), 1.7 litre (1721 cc), 1.8 litre (1794 cc) and 2.0 litre (1998 cc) petrol engines

Does not cover diesel engine

© Haynes Publishing 1999

A book in the **Haynes Service and Repair Manual Series**

ABCDE
FGHIJ
KLMNO
PQRST
2

ISBN 1 85960 565 6

British Library Cataloguing in Publication Data
A catalogue record for this book is available from the British Library.

Printed in the USA

Haynes Publishing
Sparkford, Yeovil, Somerset BA22 7JJ, England

Haynes North America, Inc
861 Lawrence Drive, Newbury Park, California 91320, USA

Editions Haynes
4, Rue de l'Abreuvoir
92415 COURBEVOIE CEDEX, France

Haynes Publishing Nordiska AB
Box 1504, 751 45 UPPSALA, Sweden

Contents

Contents

REPAIRS & OVERHAUL

Engine and associated systems

Transmission

Brakes and suspension

Body equipment

Wiring diagrams

REFERENCE

Index

The first of the Dutch-built front-wheel-drive Volvo 400 series models, the 3-door 480 Coupe, was unveiled in the UK in June 1987. The 5-door 440 Hatchback and the 4-door 460 Saloon appeared in April 1989 and April 1990 respectively. Originally only available with a 1.7 litre engine, a 1.8 litre unit was offered on the 440 and 460 from October 1991, and an entry-level 1.6 litre engine was offered on 440 models from February 1992. Finally, a 2.0 litre engine became available across the range from September 1992.

Volvo 480 ES (1987)

The 440 and 460 models received a minor facelift for 1994 model year (October 1993), with the radiator grille being incorporated into the bonnet, and minor changes to the interior switchgear.

All engines covered by this manual are of overhead camshaft type, incorporating an aluminium cylinder head and cast-iron cylinder block, with the cylinders bored directly into the block. The camshaft is driven by a toothed belt from the crankshaft. Carburettor and fuel-injection models are available, with power units ranging from the regular carburettor engine to the multipoint fuel-injected turbo-intercooler engine. A three-way catalytic converter was fitted to all models as standard from September 1990 onwards.

In keeping with the Volvo reputation for safety, the body incorporates a tough steel cage for the passenger compartment, which is further protected by crumple zones at the front and rear. The side doors on models from October 1993 onwards have high-strength steel intrusion bars built into them. A driver's airbag and front seat belt tensioners were also fitted from October 1993 onwards.

A wide range of standard and optional equipment is available within the range to suit most tastes, including central locking and electric windows; ABS and air conditioning were available as options.

Provided that regular servicing is carried out in accordance with the manufacturer's recommendations, the Volvo 400 should prove a reliable and economical car. The engine compartment is well-designed, and most of the items needing frequent attention are easily accessible.

Your Volvo 400 manual

The aim of this manual is to help you get the best value from your vehicle. It can do so in several ways. It can help you decide what work must be done (even should you choose to get it done by a garage). It will also provide information on routine maintenance and servicing, and give a logical course of action and diagnosis when random faults occur. However, it is hoped that you will use the manual by tackling the work yourself. On simpler jobs it may even be quicker than booking the car into a garage and going there twice, to leave and collect it. Perhaps most important, a lot of money can be saved by avoiding the costs a garage must charge to cover its labour and overheads.

The manual has drawings and descriptions to show the function of the various components so that their layout can be understood. Tasks are described and photographed in a clear step-by-step sequence. The illustrations are numbered by the Section number and paragraph number to which they relate - if there is more than one illustration per paragraph, the sequence is denoted alphabetically.

References to the 'left' or 'right' of the vehicle are in the sense of a person in the driver's seat, facing forwards.

Volvo 460 SE (1994)

Acknowledgements

Thanks are due to Champion Spark Plug, who supplied the illustrations showing spark plug conditions, and to Duckhams Oils, who provided lubrication data. Certain other illustrations are the copyright of AB Volvo, and are used with their permission. Thanks are also due to Draper Tools Ltd, who supplied some of the workshop tools, and to all the staff at Sparkford who assisted in the production of this manual, especially Christine Smith, whose car was used for some of the photographic work.

We take great pride in the accuracy of information given in this manual, but vehicle manufacturers make alterations and design changes during the production run of a particular vehicle of which they do not inform us. No liability can be accepted by the authors or publishers for loss, damage or injury caused by any errors in, or omissions from, the information given.

Volvo 440 GLE (1990)

Working on your car can be dangerous. This page shows just some of the potential risks and hazards, with the aim of creating a safety-conscious attitude.

General hazards

Scalding

• Don't remove the radiator or expansion tank cap while the engine is hot.
• Engine oil, automatic transmission fluid or power steering fluid may also be dangerously hot if the engine has recently been running.

Burning

• Beware of burns from the exhaust system and from any part of the engine. Brake discs and drums can also be extremely hot immediately after use.

Crushing

• When working under or near a raised vehicle, always supplement the jack with axle stands, or use drive-on ramps. *Never venture under a car which is only supported by a jack.*

• Take care if loosening or tightening high-torque nuts when the vehicle is on stands. Initial loosening and final tightening should be done with the wheels on the ground.

Fire

• Fuel is highly flammable; fuel vapour is explosive.
• Don't let fuel spill onto a hot engine.
• Do not smoke or allow naked lights (including pilot lights) anywhere near a vehicle being worked on. Also beware of creating sparks (electrically or by use of tools).
• Fuel vapour is heavier than air, so don't work on the fuel system with the vehicle over an inspection pit.
• Another cause of fire is an electrical overload or short-circuit. Take care when repairing or modifying the vehicle wiring.
• Keep a fire extinguisher handy, of a type suitable for use on fuel and electrical fires.

Electric shock

• Ignition HT voltage can be dangerous, especially to people with heart problems or a pacemaker. Don't work on or near the ignition system with the engine running or the ignition switched on.

• Mains voltage is also dangerous. Make sure that any mains-operated equipment is correctly earthed. Mains power points should be protected by a residual current device (RCD) circuit breaker.

Fume or gas intoxication

• Exhaust fumes are poisonous; they often contain carbon monoxide, which is rapidly fatal if inhaled. Never run the engine in a confined space such as a garage with the doors shut.

• Fuel vapour is also poisonous, as are the vapours from some cleaning solvents and paint thinners.

Poisonous or irritant substances

• Avoid skin contact with battery acid and with any fuel, fluid or lubricant, especially antifreeze, brake hydraulic fluid and Diesel fuel. Don't syphon them by mouth. If such a substance is swallowed or gets into the eyes, seek medical advice.
• Prolonged contact with used engine oil can cause skin cancer. Wear gloves or use a barrier cream if necessary. Change out of oil-soaked clothes and do not keep oily rags in your pocket.
• Air conditioning refrigerant forms a poisonous gas if exposed to a naked flame (including a cigarette). It can also cause skin burns on contact.

Asbestos

• Asbestos dust can cause cancer if inhaled or swallowed. Asbestos may be found in gaskets and in brake and clutch linings. When dealing with such components it is safest to assume that they contain asbestos.

Special hazards

Hydrofluoric acid

• This extremely corrosive acid is formed when certain types of synthetic rubber, found in some O-rings, oil seals, fuel hoses etc, are exposed to temperatures above 400°C. The rubber changes into a charred or sticky substance containing the acid. *Once formed, the acid remains dangerous for years. If it gets onto the skin, it may be necessary to amputate the limb concerned.*
• When dealing with a vehicle which has suffered a fire, or with components salvaged from such a vehicle, wear protective gloves and discard them after use.

The battery

• Batteries contain sulphuric acid, which attacks clothing, eyes and skin. Take care when topping-up or carrying the battery.
• The hydrogen gas given off by the battery is highly explosive. Never cause a spark or allow a naked light nearby. Be careful when connecting and disconnecting battery chargers or jump leads.

Air bags

• Air bags can cause injury if they go off accidentally. Take care when removing the steering wheel and/or facia. Special storage instructions may apply.

Diesel injection equipment

• Diesel injection pumps supply fuel at very high pressure. Take care when working on the fuel injectors and fuel pipes.

⚠️ *Warning: Never expose the hands, face or any other part of the body to injector spray; the fuel can penetrate the skin with potentially fatal results.*

Remember...

DO

• Do use eye protection when using power tools, and when working under the vehicle.

• Do wear gloves or use barrier cream to protect your hands when necessary.

• Do get someone to check periodically that all is well when working alone on the vehicle.

• Do keep loose clothing and long hair well out of the way of moving mechanical parts.

• Do remove rings, wristwatch etc, before working on the vehicle – especially the electrical system.

• Do ensure that any lifting or jacking equipment has a safe working load rating adequate for the job.

DON'T

• Don't attempt to lift a heavy component which may be beyond your capability – get assistance.

• Don't rush to finish a job, or take unverified short cuts.

• Don't use ill-fitting tools which may slip and cause injury.

• Don't leave tools or parts lying around where someone can trip over them. Mop up oil and fuel spills at once.

• Don't allow children or pets to play in or near a vehicle being worked on.

The following pages are intended to help in dealing with common roadside emergencies and breakdowns. You will find more detailed fault finding information at the back of the manual, and repair information in the main chapters.

If your car won't start and the starter motor doesn't turn

☐ If it's a model with automatic transmission, make sure the selector is in 'P' or 'N'.
☐ Open the bonnet and make sure that the battery terminals are clean and tight.
☐ Switch on the headlights and try to start the engine. If the headlights go very dim when you're trying to start, the battery is probably flat. Get out of trouble by jump starting (see next page) using a friend's car.

If your car won't start even though the starter motor turns as normal

☐ Is there fuel in the tank?
☐ Is there moisture on electrical components under the bonnet? Switch off the ignition, then wipe off any obvious dampness with a dry cloth. Spray a water-repellent aerosol product (WD-40 or equivalent) on ignition and fuel system electrical connectors like those shown in the photos. Pay special attention to the ignition coil wiring connector and HT leads.

A Check the security and condition of the battery terminals.

B Check that the HT leads are securely connected to the spark plugs.

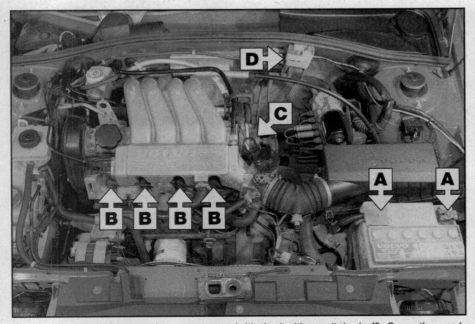

Check that electrical connections are secure (with the ignition switched off). Spray the spark plug and ignition coil connector plugs with a water-dispersant spray like WD40 if you suspect a problem due to damp.

C Also check the HT lead connections to the distributor cap.

D Check that the ignition coil wiring is securely connected.

Jump starting

HAYNES HINT *Jump starting will get you out of trouble, but you must correct whatever made the battery go flat in the first place. There are three possibilities:*

1 *The battery has been drained by repeated attempts to start, or by leaving the lights on.*

2 *The charging system is not working properly (alternator drivebelt slack or broken, alternator wiring fault or alternator itself faulty).*

3 *The battery itself is at fault (electrolyte low, or battery worn out).*

When jump-starting a car using a booster battery, observe the following precautions:

✔ Before connecting the booster battery, make sure that the ignition is switched off.

✔ Ensure that all electrical equipment (lights, heater, wipers, etc) is switched off.

✔ Take note of any special precautions printed on the battery case.

✔ Make sure that the booster battery is the same voltage as the discharged one in the vehicle.

✔ If the battery is being jump-started from the battery in another vehicle, the two vehicles MUST NOT TOUCH each other.

✔ Make sure that the transmission is in neutral (or PARK, in the case of automatic transmission).

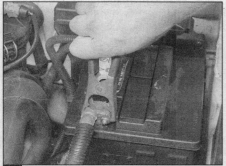

1 Connect one end of the red jump lead to the positive (+) terminal of the flat battery

2 Connect the other end of the red lead to the positive (+) terminal of the booster battery.

3 Connect one end of the black jump lead to the negative (-) terminal of the booster battery

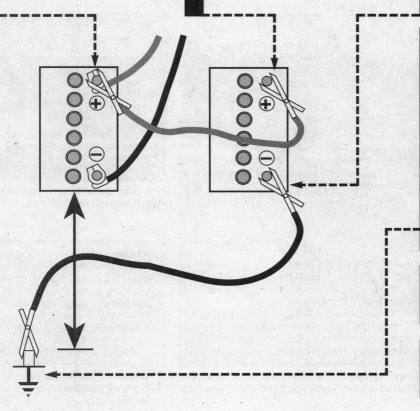

4 Connect the other end of the black jump lead to a bolt or bracket on the engine block, well away from the battery, on the vehicle to be started.

5 Make sure that the jump leads will not come into contact with the fan, drive-belts or other moving parts of the engine.

6 Start the engine using the booster battery and run it at idle speed. Switch on the lights, rear window demister and heater blower motor, then disconnect the jump leads in the reverse order of connection. Turn off the lights etc.

Wheel changing

Some of the details shown here will vary according to model. For instance, the location of the spare wheel and jack is not the same on all cars. However, the basic principles apply to all vehicles.

⚠️ *Warning: Do not change a wheel in a situation where you risk being hit by another vehicle. On busy roads, try to stop in a lay-by or a gateway. Be wary of passing traffic while changing the wheel - it is easy to become distracted by the job in hand.*

Preparation

- ☐ When a puncture occurs, stop as soon as it is safe to do so.
- ☐ Park on firm level ground, if possible, and well out of the way of other traffic.
- ☐ Use hazard warning lights if necessary.
- ☐ If you have one, use a warning triangle to alert other drivers of your presence.
- ☐ Apply the handbrake and engage first or reverse gear (or Park on models with automatic transmission.
- ☐ Chock the wheel diagonally opposite the one being removed – a couple of large stones will do for this.
- ☐ If the ground is soft, use a flat piece of wood to spread the load under the jack.

Changing the wheel

1 The spare wheel, jack and tools are stored in a recess under the boot floor on 440 and 460 models, and at the rear of the boot area on 480 models. Lift off the covering, then unscrew the spare wheel retainer, and lift the wheel and the tools out of the car.

2 Use the end of the wheelbrace to remove the wheel trim or centre cap, as applicable.

3 Slacken each wheel bolt by a half turn, using the wheelbrace. If the bolts are too tight, DON'T stand on the wheelbrace to undo them - call for assistance. On models with alloy wheels, a special Volvo socket may be needed to remove the security bolt - the socket should be in the tool tray in the boot.

4 Select the nearest jacking point to the damaged wheel, then slot the jack head fully onto the tongue in the lower edge of the sill (don't jack the vehicle at any other point of the sill).

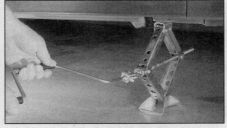

5 Engage the jack handle with the end fitting on the jack, then turn the handle clockwise until the wheel is raised clear of the ground.

6 Unscrew the wheel bolts and remove the wheel.

7 Fit the spare wheel, and screw in the bolts. Lightly tighten the bolts with the wheelbrace, then lower the vehicle to the ground. Securely tighten the wheel bolts, then refit the wheel trim or centre cap, as applicable.

Note: *Some models are supplied with a special lightweight space-saver spare wheel, the tyre being narrower than standard, and marked TEMPORARY USE ONLY. The space-saver spare wheel is intended only for temporary use, and **must** be replaced with a standard wheel as soon as possible. Drive with particular care with this wheel fitted, especially through corners - Volvo recommend a maximum speed of 50 mph (80 kmh) when the special spare wheel is in use.*

Finally...

- ☐ Remove the wheel chocks.
- ☐ Stow the jack and tools in the correct locations in the car.
- ☐ Check the tyre pressure on the wheel just fitted. If it is low, or if you don't have a pressure gauge with you, drive slowly to the nearest garage and inflate the tyre to the right pressure. In the case of the space-saver spare wheel, this pressure is much higher than for a normal tyre.
- ☐ The wheel bolts should be slackened and retightened to the specified torque at the earliest possible opportunity.
- ☐ Have the damaged tyre or wheel repaired as soon as possible.

Identifying leaks

Puddles on the garage floor or drive, or obvious wetness under the bonnet or underneath the car, suggest a leak that needs investigating. It can sometimes be difficult to decide where the leak is coming from, especially if the engine bay is very dirty already. Leaking oil or fluid can also be blown rearwards by the passage of air under the car, giving a false impression of where the problem lies.

Warning: Most automotive oils and fluids are poisonous. Wash them off skin, and change out of contaminated clothing, without delay.

 HAYNES HiNT *The smell of a fluid leaking from the car may provide a clue to what's leaking. Some fluids are distinctively coloured. It may help to clean the car carefully and to park it over some clean paper overnight as an aid to locating the source of the leak. Remember that some leaks may only occur while the engine is running.*

Sump oil

Engine oil may leak from the drain plug...

Oil from filter

...or from the base of the oil filter.

Gearbox oil

Gearbox oil can leak from the seals at the inboard ends of the driveshafts.

Antifreeze

Leaking antifreeze often leaves a crystalline deposit like this.

Brake fluid

A leak occurring at a wheel is almost certainly brake fluid.

Power steering fluid

Power steering fluid may leak from the pipe connectors on the steering rack.

Towing

When all else fails, you may find yourself having to get a tow home – or of course you may be helping somebody else. Long-distance recovery should only be done by a garage or breakdown service. For shorter distances, DIY towing using another car is easy enough, but observe the following points:

☐ Use a proper tow-rope – they are not expensive. The vehicle being towed must display an ON TOW sign in its rear window.
☐ Always turn the ignition key to the 'on' position when the vehicle is being towed, so that the steering lock is released, and that the direction indicator and brake lights will work.
☐ Only attach the tow-rope to the towing eyes provided **(see illustration)**.

☐ Before being towed, release the handbrake and select neutral on the transmission.
☐ Note that greater-than-usual pedal pressure will be required to operate the brakes, since the vacuum servo unit is only operational with the engine running.
☐ On models with power steering, greater-than-usual steering effort will also be required.
☐ The driver of the car being towed must keep the tow-rope taut at all times to avoid snatching.
☐ Make sure that both drivers know the route before setting off.
☐ Only drive at moderate speeds and keep the distance towed to a minimum. Drive smoothly and allow plenty of time for slowing down at junctions.

☐ On models with automatic transmission, special precautions apply. If in doubt, do not tow, or transmission damage may result.

Rear towing eye

Introduction

There are some very simple checks which need only take a few minutes to carry out, but which could save you a lot of inconvenience and expense.

These Weekly checks require no great skill or special tools, and the small amount of time they take to perform could prove to be very well spent, for example;

☐ Keeping an eye on tyre condition and pressures, will not only help to stop them wearing out prematurely, but could also save your life.

☐ Many breakdowns are caused by electrical problems. Battery-related faults are particularly common, and a quick check on a regular basis will often prevent the majority of these.

☐ If your car develops a brake fluid leak, the first time you might know about it is when your brakes don't work properly. Checking the level regularly will give advance warning of this kind of problem.

☐ If the oil or coolant levels run low, the cost of repairing any engine damage will be far greater than fixing the leak, for example.

Underbonnet check points

◀ **1.7 litre carburettor engine**

A *Engine oil level dipstick*
B *Engine oil filler cap*
C *Coolant expansion tank*
D *Brake fluid reservoir*
E *Power sterring fluid reservoir*
F *Screen washer fluid reservoir*
G *Battery*

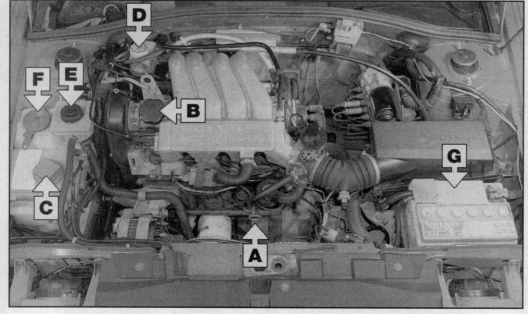

◀ **2.0 litre fuel injection engine**

A *Engine oil level dipstick*
B *Engine oil filler cap*
C *Coolant expansion tank*
D *Brake fluid reservoir*
E *Power sterring fluid reservoir*
F *Screen washer fluid reservoir*
G *Battery*

Engine oil level

Before you start

✔ Make sure that your car is on level ground.
✔ Check the oil level before the car is driven, or at least 5 minutes after the engine has been switched off.

 HAYNES HiNT *If the oil is checked immediately after driving the vehicle, some of the oil will remain in the upper engine components, resulting in an inaccurate reading on the dipstick.*

The correct oil

Modern engines place great demands on their oil. It is very important that the correct oil for your car is used (See Lubricants and fluids) on page 0•16).

Car Care

● If you have to add oil frequently, you should check whether you have any oil leaks. Place some clean paper under the car overnight, and check for stains in the morning. If there are no leaks, the engine may be burning oil *(see Fault Finding)*.
● Always maintain the level between the upper and lower dipstick marks (see photo 3). If the level is too low severe engine damage may occur. Oil seal failure may result if the engine is overfilled by adding too much oil.
● On models equipped with an information centre display, don't be tempted to rely on the automatic check alone - verify the level using the dipstick on a regular basis. Equally, don't ignore the display if it warns of low oil level.

1 The engine oil level is checked with a dipstick located at the front of the engine. Withdraw the dipstick.

2 Using a clean rag or paper towel remove all oil from the dipstick. Insert the clean dipstick into the tube as far as it will go, then withdraw it again.

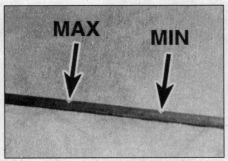

MAX   MIN

3 Note the oil level on the end of the dipstick, which should be between the MAX and MIN marks. If the oil level is only just above, or below, the MIN mark, topping-up is required.

4 Oil is added through the filler cap. Unscrew the cap and top-up the level; a funnel may be useful in reducing spillage. Add the oil slowly, checking the level on the dipstick often, and allowing time for the oil to run to the sump. Add oil until the level is just up to the MAX mark on the dipstick - don't overfill (see *Car care*).

Coolant level

 Warning: DO NOT attempt to remove the expansion tank pressure cap when the engine is hot, as there is a very great risk of scalding. Do not leave open containers of coolant about, as it is poisonous.

Car Care

● With a sealed-type cooling system, adding coolant should not be necessary on a regular basis. If frequent topping-up is required, it is likely there is a leak. Check the radiator, all hoses and joint faces for signs of staining or wetness, and rectify as necessary.

● It is important that antifreeze is used in the cooling system all year round, not just during the winter months. Don't top-up with water alone, as the antifreeze will become too diluted.

1 The coolant level varies with engine temperature - the level will always be higher when the engine is hot. The level can be seen through the reservoir, and should be above the MIN mark at all times.

2 If topping up is necessary, **wait until the engine is cold.** Slowly unscrew the expansion tank cap, to release any pressure present in the cooling system, and remove it.

3 Add a mixture of water and antifreeze to the expansion tank until the coolant level is between the MAX and MIN marks. Refit the cap and tighten it securely.

Brake fluid level

Warning:
● **Brake fluid can harm your eyes and damage painted surfaces, so use extreme caution when handling and pouring it.**

● **Do not use fluid that has been standing open for some time, as it absorbs moisture from the air, which can cause a dangerous loss of braking effectiveness.**

HAYNES HiNT ● **The fluid level in the reservoir will drop slightly as the brake pads wear down, but the fluid level must never be allowed to drop below the MIN mark.**

Before you start

✔ Make sure that your car is on level ground.

Safety First!

● If the reservoir requires repeated topping-up this is an indication of a fluid leak somewhere in the system, which should be investigated immediately.

● If a leak is suspected, the car should not be driven until the braking system has been checked. Never take any risks where brakes are concerned.

1 The brake fluid reservoir is located at the rear of the engine compartment, next to the suspension strut top mounting. On models without ABS, the reservoir is on the right-hand side; models with ABS may have the reservoir on the opposite side.

3 Where necessary, unplug the level switch wiring connector, then unscrew the reservoir cap and carefully lift it out of position. Place the cap on a piece of clean rag. Inspect the reservoir; if the fluid is dirty, the hydraulic system should be drained and refilled (see Chapter 1).

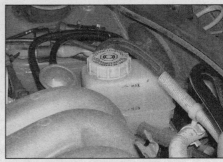

2 The MAX and MIN marks are indicated on the side or front of the reservoir, depending on whether or not ABS is fitted. The fluid level must be kept between the marks at all times.

4 Carefully add fluid, taking care not to spill it onto the surrounding components. Use only the specified fluid; mixing different types can cause damage to the system. After topping-up to the correct level, securely refit the cap (reconnect the wiring plug, where applicable) and wipe off any spilt fluid.

Power steering fluid level

Before you start

✔ Park the vehicle on level ground.
✔ Set the steering wheel straight-ahead.
✔ Ensure that the ignition is switched off.

HAYNES HiNT *For the check to be accurate, the steering must not be turned once the engine has been stopped.*

Safety First!

● The need for frequent topping-up indicates a leak, which should be investigated immediately.

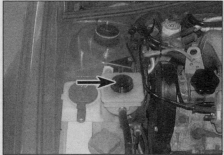

1 The reservoir is located at the right-hand side of the engine compartment, next to and above the screenwash reservoir.

2 When the system is cold, the level should be above the MIN mark. With the system at operating temperature (after a run), the level should be between the MAX and MIN marks. If topping-up is required, wipe clean the area around the reservoir filler neck and unscrew the filler cap from the reservoir.

3 When topping-up, use the specified type of fluid, and do not overfill the reservoir. When the level is correct, securely refit the cap.

Screen washer fluid level

Note: On models with a headlight washer system, the screen wash is also used to clean the headlights. The underbonnet reservoir also serves the tailgate washer.

Screenwash additives not only keep the winscreen clean during foul weather, they also prevent the washer system freezing in cold weather - which is when you are likely to need it most. Don't top up using plain water as the screenwash will become too diluted, and will freeze during cold weather. **On no account use coolant antifreeze in the washer system - this could discolour or damage paintwork.**

1 The screen washer fluid reservoir is located on the right-hand side of the engine compartment.

2 The screen washer level can be seen through the reservoir body, but if necessary, remove the filler cap, and look inside.

3 When topping-up the reservoir, add a screenwash additive in the quantities recommended on the additive bottle. The exact level is not critical - add fluid slowly until the reservoir is almost full. Refit the filler cap securely on completion.

Wiper blades

Note: Fitting details for wiper blades vary according to model, and according to whether genuine Volvo wiper blades have been fitted. Use the procedures and illustrations shown as a guide for your car.

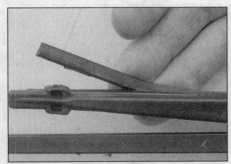

1 Check the condition of the wiper blades; if they are cracked or show any signs of deterioration, or if the glass swept area is smeared, renew them. Wiper blades should be renewed annually, regardless of their apparent condition.

HAYNES HiNT *If smearing is still a problem despite fitting new wiper blades, try cleaning the windscreen with neat screen-wash additive or methylated spirit.*

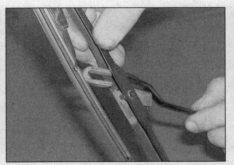

2 To remove a windscreen wiper blade, lift the arm away from the screen until it locks. Depress the locking tab, and slide the blade down, around and out of the arm's hooked end.

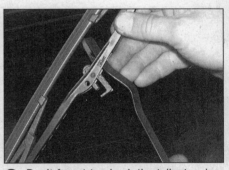

3 Don't forget to check the tailgate wiper blade as well, where applicable. On models with a rear spoiler, operate the wiper to its halfway point, then switch off the ignition, to position the arm so that the blade can be lifted. The blade is removed in the same way as the windscreen wipers.

Tyre condition and pressure

It is very important that tyres are in good condition, and at the correct pressure - having a tyre failure at any speed is highly dangerous. Tyre wear is influenced by driving style - harsh braking and acceleration, or fast cornering, will all produce more rapid tyre wear. As a general rule, the front tyres wear out faster than the rears. Interchanging the tyres from front to rear ("rotating" the tyres) may result in more even wear. However, if this is completely effective, you may have the expense of replacing all four tyres at once! Remove any nails or stones embedded in the tread before they penetrate the tyre to cause deflation. If removal of a nail does reveal that the tyre has been punctured, refit the nail so that its point of penetration is marked. Then immediately change the wheel, and have the tyre repaired by a tyre dealer.

Regularly check the tyres for damage in the form of cuts or bulges, especially in the sidewalls. Periodically remove the wheels, and clean any dirt or mud from the inside and outside surfaces. Examine the wheel rims for signs of rusting, corrosion or other damage. Light alloy wheels are easily damaged by "kerbing" whilst parking; steel wheels may also become dented or buckled. A new wheel is very often the only way to overcome severe damage.

New tyres should be balanced when they are fitted, but it may become necessary to re-balance them as they wear, or if the balance weights fitted to the wheel rim should fall off. Unbalanced tyres will wear more quickly, as will the steering and suspension components. Wheel imbalance is normally signified by vibration, particularly at a certain speed (typically around 50 mph). If this vibration is felt only through the steering, then it is likely that just the front wheels need balancing. If, however, the vibration is felt through the whole car, the rear wheels could be out of balance. Wheel balancing should be carried out by a tyre dealer or garage.

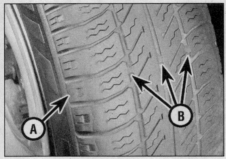

1 *Tread Depth - visual check*
The original tyres have tread wear safety bands (B), which will appear when the tread depth reaches approximately 1.6 mm. The band positions are indicated by a triangular mark on the tyre sidewall (A).

2 *Tread Depth - manual check*
Alternatively, tread wear can be monitored with a simple, inexpensive device known as a tread depth indicator gauge.

3 *Tyre Pressure Check*
Check the tyre pressures regularly with the tyres cold. Do not adjust the tyre pressures immediately after the vehicle has been used, or an inaccurate setting will result. Tyre pressures are shown on page 0•16.

Tyre tread wear patterns

Shoulder Wear

Underinflation (wear on both sides)
Under-inflation will cause overheating of the tyre, because the tyre will flex too much, and the tread will not sit correctly on the road surface. This will cause a loss of grip and excessive wear, not to mention the danger of sudden tyre failure due to heat build-up.
Check and adjust pressures
Incorrect wheel camber (wear on one side)
Repair or renew suspension parts
Hard cornering
Reduce speed!

Centre Wear

Overinflation
Over-inflation will cause rapid wear of the centre part of the tyre tread, coupled with reduced grip, harsher ride, and the danger of shock damage occurring in the tyre casing.
Check and adjust pressures

If you sometimes have to inflate your car's tyres to the higher pressures specified for maximum load or sustained high speed, don't forget to reduce the pressures to normal afterwards.

Uneven Wear

Front tyres may wear unevenly as a result of wheel misalignment. Most tyre dealers and garages can check and adjust the wheel alignment (or "tracking") for a modest charge.
Incorrect camber or castor
Repair or renew suspension parts
Malfunctioning suspension
Repair or renew suspension parts
Unbalanced wheel
Balance tyres
Incorrect toe setting
Adjust front wheel alignment
Note: *The feathered edge of the tread which typifies toe wear is best checked by feel.*

Battery

Caution: Before carrying out any work on the vehicle battery, read the precautions given in Safety first at the start of this manual.

✔ Make sure that the battery tray is in good condition, and that the clamp is tight. Corrosion on the tray, retaining clamp and the battery itself can be removed with a solution of water and baking soda. Thoroughly rinse all cleaned areas with water. Any metal parts damaged by corrosion should be covered with a zinc-based primer, then painted.

✔ Periodically (approximately every three months), check the charge condition of the battery as described in Chapter 5A.

✔ If the battery is flat, and you need to jump start your vehicle, see *Roadside Repairs*.

1 The battery is located on the left-hand side of the engine compartment. The exterior of the battery should be inspected periodically for damage such as a cracked case or cover.

2 Check the tightness of battery clamps to ensure good electrical connections. You should not be able to move them. Also check each cable for cracks and frayed conductors.

Battery corrosion can be kept to a minimum by applying a layer of petroleum jelly to the clamps and terminals after they are reconnected.

3 If corrosion (white, fluffy deposits) is evident, remove the cables from the battery terminals, clean them with a small wire brush, then refit them. Automotive stores sell a tool for cleaning the battery post . . .

4 . . . as well as the battery cable clamps

Electrical system

✔ Check all external lights and the horn. Refer to the appropriate Sections of Chapter 12 for details if any of the circuits are found to be inoperative.

✔ Visually check all accessible wiring connectors, harnesses and retaining clips for security, and for signs of chafing or damage.

 If you need to check your brake lights and indicators unaided, back up to a wall or garage door and operate the lights. The reflected light should show if they are working properly.

1 If a single indicator light, stop-light or headlight has failed, it is likely that a bulb has blown and will need to be replaced. Refer to Chapter 12 for details. If both stop-lights have failed, it is possible that the switch on the brake pedal has failed (see Chapter 9).

2 If more than one indicator light or tail light has failed, it is likely that either a fuse has blown or that there is a fault in the circuit (see Chapter 12). The main fuses are located in a triangular box at the rear of the engine compartment, or behind a cover under the driver's side of the facia, depending on model. Certain additional fuses may be located behind the glovebox.

3 To replace a blown fuse, simply pull it out using the tweezer tool provided, and fit a new fuse of the correct rating (see Chapter 12). If the fuse blows again, it is important that you find out why.

Lubricants and fluids

Engine	Multigrade engine oil, viscosity SAE 10W/30, 10W/40 or 15W/40, API SG or SH *(Duckhams QXR Premium Petrol Engine Oil, or Duckhams Hypergrade Petrol Engine Oil)*
Cooling system	Ethylene glycol-based antifreeze with corrosion inhibitor *(Duckhams Antifreeze and Summer Coolant)*
Manual gearbox Up to 1988	Gear oil, viscosity SAE 80W *(Duckhams Hypoid Gear Oil 80W GL-4)*
1989 onwards	Volvo special oil - part number 3343922-5
Automatic transmission	Volvo special oil - Dexron II type ATF
Brake hydraulic system	Hydraulic fluid to FMVSS 116 DOT 4 *(Duckhams Universal Brake & Clutch Fluid)*
Power steering	Dexron type ATF *(Duckhams ATF Autotrans III)*

Choosing your engine oil

Engines need oil, not only to lubricate moving parts and minimise wear, but also to maximise power output and to improve fuel economy. By introducing a simplified and improved range of engine oils, Duckhams has taken away the confusion and made it easier for you to choose the right oil for your engine.

HOW ENGINE OIL WORKS

• *Beating friction*

Without oil, the moving surfaces inside your engine will rub together, heat up and melt, quickly causing the engine to seize. Engine oil creates a film which separates these moving parts, preventing wear and heat build-up.

• *Cooling hot-spots*

Temperatures inside the engine can exceed 1000° C. The engine oil circulates and acts as a coolant, transferring heat from the hot-spots to the sump.

• *Cleaning the engine internally*

Good quality engine oils clean the inside of your engine, collecting and dispersing combustion deposits and controlling them until they are trapped by the oil filter or flushed out at oil change.

OIL CARE - FOLLOW THE CODE

To handle and dispose of used engine oil safely, always:

OIL CARE FOLLOW THE CODE
OIL BANK LINE
0800 66 33 66

• *Avoid skin contact with used engine oil. Repeated or prolonged contact can be harmful.*
• *Dispose of used oil and empty packs in a responsible manner in an authorised disposal site. Call 0800 663366 to find the one nearest to you. Never tip oil down drains or onto the ground.*

DUCKHAMS ENGINE OILS

For the driver who demands a premium quality oil for complete reassurance, we recommend synthetic formula **Duckhams QXR Premium Engine Oils**.
For the driver who requires a straightforward quality engine oil, we recommend **Duckhams Hypergrade Engine Oils**.

For further information and advice, call the Duckhams UK Helpline on 0800 212988.

Tyre pressures

Tyre pressures (cold):	Front	Rear
Up to 4 passengers:		
All models	2.1 bars (30 psi)	1.9 bars (28 psi)
4 passengers and luggage:		
440 and 460 models	2.3 bars (33 psi)	2.1 bars (30 psi)
480 models	2.2 bars (32 psi)	2.0 bars (29 psi)
Space-saver spare wheel (where applicable)	4.1 bars (60 psi)	4.1 bars (60 psi)

Note 1: *Tyre pressure information may be given on a decal below the driver's door lock. If the information shown there differs from that given above, consult a Volvo dealer for advice.*

Note 2: *Pressures apply to original-equipment tyres, and may vary if any other make of tyre is fitted; check with the tyre manufacturer or supplier for the correct pressures if necessary.*

Chapter 1
Routine maintenance and servicing

Contents

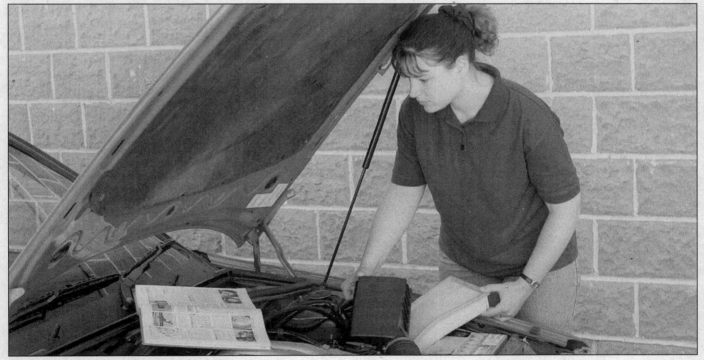

Degrees of difficulty

Easy, suitable for novice with little experience

Fairly easy, suitable for beginner with some experience

Fairly difficult, suitable for competent DIY mechanic

Difficult, suitable for experienced DIY mechanic

Very difficult, suitable for expert DIY or professional

Note: *Many of the specifications below contain references to engine codes (eg, B18FT). The engine code is part of the engine number, which appears on a small plate on the front face of the engine block, next to the engine oil dipstick tube. A photo showing a typical engine number plate appears in* Vehicle identification numbers *at the end of this manual.*

Lubricants and fluids . . . .   See end of *Weekly checks* on page 0•16

Capacities

Engine oil (including oil filter)

	Capacity	Dipstick MIN to MAX
All engines up to 1992	5.3 litres	1.7 litres
All engines, 1993 to 1994	5.0 litres	1.4 litres
1.6, 1.7 and 1.8 litre engines, 1994 onwards	4.6 litres	1.4 litres
2.0 litre engines, 1994 onwards	5.7 litres	2.2 litres

Cooling system
Carburettor engines . . . .   6.0 litres approx.
Fuel injection engines . . . .   7.0 litres approx.

Fuel tank
All models up to 1991 . . . .   48 litres approx.
All models from 1991 onwards . . . .   60 litres approx.

Manual gearbox
All models . . . .   3.4 litres

Automatic transmission
Total capacity . . . .   5.5 litres
Drain and refill (fluid change) . . . .   3.2 to 3.4 litres
Difference between MAX and MIN dipstick marks . . . .   0.3 litres

Power-assisted steering reservoir
All models . . . .   0.7 litres

Engine
Valve clearances:
  Inlet:
    Checking . . . .   0.15 to 0.25 mm
    Adjusting . . . .   0.20 mm
  Exhaust:
    Checking (except B18FT) . . . .   0.35 to 0.45 mm
    Checking (B18FT) . . . .   0.45 to 0.55 mm
    Adjusting (except B18FT) . . . .   0.40 mm
    Adjusting (B18FT) . . . .   0.50 mm
Oil filter type (all engines) . . . .   Champion F103

Cooling system

Antifreeze mixtures:

	Antifreeze	Water
Protection down to -23°C	35%	65%
Protection down to -40°C	50%	50%

Fuel system
Idle speed (carburettor engines):
  B18K, B18K(D) . . . .   800 to 900 rpm
  B18KP, B18KP(D) . . . .   750 to 900 rpm
Idle mixture CO content (carburettor engines):
  B18K, B18K(D) . . . .   0.5% to 2.5%
  B18KP, B18KP(D) . . . .   1.0% to 2.5%
Air filter element:
  Carburettor engines . . . .   Champion type not available
  Fuel injection engines . . . .   Champion U634
Fuel filter:
  Carburettor engines . . . .   Champion type not available
  Fuel injection engines . . . .   Champion L205
Fuel octane requirement:
  Models without a catalytic converter . . . .   98 RON leaded (4-star)*, 98 RON super unleaded, or 95 RON unleaded
  Models with a catalytic converter . . . .   98 RON super unleaded or 95 RON unleaded only - **do not** use leaded 4-star

* *Leaded petrol is being phased out in the UK market by January 2000 to be replaced by Lead Replacement Petrol (LRP). Cars which previously ran on leaded (4-star) petrol should run satisfactorily on LRP but, if in doubt, consult the vehicle manufacturer.*

Ignition system

Firing order	1-3-4-2
Location of No 1 cylinder	Flywheel (transmission) end
Direction of crankshaft rotation	Clockwise
Direction of distributor rotor arm rotation	Anti-clockwise

Spark plugs:
  Type:
    1.6 and 1.8 litre engines .... Champion RN9LCC
    1.7 litre (1721 cc) engines:
      Engine codes B18E, ES, ED, FT and FTM .... Champion RN7LCC
      All other engine codes .... Champion RN9LCC
    2.0 litre engines .... Champion RN7LCC
  Electrode gap .... 0.8 mm

Note: *Information on spark plug types and electrode gap is as recommended by Champion Spark Plug. Where alternative types are used, refer to their manufacturer's recommendations*

Clutch

Clutch pedal height (early models):
  Non-ABS models .... 15.0 to 20.0 mm above the brake pedal
  ABS models .... 25.0 to 30.0 mm above the brake pedal
Clutch pedal stroke (later models):
  Long release arm (ie with extra bracket bolted to the gearbox) ..... 30.0 ± 1.0 mm
  Short release arm .... 22.0 ± 1.0 mm

Braking system

Minimum front brake pad lining thickness .... 2.0 mm
Front brake disc minimum service thickness:
  Solid discs .... 10.35 mm
  Ventilated discs .... 19.30 mm
Minimum rear brake pad lining thickness .... 2.0 mm
Rear brake disc minimum service thickness .... 8.0 mm
Minimum rear brake shoe lining thickness .... 1.0 mm
Rear brake drum maximum service inside diameter .... 204.7 mm
Handbrake adjustment .... Wheels locked after 5 to 7 notches

Suspension and steering

Power steering pump drivebelt deflection .... 3.0 to 5.0 mm
Tyre pressures .... See end of *Weekly checks*

Torque wrench settings

	Nm	lbf ft
Automatic transmission drain plug	15	11
Manual gearbox drain plug	15	11
Radiator drain plug	4	3
Roadwheel bolts	110	81
Spark plugs	25	18
Sump drain plug	25	18

1

The maintenance intervals in this manual are provided with the assumption that you, not the dealer, will be carrying out the work. These are the minimum maintenance intervals recommended by us for vehicles driven daily. If you wish to keep your vehicle in peak condition at all times, you may wish to perform some of these procedures more often. We encourage frequent maintenance, because it enhances the efficiency, performance and resale value of your vehicle.

If the vehicle is driven in dusty areas, used to tow a trailer, or driven frequently at slow speeds (idling in traffic) or on short journeys, more frequent maintenance intervals are recommended.

When the vehicle is new, it should be serviced by a factory-authorised dealer service department, in order to preserve the factory warranty.

Every 250 miles (400 km) or weekly

☐ Refer to *Weekly checks*

Every 6000 miles (10 000 km) or 6 months - whichever comes first

☐ Renew the engine oil and filter (Section 3)
☐ Check for oil and coolant leaks (Section 4)
☐ Check the condition and tension of all auxiliary drivebelts (Section 5)
☐ Check the brake vacuum servo unit - non-ABS models (Section 6)
☐ Check the battery electrolyte level (Section 7)
☐ Check the operation of all lights, indicators, instruments and windscreen washer system(s) (Section 8)

Every 12 000 miles (20 000 km) or 12 months - whichever comes first

In addition to all the items listed above, carry out the following:
☐ Check/adjust the front wheel alignment (Section 9)
☐ Check the antifreeze concentration (Section 10)
☐ Check exhaust manifold for leakage, and tighten nuts (Section 11)
☐ Check/adjust the idle speed and CO content - carburettor engines (Section 12)
☐ Check fuel lines for damage and leakage (Section 13)
☐ Check the exhaust system for condition, leakage and security (Section 14)
☐ Renew the spark plugs (Section 15)
☐ Check/adjust clutch pedal height and cable free play (Section 16)
☐ Check/top-up the manual gearbox oil level (Section 17)
☐ Check/top-up the automatic transmission fluid level (Section 18)
☐ Check the driveshafts and rubber gaiters for damage and leakage (Section 19)
☐ Check all brake lines for damage and leakage (Section 20)
☐ Check the front and rear brake pads/brake shoe linings for wear (Section 21)
☐ Adjust the handbrake (Section 22)
☐ Tighten all suspension nuts and bolts - at first annual service (Section 23)
☐ Check suspension and steering components for wear and security (Section 24)
☐ Visually examine the underbody, wheel arches and body panels for damage (Section 25)

Every 12 000 miles (20 000 km) or 12 months - whichever comes first (continued)

☐ Check seat belts for wear and damage (Section 26)
☐ Lubricate all doors, bonnet and tailgate/bootlid (Section 27)
☐ Check and adjust the headlight beam alignment (Section 28)
☐ Engine management system fault code check (Section 29)
☐ Carry out a road test (Section 30)

Every 24 000 miles (40 000 km) or 2 years - whichever comes first

In addition to all the items listed above, carry out the following:
☐ Check engine cylinder compressions (Section 31)
☐ Clean the crankcase ventilation system hoses (Section 32)
☐ Renew the air filter (Section 33)
☐ Check air cleaner temperature control system - carburettor engines (Section 34)
☐ Renew the fuel filter (Section 35)
☐ Clean exhaust gas recirculation (EGR) system - where fitted (Section 36)
☐ Check automatic transmission selector and kickdown cable adjustment (Section 37)

Every 36 000 miles (60 000 km) or 3 years - whichever comes first

In addition to all the items listed above, carry out the following:
☐ Renew manual gearbox oil - 480 models up to 1988 only (Section 38)
☐ Renew automatic transmission fluid (Section 39)

Every 48 000 miles (80 000 km) or 4 years - whichever comes first

In addition to all the items listed above, carry out the following:
☐ Renew the timing belt (Section 40)
☐ Adjust valve clearances (Section 41)
☐ Renew all auxiliary drivebelts (Section 42)

Every 2 years, regardless of mileage

☐ Drain, flush and refill the cooling system, and renew the antifreeze (Section 43)
☐ Renew the brake hydraulic fluid (Section 44)

Underbonnet view of a 1.7 litre carburettor 440 model

1 Fusebox and relays
2 Fuel vapour separator
3 Fuel pump
4 Brake vacuum servo
5 Windscreen wiper motor
6 Carburettor (air cleaner removed for clarity)
7 Air duct for carburettor cooling
8 Carburettor vent valve
9 Ignition computer module
10 Front suspension strut upper mounting
11 Distributor cap and HT leads
12 Battery
13 Radiator top hose
14 Vacuum control motor for carburettor cooling system
15 Oil filter
16 Engine oil level dipstick
17 Radiator
18 Clutch cable
19 Accelerator cable
20 Cooling system vent/bleed screw
21 Alternator
22 Headlamp
23 Cooling system expansion tank
24 Windscreen washer fluid reservoir
25 Power steering fluid reservoir
26 Engine oil filler cap
27 Choke cable
28 Brake fluid reservoir

Underbonnet view of a 1.8 litre fuel injection 440 model

1 Relay box
2 Brake fluid reservoir
3 Windscreen wiper motor
4 Air inlet duct
5 Ignition coil
6 Front suspension strut upper mounting
7 Diagnostic socket
8 Air cleaner
9 Battery
10 Distributor cap and HT leads
11 Crankcase ventilation system oil separator
12 Engine oil dipstick
13 Oil filter
14 Alternator
15 Spark plugs
16 Engine oil filler cap
17 Power steering fluid reservoir
18 Cooling system expansion tank
19 Windscreen washer fluid reservoir

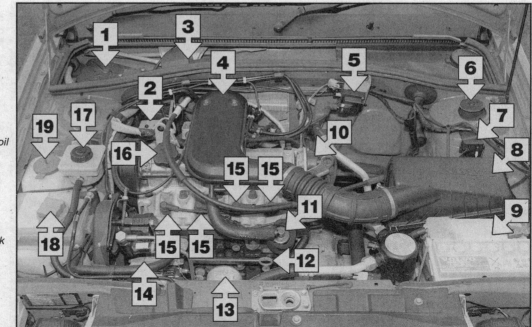

1

Underbonnet view of a 2.0 litre fuel injection 440 model

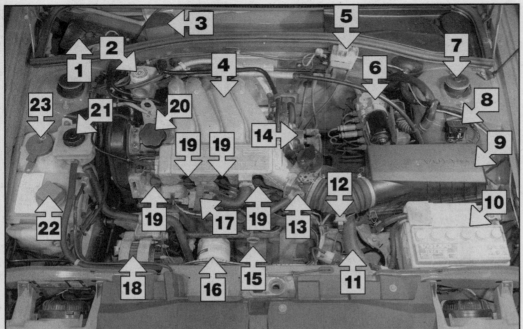

1 Relay box
2 Brake fluid reservoir
3 Windscreen wiper motor
4 Inlet manifold (upper section)
5 Ignition coil
6 ABS unit
7 Front suspension strut upper mounting
8 Diagnostic socket
9 Air cleaner
10 Battery
11 Radiator top hose
12 Inlet air temperature sensor
13 Throttle housing
14 Distributor cap and HT leads
15 Engine oil dipstick
16 Oil filter
17 Idle speed regulating valve
18 Alternator
19 Spark plugs
20 Engine oil filler cap
21 Power steering fluid reservoir
22 Cooling system expansion tank
23 Windscreen washer fluid reservoir

Front underbody view (1.7 litre 440 model shown, others similar)

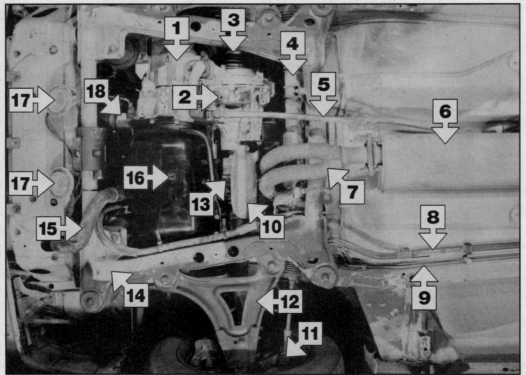

1 Manual gearbox
2 Gearbox oil drain plug
3 Left-hand driveshaft
4 Steering gear
5 Gearchange linkage
6 Exhaust silencer
7 Exhaust downpipe
8 Fuel feed and return lines
9 Hydraulic brake lines
10 Heat shield
11 Tie-rod end
12 Front suspension lower arm
13 Starter motor
14 Subframe
15 Radiator bottom hose
16 Engine oil drain plug
17 Horns
18 Electric cooling fan

Rear underbody view (440 model shown, others similar)

1 Rear suspension trailing arm
2 Rear axle
3 Panhard rod
4 Exhaust tailpipe and silencer
5 Rear towing eye
6 Rear suspension radius arm
7 Fuel tank filler pipe and vent hoses
8 Rear brake flexible hydraulic hose
9 Rear coil spring
10 Rear shock absorber
11 Fuel tank
12 Exhaust intermediate pipe

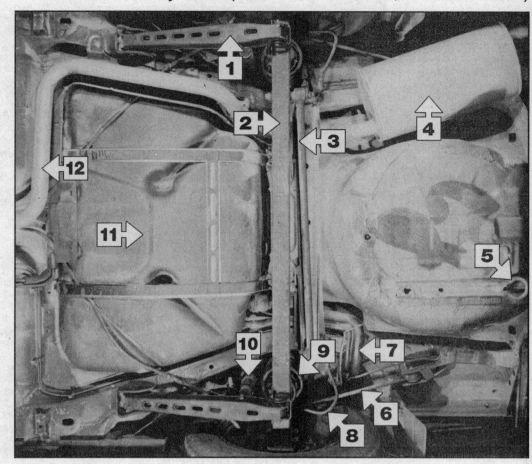

Maintenance procedures

1 Introduction

This Chapter is designed to help the home mechanic maintain their vehicle for safety, economy, long life and peak performance.

The Chapter contains a master maintenance schedule, followed by Sections dealing specifically with each task in the schedule. Visual checks, adjustments, component renewal and other helpful items are included. Refer to the accompanying illustrations of the engine compartment and the underside of the vehicle for the locations of the various components.

Servicing your vehicle in accordance with the mileage/time maintenance schedule and the following Sections will provide a planned maintenance programme, which should result

in a long and reliable service life. This is a comprehensive plan, so maintaining some items but not others at the specified service intervals, will not produce the same results.

As you service your vehicle, you will discover that many of the procedures can - and should - be grouped together, because of the particular procedure being performed, or because of the proximity of two otherwise-unrelated components to one another. For example, if the vehicle is raised for any reason, the exhaust can be inspected at the same time as the suspension and steering components.

The first step in this maintenance programme is to prepare yourself before the actual work begins. Read through all the Sections relevant to the work to be carried out, then make a list and gather all the parts and tools required. If a problem is encountered, seek advice from a parts specialist, or a dealer service department.

Service intervals - models from 1991 onwards

From 1991 model year onwards, Volvo have changed the service intervals for the 400 series. The 6000 mile and the 12 000 mile services have been amalgamated into a single 10 000 mile/12-month main service. In view of this, high-mileage users may wish to amend their servicing intervals (on 1991-on cars **only**) from those given in this manual, but the advice of a Volvo dealer should be sought first. However, we recommend that most owners keep to the original schedule shown here. We encourage frequent maintenance, because it enhances the efficiency, performance and resale value of your vehicle. If the vehicle is driven in dusty areas, used to tow a trailer, or driven frequently at slow speeds (idling in traffic) or on short journeys, more shorter maintenance intervals are recommended. In particular, the engine will benefit greatly from more frequent oil and filter changes.

1

2 Regular maintenance

1 If, from the time the vehicle is new, the routine maintenance schedule is followed closely, and frequent checks are made of fluid levels and high-wear items, as suggested throughout this manual, the engine will be kept in relatively good running condition, and the need for additional work will be minimised.
2 It is possible that there will be times when the engine is running poorly due to the lack of regular maintenance. This is even more likely if a used vehicle, which has not received regular and frequent maintenance checks, is purchased. In such cases, additional work may need to be carried out, outside of the regular maintenance intervals.

3 If engine wear is suspected, a compression test (refer to Chapter 2A) will provide valuable information regarding the overall performance of the main internal components. Such a test can be used as a basis to decide on the extent of the work to be carried out. If, for example, a compression test indicates serious internal engine wear, conventional maintenance as described in this Chapter will not greatly improve the performance of the engine, and may prove a waste of time and money, unless extensive overhaul work is carried out first.
4 The following series of operations are those most often required to improve the performance of a generally poor-running engine:

Primary operations

a) *Clean, inspect and test the battery (refer to* Weekly checks*).*
b) *Check all the engine-related fluids (refer to* Weekly checks*).*

c) *Check the condition and tension of the auxiliary drivebelt (Section 5).*
d) *Renew the spark plugs (Section 15).*
e) *Check the condition of the air filter, and renew if necessary (Section 33).*
f) *Renew the fuel filter (Section 35).*
g) *Check the condition of all hoses, and check for fluid leaks (Section 4).*

5 If the above operations do not prove fully effective, carry out the following secondary operations:

Secondary operations

All items listed under *Primary operations*, plus the following:
a) *Check the charging system (refer to Chapter 5A).*
b) *Check the ignition system (refer to Chapter 5B).*
c) *Check the fuel system (refer to Chapter 4A or 4B).*

Every 6000 miles (10 000 km) or 6 months

3 Engine oil and filter renewal

Frequent oil and filter changes are the most important preventative maintenance procedures that can be undertaken by the DIY owner. As engine oil ages, it becomes diluted and contaminated, which leads to premature engine wear.
1 Before starting this procedure, gather together all the necessary tools and materials **(see illustration)**. Also make sure that you have plenty of clean rags and newspapers handy to mop up any spills.
2 Ideally, the engine should be warm, as the oil will drain better and more built-up sludge will be removed with it. Take care, however, not to touch the exhaust or any other hot parts of the engine when working under the vehicle. To avoid any possibility of scalding, and to protect yourself from possible skin irritants and other harmful contaminants in used engine oils, it is advisable to wear gloves when carrying out this work.
3 Access to the underside of the vehicle will be greatly improved if it can be raised on a lift,

driven onto ramps or jacked up and supported on axle stands. Whichever method is chosen, make sure that the car remains as level as possible, as the drain plug is located in the centre of the sump.
4 If necessary, remove the access cover to the sump drain plug, then position a suitable container beneath the hole. Clean the drain plug and the area around it, then slacken it half a turn using a special drain plug key **(see illustration)**. Remove the drain plug, and allow the oil to drain.

> **HAYNES HINT** *Keep the plug pressed into the sump while unscrewing it by hand the last couple of turns. As the plug releases from the threads, move it away sharply, so the stream of oil issuing from the sump runs into the pan, not up your sleeve.*

5 Allow some time for the old oil to drain, noting that it may be necessary to reposition the container as the oil flow slows to a trickle.
6 After all the oil has drained, wipe off the drain plug with a clean rag, and renew the sealing washer. Clean the area around the drain plug

opening and refit the plug. Tighten the plug securely, preferably to the specified torque using a torque wrench - do not overtighten.
7 Move the container into position under the oil filter, which is located on the front face of the cylinder block.
8 Using an oil filter removal tool, slacken the filter initially, then unscrew it by hand the rest of the way. Empty the oil in the old filter into the container.
9 Use a clean rag to remove all oil, dirt and sludge from the filter sealing area on the engine. Check the old filter to make sure that the rubber sealing ring hasn't stuck to the engine. If it has, carefully remove it.
10 Apply a light coating of clean engine oil to the sealing ring on the new filter, then screw it into position on the engine **(see illustration)**. Tighten the filter firmly by hand only - do not use any tools. Wipe clean the exterior of the oil filter.
11 Remove the old oil and all tools from under the car, then (if applicable) lower the car to the ground.
12 Remove the oil filler cap on the right-hand end of the valve cover, and fill the engine, using the correct grade and type of oil **(see illustrations)**. Pour the oil in slowly, otherwise

3.1 Tools necessary for the engine oil change and filter renewal

3.4 Using a special drain plug key to unscrew the drain plug from the sump

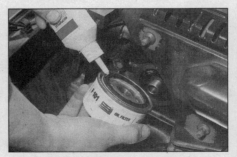

3.10 Apply a light coating of clean oil to the sealing ring before fitting the new oil filter

3.12a Remove the filler cap on the right-hand side of the valve cover . . .

3.12b . . . and add engine oil until the level reaches the dipstick MAX mark

it may overflow from the top of the valve cover. Check that the oil level is up to the maximum mark on the dipstick.

13 Start the engine and run it for a few minutes, while checking for leaks around the oil filter seal and the sump drain plug.

14 Switch off the engine, and wait a few minutes for the oil to settle in the sump once more. With the new oil circulated and the filter now completely full, recheck the level on the dipstick, and add more oil as necessary.

15 Dispose of the used engine oil safely with reference to *General repair procedures*.

4 Underbonnet hose and fluid leak check

Engine

1 Visually inspect the engine joint faces, gaskets and seals for any signs of water or oil leaks. Pay particular attention to the areas around the valve cover, cylinder head, oil filter and sump joint faces.

2 Bear in mind that over a period of time, some very slight seepage from these areas is

A leak in the cooling system will usually show up as white- or rust-coloured deposits on the area adjoining the leak

to be expected - what you are really looking for is any indication of a serious leak.

3 Should a leak be found, renew the offending gasket or oil seal by referring to the appropriate Chapters in this manual.

4 Check the security and condition of all the engine-related pipes and hoses.

5 Ensure that all cable ties or securing clips are in place, and in good condition. Clips which are broken or missing can lead to chafing of the hoses, pipes or wiring, which could cause more serious problems in the future.

Cooling system

6 The engine should be cold for the cooling system checks, so either perform the following procedure before driving the vehicle, or after it has been shut off for at least three hours.

7 Remove the expansion tank filler cap (see above), and clean it thoroughly inside and out with a rag. Also clean the filler neck on the expansion tank. The presence of rust or corrosion in the filler neck indicates that the coolant should be changed. The coolant inside the expansion tank should be relatively clean and transparent. If it is rust-coloured, drain and flush the system, and refill with a fresh coolant mixture.

8 Carefully check the radiator hoses and heater hoses along their entire lengths. Renew any hose which is cracked, swollen or deteriorated; cracks will show up better if the hose is squeezed. Pay close attention to the hose clips which secure the hoses to the cooling system components. Hose clips can pinch and puncture hoses, resulting in cooling system leaks. If wire-type hose clips are used, it may be a good idea to replace them with screw-type clips.

9 Inspect all the cooling system components (hoses, joint faces, etc.) for leaks (**see Haynes Hint**). Where any problems are found on system components, renew the component or gasket with reference to Chapter 3.

10 Clean the front of the radiator with a soft brush to remove all insects, leaves, etc. imbedded in the radiator fins. Be extremely careful not to damage the radiator fins, and take care not to cut your fingers on them.

5 Auxiliary drivebelt check, adjustment, removal and refitting

1 The water pump drivebelt arrangement varies according to the engine type, and according to whether power steering and/or air conditioning is fitted. In all cases, the water pump pulley is driven by the back (smooth side) of the drivebelt. On models fitted with both power steering and air conditioning, the alternator is driven by a small drivebelt from the air conditioning compressor pulley.

2 Since the drivebelt is located very close to the right-hand side of the engine compartment, it is possible to gain better access by raising the front of the car and removing the right-hand wheel, then removing the inner plastic cover which covers the lower part of the engine.

3 With the engine switched off, inspect the full length of the drivebelt for cracks and deterioration (**see illustration**). It will be

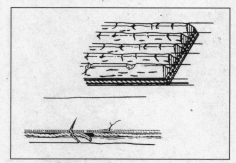

5.3 Check the multi-ribbed drivebelt for wear as shown

5.4a Checking the water pump drivebelt tension with the special Volvo tool (5197) on models without power steering or air conditioning

1 *Adjustment nut*
2 *Alternator pivot bolt and lock-bolt*

5.4b Checking the water pump drivebelt tension with the special Volvo tool (5197) on models with power steering

1 *Adjustment nut*
2 *Alternator pivot bolt and lock-bolt*

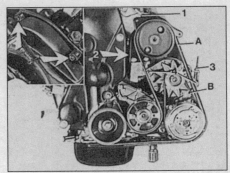

5.4c Checking the water pump drivebelt tension with the special Volvo tool on models with air conditioning and power steering

1 *Power steering pump adjustment nut*
2 *Power steering pump pivot bolt and lock-bolt*
3 *Alternator adjustment nut*
A *Water pump drivebelt*
B *Alternator drivebelt*

necessary to turn the engine in order to move the belt from the pulleys so that the belt can be inspected thoroughly. Twist the belt between the pulleys so that both sides can be viewed. Also check for fraying, and for glazing which gives the belt a shiny appearance. Check the pulleys for nicks, cracks, distortion and corrosion.

4 The tension of the drivebelt is checked by pushing on it midway between the pulleys on the longest run and checking the deflection. Volvo technicians use a special spring-tensioned tool which applies a specific force to the belt, and the tension of the belt is then adjusted to bring a mark in line on the tool. If at all possible this tool should be used; alternatively, press on the drivebelt with a finger or thumb, and check that the deflection is between 3.0 mm and 5.0 mm **(see illustrations)**.

5 If adjustment is necessary on models without air conditioning, loosen the alternator pivot and tension lock-bolts, then turn the adjustment nut clockwise to tension the belt, or anti-clockwise to slacken the belt **(see illustration)**. Tighten the pivot and lock-bolts after making the adjustment.

6 On models with air conditioning and power steering, loosen the power steering pivot and lock-bolts, then turn the adjustment nut clockwise to tension the belt, or anti-clockwise to slacken the belt. Tighten the pivot and lock-bolts after making the adjustment. To adjust

the small alternator drivebelt on these models, proceed as described in the previous paragraph. It is preferable to adjust the small drivebelt before the main drivebelt.

7 Run the engine for about five minutes, then recheck the tension and adjust if necessary.

8 To renew the drivebelt, slacken the belt tension fully as described above, then slip the belt off the pulleys. Fit the new belt ensuring that it is routed correctly, and adjust the tension as previously described. Note that on models with air conditioning and power steering, the main drivebelt must be removed first in order to remove the small alternator drivebelt.

6 Vacuum servo unit check (non-ABS models)

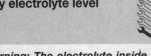

1 To test the operation of the servo unit, depress the footbrake four or five times to exhaust the vacuum, then start the engine. As the engine starts, there should be a noticeable give in the brake pedal as vacuum builds up.

2 Allow the engine to run for at least two minutes, and then switch it off. If the brake pedal is depressed now, a hiss should be heard from the servo; after about four or five applications, no further hissing should be heard, and the pedal should feel considerably firmer.

3 Check the condition of the vacuum hose to the brake servo, and ensure that its connection at the servo is secure.

7 Battery electrolyte level check

⚠ Warning: The electrolyte inside a battery is diluted acid - it is a good idea to wear suitable rubber gloves. When topping-up, don't overfill the cells so that the electrolyte overflows. In the event of any spillage, rinse the electrolyte off without delay. Refit the cell covers and rinse the battery with copious quantities of clean water. Don't attempt to siphon out any excess electrolyte.

Note: *Some models covered by this Manual may be fitted with a maintenance-free battery as standard equipment, or may have had one fitted as a replacement. If the battery in your vehicle is marked Freedom, Maintenance-Free or similar, no electrolyte level checking is required (the battery is often completely sealed, preventing any topping-up).*

1 The battery is located in the front left-hand corner of the engine compartment.

2 Batteries which do require their electrolyte level to be checked can be recognised by the presence of removable covers over the six battery cells - the battery casing is also sometimes translucent, so that the electrolyte level can be more easily checked. One of the project vehicles seen in our workshop had a battery marked 'maintenance-free', which still had removable cell caps - in this case, check the electrolyte level as described, but consult a Volvo dealer if topping-up appears to be required.

3 Remove the cell caps or covers **(see illustration)**, and either look down inside the

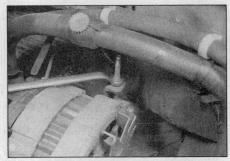

5.5 Adjusting the water pump drivebelt tension on models without air conditioning

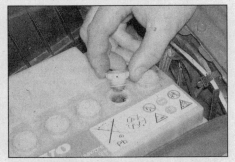

7.3 Unscrew the cell caps, and check the electrolyte level

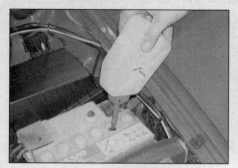

7.4 Topping-up the electrolyte level

8.3a Removing the cover from the windscreen wiper arm

8.3b Lifting the hinged cover from the tailgate wiper arm

battery to see the level web, or check the level using any markings provided on the battery casing. The electrolyte should cover the battery plates by approximately 15 mm.

4 If necessary, top up a little at a time with distilled (de-ionised) water until the level in all six cells is correct - don't fill the cells up to the brim **(see illustration)**. Wipe up any spillage, then refit the cell covers.

5 Further information on the battery, charging and jump starting can be found at the start of this manual and in Chapter 5A.

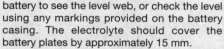

8 Ancillary systems check

Wiper blades

1 See *Weekly checks*.

Wiper arms

2 Check the wiper arms for worn hinges and weak springs, and renew as necessary.

3 If working on the windscreen wiper arm, prise out the cover for access to the retaining nut. If working on the tailgate wiper arm, lift up the hinged cover **(see illustrations)**.

4 Make sure that the wiper is in its rest (or park) position; if necessary, switch the wiper(s) on and off in order to allow them to return to the park position. Note this position for correct refitting - stick a piece of masking tape to the glass, to indicate the wiper blade line.

8.5a Removing the windscreen wiper arm from the splined spindle

8.5b Tailgate wiper arm components

5 Unscrew the retaining nut and pull the arm from the spindle splines **(see illustrations)**. If necessary, use a screwdriver to prise off the arm, being careful not to damage the paintwork.

6 Fit the new arm using a reversal of the removal procedure.

Washer system

7 If topping-up the windscreen/headlight washer fluid reservoir, refer to *Weekly checks*.

8 Check that the washer jets direct the fluid onto the upper part of the windscreen/ tailgate/headlight **(see illustration)**. If necessary, adjust the windscreen/tailgate washer jets using a 0.6 mm diameter piece of wire - not a pin or needle.

9 To adjust the headlight washer jets, make up a tool out of 2.5 mm sheet steel **(see illustration)**. Never attempt to open the jet itself, otherwise an incorrect spray pattern will result. The headlight main beam must be switched on before the headlight washers are functional - on 480 models, the headlights must be switched on and off each time the washers are checked.

10 Adjust the headlight washer jets to a point between the top of the headlight and 5.0 mm below **(see illustration)**.

Lights and instruments

11 Check the operation of all lights, indicators and instruments; refer to Chapter 12 if any problems are discovered.

 1

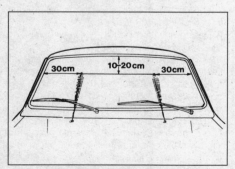

8.8 Windscreen washer jet setting diagram

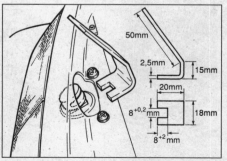

8.9 Headlamp washer jet adjustment tool dimensions

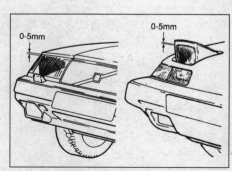

8.10 Headlamp washer jet setting diagram

Every 12 000 miles (20 000 km) or 12 months

9 Front wheel alignment check

Checking the front wheel alignment requires specialist knowledge and equipment (see Chapter 10, Section 29). For most owners, this task should therefore be referred to a Volvo dealer, suitably-equipped garage, or tyre-fitting centre. Unless abnormal tyre wear has been noted, this check should not normally be strictly necessary on a regular basis.

10 Antifreeze concentration check

If the antifreeze concentration drops below the levels indicated in the Specifications at the start of this Chapter, the cooling system will be at risk from premature freezing in cold weather, and from internal corrosion. Special antifreeze testers are available from motor accessory shops - use their manufacturers instructions to check the antifreeze concentration.

However, provided that coolant renewal has been carried out at regular intervals, and any topping-up has only been done using antifreeze mixture (not plain water), there is no reason to assume the required concentration won't be present in the system. If the history of the car is not known, it may be advisable to renew the coolant as described in Section 43.

11 Exhaust manifold check

Check the exhaust manifold for any signs of leakage, and check the tightness of the exhaust manifold nuts. On older engines, take care when tightening the nuts that the spanner or socket does not slip - if the nuts are old and rusty, it may be preferable to leave them alone, as long as there is no indication of a leak.

If there is evidence of leakage, the manifolds will have to be removed and the gasket renewed. It may be advisable to renew the manifold studs and nuts at the same time, if they are in less-than-perfect condition.

12 Idle speed and mixture check and adjustment - carburettor engines

Note: *The idle speed and mixture settings on fuel injection engines should not require routine checking, and this task does not feature in the current Volvo schedules. In most cases, the idle speed cannot be adjusted, and the mixture screw should not be interfered with unless an accurate CO meter is available, particularly on models with a catalytic converter.*

1 Before making any adjustments, note the following points:
   a) *The engine should be in good condition, with balanced compressions, correct valve clearances, plugs clean and correctly gapped, and correct ignition timing.*
   b) *The air filter element should be checked, to ensure that it is not excessively dirty.*
   c) *The accelerator and choke cables should be correctly adjusted, and all crankcase ventilation hoses should be clean.*
   d) *The engine must be at normal operating temperature (indicated by the engine cooling fan having cut in and out - but see e below).*
   e) *An exhaust gas analyser and tachometer will be required.*

   f) *Adjustments must not be made while the electric cooling fan is in operation.*
   g) *On models fitted with a catalytic converter, the CO content must be measured ahead of the catalytic converter by unscrewing the special plug and using an adaptor. Where an oxygen sensor is fitted, its wiring must be disconnected.*
   h) *On models not fitted with a catalytic converter, the CO meter probe must be inserted at least 45 cm into the end of the exhaust tailpipe.*
   i) *On automatic transmission models, select position N before adjustments are carried out.*
   j) *On models with air conditioning, make sure that the air conditioning is switched off, unless otherwise stated.*

2 Connect an exhaust gas analyser and tachometer to the engine, in accordance with the equipment manufacturer's instructions.
3 Check that the idle speed is as given in the Specifications. If the speed is not within the specified range, turn the adjustment screw using a screwdriver inserted through the special hole in the top of the air cleaner **(see illustration)**. Turning it clockwise increases the speed, and turning it anti-clockwise decreases the speed.
4 With the engine idling, check that the CO content is within the limits given in the Specifications. If adjustment is necessary, remove the tamperproof plug (where fitted) covering the mixture adjustment screw, using a scriber or small screwdriver **(see illustration)**. Turn the adjustment screw by about a half-turn, then wait a few seconds for the gases to reach the exhaust gas analyser before noting the CO reading. Increase the engine speed to 2000 rpm for 30 seconds once every 3 minutes, to ensure that any excess fuel is cleared from the inlet manifold.

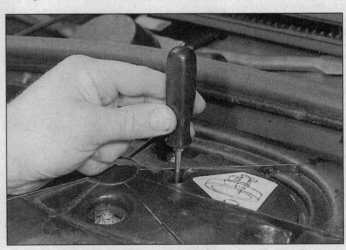

12.3 Adjusting the idle speed on the carburettor engine

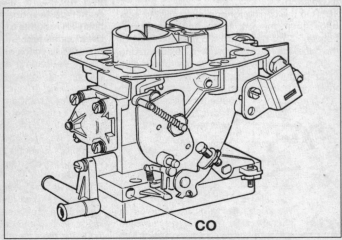

12.4 CO adjustment screw location on the Solex CISAC carburettor

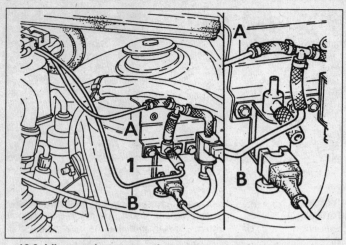

12.9 Idle speed compensation system on carburettor models fitted with air conditioning

1 Three-way valve
Inset shows method of connecting hoses A and B together

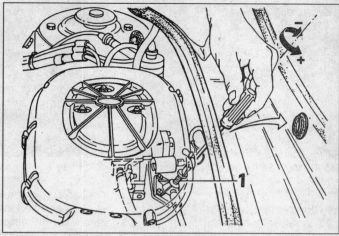

12.10 Adjusting the idle speed compensation system screw (1) on the vacuum diaphragm unit

5 If the mixture is adjusted, it will be necessary to check and if necessary adjust the idle speed again. Repeat the two adjustments until *both* are correct.
6 On completion, switch off the engine and fit a new tamperproof plug. Remove the exhaust gas analyser and tachometer.

Models with air conditioning

7 The idle speed and mixture are adjusted as described in paragraphs 2 to 6 above. On models with air conditioning, an idle speed compensation system is fitted, and this should be checked and if necessary adjusted after carrying out the previous work.
8 The headlight dipped beams should be switched on, and the air conditioning disengaged.
9 Refer to the accompanying illustration and disconnect hoses A and B from the three-way valve, then connect the hoses to each other - do not detach any other connections **(see illustration).**
10 Run the engine for approximately 10 seconds, then check that the engine speed is between 1375 rpm and 1425 rpm. If this is not the case, the idle speed should be adjusted to 1400 rpm as follows. Remove the rubber plug in the plenum chamber below the windscreen, then turn the adjusting screw on the vacuum diaphragm unit as required **(see illustration).**
11 After making the adjustment, refit the rubber plug and reconnect the hoses.

13 Fuel system checks

⚠ **Warning: Certain procedures in this Section require the removal of fuel lines and connections which may result in some fuel spillage. Before carrying out any operation on the** fuel system, refer to the precautions given in Safety first! at the beginning of this manual, and follow them implicitly. Petrol is a highly dangerous and volatile liquid, and the precautions necessary when handling it cannot be overstressed.

1 The fuel system is most easily checked with the vehicle raised on a hoist, or suitably supported on axle stands, so that the components underneath are readily visible and accessible.
2 If the smell of petrol is noticed while driving or after the vehicle has been parked in the sun, the system should be thoroughly inspected immediately.
3 Remove the petrol tank filler cap, and check for damage, corrosion and an unbroken sealing imprint on the gasket. Renew the cap if necessary.
4 With the vehicle raised, inspect the fuel tank and filler neck for punctures, cracks and other damage. The connection between the filler neck and tank is especially critical. Sometimes a rubber filler neck or connecting hose will leak due to loose retaining clamps or deteriorated rubber.
5 Carefully check all rubber hoses and metal fuel lines leading away from the fuel tank. Check for loose connections, deteriorated hoses, crimped lines and other damage. Pay particular attention to the vent pipes and hoses, which often loop up around the filler neck and can become blocked or crimped. Follow the lines to the front of the vehicle, carefully inspecting them all the way **(see illustration).** Renew damaged sections as necessary.
6 From within the engine compartment, check the security of all fuel hose attachments, and inspect the fuel hoses and vacuum hoses for kinks, chafing and deterioration.
7 Check the operation of the throttle linkage, and lubricate the linkage components with a few drops of light oil.

14 Exhaust system check

1 With the engine cold, check the complete exhaust system from the engine to the end of the tailpipe. Ideally the inspection should be carried out with the vehicle on a hoist, to permit unrestricted access. If a hoist is not available, raise and support the vehicle on axle stands.
2 Check the exhaust pipes and connections for evidence of leaks, severe corrosion and damage. Make sure that all brackets and mountings are in good condition, and that the securing nuts and bolts are tight. Leakage at any of the joints or in other parts of the system will usually show up as a black sooty stain in the vicinity of the leak.
3 Rattles and other noises can often be traced to the exhaust system, especially the brackets and mountings. Try to move the pipes and silencers. If the components can come into contact with the body or suspension parts, either secure the system with new mountings or if possible, separate the joints and twist the pipes as necessary to provide additional clearance.

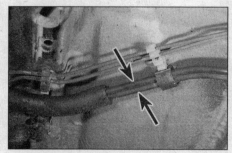

13.5 Fuel feed and return lines (arrowed) on the underbody

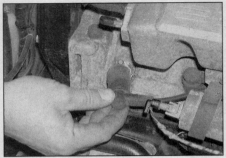

15.2 Pull the HT lead from the first spark plug

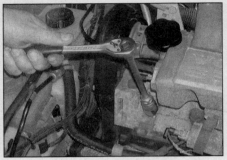

15.4a Using a suitable socket and extension bar . . .

15.4b . . . unscrew and remove the spark plugs from the cylinder head

15 Ignition system checks

Spark plugs

⚠ *Warning: Voltages produced by an electronic ignition system (such as that fitted to the Volvo 400 series) are considerably higher than those produced by conventional systems. Extreme care must be taken when working on the system with the ignition switched on. Persons with surgically-implanted cardiac pacemaker devices should keep well clear of the ignition circuits, components and test equipment.*

1 The correct functioning of the spark plugs is vital for the correct running and efficiency of the engine. It is essential that the plugs fitted are appropriate for the engine, and the suitable type is specified at the beginning of this Chapter. If this type is used and the engine is in good condition, the spark plugs should not need attention between scheduled replacement intervals. Spark plug cleaning is rarely necessary, and should not be attempted unless specialised equipment is available, as damage can easily be caused to the firing ends.

2 To remove the plugs, first open the bonnet and mark the HT leads for position. Wrap a piece of tape round each lead, and number them one to four, to correspond to the cylinder the lead serves (number one cylinder is at the left-hand, flywheel/transmission, end

of the engine). Pull the HT leads from the plugs by gripping the end fitting, not the lead, otherwise the lead connection may be fractured **(see illustration)**.

3 It is advisable to remove the dirt from the spark plug recesses using a clean brush, vacuum cleaner or compressed air before removing the plugs, to prevent any dirt dropping into the cylinders.

4 Unscrew the plugs using a spark plug spanner, suitable box spanner, or a deep socket and extension bar **(see illustrations)**. Keep the socket in alignment on the spark plugs - if it is forcibly moved to either side, the porcelain top of the spark plug may be broken off. As each plug is removed, examine it as follows.

5 Examination of the spark plugs will give a good indication of the condition of the engine. If the insulator nose of the spark plug is clean and white, with no deposits, this is indicative of a weak mixture or too hot a plug (a hot plug transfers heat away from the electrode slowly, a cold plug transfers heat away quickly).

6 If the tip and insulator nose are covered with hard black-looking deposits, then this is indicative that the mixture is too rich. Should the plug be black and oily, then it is likely that the engine is fairly worn, as well as the mixture being too rich.

7 If the insulator nose is covered with light-tan to greyish-brown deposits, then the mixture is correct and it is likely that the engine is in good condition.

8 The spark plug gap is of considerable importance - if it is too large or too small, the size of the spark and its efficiency will be

seriously impaired. For the best results, the spark plug gap should be set in accordance with the Specifications at the beginning of this Chapter.

9 To set the plug gap, measure the gap with a feeler gauge, and then bend the outer plug electrode until the correct gap is achieved **(see illustrations)**. The centre electrode should never be bent, as this may crack the insulation and cause plug failure, if nothing worse.

10 Special spark plug electrode gap adjusting tools are available from most motor accessory shops **(see illustration)**.

11 Before fitting the spark plugs, check that the threaded connector sleeves are tight, and that the plug exterior surfaces and threads are clean. To make removal of the plugs easier next time, apply a smear of copper-based brake grease to the plug threads.

12 Screw in the spark plugs by hand where possible, then tighten them to the specified torque. Take extra care to enter the plug threads correctly, as the cylinder head is of aluminium alloy **(see Tool Tip)**. Refit the remaining spark plugs in the same manner.

13 Reconnect the HT leads in their correct order.

HT leads, distributor cap and rotor arm

14 The spark plug HT leads should be checked whenever new spark plugs are installed in the engine.

15 Ensure that the leads are numbered before removing them, to avoid confusion when refitting (refer to paragraph 2 above).

15.9a Measuring the spark plug electrode gap with a feeler gauge

15.9b Measuring the spark plug electrode gap with a wire gauge

15.10 Adjusting the spark plug electrode gap with the adjuster on the wire gauge

TOOL TiP

To prevent cross-threading, fit a short length of rubber hose over the end of each spark plug before inserting it. The flexible hose acts as a universal joint to help align the plug with the plug hole. Should the plug begin to cross-thread, the hose will slip on the spark plug, preventing thread damage to the aluminium cylinder head. Remove the rubber hose and tighten the plug to the specified torque using the spark plug socket and a torque wrench

Pull the HT leads from the plugs by gripping the end fitting, not the lead, otherwise the lead connection may be fractured.

16 Check inside the end fitting for signs of corrosion, which will look like a white crusty powder. Push the end fitting back onto the spark plug, ensuring that it is a tight fit on the plug. If it isn't, remove the lead again and use pliers to carefully crimp the metal connector inside the end fitting until it fits securely on the end of the spark plug.

17 Using a clean rag, wipe the entire length of the lead to remove any built-up dirt and grease. Once the lead is clean, check for burns, cracks and other damage. Do not bend the lead excessively or pull the lead lengthways - the conductor inside might break.

18 Disconnect the other end of the lead from the distributor cap. Again, pull only on the end fitting. Unless you mark the distributor cap for lead position, do not remove all the leads from the cap at once. Check for corrosion and a tight fit in the same manner as the spark plug end. If an ohmmeter is available, check the resistance of the HT lead by connecting the meter between the spark plug end of the lead and the segment inside the distributor cap **(see illustration)**. Refit the lead securely on completion.

19 Check the remaining HT leads one at a time, in the same way.

20 Refer to Chapter 5B and remove the distributor cap. Wipe it clean and carefully inspect it inside and out for signs of cracks, carbon tracks (tracking) and worn, burned or loose contacts. Similarly inspect the rotor arm. Renew these components if any defects are found. It is common practice to renew the cap and rotor arm whenever new HT leads are fitted.

HAYNES HiNT *When fitting a new distributor cap, remove the HT leads from the old cap one at a time, and fit them to the new cap in the exact same location - do not simultaneously remove all the leads from the old cap, or firing-order confusion may occur.*

21 Even with the ignition system in first class condition, some engines may still occasionally experience poor starting, attributable to damp ignition components. The application at regular intervals of a water-dispersant spray can be an excellent preventative measure.

22 Particularly if running problems have been experienced, check carefully all earth connections around the engine compartment **(see illustration)**. Even if they appear to be sound, it is worthwhile dismantling the connection, cleaning it thoroughly, and applying a coat of water-dispersant aerosol, or a suitable grease. A Volvo dealer may be able to recommend a product which will ensure a continued good earth connection.

16 Clutch pedal adjustment

Early models

1 As the linings on the clutch friction disc wear, the clutch pedal height will rise, so it is necessary to check the adjustment at the specified intervals.

2 If adjustment is necessary, open the bonnet and locate the clutch cable mounting on the gearbox.

3 Insert a screwdriver between the adjustment nut on the outer cable and the plastic casing **(see illustration)**. Turn the screwdriver as required so that the adjustment nut turns, and continue to do this until the correct pedal height is achieved. Turning the screwdriver anti-clockwise will raise the pedal, and turning it clockwise will lower the pedal.

15.18 Checking the resistance of the spark plug HT leads using a digital ohmmeter

15.22 Typical engine compartment earth connection (arrowed) - also check those around the battery, etc

4 After each adjustment, operate the clutch pedal several times and recheck the setting.

Later models

5 On later models, the clutch cable is adjusted with a nut on the end of the inner cable. Some models are fitted with a short release arm, and some with a longer arm. The models with the longer arm can be recognised by an additional mounting bracket bolted to the gearbox housing to locate the cable in line with the release arm.

Models with the longer release arm

6 Measure the distance A between the release fork and the special bracket, without depressing the clutch pedal **(see illustration)**.

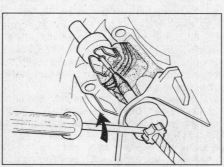

16.3 Clutch pedal height adjustment - early models

Turning nut anti-clockwise will raise the clutch pedal

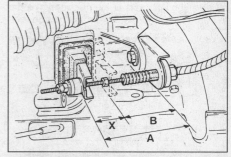

16.6 Clutch pedal stroke adjustment dimensions on later models with longer type release fork

$A - B = 30.0 ± 1.0 mm (X)$

1

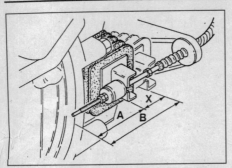

16.11 Clutch pedal stroke adjustment dimensions on later models with the shorter type release fork

$B - A = 22.0 \pm 1.0 \; mm \; (X)$

7 Have an assistant depress the clutch pedal fully, and measure between the same points on the release arm and bracket. If necessary, a length of wood can be used against the front seat to hold the clutch pedal fully depressed.

8 The difference between the two dimensions is the clutch pedal stroke, and this should be as specified.

9 If the stroke is incorrect, loosen the locknut and turn the adjustment nut as required until the difference is correct. When correct, tighten the locknut.

Models with the shorter release arm

10 First remove the pedal stop screw (if fitted) below the pedal on the bracket inside the car. Also remove the floor mat under the pedal.

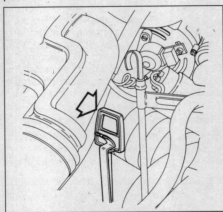

18.5a Automatic transmission fluid level dipstick location

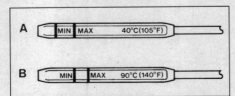

18.5b Markings on each side of the automatic transmission fluid level dipstick

A Markings for checking when cold
B Markings for checking when hot

11 Measure the distance A between the release fork and the engine-to-gearbox joint surface, without depressing the clutch pedal **(see illustration)**.

12 Now have an assistant fully depress the clutch pedal, measure between the same points and record dimension B. If necessary, a length of wood can be used against the front seat to hold the clutch pedal fully depressed.

13 The difference between the two dimensions (A - B) represents the clutch pedal stroke, and should be as specified.

14 If the stroke is incorrect, loosen the locknut and turn the adjustment nut as required. Tighten the locknut on completion.

17 Manual gearbox oil level check

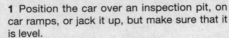

1 Position the car over an inspection pit, on car ramps, or jack it up, but make sure that it is level.

2 Remove the engine splash guard.

3 Using a suitable square key, unscrew the filler/level plug from the front-facing side of the gearbox **(see illustration)**.

4 Check that the level of the oil is up to the bottom edge of the plug hole. If necessary, use a screwdriver or length of wire to confirm this, but don't drop anything into the hole!

5 Where necessary, top-up the level using the correct grade of oil. If too much oil is added, and oil begins to come out, wait for the level to stabilise before refitting the filler plug.

6 Check and if necessary renew the sealing washer, then refit and tighten the filler plug.

7 If the gearbox requires frequent topping-up, check it for leakage, especially around the driveshaft oil seal/rubber boot, and repair as necessary.

8 Refit the engine splash guard.

9 Lower the car to the ground.

18 Automatic transmission fluid level check

1 Ideally, this check should be carried out with the engine and transmission at normal operating temperature, such as immediately after a journey of at least 5 miles. If necessary, the check can also be performed with the engine cold, but the result will not be as accurate an indication.

2 Position the car on level ground, then firmly apply the handbrake and select P with the selector lever. Start the engine, and allow it to idle.

3 Move the selector lever between all the positions, stopping in each position for 2 to 3 seconds.

4 Select position P, and allow the engine to idle for further 2 minutes.

5 With the engine still idling, withdraw the dipstick from the front of the transmission

17.3 Removing the manual gearbox filler/level plug

housing, and wipe it on a clean cloth. Note that there are level marks on both sides of the dipstick - the marks on one side are for checking when the transmission is cold, and the higher marks on the other side are for the (more accurate) hot check **(see illustrations)**.

6 Insert the dipstick again, making sure that the applicable side (according to the transmission temperature) is facing **towards** the transmission. Wait at least four seconds, then withdraw the dipstick once more and read off the level. Ideally, the level should be up to the MAX mark.

7 If the level is too low, check the transmission for leakage. Also note that a low reading may result if the ambient temperature is below 5°C, and in this case, the level should be checked again when the temperature is higher.

8 If the level is too high, check for water in the fluid, which will produce a milky colour. In this case, the fluid should be drained and the fluid cooler renewed, then the transmission filled with new fluid. Note also that heavy loading or driving at excessive speeds may overheat the fluid, resulting in a reading which is too high. Wait until the transmission has cooled down before checking the level again.

9 If topping-up is necessary, slowly add a quantity of the specified fluid (refer to the end of *Weekly checks*) to the transmission through the dipstick tube, with the engine still running. Use a funnel with a fine-mesh screen, to avoid spillage and to ensure that any foreign matter is trapped **(see illustration)**. The difference between the MIN and MAX marks is 0.3 litres. Do not overfill the transmission, otherwise there is a risk of overheating. After adding

18.9 Topping-up the automatic transmission fluid level

fluid, allow the engine to idle for several minutes before rechecking the level.

10 If the level is too high, drain a quantity of fluid from the transmission by unscrewing the drain plug.

 Warning: Take precautions to prevent scalding, as the fluid may be very hot.

11 If the fluid is discoloured or has a burnt smell, the advice of a Volvo dealer or an automatic transmission specialist should be sought.

12 Re-insert the dipstick, and switch off the engine.

19 Driveshaft rubber boot and CV joint check

1 With the vehicle raised and securely supported on axle stands, turn the steering onto full-lock then slowly rotate the roadwheel. Inspect the condition of the outer constant velocity (CV) joint rubber boots, squeezing the boots to open out the folds. Check for signs of cracking, splits or deterioration of the rubber, which may allow the grease to escape and lead to water and grit entry into the joint. Also check the security and condition of the retaining clips. Repeat these checks on the inner CV joints. If any damage or deterioration is found, the boots should be renewed as described in Chapter 8.

2 At the same time, check the general condition of the CV joints themselves by first holding the driveshaft and attempting to rotate the wheel. Repeat this check by holding the inner joint and attempting to rotate the driveshaft. Any appreciable movement indicates wear in the joints, wear in the driveshaft splines, or a loose driveshaft retaining nut.

20 Brake pipes and hoses check

1 Either position the car over an inspection pit, or alternatively jack it up and support on axle stands.

2 Check all brake hoses and hydraulic pipes/lines for leakage and damage. Check that the brake hoses are positioned well clear of suspension and underbody components, which may chafe them when the car is in motion.

3 Examine the brake hoses closely for cracking and deterioration.

21 Brake pads and shoes check

Front pads and discs

1 Loosen the front wheel bolts. Apply the handbrake, then jack up the front of the car and support on axle stands. Remove the front wheels.

2 Looking through the aperture on the front of the caliper, check that each front brake pad has at least a 2.0 mm thickness of friction material or lining left (do not confuse the lining with the pad backing plate).

3 If any one pad thickness is less than the minimum amount, renew all the front pads with reference to Chapter 9.

4 Check the front brake discs for excessive wear and scoring. Slight scoring is permissible, but if it is excessive, both front discs should be renewed.

5 Using a micrometer if possible, check that the disc thickness is not less than the minimum amount given in the Specifications. It is normal to find a lip of rust around the outer edge of the disc, which can build up sufficiently to disguise the true thickness of the disc. Remove the lip with a file if necessary, but take care not to damage the disc friction surface.

Rear pads and discs

6 Loosen the rear wheel bolts. Chock the front wheels, then jack up the rear of the car and support on axle stands. Remove the rear wheels.

7 Looking through the aperture on the rear of the caliper, check that each rear brake pad has at least a 2.0 mm thickness of friction material or lining left (do not confuse the lining with the pad backing plate).

8 If any one pad thickness is less that the minimum amount, renew all the rear pads with reference to Chapter 9.

9 Check the rear brake discs as described in paragraphs 4 and 5.

Rear shoes and drums

10 Loosen the rear wheel bolts. Chock the front wheels, then jack up the rear of the car and support it on axle stands. Remove the rear wheels.

11 Remove both rear brake drums, with reference to Chapter 9.

12 Clean away the accumulated dust from the shoes and backplates.

 Warning: The dust may contain asbestos, which is a health hazard. Do not inhale the dust; clean it away using brake cleaner or methylated spirit only.

13 Check that each brake shoe lining has at least a 1.0 mm thickness of friction material or lining left (do not confuse the lining with the shoe backing plate).

14 If the lining on any one shoe is less than the minimum amount, renew all the rear brake shoes with reference to Chapter 9.

15 Check the wheel cylinders for signs of leakage, and repair as necessary.

16 Clean the brake drums, and examine them for excessive wear and scoring. Check that the inside diameter of the drum does not exceed the maximum amount given in the Specifications. Slight scoring of the drums is permissible, but if it is excessive, both rear brake drums should be renewed.

22 Handbrake check and adjustment

1 Chock the front wheels, then jack up the rear of the car and support on axle stands.

2 Apply the handbrake lever by 5 to 7 notches, and check that both rear wheels are locked. To check this, try to turn each rear wheel by hand.

3 If adjustment is required, unbolt and remove the exhaust system heat shield from the underbody, for access to the handbrake compensator and adjuster **(see illustration)**.

4 With the handbrake applied by 6 notches, first back off the adjuster nut until the rear wheels can be turned, then tighten the adjuster nut until both rear wheels are locked.

5 Fully release the handbrake, and check that the rear wheels can be turned freely. If not, check for seized handbrake cables and/or faulty rear brake shoe/disc pad operation.

6 On models with rear disc brakes, check that, with the handbrake fully released, the levers on the rear calipers are just contacting the stops (refer to illustration 22.3). The help of an assistant will be needed to do this - have the assistant apply and release the handbrake, and tell you when it is fully off.

7 Lower the car to the ground on completion.

23 Suspension fastener tightness check

This task is included in the Volvo schedule, and need only be carried out at the first annual service. With reference to the torque wrench settings in Chapter 10, the tightness of all front and rear suspension nuts and bolts should be checked. It may be of value to carry out this check even after the first service, especially at higher mileages, or if the car's history is not known.

22.3 Handbrake adjustment

1 Locknut   *2 Adjuster bolt*

Inset shows caliper stop and lever on models with rear disc brakes

1

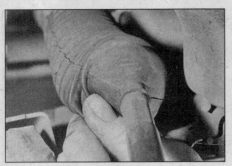

24.2 Checking the condition of the steering rack rubber bellows

24.4 Checking for wear in the front suspension and hub bearings

24 Suspension and steering check

Front

1 Raise the front of the vehicle, and securely support it on axle stands.

2 Visually inspect the balljoint dust covers and the steering rack rubber bellows for splits, chafing or deterioration (see illustration). Any wear of these components will cause loss of lubricant, and will permit dirt and water entry, resulting in rapid deterioration of the balljoints or steering gear.

3 On vehicles with power steering, check the fluid hoses for chafing or deterioration, and the pipe and hose unions for fluid leaks. Also check for signs of fluid leakage under pressure from the steering gear rubber bellows, which would indicate failed fluid seals within the steering gear. To pressurise the system, simply turn the steering towards full-lock, but do not hold it on full-lock for more than a few seconds, as this strains the pump.

4 Grasp the roadwheel at the 12 o'clock and 6 o'clock positions, and try to rock it (see illustration). Very slight free play may be felt, but if the movement is appreciable, further investigation is necessary to determine the source. Continue rocking the wheel while an assistant depresses the footbrake. If the movement is now eliminated or significantly reduced, it is likely that the hub bearings are at fault. If the free play is still evident with the footbrake depressed, then there is wear in the suspension joints or mountings.

5 Now grasp the wheel at the 9 o'clock and 3 o'clock positions, and try to rock it as before. Any movement felt now may again be caused by wear in the hub bearings or the steering track-rod balljoints. If the outer balljoint is worn, the visual movement will be obvious - wear in the steering track rod ends can be checked by attempting to compress the balljoints as shown (see illustration). If the inner joint is suspect, it can be felt by placing a hand over the rack-and-pinion rubber bellows and gripping the track-rod. If the wheel is now rocked, movement will be felt at the inner joint if wear has taken place. The maximum play allowed is 0.5 mm in the steering rack, and 0.5 mm in each of the track-rod balljoints.

6 Using a large screwdriver or flat bar, check for wear in the suspension mounting bushes by levering between the relevant suspension component and its attachment point (see illustration). Check the anti-roll bar mountings in the same way. Some movement is to be expected, as the mountings are made of rubber, but excessive wear should be obvious. Also check the condition of any visible rubber bushes, looking for splits, cracks or contamination of the rubber.

7 Check all of the front suspension mounting bolts for security and tightness.

8 With the car standing on its wheels, have an assistant turn the steering wheel back and forth about an eighth of a turn each way. There should be very little, if any, lost movement between the steering wheel and roadwheels. If this is not the case, closely observe the joints and mountings previously described, but in addition check the steering column universal joints for wear, and also check the rack-and-pinion steering gear itself.

Rear

9 Chock the front wheels, then raise the rear of the vehicle and securely support it on axle stands.

10 Using a large screwdriver or flat bar, check for wear in the rear suspension trailing arm and radius arm bushes. There will be some movement as the mountings are made of rubber, but excessive wear should be obvious.

11 Similarly check the anti-roll bar and link mounting bushes, and also the Panhard rod mounting bushes.

12 Check the rear axle beam for signs of damage.

13 Check all of the rear suspension mounting bolts for security and tightness.

Strut/shock absorber check

14 Check for any signs of fluid leakage around the suspension strut/shock absorber body, or from the seal around the piston rod. **Note:** *Suspension struts/shock absorbers should always be renewed in pairs on the same axle.*

15 The efficiency of the suspension strut/shock absorber may be checked by bouncing the vehicle at each corner. Generally speaking, the body will return to its normal position and stop after being depressed. If it rises and returns on a rebound, the suspension strut/shock absorber is probably suspect. Also examine the suspension strut/shock absorber upper and lower mountings for any signs of wear.

25 Bodywork check

Body paintwork and underseal

1 Check all of the body paintwork for damage from stones and scratching. Treat bare metal with rust inhibitor, and touch-up chipped paintwork.

2 With the car raised and supported on axle stands, check for damage to the underbody, and renew any underseal as necessary.

Rubber door seal protection

3 Before Winter, dust all door and tailgate/boot lid rubber weatherseals with talcum powder (or silicone spray), to keep them in good condition and to prevent them sticking to the body.

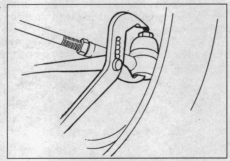

24.5 Using adjustable grips to check the steering track rod end balljoints for wear

24.6 Using a lever to check for wear in the anti-roll bar mountings

26 Seat belt check

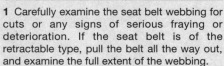

1 Carefully examine the seat belt webbing for cuts or any signs of serious fraying or deterioration. If the seat belt is of the retractable type, pull the belt all the way out, and examine the full extent of the webbing.
2 The seat belts are designed to lock up during a sudden stop or impact, yet allow free movement during normal driving. Fasten and unfasten the belt, ensuring that the locking mechanism holds securely and releases properly when intended. Check also that the retracting mechanism operates correctly when the belt is released.

27 Hinge and lock lubrication

1 Lightly lubricate all door, boot lid/tailgate and bonnet hinges with a little oil **(see illustration)**.
2 Lubricate all catches with a little grease.
3 Apply a little petroleum jelly to the door and boot lid strikers, and to the bonnet safety catch.

28 Headlight beam alignment check

Have the headlight beam alignment accurately adjusted by a Volvo dealer or suitably-equipped garage. It is not possible to accurately adjust the alignment without precision equipment, and as this is tested during the MOT test, accurate setting is vital.

29 Engine management system fault code check - Fenix fuel injection models

1 This check is part of the manufacturer's maintenance schedule, and involves 'interrogating' the engine management control unit using special dedicated test equipment. Such testing will allow the test equipment to read any fault codes stored in the electronic control unit memory.

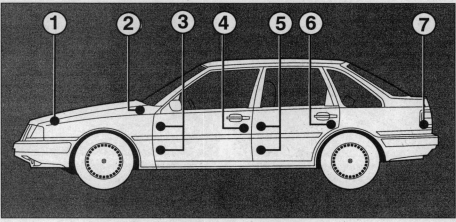

27.1 Body lubricating points

1 Engine bonnet catch
2 Bonnet hinges
3 Front door hinges
4 Front door locks
5 Rear door hinges
6 Rear door locks
7 Tailgate/boot lid hinges, locks and striker

2 Unless a fault is suspected, this test is not essential, although it should be noted that it is recommended by the manufacturers.
3 It is possible for quite serious faults to occur in the engine management system without the owner being aware of it. Certain engine management system faults will cause the system to enter an emergency back-up mode, which is often so sophisticated that engine performance is not apparently much affected. If a problem has caused the system to enter its back-up mode, this will usually be most apparent when starting and running from cold.

30 Road test

Instruments and electrical equipment

1 Check the operation of all instruments and electrical equipment.
2 Make sure that all instruments read correctly, and switch on all electrical equipment in turn, to check that it functions properly.

Steering and suspension

3 Check for any abnormalities in the steering, suspension, handling or road feel.
4 Drive the vehicle, and check that there are no unusual vibrations or noises.

5 Check that the steering feels positive, with no excessive sloppiness, or roughness, and check for any suspension noises when cornering and driving over bumps.

Drivetrain

6 Check the performance of the engine, clutch, transmission and driveshafts.
7 Listen for any unusual noises from the engine, clutch and transmission.
8 Make sure that the engine runs smoothly when idling, and that there is no hesitation when accelerating.
9 Check that the clutch action is smooth and progressive, that the drive is taken up smoothly, and that the pedal travel is not excessive. Also listen for any noises when the clutch pedal is depressed.
10 Check that all gears can be engaged smoothly without noise, and that the gear lever action is not abnormally vague or notchy.

Braking system

11 Make sure that the vehicle does not pull to one side when braking, and that the wheels do not lock prematurely when braking hard.
12 Check that there is no vibration through the steering when braking.
13 Check that the handbrake operates correctly without excessive movement of the lever, and that it holds the vehicle stationary on a slope.
14 On models without ABS, test the operation of the brake servo unit as described in Section 6.

1

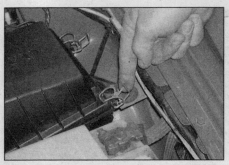

33.1 Release the over-centre wire clips securing the air cleaner top cover

33.4a Removing the air cleaner element on a carburettor engine . . .

33.4b . . . and on a fuel injection engine

Every 24 000 miles (40 000 km) or 2 years

31 Compression test

Refer to Chapter 2A and carry out a check of all cylinder compressions. This is part of the Volvo schedule, and is not absolutely essential if the engine is running well, but can give valuable diagnostic clues if the engine has been running poorly.

32 Crankcase ventilation hoses - cleaning

1 Disconnect the crankcase ventilation system hoses, and clean them out thoroughly; refer to Chapter 4C if necessary. Where applicable, clean any calibrated orifices.
2 Reconnect the hoses after cleaning them.

33 Air cleaner filter element renewal

1 Release the spring clips securing the air cleaner cover to the main body **(see illustration)**.
2 On carburettor models, unscrew the central screw and if necessary unscrew the nuts securing the main body to the carburettor.
3 Separate the cover from the main body, and move it to one side.
4 Remove the air cleaner element from inside the main body, noting which way round it is fitted **(see illustrations)**.
5 Wipe clean the inside of the main body and cover.
6 Locate a new filter element in the main body. On fuel injection models, make sure that the seal is uppermost.
7 Refit the cover, and secure with the clips and screws as applicable.

34 Air cleaner temperature control system check - carburettor engines

1 Disconnect the inlet air hose and exhaust manifold warm air hose from the air cleaner temperature control unit.
2 Pull the temperature control unit from the air cleaner body.
3 An accurate thermometer, and a hot air blower such as a hairdryer, will be required for the following check. Heat the thermostat capsule, and check that the valve flap closes at a temperature above 35°C. Now cool the thermostat, and check that the valve flap opens at a temperature below 20°C.
4 To renew the thermostat, press back the tabs at the sides and front, and separate the two halves of the housing. Press the thermostat out of the housing. Refitting is a reversal of the removal procedure, but check its operation as described previously.

35 Fuel filter renewal

⚠️ **Warning: Procedures in this Section require the removal of fuel lines and connections which may result in some fuel spillage. Before carrying out any operation on the fuel system, refer to the precautions given in Safety first! at the beginning of this manual, and follow them implicitly. Petrol is a highly dangerous and volatile liquid, and the precautions necessary when handling it cannot be overstressed.**

1 Wait until the engine is completely cold before starting this procedure. Anticipate some fuel spillage, and have some clean rag to hand to mop up any spills quickly.

Carburettor engines

2 A gauze filter is fitted in the fuel delivery union on the side of the carburettor. To remove it, unscrew the plug and pull out the filter.
3 Clean the filter in fuel, then insert it in the union. Check the washer, and renew it if necessary before refitting and tightening the plug.

Fuel injection engines

4 Depressurise the fuel system as described in Chapter 4B. This is essential, both to reduce the amount of fuel lost in changing the filter, and to ensure that it does not spray out uncontrollably.
5 The fuel filter is located on the right-hand side of the fuel tank, beneath the rear underbody. First chock the front wheels, then jack up the rear of the car and support on axle stands.
6 Before removing the filter, note the orientation of the direction-of-flow arrow on the filter body. Loosen the clips, then disconnect the hoses and remove the fuel filter.
7 Check the condition of the clips and hoses, and if necessary renew them. Check particularly for signs of cracking on the hose ends - remember, the system operates at high pressure, so renew any hose which is at all suspect.
8 Fit the new filter using a reversal of the removal procedure, making sure that the fuel flow direction arrow on the filter points away from the fuel tank. Tighten the clips securely.

36 Exhaust gas recirculation (EGR) system cleaning

1 Disconnect the EGR pipes and valve, and clean them thoroughly. Tap the components to remove internal carbon deposits.
2 After reconnecting the components, check that the valve operates correctly with reference to Chapter 4C. The valve should only operate when the engine is at its normal operating temperature, and at engine speeds above idle.

37 Automatic transmission selector and kickdown cables - adjustment

Refer to Chapter 7B.

Every 36 000 miles (60 000 km) or 3 years

38 Manual gearbox oil renewal

1 Gearbox oil renewal is best carried out shortly after a run of five miles or more, when the gearbox oil is hot.
2 Position the car over an inspection pit, on car ramps, or jack it up, but make sure that it is level.
3 Remove the engine splash guard.
4 Position a suitable container beneath the drain plug on the bottom of the gearbox.
5 Using a suitable square key, unscrew both the filler/level plug and the drain plug, and allow the oil to drain for several minutes.
6 Check and if necessary renew the plug sealing washers, then refit and tighten the drain plug.
7 Fill the gearbox with the correct quantity and grade of oil through the filler/level plug hole, and check that the level is up to the bottom edge of the hole (see Section 17).

8 Refit and tighten the filler/level plug.
9 Refit the engine splash guard.
10 Lower the car to the ground.

39 Automatic transmission fluid renewal

1 To avoid any chance of scalding, renew the fluid when the transmission is cold or only warm. Position the car over an inspection pit, on car ramps, or jack it up and support on axle stands.
2 Place a suitable container beneath the transmission drain plugs located on the right-hand side of the oil pan and differential casing **(see illustration)**.
3 Unscrew and remove the plugs, and allow the fluid to drain for several minutes. Check and if necessary renew the sealing washers on the plugs. On completion, refit and tighten the plugs.
4 Measure out the specified quantity of fluid

39.2 Automatic transmission fluid drain plugs

necessary to refill the transmission, then pour it slowly through the dipstick tube using a funnel with a fine-mesh screen, to avoid spillage and to ensure that any foreign matter is trapped.
5 With the car level, check and if necessary top-up the fluid level with reference to Section 18.

Every 48 000 miles (80 000 km) or 4 years

40 Timing belt renewal

The timing belt must be renewed at the specified interval, following the procedure described in Chapter 2A. Failure to do this may result in the belt breaking in service, with consequent serious damage to the engine. If the history of the car is not known, timing belt renewal must be regarded as a high priority.

41 Valve clearance adjustment

1 On carburettor models, remove the air cleaner assembly with reference to Chapter 4A.
2 On fuel injection models, remove the upper section of the inlet manifold with reference to Chapter 4B.
3 Unscrew the nuts and remove the valve cover from the top of the cylinder head **(see illustration)**. Remove the gasket.
4 Remove the spark plugs with reference to Section 15, in order to make turning the engine easier.
5 Draw the valve positions on a piece of paper, numbering them 1 to 8 from the flywheel end of the engine. Identify them as inlet or exhaust (ie 1E, 2I, 3E, 4I, 5I, 6E, 7I, 8E).
6 Using a socket or spanner on the crankshaft pulley bolt, turn the engine until the valves of No 1 cylinder (flywheel end) are rocking; the

exhaust valve will be closing, and the inlet valve will be opening. The piston of No 4 cylinder will be at the top of its compression stroke, both valves will be fully closed, and the valve clearances for both valves of No 4 cylinder may be checked at the same time.
7 Insert a feeler blade of the correct thickness between the cam lobe and the shim on the top of the tappet bucket, and check that it is a firm sliding fit **(see illustration)**. If it is not, use other feeler blades to ascertain the clearance present, and record this in order to calculate the new shim thickness required. Note that the inlet and exhaust valve clearances are different - refer to the Specifications.
8 With No 4 cylinder valve clearances checked, turn the engine through half a turn so that No 3 valves are rocking, then check the valve clearances of No 2 cylinder in the same way. Similarly check the remaining valve

clearances in the following sequence:

Valves rocking in cylinder	Check clearances in cylinder
1	4
3	2
4	1
2	3

9 Where a valve clearance differs from the specified value, the shim for that valve must be replaced with a thinner or thicker shim accordingly. The size of shim required can be calculated as follows.
10 If the measured clearance is less than specified, subtract the measured clearance from the specified clearance and deduct the result from the thickness of the existing shim.
11 If the measured clearance is more than specified, subtract the specified clearance from the measured clearance and add the result to the thickness of the existing shim.

41.3 Removing the valve cover

41.7 Measuring the valve clearances

41.12 Shim thickness engraved on the underside

12 The shim size is stamped on the bottom face of the shim but its thickness should be checked with a micrometer **(see illustration)**.
13 The shims can be removed from their locations on top of the tappet buckets without removing the camshaft, if the Volvo tool shown in the accompanying illustration can be borrowed, or a suitable alternative fabricated **(see illustration)**. On carburettor models, the fuel pump must also be removed if the tool is being used on No 4 cylinder valves.
14 To remove the shim, the tappet bucket has to be pressed down against valve spring pressure just far enough to allow the shim to be slid out. This can be done by levering against the camshaft between the cam lobes with a suitable pad or screwdriver to push the buckets down, but if at all possible, the Volvo tool should be used. **Note:** *The engine should not be at TDC, otherwise the valves may strike the tops of the pistons as the buckets are pressed down - turn the engine a quarter-turn past the TDC position.*
15 With the tappet bucket levered down, the valve will be open, and it will be possible to remove the shim using a small screwdriver to prise it up **(see illustration)**. Make sure that

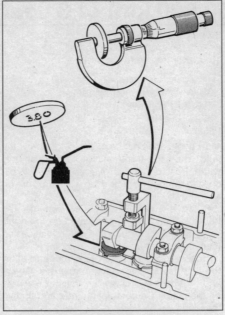

41.13 Valve tappet shim removal and checking

the relevant cam lobe peaks are uppermost when doing this, and rotate the buckets so that the notches are at right angles to the camshaft centreline, to make removal of the shims easier. When refitting the shims, ensure that the size markings face the tappet buckets (ie face downwards), and lubricate them generously with engine oil.
16 If difficulty is experienced in removing the shims, the alternative method is to remove the camshaft complete, with reference to Chapter 2A. Direct access to each of the shims will then be much easier.
17 Remove the socket or spanner from the crankshaft pulley bolt.

41.15 Using a screwdriver to depress the tappet buckets, and a smaller screwdriver to prise up the shim

18 Refit the spark plugs with reference to Chapter 1, Section 15, then refit the valve cover together with a new gasket where necessary. On fuel injection models, refit the inlet manifold; on carburettor models, refit the air cleaner.

42 Auxiliary drivebelt renewal

This is part of the Volvo schedule. Arguably, if a regular check is made of drivebelt condition (as described in Section 5), signs of premature wear should be noticed in time to prevent a drivebelt failing in service. However, if a high mileage has been completed, or if the history of the car is not known, it would be prudent to renew the drivebelt(s), if only for peace of mind. Drivebelt failure could lead to engine damage through overheating - the water pump would stop working. On power steering models, belt failure would cause a sudden loss of power assistance, which could be highly dangerous.

Every 2 years, regardless of mileage

43 Coolant renewal

⚠️ *Warning: Wait until the engine is cold before starting this procedure. Do not allow antifreeze to come in contact with your skin, or with the painted surfaces of the vehicle. Rinse off spills immediately with plenty of water.*

Draining

1 With the engine cold, unscrew the pressure cap from the top of the expansion tank.
2 On 440 and 460 models, unscrew the screws and pull down the front section of the engine splash guard for access to the radiator drain tap.
3 On 480 models, unscrew the self-tapping screws from the front skirt, and pull it down for access to the radiator drain tap.
4 Position a suitable container beneath the radiator. If necessary, a length of tubing may be fitted over the drain plug to prevent coolant

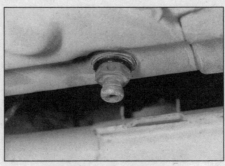

43.5 Radiator drain plug

spillage. Bear in mind that antifreeze is poisonous, and it has a sweet smell which may attract children or animals - always try to reduce the risk of spillage.
5 Loosen the drain plug and allow the coolant to drain into the container **(see illustration)**. On completion, remove the tubing and tighten the plug.
6 If it is required to drain the cylinder block as well, move the container beneath the right-hand end of the engine, and unscrew the cylinder block drain plug located below the inlet manifold near the oil pressure switch. Allow the coolant to drain.
7 If the system needs to be flushed after draining, refer to the following paragraphs; otherwise refit and tighten the drain plug.

Flushing

8 With time (and particularly if regular coolant changes are neglected), the cooling system may gradually lose its efficiency as the radiator matrix becomes choked with rust and scale deposits. If this condition is suspected, the system must be flushed as follows.

9 First drain the coolant as already described. Loosen the clips and disconnect the top and bottom hoses from the radiator. Insert a garden hose in the radiator top hose connection stub, and allow the water to circulate through the radiator until it runs clear from the bottom outlet.

10 To flush the engine and the remainder of the system, remove the thermostat as described in Chapter 3, then insert the garden hose in the thermostat opening in the cylinder head, and allow the water to circulate through the engine until it runs clear from the bottom hose and cylinder block drain plug opening.

11 In severe cases of contamination, the radiator should be reverse-flushed. To do this, first remove it from the car, as described in Chapter 3, invert it and insert a hose in the bottom outlet. Continue flushing until clear water runs from the top hose outlet.

12 If, after a reasonable period, the water still does not run clear, the radiator should be flushed with a good proprietary cleaning system. The regular renewal of corrosion-inhibiting antifreeze should prevent such severe contamination of the system.

Filling

13 Refit and tighten the cylinder block drain plug. If the system has just been flushed, also refit the radiator top and bottom hoses, and any other hoses which were removed.

14 Loosen the bleed screw, which, depending on model, is located in the hose near the thermostat housing (B18U engine), on the T-piece into the cylinder head (B18EP/FP and B20F engines), or on the expansion tank-to-radiator supply hose **(see illustrations)**.

15 Pour the appropriate mixture of water and antifreeze into the expansion tank, and close the bleed screw as soon as a continuous flow of bubble-free coolant can be seen flowing from it. Continue to fill the expansion tank until the coolant is at the maximum level.

16 Start the engine and run it at a fast idle speed for three or four minutes. Keep the expansion tank topped-up to the maximum level during this period.

17 Refit and tighten the expansion tank cap, then run the engine at a fast idle speed until it reaches its normal operating temperature (indicated by the electric cooling fan cutting in). During this period, the coolant will circulate around the engine, and any remaining air will be purged to the expansion tank.

18 Switch off the engine and allow it to cool, then check the coolant level as described earlier and top-up if necessary.

Antifreeze

19 The antifreeze should always be renewed at the specified intervals. This is necessary not only to maintain the antifreeze properties, but also to prevent corrosion which would otherwise occur as the corrosion inhibitors in a good-quality antifreeze become progressively less effective.

20 Always use an ethylene-glycol based antifreeze which is suitable for use in mixed-metal cooling systems. The quantity of antifreeze and levels of protection are indicated in the Specifications.

21 Before adding antifreeze, the cooling system should be completely drained, preferably flushed, and all hoses checked for condition and security.

22 After filling with antifreeze, a label should be attached to the radiator or expansion tank stating the type and concentration of antifreeze used and the date installed. Any

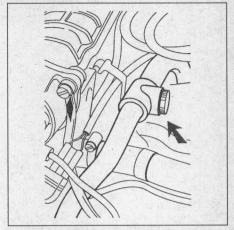

43.14a Bleed screw location on B18U engine . . .

subsequent topping-up should be made with the same type and concentration of antifreeze **(see illustration)**.

23 Do not use engine antifreeze in the windscreen or tailgate washer system, as it will cause damage to the vehicle paintwork. A screen wash should be added to the washer system in the screen wash manufacturer's recommended quantities.

44 Brake fluid renewal

The procedure is similar to that for the bleeding of the hydraulic system described in Chapter 9, except that the brake fluid reservoir should be emptied by syphoning, using a clean poultry baster or similar before starting, and allowance should be made for the old fluid to be removed from the circuit when bleeding each section of the circuit.

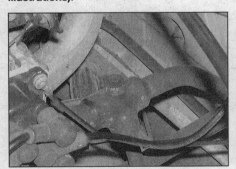

43.14b . . . B18EP/F and B20F engines . . .

43.14c . . . and bleed screw located on the expansion tank-to-radiator supply hose

43.22 Topping-up the cooling system with antifreeze

Chapter 2 Part A:
Engine in-car repair procedures

Contents

Degrees of difficulty

Easy, suitable for novice with little experience	Fairly easy, suitable for beginner with some experience	Fairly difficult, suitable for competent DIY mechanic	Difficult, suitable for experienced DIY mechanic	Very difficult, suitable for expert DIY or professional 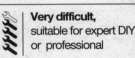

2A

Specifications

Engine codes

B16F	1596 cc (1.6 litre), Fenix 3B fuel injection, catalytic converter
B18K	1721 cc (1.7 litre), economy carburettor, no catalytic converter
B18K(D)	1721 cc (1.7 litre), economy carburettor, catalytic converter
B18KP	1721 cc (1.7 litre), carburettor, no catalytic converter
B18KP(D)	1721 cc (1.7 litre), carburettor, catalytic converter
B18E, B18ES	1721 cc (1.7 litre), Fenix 1 or 3.2 fuel injection, no catalytic converter. B18ES has EGR and Pulsair system
B18E(D)	1721 cc (1.7 litre), Fenix 1 or 3.2 fuel injection, catalytic converter
B18EP	1721 cc (1.7 litre), high torque, Fenix 3B fuel injection, no catalytic converter
B18FP	1721 cc (1.7 litre), high torque, Fenix 3B fuel injection, catalytic converter
B18F	1721 cc (1.7 litre), Bosch LH-Jetronic fuel injection, full emissions, catalytic converter
B18FT	1721 cc (1.7 litre), turbo, Bosch LH-Jetronic fuel injection, catalytic converter, EVAP fuel evaporation control
B18FT(M)	1721 cc (1.7 litre), turbo, Bosch LH-Jetronic fuel injection, no catalytic converter
B18U	1794 cc (1.8 litre), Bosch/Siemens single-point fuel injection (SPI), catalytic converter
B20F	1998 cc (2.0 litre), Fenix 3B fuel injection, catalytic converter

Engine (general)

Type	Four-cylinder, in-line, overhead camshaft
Bore:	
1.6 litre	78.0 mm
1.7 litre	81.0 mm
1.8 and 2.0 litre	82.7 mm
Stroke:	
1.6, 1.7 and 1.8 litre	83.5 mm
2.0 litre	93.0 mm
Firing order	1-3-4-2 (No 1 cylinder at flywheel end)
Direction of crankshaft rotation	Clockwise
Power output:	
B16F	62 kW at 5700 rpm
B18K	59 kW at 5400 rpm
B18K(D)	57 kW at 5400 rpm
B18KP	66 kW at 5800 rpm
B18KP(D)	64 kW at 5700 rpm
B18E, B18ES	80 kW at 5800 rpm
B18E(D)	78 kW at 5800 rpm
B18EP	78 kW at 5600 rpm
B18FP	75 kW at 5600 rpm
B18F	70 kW at 5400 rpm
B18FT	88 kW at 5400 rpm
B18FT(M)	90 kW at 5400 rpm
B18U	66 kW at 6000 rpm
B20F	80 kW at 5500 rpm
Compression ratio:	
B16F	10.0 : 1
B18K, B18K(D), B18KP, B18KP(D), B18F	9.5 : 1
B18E, B18E(D), B18E(S)	10.5 : 1
B18EP, B18FP	10.0 : 1
B18FT, B18FT(M)	8.1 : 1
B18U	9.7 : 1
B20F	9.8 : 1
Compression pressure:	
All engines except B18FT, B18FT(M)	11 to 13 bar
B18FT, B18FT(M) engines	12 to 14 bar

Lubrication system

System pressure (new filter, hot engine):	
1000 rpm	2.0 bars
3000 rpm	3.5 bars
Oil pump type	Two-gear
Oil pump clearances:	
Gear endfloat	0.02 to 0.08 mm
Maximum clearance between gears and body	0.1 mm
Backlash between gears	0.10 to 0.24 mm
Oil pump pressure relief valve spring free length	74.6 mm

Cylinder head

Material	Aluminium alloy
Height	169.5 ± 0.05 mm
Maximum acceptable gasket face distortion	0.05 mm
Valve seat angle:	
Inlet valve:	
1.6 and 1.7 litre	60°
1.8 and 2.0 litre	45°
Exhaust valve	45°
Valve seat width	1.7 ± 0.2 mm
Seat cutter correction angle:	
Inlet valve	45°
Exhaust valve	30°

Camshaft

Drive	Toothed belt
Number of bearings	5
Bearing journal running clearance	0.050 to 0.150 mm
Camshaft endfloat	0.048 to 0.133 mm

Auxiliary shaft

Bearing bush diameter:	
Inner bush	39.5 mm
Outer bush	40.5 mm
Auxiliary shaft endfloat	0.07 to 0.15 mm

Valves

	Inlet	Exhaust
Seat angle:		
1.6 and 1.7 litre	60°	45°
1.8 and 2.0 litre	45°	45°
Seat width	1.7 ± 0.2 mm	
Head diameter:	Inlet	Exhaust
1.6 litre, and 1.7 litre (non-turbo)	38.1 mm	32.62 mm
1.7 litre (turbo)	38.22 mm	32.62 mm
1.8 and 2.0 litre	40.1 mm	32.62 mm
Valve spring free length:		
B16, B18E/EP/FP	42.6 mm	
B18K/F/FT(M)	44.2 mm	
B18U	49.7 mm	
B20F	47.6 mm	
Valve guide internal diameter	8.0 mm	
Valve guide outside diameter:		
Standard (no grooves)	13.0 mm	
Oversize 1 (two grooves)	13.25 mm	

Torque wrench settings

	Nm	lbf ft
Auxiliary shaft housing	15	11
Auxiliary shaft sprocket	50	37
Auxiliary shaft thrustplate	15	11
Big-end bearing cap	45	33
Camshaft bearing cap:		
M6	9	7
M8	20	15
Camshaft sprocket	50	37
Crankshaft oil seal housing	15	11
Crankshaft pulley bolt	95	70
Cylinder block drain plug	20	15
Cylinder head bolts (oiled):		
Stage 1	30	22
Stage 2	70	52
Stage 3	Wait at least 3 minutes, then slacken	
Stage 4	20	15
Stage 5	Angle-tighten by 123° ± 2°	
Cylinder head studs	10	7
Engine mountings (front)	40	30
Engine-to-transmission bracket	50	37
Flywheel/driveplate (use new bolts)	53	39
Main bearing cap	65	48
Oil cooler	15	11
Oil level sensor	23	17
Oil pressure sensor	35	26
Oil pump body and cover bolts:		
M6	9	7
M8	23	17
Oil temperature sensor	25	18
Speedometer sensor	25	18
Sump bolts	13	10
Sump drain plug	25	18
Timing belt idler wheel	27	20
Timing belt tensioner bolt	15	11
Timing belt tensioner nut	40	30
Timing cover	6	4
Turbocharger oil pipe:		
Lower	35	26
Upper	22	16
Valve cover	5	4
Water pump housing and cover	13	10

2A

1 General information

How to use this Chapter

This Part of Chapter 2 describes the repair procedures that can reasonably be carried out on the engine while it remains in the car. If the engine has been removed from the car and is being dismantled as described in Part B, any preliminary dismantling procedures can be ignored.

Note that while it may be possible physically to overhaul items such as the piston/connecting rod assemblies while the engine is in the car, such tasks are not usually carried out as separate operations, and usually require the execution of several additional procedures (not to mention the cleaning of components and of oilways); for this reason, all such tasks are classed as major overhaul procedures, and are described in Part B of this Chapter.

Part B describes the removal of the engine/transmission unit from the car, and the full overhaul procedures that can then be carried out.

For ease of reference, all specifications are given in the one Specifications Section at the beginning of the Chapter.

Engine description

The engine is of four-cylinder, in-line, overhead camshaft type, mounted transversely at the front of the car.

The crankshaft is supported in five shell-type main bearings. Thrustwashers are fitted to No 2 main bearing, to control crankshaft endfloat.

The connecting rods are attached to the crankshaft by horizontally-split shell-type big-end bearings, and to the pistons by gudgeon pins. The gudgeon pins are fully-floating and retained by circlips on all engines except the B18K and B18U; on the B18K and B18U engines, they are a press-fit in the connecting rods. The aluminium alloy pistons are fitted with three piston rings; two compression rings and a scraper-type oil control ring.

The overhead camshaft is mounted directly in the cylinder head, and is driven by the crankshaft via a toothed rubber timing belt. The camshaft operates the valves via inverted bucket-type tappets, which operate in bores machined directly in the cylinder head. Valve clearance adjustment is by selected shims located externally between the tappet bucket and the cam lobe. The inlet and exhaust valves are mounted vertically in the cylinder head, and are each closed by a single valve spring **(see illustration)**.

An auxiliary shaft located alongside the crankshaft is also driven by the toothed timing belt, and actuates the oil pump via a skew gear.

A semi-closed crankcase ventilation system is employed; crankcase fumes are drawn from an oil separator on the cylinder block and passed via a hose to the inlet manifold.

Engine lubrication is by pressure feed from a gear-type oil pump, located beneath the crankshaft. Engine oil is fed through an externally-mounted oil filter to the main oil gallery feeding the crankshaft, auxiliary shaft and camshaft **(see illustration)**.

The distributor rotor (and the fuel pump on carburettor engines) are driven by the camshaft.

Repair operations possible with the engine in the vehicle

The following operations can be carried out without having to remove the engine from the car.

a) *Removal and refitting of the timing belt and sprockets.*
b) *Renewal of the camshaft oil seals.*
c) *Removal and refitting of the camshaft.*
d) *Removal and refitting of the auxiliary shaft.*
e) *Removal and refitting of the cylinder head.*
f) *Removal and refitting of the sump.*
g) *Removal and refitting of the oil pump.*
h) *Removal and refitting of the big-end bearings, connecting rods, and piston*.*
i) *Renewal of the crankshaft oil seals.*
j) *Renewal of the auxiliary shaft oil seal.*
k) *Removal and refitting of the flywheel/driveplate.*
l) *Renewal of the engine mountings.*

*Note: *Although the operation marked with an asterisk can be carried out with the engine in the car (after removal of the sump), it is better for the engine to be removed, in the interests of cleanliness and improved access. For this reason, the procedure is described in Part B of this Chapter.*

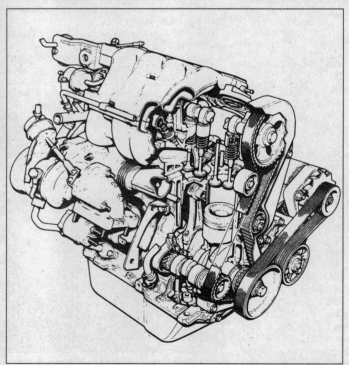

1.8 Cutaway view of the 1721 cc B18FT turbocharged engine

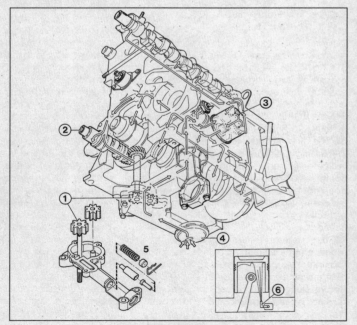

1.11 Lubrication circuit

1 *Oil pump*
2 *Auxiliary shaft*
3 *Oil filter*
4 *Oil pump pick-up tube and filter*
5 *Oil pump pressure regulating valve*
6 *Oil lubricating jets*

2 Compression test - description and interpretation

1 When engine performance is down, or if misfiring occurs which cannot be attributed to the ignition or fuel systems, a compression test can provide diagnostic clues as to the engine's condition. If the test is performed regularly, it can give warning of trouble before any other symptoms become apparent. **Note:** *The engine must be at normal operating temperature, and the battery must be fully-charged, for this test.*
2 Begin by cleaning the area around the spark plugs before you remove them (a small brush or a bicycle tyre pump will do this quite effectively). The idea is to prevent dirt from getting into the cylinders as the compression test is being done.
3 Remove all of the spark plugs from the engine (see Chapter 1, Section 15).
4 Disconnect the wiring to the flywheel sensor, to prevent the ignition system from functioning. Alternatively, disconnect the LT wiring from the ignition coil.
5 Fit a compression tester to the No 1 spark plug hole - the type of tester which screws into the plug thread is to be preferred **(see illustration)**.
6 Have your assistant hold the accelerator pedal fully depressed to the floor, at the same time cranking the engine over several times on the starter motor; after one or two revolutions, the compression pressure should build up to a maximum figure and then stabilise. Record the highest reading obtained.
7 Repeat the test on the remaining cylinders, recording the pressure in each.
8 All cylinders should produce very similar pressures; any pressures outside of the specified tolerance indicates the existence of a fault.
9 Note that the compression should build up quickly in a healthy engine; low compression on the first stroke, followed by gradually increasing pressure on successive strokes, indicates worn piston rings. A low compression reading on the first stroke, which does not build up during successive strokes, indicates leaking valves or a blown head gasket (a cracked head could also be the cause).
10 If the pressure in any cylinder is reduced to the specified minimum or less, carry out the following test to isolate the cause. Introduce a teaspoonful of clean oil (or about three squirts from a plunger-type oil can) into that cylinder through its spark plug hole, and repeat the test.
11 If the addition of oil temporarily improves the compression pressure, this indicates that bore or piston wear is responsible for the pressure loss. No improvement suggests that leaking or burnt valves, or a blown head gasket, may be to blame.

2.5 Typical compression gauge in use

12 A low reading from two adjacent cylinders is almost certainly due to the head gasket having blown between them; the presence of coolant in the engine oil will confirm this.
13 On completion of the test, refit the spark plugs and reconnect the flywheel sensor or ignition coil wiring.

3 Top dead centre (TDC) for No 1 piston - locating

1 Top dead centre (TDC) is the highest point in the cylinder that each piston reaches as the crankshaft turns. Each piston reaches TDC at the end of the compression stroke, and again at the end of the exhaust stroke; for the purpose of timing the engine, TDC refers to the position of No 1 piston at the end of its compression stroke. On all engines in this manual, No 1 piston and cylinder is at the flywheel (transmission) end of the engine.
2 Disconnect the negative and positive battery leads, in that order.
3 Loosen the wheel bolts on the right-hand front wheel. Apply the handbrake, then jack up the front right-hand side of the car, and support on axle stands. Remove the wheel.
4 Remove the plastic cover from within the right-hand wheelarch, to gain access to the crankshaft pulley.
5 Turn the engine in a clockwise direction, using a socket on the crankshaft pulley bolt, until the TDC mark on the camshaft sprocket is uppermost and in line with the pointer on the timing cover **(see illustration)**. Turning the engine will be easier if the spark plugs are first removed (see Chapter 1, Section 15).
6 If the distributor cap is now removed, the rotor arm should be in alignment with the No 1 HT lead segment.
7 Remove the plug on the lower front-facing side of the engine, at the flywheel end, and obtain an 8.0 mm diameter bolt or metal rod which will fit in the plug hole. Turn the crankshaft slightly as necessary to the TDC position, then push the rod through the hole to locate in the slot in the crankshaft web **(see illustration)**. Make sure that the crankshaft is exactly at TDC for No 1 piston by aligning the timing notch on the flywheel/driveplate with

3.5 Camshaft sprocket mark aligned with pointer

the corresponding mark on the transmission bellhousing. If the crankshaft is not positioned accurately, it is possible to engage the rod with a balance hole in the crankshaft web, which is not the TDC slot.
8 On completion, remove the metal rod and refit the plug.
9 Refit the distributor cap.
10 Refit the plastic cover to the right-hand wheelarch, then refit the roadwheel and lower the car to the ground.
11 Reconnect the battery leads to complete.

4 Timing belt - removal, inspection and refitting

Removal

1 Disconnect the battery negative and positive leads, in that order.
2 Remove the alternator and water pump drivebelts (Chapter 1).
3 Loosen the wheel bolts on the right-hand front wheel. Apply the handbrake, then jack up the front right-hand side of the car, and support it on axle stands. Remove the wheel.
4 Remove the plastic cover from within the right-hand wheelarch, to gain access to the crankshaft pulley.
5 Set the engine at the TDC position for No.1 piston as described in Section 3, but don't fit the metal locating rod into the crankshaft at this stage.

3.7 Bolt (arrowed) inserted through the cylinder block and into the TDC hole in the crankshaft web

2A

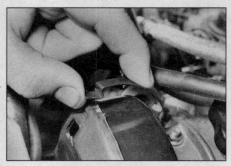

4.6a Release the spring clip . . .

4.6b . . . and lift off the timing belt outer cover

4.6c Camshaft sprocket and rear timing cover timing marks - not applicable to all engines

6 Release the spring clip where fitted, then unscrew the bolts and lift off the timing belt outer cover. For improved access, move the power steering fluid reservoir (where fitted) to one side after releasing the retaining bolt. With the outer cover removed, on some models there is a further timing mark on the rear timing cover - the camshaft sprocket mark should be aligned with this mark **(see illustrations)**.

7 Unscrew the crankshaft pulley bolt, while holding the crankshaft stationary. To do this, have an assistant insert a screwdriver in the starter ring gear teeth through the access hole in the top of the transmission bellhousing. Take care not to damage the ignition timing sensor.

8 Remove the crankshaft pulley from the nose of the crankshaft **(see illustration)**. If it is tight, use a puller.

9 Ensure that the engine is still at the TDC position for No. 1 piston, as described in

Section 3, and insert the metal locating rod to engage the crankshaft.

10 Check whether the timing belt is marked with arrows to indicate its running direction, and if not, make suitable marks yourself (if you intend to refit the belt rather than renew it, but this is not recommended).

11 Loosen the timing belt tensioner nut, and turn the tensioner to release the tension from the belt; when the belt is slack, re-tighten the nut.

12 Release the belt from the camshaft sprocket, idler/tensioner wheels, auxiliary shaft sprocket and crankshaft sprocket, and remove it from the engine.

13 Clean the sprockets and idlers/tensioners, and wipe them dry; do not apply excessive amounts of solvent to the idler/tensioner wheels, otherwise the bearing lubricant may be contaminated. Also clean the front of the cylinder head and block.

Inspection

14 Examine the timing belt carefully for any signs of cracking, fraying or general wear, particularly at the roots of the teeth. Renew the belt if there is any sign of deterioration of this nature, or if there is any oil or grease contamination. The belt must, of course, be renewed if it has completed the service mileage interval given in Chapter 1. If the belt is being removed as part of another engine operation, it would be worthwhile fitting a new belt on reassembly, rather than risking the expense of an old belt failing in service.

Refitting

15 Check that the crankshaft is at the TDC position for No 1 cylinder, and that the crankshaft is locked in this position using the metal rod or bolt through the hole in the crankcase.

16 Check that the timing mark on the camshaft sprocket is facing upwards. Temporarily locate the outer timing cover over the sprocket to check that it is on the exact position.

17 Align the timing mark bands on the belt with those on the sprockets, noting that the running direction arrows on the belt should be positioned between the auxiliary shaft sprocket and the tensioner. The crankshaft sprocket mark is in the form of a notch in its rear guide perimeter **(see illustrations)**. The auxiliary shaft sprocket has no timing mark.

18 Fit the timing belt over the crankshaft sprocket first, then the auxiliary shaft sprocket, followed by the tensioner/idler, camshaft sprocket and tensioner/idler. Note that there is only one tensioner, but it is located in one of two positions according to the engine type.

19 Check that all the timing marks are still aligned, then temporarily tension the belt by turning the tensioner pulley anti-clockwise and tightening the retaining nut. As a rough guide to the correct tension, it should just be possible to turn the belt through 90°, using a finger and thumb placed approximately midway between the auxiliary shaft sprocket and the tensioner/idler wheel.

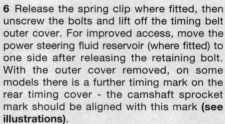

4.8 Removing the crankshaft pulley

4.17a Timing belt band aligned with the notch (arrowed) in the crankshaft sprocket

4.17b Timing belt band aligned with the mark on the camshaft sprocket

4.17c The timing belt running direction arrows should be positioned between the auxiliary shaft sprocket and the tensioner

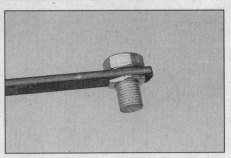

4.20a Home-made tool consisting of a bolt attached to the end of a metal bar, for tensioning the timing belt

4.20b Tensioning the timing belt with the home-made tool

4.26 Tensioning the timing belt using the Volvo special tool 5197

20 Where the tensioner pulley is located next to the camshaft sprocket, it may be turned with a suitable tool inserted in the back bracket which incorporates a hole. In practice, it was found that a bolt attached to the end of a length of metal bar could be used effectively - insert the bolt in the pulley bracket and press on the bar to tension the belt **(see illustrations)**.

21 Remove the TDC locating rod or bolt.

22 Refit the crankshaft pulley and retaining bolt. Prevent the crankshaft turning using the method given in the dismantling procedure, and tighten the bolt to the specified torque.

23 Using a socket or spanner on the crankshaft pulley bolt, turn the crankshaft two complete turns in the normal direction of rotation, then return it to the TDC position with No 1 cylinder on compression, and insert the TDC locating rod again.

24 Check that the timing marks on the sprockets are still aligned. The bands on the timing belt will not now be aligned, but this is of no significance - the bands are only used for alignment purposes when the belt is being initially fitted to the sprockets.

25 The belt deflection must now be checked. To do this, first make a mark on the front of the engine, in line with the outer surface of the timing belt, midway between the auxiliary shaft sprocket and tensioner/idler wheel above it.

26 A force of 30 N must now be applied to the timing belt, and its deflection checked to be 7.5 mm with the engine cold. Should the deflection be checked with the engine hot, the

deflection should be 5.5 mm. Volvo technicians use a special tool to do this **(see illustration)**, but an alternative arrangement can be made by using a spring balance and steel rule. Apply the force with the spring balance, and read off the deflection on the steel rule.

27 If the tension is incorrect, adjust the tensioner as necessary, then re-tighten the nut to the specified torque. *This torque is critical, since if the nut were to come loose, considerable engine damage would result.*

28 Remove the TDC locating rod or bolt, and refit the plug.

29 Refit the plastic cover to the right-hand wheelarch.

30 Refit the roadwheel, and lower the car to the ground.

31 Refit the timing belt cover, and tighten the bolts. Refit the spring clip (where removed).

32 Refit and tension the alternator and water pump drivebelts, with reference to Chapter 1.

33 Refit the power steering fluid reservoir if moved for access.

34 Reconnect the battery positive and negative leads, in that order.

5 Timing belt sprockets and tensioners - removal, inspection and refitting

Removal

1 Remove the timing belt, as described in Section 4.

2 To remove the camshaft sprocket, hold the sprocket stationary using a metal bar with two bolts through it, inserted in the holes in the sprocket, then unscrew the sprocket bolt. Alternatively, hold the sprocket stationary by wrapping an old timing belt around the sprocket and hold firm with a pair of grips, or else use a special gear-holding tool (refer to illustration 5.14 and **Tool Tip**).

3 Pull the sprocket from the end of the camshaft, if necessary using two levers or screwdrivers **(see illustration)**. Check whether the locating Woodruff key is likely to drop out of its camshaft slot; if so, remove it and store it safely.

4 The sprocket can be removed from the auxiliary shaft in the same manner **(see illustration)**. Again check that the Woodruff key is firmly in the slot in the shaft, or remove it for safekeeping.

5 A puller may be necessary to remove the crankshaft sprocket. It is a simple matter to make up a puller using two bolts, a metal bar and the existing crankshaft pulley bolt. By unscrewing the crankshaft pulley bolt, the sprocket is pulled from the end of the crankshaft **(see illustration)**. If necessary, remove the Woodruff key from the slot in the crankshaft.

6 Unscrew the nut or bolt, and remove the upper timing belt idler wheel or tensioner, as applicable. If necessary, the upper and lower rear timing covers may be unbolted at this stage, but it will be necessary to unscrew the tensioner/idler stud first **(see illustrations)**.

7 Unscrew the nut or bolts, and remove the

2A

5.3 Removing the camshaft sprocket

5.4 Removing the bolt from the auxiliary shaft sprocket

5.5 Removing the crankshaft sprocket

5.6a Tensioner located on the cylinder head

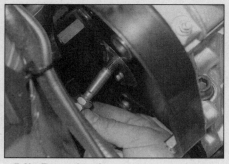

5.6b Removing the tensioner stud from the cylinder head

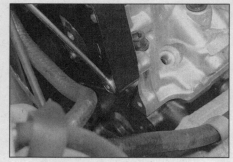

5.6c Unscrew the bolts . . .

5.6d . . . and remove the upper rear timing cover . . .

5.6e . . . and lower rear timing cover

5.7 Removing the lower timing belt idler wheel assembly

lower timing belt idler wheel or tensioner, as applicable **(see illustration)**.

Inspection

8 Inspect the teeth of the sprockets for signs of nicks and damage. The teeth are not prone to wear, and should normally last the life of the engine.

9 Spin the tensioner and idler wheel by hand, and check it for any roughness or tightness. Do not attempt to clean them with solvent, as this may enter the bearings. If wear is evident, renew the tensioner and/or idler wheel.

Refitting

10 Refit the timing belt idler wheel, and tighten the nut or bolts to the specified torque.
11 Refit the tensioner, but do not tighten the adjustment nut at this stage.
12 Refit the upper and lower timing belt rear covers, and tighten the bolts.

13 Check that the Woodruff key is in the crankshaft slot, then slide on the crankshaft pulley. Use a piece of metal tube to tap it fully home.
14 Check that the Woodruff key is in the auxiliary shaft slot, then slide on the sprocket. Use a metal tube to tap it home, if necessary. Apply a little locking fluid to the bolt, then fit the bolt and washer, tightening the bolt to the specified torque while holding it stationary using one of the methods described in paragraph 2 **(see illustration and Tool Tip)**.
15 Fit the camshaft sprocket in the same way, and tighten the bolt to the specified torque.
16 Refit the timing belt with reference to Section 4.

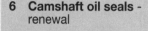

6 Camshaft oil seals - renewal

Right-hand (timing belt end)

1 Remove the timing belt as described in Section 4.
2 Unscrew the bolt, and remove the camshaft sprocket with reference to Section 5. Prise the Woodruff key from the groove in the end of the camshaft.
3 Note the fitted depth of the oil seal, then prise it out using a small screwdriver **(see illustration)**.

 HAYNES HiNT *A small hole may be drilled in an oil seal and a self-tapping screw used with a pair of pliers to pull it out.*

5.14 Using a special tool to hold the auxiliary shaft sprocket stationary while tightening the bolt

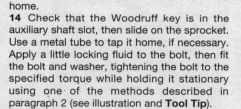 **TOOL TiP**

Hold the sprocket stationary with a home-made tool made from two strips of steel bolted together at one end

6.3 Using a screwdriver to prise out the right-hand (timing belt end) camshaft oil seal

6.10 Using a screwdriver to prise out the left-hand (distributor end) camshaft oil seal

4 Wipe clean the seating in the cylinder head.
5 Smear a little fresh oil on the outer surface of the new oil seal, locate it squarely in the cylinder head, and drive it into position using a metal tube of diameter slightly less than that of the bore in the cylinder head. Make sure that the oil seal is the correct way round (with its sealed face outwards) and fitted to the previously noted depth.
6 Fit the Woodruff key to its groove in the end of the camshaft.
7 Refit the camshaft sprocket with reference to Section 5.
8 Refit the timing belt as described in Section 4.

Left-hand (distributor end)

9 Remove the distributor cap, rotor arm and baseplate, with reference to Chapter 5B.
10 Note the fitted depth of the oil seal, then prise it out using a small screwdriver **(see illustration)**. Alternatively, a small hole may

be drilled in the oil seal, and a self-tapping screw used with a pair of pliers to pull it out.
11 Wipe clean the seating in the cylinder head.
12 Smear a little fresh oil on the outer surface of the new oil seal, locate it squarely in the cylinder head, and drive it into position using a metal tube of diameter slightly less than that of the bore in the cylinder head. Make sure that the oil seal is the correct way round (with its sealed face outwards) and fitted to the previously noted depth.
13 Refit the distributor baseplate, rotor arm and cap, with reference to Chapter 5B.

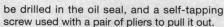

7 Camshaft - removal, inspection and refitting

Removal

1 Remove the timing belt and camshaft sprocket, with reference to Sections 4 and 5.
2 Unbolt and remove the timing belt rear cover.
3 Disconnect the HT leads, and remove the distributor cap and rotor arm with reference to Chapter 5B. Also unbolt and remove the baseplate **(see illustration)**.
4 Refer to Chapter 4A or 4B and remove the air cleaner (carburettor and single-point injection models), or the upper section of the inlet manifold (multi-point injection models).
5 Unscrew the nuts, and remove the valve cover and gasket from the top of the cylinder head.
6 On carburettor models, remove the fuel pump with reference to Chapter 4A.

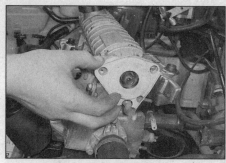

7.3 Removing the distributor cap baseplate

7 Using a dial gauge, measure the endfloat of the camshaft, and compare with the figure quoted in the Specifications. This will give an indication of the amount of wear present on the thrust surfaces.
8 If necessary, make identifying marks on the camshaft bearing caps, so that they can be refitted in the same positions and the same way round **(see illustration)**.
9 Progressively slacken the bearing cap bolts until all valve spring pressure is released. Remove the bolts, and the bearing caps themselves **(see illustration)**.
10 Note the fitted depth of the oil seals then lift out the camshaft, together with the oil seals **(see illustration)**.
11 Remove the tappets, each with its shim. Place them in a compartmented box, or on a sheet of card divided into eight sections, so that they may be refitted to their original locations **(see illustrations** and **Haynes Hint)**.

2A

7.8 Camshaft bearing cap marking

7.9 Removing the camshaft bearing caps

7.10 Lifting the camshaft together with oil seals from the top of the cylinder head

7.11a Removing a tappet

7.11b Underside of a tappet bucket

7.11c Store the tappets in a compartmented box

It is a good idea to write the shim thickness on the card alongside each bucket, in case the shims are accidentally knocked off their buckets and mixed up. The size is etched on the shim bottom face

Inspection

12 Examine the camshaft bearing surfaces, cam lobes and fuel pump eccentric for wear ridges, pitting or scoring. Renew the camshaft if such wear is evident.

13 Renew the oil seals at the ends of the camshaft as a matter of course. Lubricate the lips of the new seals before fitting them, and store the camshaft so that its weight is not resting on the seals.

14 Examine the camshaft bearing surfaces in the cylinder head and bearing caps. Deep scoring or other damage means that the cylinder head must be renewed.

15 Inspect the tappet buckets and shims for

7.19 Tightening the camshaft bearing cap bolts

scoring, pitting and wear ridges. Renew as necessary.

Refitting

16 Oil the tappets, and fit them to the bores from which they were removed. Fit the correct shim, numbered side downwards, to each tappet.

17 Oil the camshaft bearings. Place the camshaft with its oil seals onto the cylinder head, making sure that the cam lobes for No 1 cylinder are angled upwards. The oil seals must be positioned so that they are at the fitted depth as previously noted.

18 Refit the camshaft bearing caps to their original locations, applying a little sealant to the end caps where they meet the cylinder head.

19 Apply a little locking fluid to the threads of the upper five bearing cap bolts. Fit all of the bolts, and tighten them progressively to the specified torque **(see illustration)**.

20 If a new camshaft has been fitted, measure the endfloat using a dial gauge, and check that it is within the specified range.

21 On carburettor models, refit the fuel pump with reference to Chapter 4A.

22 Check and adjust the valve clearances as described in Chapter 1.

23 Refit the valve cover together with a new gasket, and tighten the nuts to the specified torque.

24 Refit the air cleaner or the upper section of the inlet manifold, as applicable, with reference to Chapter 4A or 4B.

25 Refit the distributor baseplate, rotor arm and cap with reference to Chapter 5B; also reconnect the HT leads.

26 Refit the timing belt rear cover, and tighten the bolts.

27 Refit the camshaft sprocket and timing belt with reference to Sections 5 and 4 respectively.

8 Auxiliary shaft - removal, inspection and refitting

Removal

1 Remove the timing belt, with reference to Section 4.

2 Remove the auxiliary shaft sprocket, with reference to Section 5.

3 Unscrew the four bolts and withdraw the auxiliary shaft housing **(see illustration)**. Access may be easier from under the car.

4 From the top, unscrew the two bolts and withdraw the oil pump drivegear cover plate and O-ring. Screw an M12 bolt into the oil pump drivegear (or use a tapered wooden shaft) and withdraw the drivegear from its location **(see illustrations)**.

5 Unscrew the two bolts and washers, and lift out the auxiliary shaft thrustplate and the auxiliary shaft **(see illustrations)**.

Inspection

6 Examine the auxiliary shaft and oil pump driveshaft for pitting, scoring or wear ridges on the bearing journals, and for chipping or wear of the gear teeth. Renew as necessary.

7 Check the auxiliary shaft bearings in the cylinder block for wear and, if worn, have

8.3 Removing the auxiliary shaft housing

8.4a Removing the oil pump drivegear cover plate . . .

8.4b . . . and drivegear

8.5a Removing the thrustplate . . .

8.5b . . . and auxiliary shaft

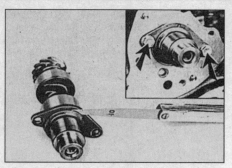

8.8 Checking the auxiliary shaft endfloat with a feeler gauge

these renewed by your Volvo dealer or a suitably-equipped engineering works. Wipe them clean if they are still serviceable.

8 Temporarily fit the thrustplate to its position on the auxiliary shaft, and use a feeler gauge to check that the endfloat is as given in the Specifications **(see illustration)**. If it is greater than the upper tolerance, a new thrustplate should be obtained, but first check the thrust surfaces on the shaft to ascertain if wear has occurred here.

Refitting

9 Clean off all traces of gasket cement from the auxiliary shaft housing, and prise out the oil seal with a screwdriver.
10 Install the new oil seal using a block of wood, tapping the seal in until it is flush with the outer face of the housing. The open side of the seal must be towards the engine **(see illustrations)**.

9.13 Wiring disconnection points on the cylinder head (arrowed)

9.14a Disconnecting the top hose from the thermostat housing . . .

8.10a Prising the auxiliary shaft oil seal from the housing

11 Liberally lubricate the auxiliary shaft, and slide it into its bearings.
12 Place the thrustplate in position (with its curved edge away from the crankshaft) and refit the two retaining bolts, tightening them to the specified torque.
13 Apply a bead of gasket cement to the auxiliary shaft housing mating face.
14 Liberally lubricate the oil seal lips, and then locate the housing in place. Refit and tighten the housing retaining bolts progressively and in a diagonal sequence to the specified torque.
15 Lubricate the oil pump drivegear, and lower the gear into its location.
16 Position a new O-ring seal on the drivegear cover plate, fit the plate and secure with the two retaining bolts.
17 Refit the auxiliary shaft sprocket and timing belt with reference to Sections 5 and 4 respectively.

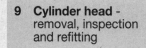

9 Cylinder head -
removal, inspection and refitting

Removal

1 Disconnect both the negative and positive battery leads, in that order.
2 Unbolt and remove the engine splash guard from under the engine compartment.
3 Drain the cooling system (including the cylinder block) with reference to Chapter 1. Refit the cylinder block drain plug after draining.

9.14b . . . and the heater hose from the coolant pipe

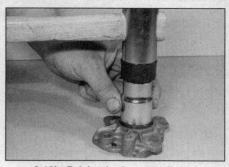

8.10b Driving in the new oil seal

4 Drain the engine oil with reference to Chapter 1. Refit the sump drain plug after draining.
5 Remove the timing belt and camshaft sprocket, with reference to Sections 4 and 5 of this Chapter.
6 Unbolt the timing belt rear cover located behind the camshaft sprocket.
7 Remove the inlet and exhaust manifolds, with reference to Chapter 4A or 4B. Tie the exhaust downpipe to one side with string or wire.
8 On carburettor models, disconnect the fuel supply line from the fuel pump, and disconnect the fuel return line from the vapour separator.
9 On fuel injection models, remove the idle control unit, and disconnect the fuel supply and return lines from the injector manifold.
10 Disconnect the HT leads from the spark plugs and ignition coil. Remove the distributor cap and rotor arm, and unbolt the baseplate from the cylinder head.
11 Where applicable, disconnect the wiring plug from the ignition unit.
12 Disconnect the wiring plug from the flywheel sensor.
13 As applicable, disconnect the wiring plug from the knock sensor, coolant temperature sensor(s), and from the injectors at the harness **(see illustration)**.
14 Loosen the clip and disconnect the radiator top hose from the thermostat housing. Similarly disconnect the coolant hoses from the coolant pipes **(see illustrations)**.
15 Unscrew the bolt securing the engine oil level dipstick tube to the cylinder head, and remove the spacer **(see illustration)**.

2A

9.15 Unbolting the engine oil level dipstick tube bracket from the cylinder head

9.18 Lifting the cylinder head off of the cylinder block

9.29a New cylinder head gasket located on the cylinder block

9.29b Check that the cylinder head gasket is located correctly over the dowels

16 Disconnect the crankcase ventilation hose at the oil separator T-piece.

17 Using a suitable hexagon-headed socket bit, slacken the cylinder head retaining bolts half a turn at a time, in the reverse order to that shown in illustration 9.32a. When the tension has been relieved, remove all of the bolts.

18 Lift the cylinder head upwards and off the engine cylinder block (see illustration). If it is stuck, tap it upwards using a hammer and block of wood. Do not try to turn it, as it is located by two dowels; make no attempt whatsoever to prise it free using a screwdriver inserted between the block and head faces.

19 Remove the cylinder head gasket from the top of the cylinder block.

Inspection

20 The mating faces of the cylinder head and block must be perfectly clean before refitting the head. Use a scraper to remove all traces of gasket and carbon, and also clean the tops of the pistons. Take particular care with the aluminium cylinder head, as the soft metal is easily damaged.

21 Make sure that the carbon and other debris is not allowed to enter the oil and water channels - this is particularly important for the oil circuit, as carbon could block the oil supply to the camshaft and tappets, or to the crankshaft main and big-end bearings. Using adhesive tape and paper, seal the water, oil and bolt holes in the cylinder block.

HAYNES HINT *To prevent carbon entering the gap between the pistons and bores, smear a little grease in the gap. After cleaning the piston, rotate the crankshaft so that the piston moves down the bore, then wipe out the grease and carbon with a rag.*

22 Check the block and head for nicks, deep scratches and other damage. If very slight, these may be removed carefully with a file, but if excessive, machining may be the only alternative.

23 Check the joint face of the cylinder head for warping using a straight-edge and feeler gauge, and make sure that any distortion is not greater than the specified amount.

24 Clean out all the bolt holes in the block using a rag and screwdriver. Make sure that all oil is removed, otherwise there is a possibility of the block being cracked by hydraulic pressure when the bolts are inserted and tightened.

25 Examine the bolt threads and the threads in the cylinder block for damage. If necessary, use the correct-size tap to chase out the threads in the block, and use a die to clean the threads on the bolts. If the bolts show any signs of stretching they should be renewed, but there is no requirement by Volvo to renew them after removal of the cylinder head.

26 The best way of checking whether the bolts have stretched is to compare with new bolts. Consider renewing all the cylinder head bolts in any case - the inconvenience and expense of having an apparently-sound used bolt shear off should not be overlooked.

Refitting

27 Ensure that the mating faces of the cylinder block and head are spotlessly clean, that the retaining bolt threads are also clean, and that they screw easily in and out of their locations.

28 Check that No 1 piston (flywheel end) is at TDC, and that No 1 cylinder valves in the head are both shut. Temporarily fit the camshaft sprocket and check that the sprocket timing mark is facing upwards - to determine the exact position of the sprocket, temporarily locate the timing cover on the cylinder head, and check that the pointer is aligned with the mark on the sprocket. Where applicable, also check that the sprocket mark is aligned with the mark on the rear timing cover.

29 Fit a new cylinder head gasket to the block, locating it over the dowels. Make sure it is the right way up (see illustrations).

30 Lower the cylinder head onto the block, engaging it over the dowels.

31 Lightly oil the cylinder head bolts, both on their threads and under their heads. Insert the bolts, and tighten them finger-tight.

32 Following the sequence shown, tighten the bolts to the torque specified for Stage 1. Repeat the sequence, this time tightening to the torque specified for Stage 2 (see illustrations).

33 Wait at least three minutes to allow the gasket to bed down, then progressively slacken all the bolts in the reverse order of the tightening sequence until completely loose - this is Stage 3.

34 Again following the tightening sequence, tighten the bolts to the torque specified for Stage 4.

35 Final tightening is carried out by turning each bolt, in the tightening sequence, through the angle specified for Stage 5. Measure the angle using a commercially-available gauge, or else make up a cardboard template cut to the angle required (see illustration). Each bolt should be angle-tightened using a single uninterrupted movement.

36 Reconnect the crankcase ventilation hose at the oil separator T-piece.

37 Refit the engine oil level dipstick tube to the cylinder head (together with the spacer) and tighten the bolt (see illustration).

38 Reconnect the coolant hoses to the coolant pipes.

39 Reconnect the radiator top hose to the thermostat housing.

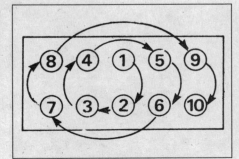

9.32a Cylinder head bolt tightening sequence

9.32b Tightening the cylinder head bolts

9.35 Angle-tightening the cylinder head bolts

9.37 Engine oil level dipstick tube bracket on the cylinder head. Note the spacer (arrowed) next to the head

11.2 Removing the oil pump from the crankcase (engine removed for clarity)

40 As applicable, reconnect the wiring to the injectors, coolant temperature sensor(s), knock sensor, flywheel sensor, and ignition unit.
41 Refit the baseplate, rotor arm and distributor cap, and reconnect the HT leads to the spark plugs and ignition coil.
42 On fuel injection models, refit the idle control unit, and reconnect the fuel supply and return lines to the injector manifold.
43 On carburettor models, reconnect the fuel supply line to the fuel pump, and the fuel return line to the vapour separator.
44 Refit the inlet and exhaust manifolds (together with a new gasket), with reference to Chapter 4A or 4B. Adjust the accelerator and choke cables as applicable.
45 Refit the timing belt rear cover, and tighten the bolts.
46 Refit the camshaft sprocket and timing belt, with reference to Sections 5 and 4 respectively.
47 Refill the engine with the correct quantity of oil, with reference to Chapter 1.
48 Refill the cooling system, with reference to Chapter 1.
49 Refit the engine splash guard beneath the engine compartment.
50 Reconnect the battery positive and negative leads, in that order.

10 Sump - removal and refitting

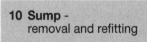

Removal

1 Apply the handbrake, then jack up the front of the car and support it on axle stands.
2 Drain the engine oil as described in Chapter 1, then refit and tighten the sump drain plug.
3 Unscrew the bolts, and remove the flywheel or torque converter cover plate and support bracket from the engine and transmission.
4 Unscrew and remove the bolts securing the sump to the crankcase. Tap the sump with a hide or plastic mallet to break the seal, then remove the sump.
5 Remove the gasket (where fitted) and clean the mating faces of the sump and crankcase.

Refitting

6 Where a gasket was removed, locate a new gasket on the sump; otherwise, apply a bead of gasket sealing compound to the sump face.
7 If a gasket is not fitted, it is important that the sump is positioned correctly first time, and not moved around after the sealing compound has touched the crankcase. Temporary long bolts or dowel rods may be used to help line the sump up, to achieve this.
8 To prevent oil dripping from the oil pump and crankcase, wipe these areas clean before refitting the sump.
9 Lift the sump into position, then insert the bolts and tighten them progressively to the specified torque.
10 Refit the flywheel or torque converter cover plate and support bracket to the engine and transmission.
11 Lower the car to the ground.
12 Fill the engine with fresh oil, with reference to Chapter 1.

11 Oil pump - removal and refitting

Removal

1 Remove the sump, as described in Section 10.
2 Unscrew the four retaining bolts at the ends of the pump body, and withdraw the pump from the crankcase and drivegear (**see illustration**).

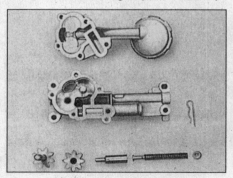

12.4 Oil pump components

Refitting

3 Wipe clean the mating faces of the oil pump and crankcase.
4 Lift the oil pump into position with its shaft engaged with the drivegear. Insert and fully tighten the retaining bolts.
5 Refit the sump, and refill the engine with oil, with reference to Section 10 and Chapter 1 respectively.

12 Oil pump - dismantling, inspection and reassembly

Dismantling

1 Unscrew the retaining bolts, and lift off the pump cover.
2 Withdraw the idler gear and the drivegear/shaft. Mark the idler gear so that it can be refitted in its same position.
3 Extract the retaining clip, and remove the oil pressure relief valve spring retainer, spring, spring seat and plunger.

Inspection

4 Clean the components and carefully examine the gears, pump body and relief valve plunger for any signs of scoring or wear (**see illustration**). Renew the pump complete if excessive wear is evident.
5 If the components appear serviceable, measure the clearance between the pump body and the gears, and the gear endfloat, using feeler gauges (**see illustrations**). If the

2A

12.5a Checking the clearance between the oil pump gears and the body

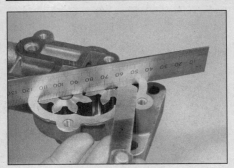

12.5b Checking the endfloat of the oil pump gears

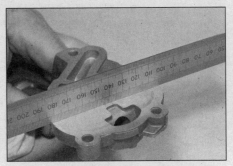

12.6 Checking the flatness of the oil pump cover

12.7 Tightening the oil pump cover bolts

clearances exceed the specified tolerances, the pump must be renewed.

6 Also check the oil pump cover for flatness - no tolerance is available for this, but if the cover is badly warped, leaks will occur, causing a loss of oil pressure **(see illustration).**

Reassembly

7 Reassembly is a reversal of dismantling, but fill the pump with oil before refitting the cover, and tighten the bolts to the specified torque **(see illustration).**

13 Crankshaft oil seals - renewal

Front/right-hand (timing belt end)

1 Remove the timing belt and crankshaft sprocket, with reference to Sections 4 and 5. Also remove the Woodruff key.
2 Carefully prise out the old oil seal with a small screwdriver, taking care not to damage the surface of the crankshaft.
3 If it is difficult to remove, the entire oil seal housing may be unbolted from the cylinder block, and the oil seal driven out on the bench using a metal tube. If this course of action is taken, the sump may also have to be removed, on models where a sump gasket is fitted and it becomes damaged. Where no sump gasket is fitted, there is no need to remove the sump, but new sealing compound will be required.
4 Lubricate the new oil seal lips with engine oil, then fit the seal using a block of wood, so that it is flush with the outer face of the housing. Ensure that the open side of the seal is fitted towards the engine.
5 Where the housing is being refitted, apply a bead of sealing compound to the mating face, making sure that the oilway cavity is not blocked, then refit the housing and insert the retaining bolts. The two bolts around the oil seal opening at the 2 o'clock and 8 o'clock positions should also have a small quantity of

the sealant applied to their threads, as they protrude into the crankcase. Progressively tighten the retaining bolts in a diagonal sequence.
6 Refit the sump where removed, with reference to Section 10.
7 Locate the Woodruff key in its groove in the crankcase, then refit the crankshaft sprocket and timing belt with reference to Sections 5 and 4 respectively.

Rear/left-hand (flywheel end)

8 Remove the flywheel/driveplate as described in Section 15.
9 Prise out the old oil seal using a small screwdriver, taking care not to damage the surface of the crankshaft **(see illustration).**
10 Alternatively, the oil seal can be removed by drilling two small holes diagonally opposite each other in the closed end of the oil seal, and inserting self-tapping screws in them. A pair of grips can then be used to pull out the oil seal, by pulling on each side in turn.
11 Wipe clean the oil seal seating, then dip the new seal in fresh engine oil, and locate it over the crankshaft with its closed side facing outwards. Make sure that the oil seal lip is not damaged as it is located on the crankshaft.
12 Using a metal tube, drive the oil seal squarely into the bore until flush. A block of wood cut to pass over the end of the crankshaft may be used instead.
13 Refit the flywheel/driveplate, with reference to Section 15.

13.9 Prising out the rear/left-hand crankshaft oil seal

14 Auxiliary shaft oil seal - renewal

1 Remove the timing belt and auxiliary shaft sprocket, with reference to Sections 4 and 5.
2 The oil seal may be removed using a small screwdriver, taking care not to damage the surface of the shaft. Alternatively, the housing may be unbolted from the cylinder block complete, and the oil seal tapped out on the bench using a suitable diameter metal tube.
3 Dip the new oil seal in engine oil, then drive it in until flush with the outer face of the housing. Use a block of wood to make sure that the seal enters squarely in the housing. The open side of the seal must be towards the engine.
4 Refit the auxiliary shaft sprocket and timing belt, with reference to Sections 5 and 4 respectively.

15 Flywheel/driveplate - removal, inspection and refitting

Removal

Note: *New flywheel/driveplate mounting bolts must be used on refitting; obtain a set of bolts before starting work.*

1 Remove the transmission, as described in Chapter 7A or 7B.
2 On manual gearbox models, remove the clutch assembly.
3 Mark the flywheel or driveplate in relation to the crankshaft. This will help during refitting, although in fact the bolt holes are spaced so that it is only possible to fit the flywheel/driveplate in one position.
4 The flywheel/driveplate must now be held stationary while the bolts are loosened. To do this, locate a long bolt in one of the transmission mounting bolt holes, and insert either a wide-bladed screwdriver or a piece of metal bar in the starter ring gear.
5 Unscrew the mounting bolts, and withdraw the flywheel/driveplate from the crankshaft.

15.11 Tightening the flywheel bolts - note the tool (arrowed) used to hold the flywheel stationary

16.10 Engine/transmission front left-hand mounting

16.11 Removing the front left-hand engine/transmission mounting from the transmission

Inspection

6 Examine the flywheel (manual gearbox models) for scoring of the clutch face, and for wear or chipping of the ring gear teeth.

7 If the clutch face is scored, the flywheel may be machined until flat, but renewal is preferable.

8 If the ring gear is worn or damaged, it may be possible to renew it separately, but this job is best left to a Volvo dealer or engineering works. The temperature to which the new ring gear must be heated for installation is critical and, if not done accurately, the hardness of the teeth will be destroyed.

9 Check the torque converter driveplate (automatic transmission models) carefully for signs of distortion, or any hairline cracks around the bolt holes or radiating outwards from the centre.

Refitting

10 Clean the flywheel/driveplate and crankshaft faces, then coat them with a little locking fluid. Locate the flywheel/driveplate on the crankshaft, making sure that any previously-made marks are aligned.

11 Apply a few drops of thread-locking fluid to the threads of the new mounting bolts, then fit the bolts and tighten them in a diagonal sequence to the specified torque **(see illustration)**.

12 On manual gearbox models, refit the clutch assembly.

13 Refit the transmission, as described in Chapter 7A or 7B.

16 Engine/transmission mountings - inspection and renewal

Inspection

1 Problems with the engine/transmission mountings will usually be indicated if there is excessive movement of the engine, particularly noticeable on acceleration and overrun.

2 With the engine stopped, try to rock the engine/transmission back and forth while looking at the mountings. Excessive movement indicates that one of the mountings may be broken or loose. Closer examination of the mountings may be made by jacking up the front of the car and supporting on axle stands.

3 An engine-movement damper is fitted to the front/right-hand end of the cylinder head. If this should be worn, movement of the engine will be excessive.

Renewal

4 Apply the handbrake, then jack up the front of the car and support it on axle stands. Remove the engine splash guard.

Front right-hand mounting

5 Take the weight of the right-hand side of the engine using a hoist. Alternatively, use a trolley jack (with a wide block of wood between the jack head and the sump) beneath the sump. A wide, flat piece of wood must be used, or the sump may be damaged by the head of the jack.

6 Unscrew the nuts, and remove the mounting from the bracket.

7 If necessary, unbolt the bracket from the cylinder block.

8 Fit the new mounting using a reversal of the removal procedure, but make sure that the locating peg enters the special hole in the subframe.

Front left-hand mounting

9 Take the weight of the front left-hand side of the engine/transmission unit using a hoist. Alternatively, use a trolley jack and block of wood beneath the transmission.

10 Unscrew the nuts, and remove the mounting from the bracket **(see illustration)**.

11 If necessary, unbolt the bracket from the transmission **(see illustration)**.

12 Fit the new mounting using a reversal of the removal procedure, but make sure that the locating peg enters the special hole in the subframe.

Transmission rear mounting

13 Take the weight of the rear left-hand side of the engine/transmission unit using a hoist, or alternatively, use a trolley jack and block of wood beneath the transmission.

14 Unscrew and remove the bolts securing the mounting bracket to the rear of the transmission.

15 Unscrew the two horizontal bolts securing the rubber mounting to the bracket. It will not be possible to remove these bolts at this stage.

16 Unscrew and remove the bolts securing the mounting to the subframe.

17 Remove the mounting and bracket from under the car, then separate them.

18 Fit the new mounting using a reversal of the removal procedure.

Engine-movement damper

19 On carburettor and single-point injection models, remove the air cleaner assembly with reference to Chapter 4A or 4B.

20 Note which way round the damper is fitted, then unscrew the two mounting bolts and remove the unit from the right-hand side of the engine **(see illustrations)**.

21 Fit the new damper using a reversal of the removal procedure.

2A

16.20a Engine-movement damper located on the right-hand end of the cylinder head

16.20b Removing the engine-movement damper

Notes

Chapter 2 Part B:
Engine removal and overhaul procedures

Contents

Degrees of difficulty

Easy, suitable for novice with little experience	Fairly easy, suitable for beginner with some experience	Fairly difficult, suitable for competent DIY mechanic	Difficult, suitable for experienced DIY mechanic	Very difficult, suitable for expert DIY or professional

Specifications

Note: *For details of engine codes, refer to Part A Specifications*

Cylinder block

Material . . . . Cast iron

Cylinder bore diameter (mm):	B16	B18	B18U/B20F
Tolerance	+0.015	+0	±0.005
Class A	78.00	81.00	82.705
Class B	78.015	81.01	82.715
Class C	-	81.02	82.722
Class U	-	81.25	82.955
Class V	-	81.26	82.965
Class W	-	81.27	82.975

Pistons and piston rings

	B18K	B18KP/E	B18 (other)
Piston diameter (mm) - 1.7 litre engines:			
Tolerance	± 0.005	± 0.005	± 0.005
Class A	80.955	80.975	80.970
Class B	80.965	80.985	80.980
Class C	80.975	80.995	80.990
Class U	81.205	81.225	81.220
Class V	81.215	81.235	81.230
Class W	81.225	81.245	81.240
Piston-to-bore clearance	0.04 to 0.06	0.02 to 0.04	0.025 to 0.045

	B16F	B18U/B20F	
Piston diameter (mm) - 1.6, 1.8 and 2.0 litre engines:			
Tolerance	± 0.005	± 0.005	
Class A	78.000	82.670	
Class B	77.990	82.680	
Class C	-	82.690	
Class U	-	82.920	
Class V	-	82.930	
Class W	-	82.940	
Piston-to-bore clearance	0.02 to 0.04	0.025 to 0.045	

Piston ring end gaps (fitted in bore):
Top compression ring	0.30 to 0.45 mm
Second compression ring	0.25 to 0.40 mm
Oil control ring:	
B18K, B18U and B20F	0.25 to 0.40 mm
B16 and B18 (except B18K and B18U)	0.25 to 0.50 mm

Piston ring-to-groove clearance:
Top compression ring	0.07 to 0.10 mm
Second compression ring:	
B18U and B20F	0.05 to 0.085 mm
All other engines	0.04 to 0.075 mm
Oil control ring	0.02 to 0.055 mm

Gudgeon pins

Diameter	21.0 mm
Clearance in piston:	
B18FT(M)	0.004 to 0.008 mm
B18K and B18U	0.006 to 0.018 mm
All other engines	0.006 to 0.012 mm
Fit in connecting rod:	
B18K and B18U	Press-fit
All other engines	Light thumb pressure (close sliding fit)

Connecting rods

Maximum difference in weight between two connecting rods:
B20F	3.0 grams
All other engines	6.0 grams

Crankshaft

Number of main bearings	5
Main bearing journal diameter:	
Standard, blue	54.785 to 54.805 mm
Standard, red	54.795 to 54.805 mm
Undersize 1	54.550 to 54.560 mm
Main bearing journal running clearance	0.04 to 0.07 mm
Maximum main bearing journal ovality	0.0025 mm
Maximum main bearing journal taper	0.0050 mm
Crankpin (big-end) journal diameter:	
Standard	48.00 to 48.02 mm
Undersize 1	47.75 to 47.77 mm
Crankpin (big-end) journal running clearance	0.031 to 0.075 mm
Maximum crankpin journal ovality	0.0025 mm
Maximum crankpin journal taper	0.0050 mm
Crankshaft endfloat	0.07 to 0.23 mm

Torque wrench settings

Refer to Part A Specifications

1 General information

Included in this Part of Chapter 2 are the engine removal procedures, and the overhaul procedures for the cylinder heads, cylinder block/crankcase and internal engine components.

The information ranges from advice concerning preparation for an overhaul and the purchase of replacement parts, to detailed step-by-step procedures covering removal, inspection, renovation and refitting of internal engine parts.

The following Sections have been compiled based on the assumption that the engine has been removed from the vehicle. For information concerning in-vehicle engine repair, as well as the removal and refitting of the external components necessary for the overhaul, refer to Part A of this Chapter, and to Section 5 of this Part.

2 Engine overhaul -
general information

It is not always easy to determine when, or if, an engine should be completely overhauled, as a number of factors must be considered.

High mileage is not necessarily an indication that an overhaul is needed, while relatively low mileage does not preclude the need for an overhaul. Frequency of servicing is probably the most important consideration. An engine which has had regular and frequent oil and filter changes, as well as other required maintenance, will most likely give many thousands of miles of reliable service. Conversely, a neglected engine may require an overhaul very early in its life.

Excessive oil consumption is an indication that piston rings, valve seals and/or valve guides are in need of attention. Make sure that oil leaks are not responsible before deciding that the rings and/or guides are worn. Perform a cylinder compression check (see Chapter 2 Part A, Section 2) to determine the extent of the work required.

Check the oil pressure with a gauge fitted in place of the oil pressure switch, and compare it with the information given in the Specifications. If it is extremely low, the main and big-end bearings and/or the oil pump are probably worn.

Loss of power, rough running, knocking or metallic engine noises, excessive valve gear noise and high fuel consumption may also point to the need for an overhaul, especially if they are all present at the same time. If a complete service does not remedy the situation, major mechanical work is the only solution.

An engine overhaul involves restoring the internal parts to the specifications of a new engine. During an overhaul, the pistons and rings are replaced, and the cylinder bores are reconditioned. New main bearings and connecting rod bearings are generally fitted, and if necessary, the crankshaft may be reground to restore the journals. The valves are also serviced as well, since they are usually in less-than-perfect condition at this point.

While the engine is being overhauled, other components, such as the starter and alternator, can be overhauled as well. The end result should be an engine that will give many trouble-free miles. **Note:** *Critical cooling system components such as the hoses, drivebelts, thermostat and water pump MUST be renewed when an engine is overhauled. The radiator should be checked carefully, to ensure that it is not clogged or leaking. It is also a good idea to renew the oil pump whenever the engine is overhauled.*

Before beginning the engine overhaul, read through the entire procedure, to familiarise yourself with the scope and requirements of the job. Overhauling an engine is not difficult if you follow all of the instructions carefully, have the necessary tools and equipment, and pay close attention to all specifications; however, it can be time-consuming.

Plan on the vehicle being off the road for a minimum of two weeks, especially if parts must be taken to an engineering works for repair or reconditioning. Check on the availability of parts, and make sure that any necessary special tools and equipment are obtained in advance.

Most work can be done with typical hand tools, although a number of precision measuring tools are required for inspecting parts to determine if they must be renewed. Often the engineering works will handle the inspection of parts, and offer advice concerning reconditioning and renewal. **Note:** *Always wait until the engine has been completely dismantled, and until all components (especially the engine block) have been inspected, before deciding what service and repair operations must be performed by an engineering works. Since the condition of the block will be the major factor to consider when determining whether to overhaul the original engine or buy a reconditioned unit, do not purchase parts or have overhaul work done on other components until the block has been thoroughly inspected. As a general rule, time is the primary cost of an overhaul, so it does not pay to fit worn or sub-standard parts.*

As a final note, to ensure maximum life and minimum trouble from a reconditioned engine, everything must be assembled with care, in a spotlessly-clean environment.

3 Engine removal -
methods and precautions

If you have decided that an engine must be removed for overhaul or major repair work, several preliminary steps should be taken.

Locating a suitable place to work in is extremely important. Adequate work space, along with storage space for the vehicle, will be needed. If a garage is not available, at the very least a flat, level, and clean work surface is required.

Cleaning the engine compartment and engine before beginning the removal procedure will help keep tools clean and organised.

An engine hoist will also be necessary. Make sure the equipment is rated in excess of the combined weight of the engine and transmission. Safety is of primary importance, considering the potential hazards involved in lifting the engine out of the vehicle.

If the engine is being removed by a novice, a helper should be available; the advice and aid from someone more experienced would also be helpful. There are many instances when one person cannot simultaneously perform all of the operations required when lifting the engine out of the vehicle.

Plan the operation ahead of time. Arrange for or obtain all of the tools and equipment you'll need prior to beginning the job. Some of the equipment necessary to perform engine removal and installation safely and with relative ease are (in addition to an engine hoist) a heavy-duty trolley jack, complete sets of spanners and sockets as described in the preliminary sections of this manual, wooden blocks, and plenty of rags and cleaning solvent for mopping-up spilled oil, coolant and fuel. If the hoist must be hired, make sure that you arrange for it in advance, and perform all of the operations possible without it beforehand. This will save you money and time.

Plan for the vehicle to be out of use for quite a while. An engineering works will be required to perform some of the work which the do-it-yourselfer cannot accomplish without special equipment. These places often have a busy schedule, so it would be a good idea to consult them before removing the engine, in order to accurately estimate the amount of time required to rebuild or repair components that may need work.

Always be extremely careful when removing and refitting the engine; serious injury can result from careless actions. Plan ahead and take your time, and a job of this nature, although major, can be accomplished successfully.

2B

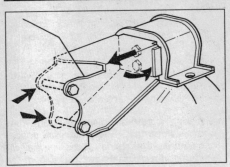

4.6 Transmission rear mounting bracket removal

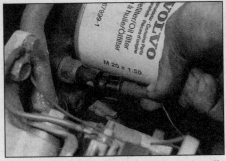

4.7 Disconnecting the wiring from the oil pressure gauge

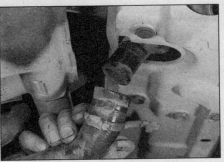

4.8 Disconnecting the bottom hose from the radiator

4 Engine - removal and refitting

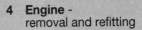

Note: *This Section describes engine removal together with the transmission; the separation of the transmission from the engine then being done on the bench. It is possible to remove the transmission separately first, then to remove the engine on its own, but this method would only be used if the gearbox has previously been removed for repairs or work on the clutch. If there is doubt whether the hoist can lift the combined weight of the engine and transmission safely (more likely on automatic transmission models), the latter method should be used.*

Removal

1 Fully open the bonnet to its service (fully-upright) position.
2 Disconnect the battery negative and positive leads, in that order.
3 Drain the cooling system, with reference to Chapter 1.
4 Drain the transmission oil/fluid, with reference to Chapter 1.
5 Disconnect the exhaust downpipe from the exhaust manifold with reference to Chapter 4C, and tie the downpipe to one side.
6 Unscrew the two nuts or bolts (as applicable) from the transmission rear mounting to release the mounting bracket **(see illustration)**. Also unscrew the nut from the front right-hand engine mounting.
7 Disconnect the wiring from the oil pressure

gauge and reversing light switch **(see illustration)**. Where applicable, also disconnect the wiring from the oil level sensor.
8 Loosen the clip and disconnect the radiator bottom hose from the radiator **(see illustration)**.
9 Loosen the left-hand front wheel bolts. Apply the handbrake, then jack up the front of the car and support on axle stands. Remove the left-hand front wheel.
10 Disconnect the remote control rod from the manual gearbox by pulling the rubber boot forwards, then unscrewing and removing the bolt. Recover the sleeve and the nylon cover.
11 Unscrew the bolts attaching the left-hand front suspension strut to the stub axle carrier. Where applicable, pull the front brake hydraulic hose from the slot in the strut.
12 Turn the steering wheel to full right-hand lock, taking care not to damage the front brake hydraulic hose (where applicable).
13 Unscrew the three bolts securing the left-hand driveshaft rubber gaiter and ring to the transmission. Withdraw the driveshaft from the transmission, and tie it to one side. Blank off the opening in the transmission, and cover the driveshaft inner joint, to prevent the entry of dust and dirt.
14 Where applicable, remove the driveshaft heat shield, after loosening the top left-hand bolt and removing the other two bolts **(see illustration)**.
15 Drive out the roll pin securing the right-hand driveshaft to the transmission side gear. Refer to Chapter 8 if necessary.
16 Remove the battery and battery tray, with reference to Chapter 5A.

17 Where applicable, unbolt and remove the engine-movement damper (see Chapter 2 Part A, Section 16).
18 Remove the air cleaner housing assembly, with reference to Chapter 4A or 4B.
19 Loosen the clip and disconnect the radiator top hose from the thermostat housing.
20 Loosen the clips and disconnect the heater hoses from the heater tubes on the bulkhead.
21 On manual gearbox models, disconnect the clutch cable from the gearbox, with reference to Chapter 6.
22 Remove the radiator cooling fan and bracket from the radiator, with reference to Chapter 3.
23 Disconnect and remove the accelerator cable and (where applicable) the choke cable, with reference to Chapter 4A or 4B, and tie them to one side.
24 Disconnect and remove the crankcase ventilation hoses (where applicable).
25 Loosen the clips and disconnect the fuel supply and return hoses from the fuel pump (carburettor engines) or injection manifold (fuel injection engines).
26 Disconnect the vacuum hoses from the inlet manifold air pressure sensor and the brake servo unit (where fitted).
27 Unscrew the nut from the transmission front mounting bracket.
28 Disconnect the cooling system expansion tank overflow hose (where applicable).
29 Where applicable, disconnect the hose unions from the Pulsair and EGR systems.
30 Disconnect the main ignition coil HT lead from the distributor cap.
31 On fuel injection models, disconnect the two-pin plug from the ignition unit.
32 Disconnect the wiring from the flywheel sensor at the connector plug.
33 On the B18U engine, disconnect the wiring from the knock sensor.
34 Disconnect the wiring from the coolant temperature sensor(s) **(see illustration)**.
35 On carburettor engines, disconnect the wiring from the thermistor **(see illustration)**.
36 On fuel injection engines, disconnect the wiring from the idle control unit, throttle butterfly switch and air inlet temperature sensor.

4.14 Heat shield located over the right-hand driveshaft

4.34 Coolant temperature sensor and wiring

4.35 Thermistor and wiring on carburettor engines

37 On carburettor engines, disconnect the earth lead from the distributor cap.

38 Disconnect all of the wiring from the rear of the alternator; refer to Chapter 5A if necessary.

39 Disconnect the wiring from the oil temperature sensor.

40 On fuel injection models, disconnect the earthing points on the engine lifting eye, and disconnect the wiring harness for the injectors.

41 Unscrew the bolt and remove the earth lead from the transmission.

42 Disconnect the speedometer cable or sensor lead, according to model.

43 Unscrew the nuts and disconnect the wiring from the starter motor.

44 Connect a hoist to the engine, and lift it carefully until its weight is taken and the mounting brackets are released.

45 Remove the bolt(s) from the transmission mounting bracket(s), and remove the brackets (as applicable).

46 Push the engine forwards at the left-hand side until the right-hand driveshaft can be disconnected from the final drive side gear.

47 Lift the engine and transmission assembly upwards out of the engine compartment, taking care not to damage the surrounding bodywork and components **(see illustration)**.

48 When the engine and transmission are raised sufficiently, move the assembly clear of the car and lower it to the floor or position it on a suitable bench for disassembly.

49 To separate the engine from the transmission, first unbolt and remove the

4.49a Bolts (arrowed) securing the flywheel/driveplate cover and support bracket to the transmission

4.47 Lifting the engine and transmission assembly out of the engine compartment

flywheel/driveplate cover and support bracket from the engine and transmission **(see illustrations)**.

50 Disconnect the wiring from the speedometer sensor (where applicable), and withdraw the starter motor/speedometer sensor wiring through the opening in the clutch housing.

51 Where applicable, release the unions from the Pulsair lines.

52 Unscrew and remove the three bolts securing the starter motor to the transmission. Where applicable, remove the heat shield from the starter motor.

53 On automatic transmission models, unscrew the four bolts securing the torque converter to the driveplate. Refer to Chapter 7B if necessary.

54 Unscrew the mounting nuts, and withdraw the transmission directly from the engine. Ensure that the transmission is adequately supported as it is withdrawn - do not allow it to hang free under its own weight when partially withdrawn (in particular, don't let it hang on the clutch, on manual gearbox models). On automatic transmission models, make sure that the torque converter remains in the transmission - refer to Chapter 7B if necessary.

Refitting

55 Refitting is a reversal of the removal procedure, noting the following additional points.

a) On manual gearbox models, apply a little high-melting-point grease to the splines of the gearbox input shaft before fitting

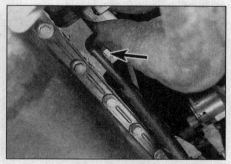

4.49b One of the bolts (arrowed) securing the support bracket to the engine crankcase

the clutch. Do not apply too much, however, otherwise there is the possibility of the grease contaminating the clutch friction disc. Make sure that the clutch release bearing is correctly located on the release arm.

b) Where other Chapters were referred to for removal, refer to them again for refitting, and make any adjustments as required.

c) When engaging the right-hand side driveshaft with the differential side gear, make sure that the roll pin holes are correctly aligned.

d) Fit new roll pins to the right-hand driveshaft, and seal the ends using a suitable sealant.

e) When refitting the sensor for the electronic speedometer, check the O-ring and renew it if necessary.

f) Tighten all nuts and bolts to the specified torques.

g) Refill the transmission with oil or fluid as necessary, with reference to Chapter 1.

h) Refill the cooling system, with reference to Chapter 1.

5 Engine overhaul - dismantling sequence

1 It is much easier to dismantle and work on the engine if it is mounted on a portable engine stand; these stands can often be hired from a tool hire shop.

2 If a stand is not available, it is possible to dismantle the engine with it mounted on blocks, on a sturdy workbench or on the floor. Be extra-careful not to tip or drop the engine when working without a stand.

3 If you are going to obtain a reconditioned engine, all external components must come off first, to be transferred to the replacement engine (just as they will if you are doing a complete engine overhaul yourself). These components include the following.

a) Alternator and brackets.

b) Distributor cap, rotor and baseplate, HT leads and spark plugs.

c) Thermostat and cover.

d) Carburettor or fuel injection components.

e) Inlet and exhaust manifolds.

f) Oil filter.

g) Fuel pump (carburettor engines).

h) Engine mountings.

i) Flywheel/driveplate.

Note: When removing the external components from the engine, pay close attention to details that may be helpful or important during refitting. Note the fitted position of gaskets, seals, spacers, washers, bolts and other small items.

4 If you are obtaining a short engine (which consists of the engine cylinder block, crankshaft, pistons and connecting rods all assembled), then the cylinder head, sump, oil pump, and timing belt will have to be removed also.

2B

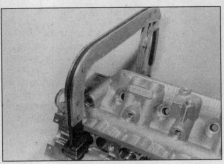

6.7a Using a valve spring compressor

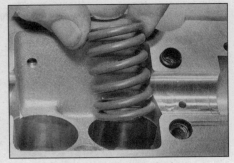

6.7b Removing a valve spring . . .

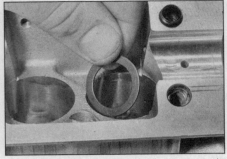

6.7c . . . and valve spring seat

5 If you are planning a complete overhaul, the engine can be dismantled and the internal components removed in the following order.
  a) Inlet and exhaust manifolds.
  b) Timing belt and sprockets.
  c) Cylinder head and camshaft.
  d) Flywheel/driveplate.
  e) Sump.
  f) Oil pump.
  g) Piston/connecting rod assemblies.
  h) Crankshaft and main bearings.
6 Before beginning the dismantling and overhaul procedures, make sure that you have all of the correct tools necessary. Refer to Section 3 and the *Tools and working facilities* Section of this manual for further information.

6 Cylinder head - dismantling

Note: *New and reconditioned cylinder heads are available from the manufacturers and from engine overhaul specialists. Due to the fact that some specialist tools are required for the dismantling and inspection procedures, and new components may not be readily available, it may be more practical and economical for the home mechanic to purchase a reconditioned head rather than dismantle, inspect and recondition the original head.*
1 If not already removed, remove the thermostat housing and thermostat, with reference to Chapter 3.
2 Unscrew and remove the temperature sensors, and unbolt the engine lifting eyes.
3 Unscrew the nut/bolt, and remove the timing belt tensioner/idler.
4 If not already removed, remove the timing belt rear cover, and the distributor cap, rotor arm and baseplate.
5 Remove the camshaft with reference to Chapter 2 Part A, Section 7.
6 Withdraw the tappet buckets, complete with shims, from their bores in the head. Place the buckets in a compartment box, or lay them out on a sheet of cardboard numbered 1 to 8 (make No 1 the flywheel-end bucket, to correspond with the cylinder numbering). It is a good idea to write the shim thickness size on the card alongside each bucket, in case

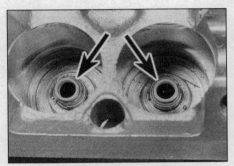

6.9a Valve stem oil seals (arrowed)

6.9b Removing a valve

the shims are accidentally knocked off their buckets and mixed up. The size is etched on the shim bottom face.
7 Using a valve spring compressor, compress each valve spring in turn until the split collets can be removed. Release the compressor, and lift off the cap, spring and spring seat **(see illustrations)**.
8 If, when the valve spring compressor is screwed down, the valve spring cap refuses to free and expose the split collets, gently tap the top of the tool, directly over the cap, with a light hammer. This will free the cap.
9 Withdraw the stem oil seal off the top of the valve guide, and then remove the valve through the combustion chamber **(see illustrations)**.
10 It is essential that the valves are kept in their correct sequence, unless they are so badly worn that they are to be renewed. If they are going to be kept and used again, place them in labelled polythene bags, or

alternatively put them in a sheet of card having eight holes numbered 1 to 8 - corresponding to the relative fitted positions of the valves **(see illustrations)**. Note that No 1 valve is nearest to the flywheel end of the engine.

7 Cylinder head and valves - cleaning, inspection and renovation

1 Thorough cleaning of the cylinder head and valve components, followed by a detailed inspection, will enable you to decide how much valve service work must be carried out during the engine overhaul.

Cleaning

2 Scrape away all traces of old gasket material and sealing compound from the cylinder head.

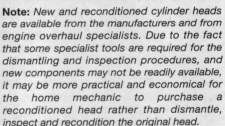

6.10a Valve components

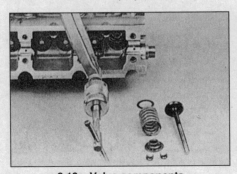

6.10b Store the valve components in a polythene bag after removal

3 Scrape away the carbon from the combustion chambers and ports, then wash the cylinder head thoroughly with paraffin or a suitable solvent.
4 Scrape off any heavy carbon deposits that may have formed on the valves, then use a power-operated wire brush to remove deposits from the valve heads and stems.

Inspection and renovation

Note: *Be sure to perform all the following inspection procedures before concluding that the services of a machine shop or engine overhaul specialist are required. Make a list of all items that require attention.*

Cylinder head

5 Inspect the head very carefully for cracks, evidence of coolant leakage, and other damage. If cracks are found, a new cylinder head should be obtained.
6 Use a straight-edge and feeler blade to check that the cylinder head surface is not distorted **(see illustration)**. If the distortion is greater than the maximum specified amount, the cylinder head should be renewed. Volvo state categorically that the cylinder head must **not** be resurfaced.
7 Examine the valve seats in each of the combustion chambers. If they are severely pitted, cracked or burned, then they will need to be renewed or re-cut by an engine overhaul specialist. If they are only slightly pitted, this can be removed by grinding the valve heads and seats together with coarse, then fine, grinding paste as described below. Note however that on the B18FT(M) engine, the exhaust valves are protected by a coating of Stellite alloy - excessive grinding may destroy the Stellite, and reduce thermal conductivity.
8 If the valve guides are worn, indicated by a side-to-side motion of the valve, new guides must be fitted. A dial gauge may be used to determine the amount of side play of the valve. Renewing the valve guides is best carried out by an engine overhaul specialist, since it is important that they are installed at the correct height.
9 The valve guides are available in two sizes - the standard size has no marking on its outer surface, while the oversize guide has two grooves. There are also two types of valve guide, and it is important to renew the guide with the same type as was removed.

Valves

10 Examine the heads of each valve for pitting, burning, cracks and general wear, and check the valve stem for scoring and wear ridges. Rotate the valve, and check for any obvious indication that it is bent. Look for pits and excessive wear on the end of each valve stem. If the valve appears satisfactory at this stage, measure the valve stem diameter at several points using a micrometer **(see illustration)**.
11 Any significant difference in the readings obtained indicates wear of the valve stem.

7.6 Checking the cylinder head surface for distortion

Should any of these conditions be apparent, the valve(s) must be renewed.
12 Note that the exhaust valves on the B18FT(M) engine are filled with sodium, and if these valves are to be discarded, they should be taken to an engine reconditioner for safe disposal.
13 If the valves are in satisfactory condition, they should be ground (lapped) into their respective seats to ensure a smooth gas-tight seal.
14 Valve grinding is carried out as follows. Place the cylinder head upside-down on a bench, supported with a block of wood at each end to give clearance for the valve stems.
15 Two basic types of grinding tool are available - either the manual dowel and rubber sucker type, or the automatic type which is driven by a rotary power tool. If the valve seats are badly pitted, or if this is the first time you have ground-in a set of valves, the automatic type is greatly preferable.
16 Smear a small quantity of coarse grinding paste on the sealing face of the valve head, and insert the valve into the correct guide. Attach the grinding tool to the valve head and using a backward/forward rotary action (or the action of the automatic tool), grind the valve head into its seat **(see illustration)**. Periodically lift the valve and rotate it to redistribute the grinding paste.
17 When a dull-matt even surface is produced on both the valve seat and the valve, wipe off the paste, and repeat the

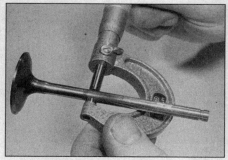

7.10 Checking the valve stem for excessive wear

process with fine carborundum paste. A light spring placed under the valve head will greatly ease this operation.
18 When a smooth unbroken ring of light grey matt finish is produced on both the valve and seat, the grinding operation is complete. Be sure to remove all traces of grinding paste (using paraffin or a suitable solvent) before reassembly of the cylinder head.
19 Record the location of each newly ground-in valve, perhaps by making up a piece of cardboard with eight numbered holes in it, for storing the valves. Alternatively, wrap a piece of masking tape around the valve stem, marked with a number from 1 to 8. No 1 cylinder is at the flywheel end of the engine - number the valves from this end.

Valve components

20 Examine the valve springs for signs of damage and discoloration, and also measure their free length using vernier calipers **(see illustration)** or by comparing the existing spring with a new component.
21 Stand each spring on a flat surface, and check it for squareness. If any of the springs are damaged, distorted or have lost their tension, obtain a complete new set of springs.
22 Inspect the tappet buckets and their shims for scoring or pitting (especially on the shims), and wear ridges. Renew any components as necessary. Note that some scuffing is to be expected, and is acceptable provided that the tappets are not scored.

2B

7.16 Grinding-in the valves using a dowel-and-sucker tool

7.20 Checking the valve spring free length

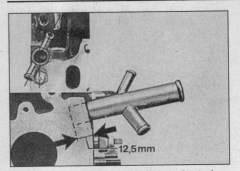
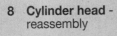

8.1 Correct fitted position of coolant pipe stub in cylinder head

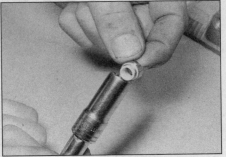

8.3 Using a socket when fitting the oil seals on the valve guides

8.5 Use grease to hold the collets in place on reassembly

8 Cylinder head - reassembly

1 If a new cylinder head is being fitted, a new coolant pipe stub must always be fitted. Clean the aperture in the head, then apply a little locking fluid to the end of the coolant pipe, and tap it into the head with a soft-faced mallet. The correct fitted position of the pipe is as shown **(see illustration)**.
2 Lubricate the stems of the valves, and insert them into their original locations. If new valves are being fitted, insert them into the locations to which they have been ground.
3 Working on the first valve, dip the oil seal in engine oil, then carefully locate it over the valve and onto the guide. Take care not to damage the seal as it is passed over the valve stem - if possible, locate a plastic cap over the end of valve stem (or wrap some tape around the stem) while the oil seal is being fitted. Use an 11.0 mm socket or metal tube **(see illustration)** to press the seal firmly onto the guide, and remove the plastic cap or tape afterwards. Make sure that the correct seals are fitted, according to the type of valve guide fitted.
4 Locate the spring seat on the guide, followed by the spring and cap. Where applicable, the spring should be fitted with its closest coils towards the head.
5 Compress the valve spring, and locate the split collets in the recess in the valve stem.

Use a little grease to hold the collets in place **(see illustration)**. Release the compressor, then repeat the procedure on the remaining valves.
6 With all the valves installed, tap the end of each valve stem using a hammer and interposed block of wood to settle the components.
7 Lubricate the tappet buckets, and insert them into their respective locations as noted during removal. Make sure that each bucket has its correct tappet shim in place on its upper face, and that the shim is installed with its etched size number facing downwards.
8 Refit the camshaft with reference to Chapter 2 Part A, Section 7.
9 Refit the distributor baseplate, rotor arm and cap, timing belt rear cover, timing belt tensioner/idler, engine lifting eyes, temperature sensors, thermostat and housing, as applicable.

9 Pistons/connecting rods - removal

1 With the cylinder head, sump and oil pump removed, proceed as follows.
2 Rotate the crankshaft so that No 1 big-end cap (nearest the flywheel position) is at the lowest point of its travel. If the big-end cap and rod are not already numbered, mark them with a centre-punch **(see illustration)**. Mark both cap and rod in relation to the cylinder

they operate in, noting that No 1 is nearest the flywheel (transmission) end of the engine.
3 Before removing the big-end caps, use a feeler blade to measure the amount of side play between the caps and the crankshaft webs **(see illustration)**, and make a note of the results.
4 Unscrew and remove the big-end bearing cap bolts, and withdraw the cap, complete with shell bearing, from the connecting rod. If only the bearing shells are being attended to, push the connecting rod up and off the crankpin, and remove the upper bearing shell. Keep the bearing shells and cap together in their correct sequence if they are to be refitted.
5 Push the connecting rod up, and remove the piston and rod from the top of the bore using the wooden handle of a hammer **(see illustration)**.
6 Using the same procedure, remove the piston and connecting rod from No 4 cylinder, then rotate the crankshaft half a turn and remove the pistons and connecting rods from Nos 2 and 3 cylinders.

10 Crankshaft - removal

1 With the front cover and flywheel removed, proceed as follows.
2 Before the crankshaft is removed, check the endfloat using a dial gauge in contact with

9.2 Big-end caps marked with a centre-punch

9.3 Checking the big-end cap side play

9.5 Using the wooden handle of a hammer to push the piston and connecting rod out of the cylinder bore

10.2 Checking the crankshaft endfloat with a dial gauge

10.5 Removing No 1 main bearing cap

10.6 Lifting the crankshaft from the crankcase

the end of the crankshaft (see illustration). Push the crankshaft fully one way, and then zero the gauge. Push the crankshaft fully the other way, and check the endfloat. The result can be compared with the specified amount, and will give an indication as to whether new thrustwashers are required.

3 If a dial gauge is not available, feeler blades can be used. First push the crankshaft fully towards the flywheel end of the engine, then slip the feeler blade between the crankshaft web and the thrustwasher of No 2 main bearing.

4 Identification numbers should be cast onto the base of each main bearing cap similar to the connecting rods and caps, but if not, number the cap and crankcase using a centre-punch.

5 Unscrew and remove the main bearing cap retaining bolts, and withdraw the caps, complete with bearing shells (see illustration).

6 Carefully lift the crankshaft from the crankcase (see illustration).

7 Remove the thrustwashers from each side of No 2 main bearing, then remove the bearing shell upper halves from the crankcase (see illustrations). Place each shell with its respective bearing cap.

8 Remove the oil seal from the rear of the crankshaft.

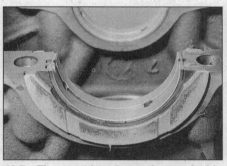

10.7a Thrustwashers located on each side of No 2 main bearing

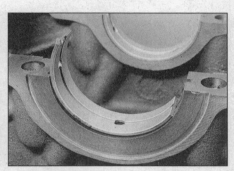

10.7b Main bearing upper shell removal

5 Remove all oil gallery plugs (where fitted). The plugs are usually very tight - they may have to be drilled out, and the holes re-tapped. Use new plugs when the engine is reassembled.

6 If the block is extremely dirty, it should be steam-cleaned.

7 Clean all oil holes and oil galleries one more time. Flush all internal passages with warm water until the water runs clear, then dry the block thoroughly, and wipe all machined surfaces with a light rust-preventative oil. If you have access to compressed air, use it to speed the drying process, and to blow out all the oil holes and galleries.

 Warning: Wear eye protection when using compressed air!

8 If the block is not very dirty, you can do an adequate cleaning job with hot soapy water and a stiff brush. Take plenty of time, and do a

thorough job. Regardless of the cleaning method used, be sure to clean all oil holes and galleries very thoroughly, dry the block completely, and coat all machined surfaces with light oil.

9 The threaded holes in the block must be clean to ensure accurate torque readings during reassembly. Run the proper-size tap into each of the holes, to remove rust, corrosion, thread sealant or sludge, and to restore damaged threads. If possible, use compressed air to clear the holes of debris produced by this operation. Now is a good time to clean the threads on the head bolts and the main bearing cap bolts as well.

10 Refit the main bearing caps, and tighten the bolts finger-tight.

11 After coating the mating surfaces of new core plugs with suitable sealant, fit them in the cylinder block. Make sure that they are driven in straight and are seated properly, or leakage

2B

11 Cylinder block/crankcase - cleaning and inspection

Cleaning

1 For complete cleaning, ideally the core plugs (where fitted) should first be removed. Drill a small hole in them, then insert a self-tapping screw and pull out the plugs using a pair of grips or a slide hammer.

2 Remove all external components and sensors.

3 Remove the oil sprayers from the bottom of each bore by unscrewing the retaining bolts (see illustrations).

4 Scrape all traces of gasket from the cylinder block, taking care not to damage the head and sump mating faces.

11.3a Oil sprayer location on the bottom of the bore

11.3b Oil sprayer removed from the engine

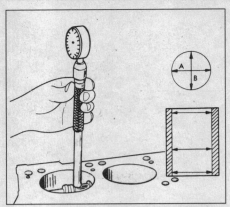

11.17 Measuring the diameter of the cylinder bores

could result. Special tools are available for this purpose, but a large socket, with an outside diameter that will just slip into the core plug, will work just as well.

12 Apply suitable sealant to the new oil gallery plugs, and insert them into the holes in the block; tighten them securely.

13 Refit the oil sprayers to the bottom of each bore, and tighten the bolts securely.

14 If the engine is not going to be reassembled right away, cover it with a large plastic bag, to keep it clean and prevent it from rusting.

Inspection

15 Visually check the block for cracks, rust and corrosion. Look for stripped threads in the threaded holes. If there has been any history of internal water leakage, it may be worthwhile having an engine overhaul specialist check the block with special equipment. If defects are found, have the block repaired, if possible, or renewed.

16 Check the cylinder bores for scuffing and scoring.

17 Measure the diameter of each cylinder at

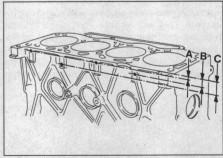

11.19 Cylinder bore class identification

5.0 mm diameter blind hole
Class A: 6.0 mm distance from the joint face
Class B: 12.0 mm distance from the joint face
Class C: 18.0 mm distance from the joint face
7.0 mm diameter blind hole
Class U: 6.0 mm distance from the joint face
Class V: 12.0 mm distance from the joint face
Class W: 18.0 mm distance from the joint face

the top (just under the ridge area), centre and bottom of the cylinder bore, parallel to the crankshaft axis **(see illustration)**.

18 Next measure each cylinder's diameter at the same three locations across the crankshaft axis. If the difference between any of the measurements is greater than 0.20 mm, indicating that the cylinder is excessively out-of-round or tapered, then remedial action must be considered.

19 Note that when the cylinder bores are originally bored, they are given a Standard or Oversize class identification. A blind drilling is made on the side of the cylinder block in the positions shown **(see illustration)**, and this makes it easy to ascertain the amount of wear which has occurred in the bores.

20 Repeat the procedure for the remaining pistons and cylinders.

21 If the cylinder walls are badly scuffed or scored, or if they are excessively out-of-round or tapered, have the cylinder block rebored. Oversize pistons will also be required.

22 If the cylinders are in reasonably good condition, then it may only be necessary to renew the piston rings. If this is the case, the bores should be honed in order to allow the new rings to bed in correctly and provide the best possible seal.

23 The conventional type of hone has spring-loaded stones, and is used with a power drill. You will also need some paraffin or honing oil and rags.

24 The hone should be moved up and down the cylinder to produce a crosshatch pattern, and plenty of honing oil should be used. Ideally, the crosshatch lines should intersect at approximately a 60° angle; do not take off more material than is necessary to produce the required finish.

25 If new pistons are being fitted, the piston manufacturers may specify a finish with a different angle, so their instructions should be followed.

26 Do not withdraw the hone from the cylinder while it is still being turned - stop it first.

27 After honing a cylinder, wipe out all traces of the honing oil.

28 If equipment of this type is not available, or if you are not sure whether you are competent to undertake the task yourself, an engine overhaul specialist will carry out the work at moderate cost.

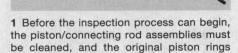

12 Pistons/connecting rods - inspection

1 Before the inspection process can begin, the piston/connecting rod assemblies must be cleaned, and the original piston rings removed from the pistons.

2 Carefully expand the old rings over the top of the pistons. The use of two or three old feeler blades will be helpful in preventing the rings dropping into empty grooves **(see illustration)**.

3 Scrape away all traces of carbon from the top of the piston. A hand-held wire brush or a piece of fine emery cloth can be used once the majority of the deposits have been scraped away.

4 Remove the carbon from the ring grooves in the piston by cleaning them using an old ring; break the old ring in half to do this, but take care, as the rings are very sharp! Be very careful to remove only the carbon deposits - don't remove any metal, and don't nick or scratch the sides of the ring grooves.

5 Once the deposits have been removed, clean the piston/connecting rod assembly with paraffin or a suitable solvent, and dry thoroughly. Make sure the oil return holes in the back sides of the ring grooves are clear.

6 If the pistons and cylinder bores are not damaged or worn excessively, and if the cylinder block does not need to be rebored, the original pistons can be re-used. Normal piston wear appears as even, vertical wear on the piston thrust surfaces, and slight looseness of the top ring in its groove.

7 Carefully inspect each piston for cracks around the skirt, at the gudgeon pin bosses and at the piston ring lands.

8 Look for scoring and scuffing on the thrust faces of the skirt, holes in the piston crown, or burned areas at the edge of the crown. If the skirt is scored or scuffed, the engine may have been suffering from overheating and/or abnormal combustion, which has caused excessively-high operating temperatures; the cooling and lubricating systems should be checked thoroughly. A hole in the piston crown is an indication that abnormal combustion (pre-ignition) has been occurring. Burned areas at the edge of the piston crown are usually evidence of knocking (detonation). If any of the above problems exist, the causes must be corrected, or damage will occur with new components. Causes of pre-ignition include inlet air leaks or incorrect fuel/air mixture, as well as incorrect ignition timing.

9 Corrosion of the piston, in the form of small pits, indicates that coolant is leaking into the combustion chamber and/or the crankcase. Again, the cause must be corrected, or the problem may persist in the rebuilt engine.

10 Even if the pistons are serviceable, new piston rings should always be used when the

12.2 Using an old feeler blade to remove the piston rings

12.11 Measuring piston ring-to-groove clearance

12.12 Measuring the pistons for ovality

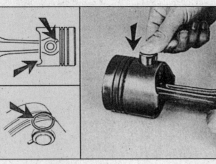

12.15 Fitting the piston to the connecting rod

engine is reassembled - re-using old rings is a very false economy.

11 Measure the piston ring-to-groove clearance by placing a new piston ring in each ring groove and measuring the clearance with a feeler blade **(see illustration)**. Check the clearance at three or four places around each groove. If the measured clearance is greater than specified, new pistons will be required.

12 Check the piston-to-bore clearance by measuring the cylinder bore (see Section 11) and the piston diameter. Measure the piston across the skirt, at a 90° angle to the gudgeon pin, approximately half-way down the skirt **(see illustration)**. Subtract the piston diameter from the bore diameter to obtain the clearance. If this is greater than the figures given in the Specifications, the block will have to be rebored, and new pistons and rings fitted.

13 Check the fit of the gudgeon pin by twisting the piston and connecting rod in opposite directions. Any noticeable play indicates excessive wear, which must be corrected.

14 If the pistons or connecting rods are to be renewed, the gudgeon pins may be removed on all engines except the B18K and B18U by extracting the circlips and pressing them out by hand. On the B18K and B18U engines, the gudgeon pins are a press fit in the connecting rods, and it will be necessary to have this work carried out by a Volvo dealer or suitable engine overhaul specialist.

15 When fitting the connecting rods to the pistons, make sure that the small-end oilway in the connecting rod is on the opposite side to the cooling recess in the piston skirt **(see illustration)**.

16 Before refitting the rings to the pistons, check their end gaps by inserting each of them in their cylinder bores. Use the piston to make sure that they are square. The rings are normally supplied with the correct end gaps, but if the gaps are too small, the ring ends may be filed carefully.

17 Install the new rings by fitting them over the top of the piston, starting with the oil control scraper ring. Note that the second compression ring is tapered, and must be fitted with the word TOP uppermost. With all the rings in position, space the ring gaps at 120° to each other **(see illustration)**.

13 Crankshaft - inspection

1 Clean the crankshaft, and dry it with compressed air if available.

⚠ **Warning: Wear eye protection when using compressed air! Be sure to clean the oil holes with a pipe cleaner or similar probe.**

2 Check the main and big-end bearing journals for uneven wear, scoring, pitting or cracking.

3 Remove all burrs from the crankshaft oil holes with a stone, file or scraper.

4 Using a micrometer, measure the diameter of the main and connecting rod journals, and compare the results with the Specifications at the beginning of this Chapter **(see illustration)**. By measuring the diameter at a number of points around each journal's circumference, you will be able to determine whether or not the journal is out-of-round. Take the measurement at each end of the journal, near the webs, to determine if the journal is tapered.

5 If any of the measurements vary by more than 0.0254 mm, or if the crankshaft journals are damaged, tapered, out-of-round or worn beyond the limits given in the Specifications, the crankshaft will have to be reground, and undersize bearings fitted.

6 Check the oil seal journals at each end of the crankshaft for wear and damage. If the seal has worn an excessive groove in the journal,

consult an engine overhaul specialist, who will be able to advise whether a repair is possible or whether a new crankshaft is necessary.

14 Main and big-end bearings - inspection

1 Even though the main and big-end bearings should be renewed during the engine overhaul, the old bearings should be retained for close examination, as they may reveal valuable information about the condition of the engine. The size of the bearing shells is stamped on the back metal, and this information should be given to the supplier of the new shells.

2 Bearing failure can occur for a number of reasons - lack of lubrication, the presence of dirt or other foreign particles, overloading the engine, or corrosion **(see illustration overleaf)**. Regardless of the cause of bearing failure, it must be corrected before the engine is reassembled, to prevent it from happening again.

3 When examining the bearings, remove them from the engine block, the main bearing caps, the connecting rods and the rod caps, and lay them out on a clean surface in the same general position as their location in the engine. This will enable you to match any bearing problems with the corresponding crankshaft journal.

4 Dirt and other foreign particles get into the engine in a variety of ways. Dirt may be left in

2B

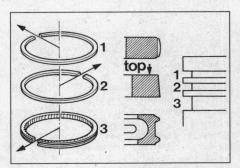

12.17 Piston ring identification and end gap spacing

13.4 Using a micrometer to check the crankshaft journals

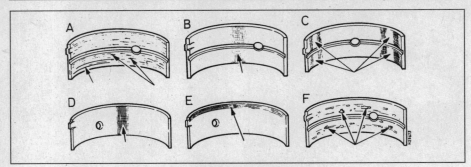

14.2 Typical bearing failures

A Scratched by dirt; dirt embedded into bearing material
B Lack of oil; overlay wiped out
C Improper seating; bright (polished) sections
D Tapered journal; overlay gone from entire surface
E Radius ride
F Fatigue failure; craters or pockets

the engine during assembly, or it may pass through filters or the crankcase ventilation system. It may get into the oil, and from there into the bearings. Metal chips from machining operations and normal engine wear are often present. Abrasives are sometimes left in engine components after reconditioning, especially when parts are not thoroughly cleaned using the proper cleaning methods.

5 Whatever the source, these foreign objects often end up embedded in the soft bearing material. Large particles will not be embedded in the bearing, and will score or gouge the bearing and journal. The best prevention for this cause of bearing failure is to clean all parts thoroughly, and keep everything spotlessly-clean during engine assembly. Frequent and regular engine oil and filter changes are also recommended.

6 Lack of lubrication (or lubrication breakdown) has a number of interrelated causes. Excessive heat (which thins the oil), overloading (which squeezes the oil from the bearing face) and oil leakage (from excessive bearing clearances, worn oil pump or high engine speeds) all contribute to lubrication breakdown.

7 Blocked oil passages, which usually are the result of misaligned oil holes in a bearing shell, will also oil-starve a bearing and destroy it. When lack of lubrication is the cause of bearing failure, the bearing material is wiped or extruded from the steel backing of the bearing. Temperatures may increase to the point where the steel backing turns blue from overheating.

8 Driving habits can have a definite effect on bearing life. Full-throttle, low-speed operation (labouring the engine) puts very high loads on bearings, which tends to squeeze out the oil film. These loads cause the bearings to flex, which produces fine cracks in the bearing face (fatigue failure). Eventually, the bearing material will loosen in pieces and tear away from the steel backing.

9 Short-trip driving leads to corrosion of bearings, because insufficient engine heat is produced to drive off the condensed water and corrosive gases. These products collect in the engine oil, forming acid and sludge. As the

oil is carried to the engine bearings, the acid attacks and corrodes the bearing material.

10 Incorrect bearing installation during engine assembly will lead to bearing failure as well. Tight-fitting bearings leave insufficient bearing oil clearance, resulting in oil starvation. Dirt or foreign particles trapped behind a bearing shell result in high spots on the bearing which lead to failure.

15 Engine overhaul -
reassembly sequence

1 Before reassembly begins, ensure that all new parts have been obtained, and that all necessary tools are available. Read through the entire procedure, to familiarise yourself with the work involved, and to ensure that all items necessary for reassembly of the engine are at hand. In addition to all normal tools and materials, a thread-locking fluid will be needed. A tube of RTV sealing compound will also be required for the joint faces that are fitted without gaskets.

2 In order to save time and avoid problems, engine reassembly can be carried out in the following order:
   a) Crankshaft and main bearings.
   b) Piston/connecting rod assemblies.
   c) Oil pump.

16.4 Fit the plain bearing shells to the caps

d) Sump.
e) Cylinder-head and camshaft.
f) Timing belt and sprockets.
g) Flywheel/driveplate.
h) Inlet and exhaust manifolds.
i) Engine external components.

16 Crankshaft -
refitting and main bearing running clearance check

1 Refitting the crankshaft is the first step in engine reassembly. It is assumed at this point that the cylinder block and crankshaft have been cleaned, inspected and repaired or reconditioned.

2 Position the cylinder block with the sump mating face uppermost.

Main bearing running clearance check

3 Clean the bearing shells and the bearing recesses in both the cylinder block and main bearing caps. If new shells are being fitted, ensure that all traces of the protective grease are cleaned off using paraffin. Wipe the shells dry with a lint-free cloth.

4 Press the bearing shells without the oil holes into the caps, ensuring that the tag on the shell engages in the notch in the cap (see illustration).

5 Press the bearing shells with the oil holes/grooves into the recesses in the cylinder block. If the original main bearing shells are being re-used, these must be refitted to their original locations in the block and caps.

6 Before the crankshaft can be permanently installed, the main bearing running clearance should be checked - this can be done in either of two ways.

7 One method is to first fit the main bearing caps to the cylinder block, with bearing shells in place. With the cap retaining bolts tightened to the specified torque, measure the internal diameter of each assembled pair of bearing shells, using a vernier dial indicator or internal micrometer. If the diameter of each corresponding crankshaft journal is measured and then subtracted from the bearing internal diameter, the result will be the main bearing running clearance.

8 The second (and more accurate) method is to use a product known as Plastigauge. This consists of a fine thread of perfectly-round plastic which is compressed between the bearing cap and the journal. When the cap is removed, the plastic is deformed, and can be measured with a special card gauge supplied with the kit; the running clearance is determined from this gauge.

9 Plastigauge is sometimes difficult to obtain in this country, but enquiries at one of the larger specialist chains of quality motor factors should produce the name of a stockist in your area. The procedure for using Plastigauge is as follows.

16.11 Thread of Plastigauge (arrowed) placed on a crankshaft main journal

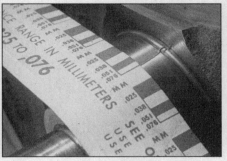

16.15 Measuring the Plastigauge width with the special gauge

16.21 Injecting sealant into the side grooves of No 1 main bearing cap

10 With the upper main bearing shells in place, carefully lay the crankshaft in position. Do not use any lubricant; the crankshaft journals and bearing shells must be perfectly clean and dry.

11 Cut several pieces of the appropriate-size Plastigauge (they should be slightly shorter than the width of the main bearings) and place one piece on each crankshaft journal axis **(see illustration)**.

12 With the bearing shells in position in the caps, fit the caps to their numbered or previously-noted locations. Take care not to disturb the Plastigauge.

13 Starting with the centre main bearing and working outwards, tighten the main bearing cap bolts progressively to their specified torque setting. Don't rotate the crankshaft at any time during this operation.

14 Remove the bolts and carefully lift off the main bearing caps, keeping them in order. Don't disturb the Plastigauge or rotate the crankshaft. If any of the bearing caps are difficult to remove, tap them from side-to-side with a soft-faced mallet.

15 Compare the width of the crushed Plastigauge on each journal with the scale printed on the Plastigauge envelope, to obtain the main bearing running clearance **(see illustration)**.

16 If the clearance is not as specified, the bearing shells may be the wrong size (or excessively-worn, if the original shells are being re-used). Before deciding that different-size shells are needed, make sure that no dirt or oil was trapped between the bearing shells and the caps or block when the clearance was measured. If the Plastigauge was wider at one end than at the other, the journal may be tapered.

17 Carefully scrape away all traces of the Plastigauge material from the crankshaft and bearing shells, using a fingernail or other object which is unlikely to score the shells.

Final crankshaft refitting

18 Carefully lift the crankshaft out of the cylinder block once more.

19 Using a little grease, stick the thrustwashers to each side of No 2 main bearing. Ensure that the oilway grooves on each thrustwasher face outwards.

20 Liberally lubricate each bearing shell in the cylinder block, and lower the crankshaft into position.

21 Lubricate the bearing shells, then fit the bearing caps in their numbered or previously-noted locations. When fitting No 1 bearing cap (flywheel end), do not press it right down onto the crankshaft, but leave it raised so that the first few threads of the main bearing bolts can just be entered. Now inject suitable sealant into each of the cap side grooves, until it enters the space below the cap and completely fills the grooves **(see illustration)**.

22 Fit all of the main bearing cap bolts, and tighten them progressively to the specified torque **(see illustration)**. Wipe away any excess sealant from No 1 main bearing cap.

23 Check that the crankshaft is free to turn, then check the endfloat (see Section 10).

24 Wipe clean the crankshaft oil seal seating, then dip the new seal in fresh engine oil, and locate it over the crankshaft with its closed side facing outwards. Make sure that the oil seal lip is not damaged as it is located on the crankshaft.

25 Using a metal tube, drive the oil seal squarely into the bore until flush. A block of wood cut to pass over the end of the crankshaft may be used instead.

16.22 Tightening the main bearing cap bolts

4 Liberally lubricate the piston and cylinder bore with clean engine oil.

5 Position the crankshaft so that No 1 crankpin is at its lowest point.

6 Fit a ring compressor to No 1 piston, then insert the piston and connecting rod into No 1 cylinder. Drive the piston carefully into the cylinder with the wooden handle of a hammer **(see illustration)**, and at the same time guide the connecting rod onto the crankpin. Make sure that the V-mark or arrow on the piston crown faces the flywheel end of the engine.

7 To measure the big-end bearing running clearance, refer to the information contained in Section 16, as the same general procedures apply.

8 If the Plastigauge method is being used, ensure that the crankpin journal and the big-end bearing shells are clean and dry, then engage the connecting rod with the crankpin.

17 Pistons/connecting rods - refitting and big-end bearing running clearance check

1 Clean the backs of the big-end bearing shells, and the recesses in the connecting rods and big-end caps. If new shells are being fitted, ensure that all traces of the protective grease are cleaned off using paraffin. Wipe the shells and connecting rods dry with a lint-free cloth.

2 Press the big-end bearing shells into the connecting rods and caps in their correct positions. Make sure that the location tabs are engaged with the cut-outs in the connecting rods.

Big-end bearing running clearance check

3 Lubricate the No 1 piston and piston rings, and check that the gaps are spaced out at 120° intervals.

17.6 Using a hammer handle to drive the piston into the cylinder

2B

Lay the Plastigauge strip on the crankpin, fit the bearing cap in its previously-noted position, then tighten the bolts to the specified torque. Do not rotate the crankshaft during this operation. Remove the cap, and check the running clearance by measuring the Plastigauge as previously described.

9 Repeat the foregoing procedures on the remaining piston/connecting rod assemblies.

Final connecting rod refitting

10 Having checked the running clearance of all the crankpin journals and taken any corrective action necessary, clean off all traces of Plastigauge from the bearing shells and crankpins.

11 Liberally lubricate the crankpin journals and big-end bearing shells, and refit the bearing caps once more, ensuring correct positioning as previously described. Tighten the bearing cap bolts to the specified torque, turning the crankshaft each time to make sure that it is free before moving on to the next assembly.

18 Engine - initial start-up after overhaul

1 With the engine refitted in the vehicle, double-check the engine oil and coolant levels.

2 With the spark plugs removed and the ignition system disabled by disconnecting the flywheel sensor wiring, crank the engine over on the starter until the oil pressure light goes out.

3 Refit the spark plugs, and connect the HT leads and flywheel sensor wiring.

4 Start the engine, noting that this may take a little longer than usual. On carburettor engines, this will be due to the fuel pump and carburettor being empty.

5 While the engine is idling, check for fuel, water and oil leaks. Don't be alarmed if there are some odd smells and smoke from parts getting hot and burning off oil deposits.

6 Keep the engine idling until hot water is felt circulating through the radiator top hose, then switch it off.

7 After a few minutes, recheck the oil and water levels, and top-up as necessary.

8 If new pistons, rings or crankshaft bearings have been fitted, the engine must be run-in for the first 500 miles (800 km). Do not operate the engine at full-throttle or allow it to labour in any gear during this period. It is recommended that the oil and filter be changed at the end of this period.

Chapter 3
Cooling, heating and ventilation systems

Contents

Degrees of difficulty

Easy, suitable for novice with little experience	Fairly easy, suitable for beginner with some experience	Fairly difficult, suitable for competent DIY mechanic	Difficult, suitable for experienced DIY mechanic	Very difficult, suitable for expert DIY or professional

Specifications

System type .... Pressurised, with front-mounted radiator and electric cooling fan. Water pump driven by external belt from crankshaft. Auxiliary electric water pump fitted to some engines

Thermostat

Type	Wax
Starts-to-open temperature:	
Except B18FT(M) engine	92°C
B18FT(M) engine	89°C
Fully-open temperature:	
Except B18FT(M) engine	106°C
B18FT(M) engine	104°C
Lift height:	
Except B18FT(M) engine	8.5 mm
B18FT(M) engine	8.9 mm

Expansion tank cap pressure .... 1.5 bar

Radiator cooling fan thermal switch

	1st stage	2nd stage*
Switch-on temperature (typical)	95°C	101°C
Switch-off temperature (typical)	90°C	96°C

Note: Not all models are fitted with a two-stage cooling fan

Auxiliary electric water pump

Delivery at 0.1 bar pressure	700 litres/hour
Operating pressure	0.2 to 0.8 bar
Engaging temperature	100°C
Disengaging temperature	95°C

3

Torque wrench settings

	Nm	lbf ft
Air conditioning compressor mounting bolts	40	30
Air conditioning compressor oil filler plug	10	7
Air conditioning condenser unions:		
Inlet	24	18
Outlet	17	13
Air conditioning evaporator unions:		
High pressure	24	18
Low pressure	41	30
Auxiliary water pump	8	6
Coolant return pipe on cylinder head	7	5
Coolant temperature sensor	20	15
Radiator	20	15
Radiator cooling fan thermal switch	18	13
Thermostat housing	8	6
Turbocharging cooling banjo bolt	45	33
Water pump	13	10
Water pump drive pulley	20	15

1 General information

The cooling system is of pressurised type, consisting of a belt-driven pump, aluminium crossflow radiator, expansion tank, electric cooling fan and a thermostat. On some fuel injection engines, an additional auxiliary electric water pump circulates a proportion of the coolant even when the engine is switched off.

The cooling system functions as follows. Cold coolant in the bottom of the radiator passes through the bottom hose to the water pump, where it is pumped around the cylinder block and head passages. After cooling the cylinder bores, combustion surfaces and valve seats, the coolant reaches the underside of the thermostat, which is initially closed. The coolant passes through the heater and inlet manifold, and is returned to the water pump.

When the engine is cold, the coolant circulates only through the cylinder block, cylinder head, heater and inlet manifold. When the coolant reaches a predetermined temperature, the thermostat opens and the coolant passes through the top hose to the radiator. As the coolant circulates through the radiator, it is cooled by the inrush of air when the car is in forward motion. The airflow is supplemented by the action of the electric cooling fan when necessary. Upon reaching the bottom of the radiator, the coolant is now cooled, and the cycle is repeated **(see illustration)**.

When the engine is at normal operating temperature, the coolant expands, and some of it is displaced into the expansion tank. This coolant collects in the tank, and is returned to the radiator when the system cools.

The electric cooling fan mounted behind the radiator is controlled by a thermostatic switch located in the left-hand side of the radiator. At a predetermined coolant temperature, the switch contacts close, thus actuating the fan.

⚠ Warning: When an air conditioning system is fitted, it is necessary to observe special precautions whenever dealing with any part of the system, its associated components, or any items which necessitate disconnection of the system. If for any reason the system must be disconnected, entrust this task to your Volvo dealer or a refrigeration engineer. The refrigeration circuit contains a potentially-harmful liquid refrigerant (Freon), and it is highly dangerous to disconnect any part of the system without specialised knowledge and equipment. The refrigerant must not be allowed to come in contact with a naked flame, otherwise a poisonous gas will be created. Further, do not allow the fluid to come in contact with the skin or eyes.

2 Radiator - removal, inspection and refitting

Removal

Note: If the reason for radiator removal is concern over coolant loss, note that minor leaks may be repaired by using a radiator sealant with the radiator in situ.

440 and 460 models

1 Drain the cooling system as described in Chapter 1.
2 Loosen the clips, and disconnect the top and bottom hoses and the expansion tank hose from the radiator. Also disconnect the wiring from the radiator cooling fan thermal switch **(see illustrations)**.

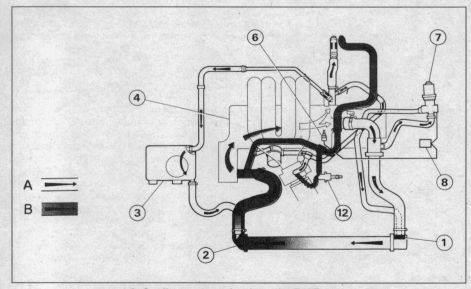

1.3 Cooling system circuit on the B18F engine

1	Non-return valve	5	Water pump	9	Throttle valve housing
2	Radiator	6	Thermal switch		heating thermostat
3	Expansion tank	7	Electric pump	A	Hot coolant
4	Cylinder head	8	Pump control unit	B	Cold coolant

2.2a Top hose connection to the radiator

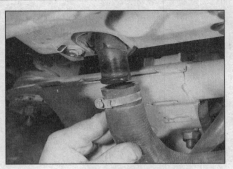

2.2b Disconnecting the bottom hose from the radiator

2.2c Radiator cooling fan thermal switch wiring at the side of the radiator

3 On later models, remove the securing bolts, and take off the radiator cover panel. Unscrew the radiator top mounting bolts, and remove the clamps **(see illustration)**.

4 Move the top of the radiator forwards from the engine compartment crossmember, then lift it up from the rubber location bushes, and withdraw it from the car **(see illustration)**.

480 models

5 Drain the cooling system as described in Chapter 1.

6 Remove the radiator front panel, together with the headlights and direction indicators, as described in Chapter 11.

7 On models with the B18FT engine, remove the intercooler by disconnecting the top and bottom hoses, and removing the clip at the top centre; lift out the intercooler **(see illustration)**.

8 Unscrew the screws and remove the shroud from the front of the radiator.

9 Loosen the clips, and disconnect the top and bottom hoses and the expansion tank hose from the radiator. Also disconnect the wiring from the radiator cooling fan thermal switch.

10 Unscrew the radiator top mounting bolts, and remove the clamps.

11 Move the top of the radiator forwards from the engine compartment crossmember, then lift it up from the rubber location bushes, and withdraw it from the car.

Inspection

12 Radiator damage which cannot be cured using a radiator sealant is best left to a specialist.

13 Clear the radiator matrix of flies and small leaves with a soft brush, or by hosing.

14 If the radiator is to be left out of the car for more than two days, precautions should be taken to prevent rusting within the matrix. Either the radiator can be thoroughly flushed with clean water and then dried out, or it can be filled with coolant and temporarily plugged at the outlets.

Refitting

15 Refitting is a reversal of the removal procedure. Check the radiator rubber mounting bushes, and renew them if necessary. The bushes may be smeared with

2.3 Removing the radiator top mounting

2.4 Lifting the radiator from the car

a little petroleum jelly before locating the radiator bottom pegs in them. Refill the system with reference to Chapter 1.

---

3 Expansion tank -
removal and refitting

Removal

1 Drain the cooling system, with reference to Chapter 1.

2 Disconnect the wiring from the coolant level warning light switch.

3 Unscrew and remove the expansion tank mounting screws. Where necessary for better access, remove the power steering fluid

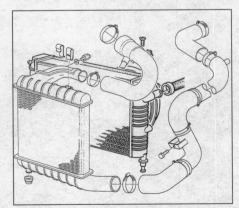

2.7 Radiator and intercooler components as fitted to the B18FT engine

reservoir (where applicable) and washer fluid reservoir.

4 Loosen the clips, and disconnect the supply hose, purge hose and return hose from the expansion tank. Withdraw the expansion tank from the engine compartment.

Refitting

5 Refitting is a reversal of the removal procedure. Refill the cooling system with reference to Chapter 1.

---

4 Thermostat -
removal, testing and refitting

1 Before assuming the thermostat is to blame for a cooling system problem, check the coolant level, auxiliary drivebelt tension and condition (see *Weekly checks* and Chapter 1) and temperature gauge operation. Also check around the water pump for signs of leakage - a failed water pump will often leak with the engine switched off, or when the engine is first started from cold.

2 If the engine seems to be taking a long time to warm up (based on heater output or temperature gauge operation), the thermostat is probably stuck open. Renew the thermostat.

3 Equally, a lengthy warm-up period might suggest that the thermostat is missing - it may have been removed or inadvertently omitted by a previous owner or mechanic. Don't drive the vehicle without a thermostat - exhaust emissions and fuel economy will suffer.

3

4.8 Disconnecting the top hose from the thermostat cover housing

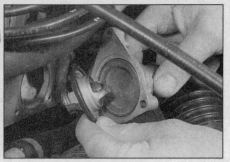

4.10 Removing the thermostat and sealing ring

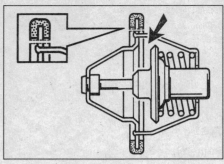

4.17 Diagram of the thermostat showing the air vent hole position

4 If the engine runs hot, use your hand to check the temperature of the radiator top hose. If the hose isn't hot, but the engine is, the thermostat is probably stuck closed, preventing the coolant inside the engine from escaping to the radiator - renew the thermostat.

5 If the radiator top hose is hot, it means that the coolant is flowing and the thermostat is open. Consult the *Fault diagnosis* section at the end of this manual to assist in tracing possible cooling system faults.

Removal

6 The thermostat is located on the left-hand (transmission) end of the cylinder head, below the distributor cap.

7 Drain the cooling system, with reference to Chapter 1.

8 Loosen the clip, and disconnect the radiator top hose from the thermostat cover housing **(see illustration)**.

9 Unscrew the bolts and remove the cover.

10 Remove the thermostat and sealing ring from its location **(see illustration)**.

Testing

11 If there is any doubt about the condition of the thermostat, the best advice is to fit a new one - they are not expensive. Testing is often inconclusive, but is described below.

12 If the thermostat remains in the open position at room temperature, it is faulty, and must be renewed as a matter of course.

13 To test it fully, suspend the (closed) thermostat on a length of string in a container of cold water, with a thermometer beside it; ensure that neither touches the side of the container.

14 Heat the water, and check the temperature at which the thermostat begins to open. The temperature at which thermostat should start to open is given in the Specifications, and is normally stamped on the unit.

15 Checking the fully-open temperature is not possible in an open container, as it is higher than the boiling point of water at atmospheric pressure. Remove the thermostat and allow it to cool down; check that it closes fully.

16 If the thermostat does not open and close as described, if it sticks in either position, or if it does not open at the specified temperature, it must be renewed.

Refitting

17 Refitting is a reversal of the removal procedure, noting the following points:
a) Renew the sealing ring, and clean the mating surfaces.
b) Where the thermostat incorporates a vent hole, this should be located at the top, to allow air to escape into the top hose **(see illustration)**.
c) Tighten the mounting bolts to the specified torque.
d) Refill the cooling system with reference to Chapter 1.

5 Radiator cooling fan - testing, removal and refitting

Testing

1 The radiator cooling fan can be tested by disconnecting the wiring plug from the thermal switch (located on the left-hand side of the radiator), and bridging the two contacts in the plug with a piece of wire. If the fan now operates with the ignition switched on, the thermal switch is faulty. If the fan is still inoperative, this proves that there is a fault in the fan motor or associated wiring (see also Section 6).

Removal

2 Disconnect the battery negative lead.

3 On 440 and 460 models, release the plastic cable-tie securing the wiring harness to the cooling fan bracket.

4 On 480 models, remove the air intake hose.

5 Unscrew and remove the two upper mounting bolts from the fan bracket **(see illustration)**.

6 Disconnect the wiring plugs for the cooling fan motor and thermal switch **(see illustration)**.

7 Lift the cooling fan assembly and bracket out of the engine compartment.

8 If necessary, the fan blades may be removed by extracting the circlip. The fan motor may also be removed from the bracket by disconnecting the wiring and unscrewing the three nuts **(see illustration)**.

5.5 Radiator cooling fan bracket upper mounting

5.6 Wiring plug for the radiator cooling fan motor

5.8 Electric cooling fan blades and motor removal

Refitting

9 Refitting is a reversal of the removal procedure.

6 Cooling system electrical switches - testing, removal and refitting

Testing

Radiator cooling fan thermal switch

1 The thermal switch is located on the left-hand side of the radiator. If it develops a fault, it is most likely to fail open-circuit, rendering the fan motor inoperative even when the coolant temperature exceeds the switch-on point. The coolant may even reach boiling point in such a case, which would almost certainly result in engine damage.

2 To test the thermal switch, remove it and suspend it in very hot (near-boiling) water. Connect an ohmmeter to the two contacts, and check that the resistance is zero, indicating that the contacts are closed. If the ohmmeter is to hand when the engine overheats, the same check can be made with the switch in position in the radiator.

Coolant/water temperature gauge sender unit

3 The water temperature gauge sender unit is located on the left-hand end of the cylinder head. No resistance values are available, but the unit is relatively inexpensive, and should be renewed if it is thought to be faulty.

Removal

Radiator cooling fan thermal switch

4 To save time draining and refilling the cooling system, it is possible to quickly remove the old switch and fit the new one with the coolant still in the radiator. If this approach is taken, the engine should be cold, to prevent the danger of scalding. The alternative is to completely drain the cooling system before removing the switch.

5 Position a container beneath the switch to catch any spilled coolant, and disconnect the switch wiring.

6 If the cooling system has not been drained, either have the new switch ready (with a new washer already fitted to it), or else make up a suitable temporary plug for when the old switch is removed - a cork might serve well.

7 Unscrew and remove the switch from the radiator, and quickly fit the new switch (or the temporary plug if the system was not drained).

Coolant/water temperature gauge sender unit

8 The procedure is similar to that for the thermal switch described in the previous paragraphs.

Refitting

Radiator cooling fan thermal switch

9 Screw the new switch (together with a new

7.7a Removing the water pump (engine shown in the car)

sealing washer) into the radiator, and tighten it to the specified torque.

10 Refit the wiring connector, then top-up or refill the cooling system with reference to Chapter 1.

Coolant/water temperature gauge sender unit

11 Refitting is a reversal of the removal procedure; top-up or refill the cooling system with reference to Chapter 1.

7 Water pump - removal and refitting

Removal

1 Loosen the right-hand front roadwheel bolts. Apply the handbrake, then jack up the front of the car and support on axle stands.

2 Remove the engine splash guard from under the subframe.

3 Remove the right-hand front roadwheel, then remove the plastic access panel covering the lower part of the engine.

4 Drain the cooling system, with reference to Chapter 1.

5 On models not fitted with air conditioning, loosen the alternator mounting and pivot bolts, then move the alternator to release the drivebelt tension by unscrewing the adjustment nut; remove the drivebelt.

TOOL TiP

Make up a tool from two strips of steel bolted together at one end - the free ends can then be bolted to the water pump pulley, to hold it stationary

7.7b Removing the water pump (engine shown out of the car for clarity)

6 On models fitted with air conditioning, loosen the power steering pivot and mounting bolts, and unscrew the adjusting nut to release the drivebelt tension. If necessary, also remove the alternator drivebelt by loosening the alternator pivot and mounting bolts, unscrewing the adjustment nut to release the drivebelt tension; remove the drivebelt(s).

7 Unscrew the water pump mounting bolts, and withdraw the water pump from the cylinder block (see illustrations). If the drive pulley is left on the water pump, it will not be possible to completely remove four of the bolts, but they can still be unscrewed enough for the pump to be removed.

8 If desired, the pulley may be unbolted and removed by holding it stationary with an oil filter strap, or with a tool made out of two lengths of metal bar and three bolts (see Tool Tip).

9 Remove the water pump gasket, and thoroughly clean the mating surfaces.

Refitting

10 Refitting is a reversal of the removal procedure, but use a new gasket, and tighten the bolts evenly and in diagonal sequence to the specified torque.

11 On completion, adjust the drivebelt tension and fill the cooling system, with reference to Chapter 1.

8 Auxiliary electric water pump - testing, removal and refitting

Testing

1 On the B18F engine, the auxiliary pump only operates with the engine switched off and the coolant temperature at or above 97°C (see illustration). Once it has started, the pump remains on for 8 to 11 minutes. The temperature sensor is located in the cylinder head, and also serves the fuel injection engine management system.

2 On the B18FT engine, the pump should continue to run for 25 seconds after the ignition has been switched off. It engages at 100°C, and disengages at 95°C. The temperature sensor is located in the turbocharger coolant outlet hose.

3

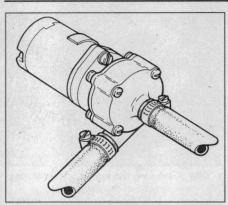

8.1 Auxiliary electric water pump

3 To check the auxiliary pump relay, first check fuses 5 and 20 in the fusebox. Remove relay B, and check that battery voltage is present at terminal 30 **(see illustration)**. Switch on the ignition, and check that battery voltage is present at terminal 15. Using an ohmmeter, check that the resistance between terminal 31 and earth is zero.

4 On models with the B18F engine, check that the resistance between terminal T and earth is 2275 ohms at a coolant temperature of 20°C, and 300 ohms at 80°C.

5 On models with the B18FT engine, check that the resistance between terminal T and earth is infinite at room temperature, and zero at a coolant temperature of 95°C to 100°C.

6 To check the pump for correct operation, connect a bridging wire between terminals A and 31 on the B18F engine, or between terminals 87 and 30 on the B18FT engine **(see illustration)**.

Removal

7 Remove the air cleaner housing, with reference to Chapter 4B.

8 Fit hose clamps to the electric pump inlet and outlet hoses.

9 Loosen the clips, and disconnect the hoses from the pump.

10 Disconnect the wiring, then unscrew the mounting bolt and remove the pump.

Refitting

11 Refitting is a reversal of the removal procedure. Top-up the cooling system with reference to Chapter 1.

9 Heating system - general information

The heating system consists of a heater housing mounted below the facia, which contains the heater matrix and, on models with air conditioning, an evaporator. The heater blower motor is mounted on the left-hand side of the bulkhead.

With the blower motor operating, air is drawn into the car through a grille in the bonnet; the air is directed through the heater housing and into the car. The heater matrix, broadly speaking, is a small radiator connected into the engine cooling system circuit; when the engine is at working temperature, the coolant flowing through the matrix is hot. The air entering the car is heated as it flows over the matrix; the heater housing contains air flaps to allow the driver to regulate the amount of heat required. With the heat temperature control set to minimum, the air flaps are closed and no heated air enters the car, although hot coolant from the engine still circulates through the matrix.

On models with air conditioning, the heater housing also contains an evaporator which extracts heat from the incoming air.

10 Heater components - removal and refitting

⚠️ *Warning: On 480 models fitted with air conditioning, the refrigerant hoses must be disconnected by a refrigeration engineer - consult your Volvo dealer if necessary.*

Heater unit

1 Remove the facia as described in Chapter 11.

2 Support the heater unit with a piece of wood.

3 Working in the engine compartment, attach hose clamps to the two heater hoses located on the left-hand side of the bulkhead. If hose clamps are not available, drain the complete cooling system with reference to Chapter 1.

4 Loosen the clips and disconnect the heater hoses from the heater outlets. Some coolant will escape, so position a container beneath the engine compartment to collect it.

5 Remove the plastic cover from the left-hand side of the bulkhead by first pulling up the moulding. Unscrew the nut from the heater inlet grille on the bulkhead **(see illustration)**.

6 Unscrew the screw securing the heat shield to the front of the bulkhead, and pull the heat shield forwards slightly. Also unscrew the heater mounting nut located above the heat shield.

7 Remove the bracket from the top of the heater fan housing.

8 Working inside the car, remove the glovebox with reference to Chapter 11.

9 Remove the two relays from the fan housing bracket, then unbolt the bracket from the tunnel.

10 Withdraw the heater unit from inside the car. Some spillage of coolant is to be expected, so cover the floor carpet with polythene sheeting and cloth rags.

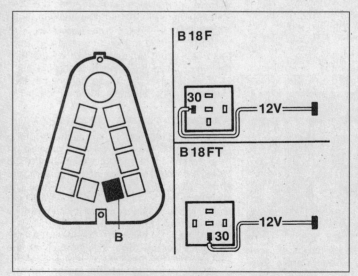

8.3 Checking for battery voltage at the auxiliary pump relay (B) terminals

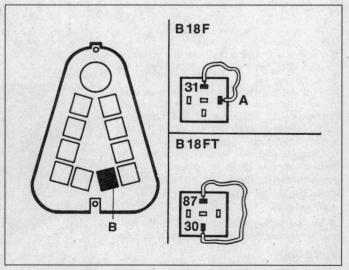

8.6 Terminal bridging connection when checking the auxiliary pump

10.5 Heater inlet grille mounting nut (arrowed)

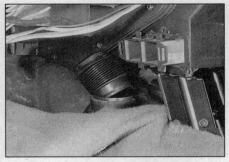

10.17 Removing the air duct hoses from under the heater unit

10.18 Lowering the bottom cover from under the heater

10.19a Removing the heater matrix from the housing

10.19b Clamp which holds the two matrix outlets to the upper heater section

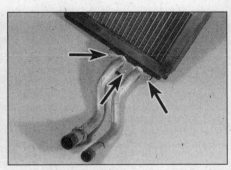

10.20 Inlet and outlet pipes on the heater matrix - clamp plate bolts arrowed

11 Refitting is a reversal of the removal procedure, but top-up and bleed the cooling system with reference to Chapter 1. Where applicable, have the air conditioning system re-charged by a refrigeration engineer. Refit the facia with reference to Chapter 11.

Heater matrix

12 Disconnect the battery negative lead.
13 Remove the centre console, with reference to Chapter 11.
14 For improved access, the glovebox may be removed (Chapter 11).
15 Working in the engine compartment, fit hose clamps to the two heater hoses on the front of the bulkhead. If hose clamps are not available, the cooling system may be completely drained with reference to Chapter 1.
16 Loosen the clips and disconnect the hoses from the heater outlets. Some coolant

will escape, so position a container beneath the engine compartment to collect it.
17 Carefully prise the two air duct hoses from under the heater unit **(see illustration)**.
18 Remove the screws, and lower the bottom cover from the heater **(see illustration)**.
19 Where fitted, unscrew the clamp bolt located under the matrix at the front end. This clamp holds the two matrix outlets to the upper heater section. Withdraw the matrix from the heater housing **(see illustrations)**.
20 On some models, the inlet and outlet pipes may be removed from the matrix by unscrewing the bolts and lifting off the clamp plate **(see illustration)**. Check the sealing O-rings, and renew them if necessary.
21 Refitting is a reversal of the removal procedure. Top-up or refill the cooling system with reference to Chapter 1.

Heater blower/fan motor

22 Disconnect the battery negative lead.
23 Remove the glovebox and lower trim panel from under the facia with reference to Chapter 11.
24 Disconnect the wiring from the motor at the connector plug **(see illustration)**.
25 Disconnect the motor air hose and the earth lead **(see illustration)**.
26 Unscrew the motor mounting bolts, noting the location of the earth lead terminal **(see illustration)**.
27 Lower the motor from the housing, and withdraw it from the car **(see illustration)**. On heater units fitted to high trim level cars, the fan wheel must be turned so that the flat section can pass the vacuum diaphragm unit.
28 The motor and housing cannot be dismantled - they are manufactured as one unit.

3

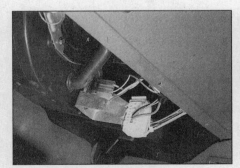

10.24 Heater blower/fan motor wiring plug

10.25 Disconnecting the air hose from the heater motor

10.26 Heater blower/fan motor and mounting bolts - earth lead terminal arrowed

10.27 Removing the heater blower/fan motor

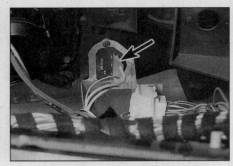

10.33 Heater resistor (arrowed)

11.4 Removing the heater control panel from the surround

29 Refitting is a reversal of the removal procedure.

Heater resistor

30 Disconnect the battery negative lead.
31 Remove the glovebox and lower trim panel from under the facia with reference to Chapter 11.
32 Disconnect the wiring, and remove the relay from the bracket.
33 Remove the screws, and lift out the mounting frame and resistor **(see illustration)**.
34 Refitting is a reversal of the removal procedure.

11 Heater control panel - removal and refitting

440 and 460 models up to 1994, and 480 models

1 Disconnect the battery negative lead.
2 Remove the facia panel surrounds with reference to Chapter 11.

Vacuum-operated valve type

3 Remove the screws, and remove the heater control panel surround.
4 Unclip the spring clip from the outer cable on the heater control panel, and disconnect the inner cable from the operating arm **(see illustration)**.
5 Disconnect the wiring at the rear of the panel.
6 Disconnect the vacuum block, complete with hoses.

7 Withdraw the heater control panel from the facia.

Mechanically-operated type

8 Working under the facia, remove the screws and release the outer cables from the clamps. Disconnect the inner cables from the operating arms.
9 The heater control panel mounting screws are removed when the facia panels are removed.
10 Withdraw the heater control panel from the facia, together with the control cables. If the control panel is being removed on its own, pull the panel part-way out; disconnect the outer cables by unclipping the spring clips, then disconnect the inner cables from the operating arms.

All types

11 Refitting is a reversal of the removal procedure. Check that the controls operate correctly, so that the valves fully open and close. If necessary, adjust the outer cables within the spring clips.

440 and 460 models, 1994 onwards

12 Disconnect the battery negative lead.
13 Using a pair of pliers with a piece of cloth or card to protect the knobs from damage, pull off the three rotary control knobs, noting their fitted locations **(see illustration)**.
14 Using a suitable flat-bladed tool, carefully prise out the heater control panel surround, and remove it **(see illustration)**. The panel illumination bulbs are now accessible, and may be pulled out if their renewal is required.

15 Loosen and remove the four screws securing the control panel to the facia **(see illustration)**.
16 The control panel can now be pulled forwards and partly withdrawn from the facia, for access to the control cables and connections. If difficulty is experienced in withdrawing the panel, remove the radio/cassette player as described in Chapter 12, and reach in through the radio aperture to push the panel out from behind.
17 Disconnect the outer cables by unclipping the spring clips, then disconnect the inner cables from the operating arms, noting their locations. Disconnect the wiring plugs and connections from the rear of the panel, and remove it from the car.
18 Refitting is a reversal of the removal procedure. Check that the controls operate correctly before refitting is completed. If necessary, the outer cables can be adjusted within the spring clips.

12 Air conditioning system - general information and precautions

Air conditioning is available on some models as an optional extra. In conjunction with the heater, the system enables any reasonable air temperature to be achieved inside the car; it also reduces the humidity of the incoming air, aiding demisting even when cooling is not required.

The refrigeration side of the air conditioning system functions in a similar way to a domestic

11.13 Pull off the control knobs using pliers with protected jaws

11.14 Prise out the panel surround using a flat-bladed tool

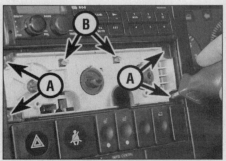

11.15 Removing the control panel screws (A) - note the illumination bulbs (B)

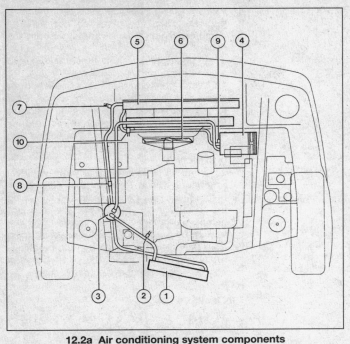

12.2a Air conditioning system components

1 Evaporator
2 Low-pressure switch
3 Accumulator/drier
4 Compressor
5 Condenser
6 Electric cooling fan
7 High-pressure switch
8 Orifice tube
9 Pressure relief valve
10 Coolant temperature switch

12.2b Air conditioning schematic diagram

1 Evaporator
2 Low-pressure switch
3 Accumulator/drier
4 Compressor
5 Condenser
6 Electric cooling fan
7 High-pressure switch
8 Orifice tube
9 Pressure relief valve

refrigerator. A compressor, belt-driven from the crankshaft pulley, draws refrigerant in its gaseous state from an evaporator. The compressed refrigerant passes through a condenser, where it loses heat and becomes a liquid. After dehydration, the refrigerant returns to the evaporator, where it absorbs heat from the air passing over the evaporator fins. The refrigerant becomes a gas again, and the cycle is repeated **(see illustrations)**.

Various subsidiary controls and sensors protect the system against excessive temperatures and pressures. Engine idle speed is increased when the system is in use, to compensate for the additional load imposed by the compressor.

Although the refrigerant is not itself toxic, in the presence of a naked flame (or a lighted cigarette), it forms a highly-toxic gas. Liquid refrigerant spilled on the skin will cause frostbite.

Considering the above points, and the need for specialised equipment for discharging and recharging the system, any work which requires the disconnection of a refrigerant line **must** be left to a specialist.

Do not allow refrigerant lines to be exposed to temperatures in excess of 110°C (230°F), as might occur for example during welding or paint-drying operations.

To prevent problems with the system hoses hardening and cracking, the system should be operated regularly, even during colder weather - bear in mind that the system is useful for demisting, for example.

Do not operate the air conditioning system if it is known to be short of refrigerant, or damage may result.

13 Air conditioning system components - removal and refitting

⚠️ *Warning: The system should be professionally discharged before carrying out any of the following work. Cap or plug the pipe lines as soon as they are disconnected, to prevent the entry of moisture. Refer to the precautions given in Section 1 before proceeding.*

Compressor

1 Have the system discharged (see *Warning* above).
2 Disconnect the battery negative lead.
3 Unbolt and remove the drivebelt guard.
4 Loosen the power steering pump pivot and mounting bolts, and back off the adjustment nut so that the drivebelt tension is released **(see illustration overleaf)**.
5 Unbolt and remove the power steering pump, leaving the fluid lines still attached. Note that one of the bolts is accessed through the pulley, and it may therefore be necessary to rotate the engine until the pulley hole is aligned with the bolt.

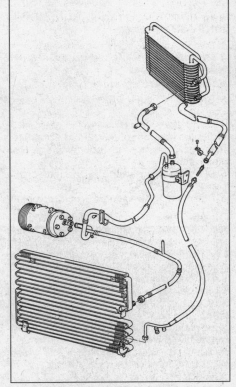

12.2c Air conditioning components and line connections

3

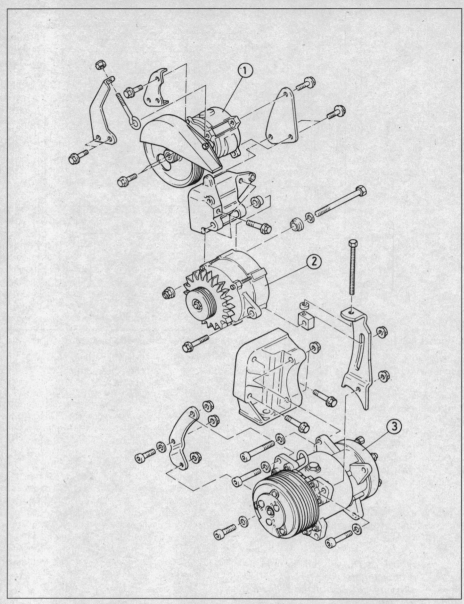

13.4 Compressor components on models with power steering

1 Power steering pump   *2 Alternator*   *3 Compressor*

6 Loosen the alternator mounting bolts, then back off the adjustment bolt so that the drive-belt tension is released. Remove the drivebelt.
7 Disconnect the wiring from the rear of the alternator, and unbolt the earth lead from the alternator bracket.
8 Unscrew and remove the pivot and adjuster bolts, and lift the alternator from the engine.
9 Apply the handbrake, then jack up the front of the car and support on axle stands. Unbolt and remove the engine splash guard. Remove the left-hand roadwheel and the plastic splash panel from the left-hand side of the engine compartment.
10 With the refrigerant lines disconnected from the compressor and plugged, unscrew the

lower mounting bolts and disconnect the compressor wiring at the connector. The compressor can now be removed from the engine.
11 If necessary, unbolt the brackets and transfer them to the new unit.
12 When the compressor is renewed or repaired, it should be filled with new oil. Refer to a Volvo dealer or air conditioning specialist for the quantity and type of oil required, as this varies with compressor type. Always fit a new O-ring to the filler plug, and tighten the plug securely.
13 Refitting is a reversal of the removal procedure. Clean the refrigerant line ports before fitting new O-ring seals and tightening the unions fully. Note that the top left compressor attachment bolt is fitted from left to right by the factory, but it should be fitted from right to left on refitting in the car. Have the system recharged by a refrigeration specialist or Volvo dealer on completion.

Condenser

14 Have the system discharged (see *Warning* at the start of this section).
15 Remove the radiator front panel with reference to Chapter 11.
16 Extract the fasteners, and remove the header cover from the front of the radiator.
17 Disconnect the refrigerant lines from the condenser, and blank off the openings.
18 Unscrew the nuts, and remove the power steering oil cooler pipe from front of the condenser **(see illustration)**.
19 Unbolt and remove the mounting straps between the condenser and the radiator, then pull the condenser upwards and out of its mountings.
20 If the condenser is being renewed, the quantity of oil in the old unit must be calculated by pouring the oil into a calibrated container, then the same quantity of new oil poured into the new unit. Blanking plugs must be fitted to the unit, and must remain in position until just prior to connecting the lines. Renew the O-rings on the connections, and smear them with compressor oil.
21 Refitting is a reversal of the removal procedure. Have the system recharged by a refrigeration specialist or Volvo dealer on completion.

Evaporator

22 Have the system discharged (see *Warning* at the start of this section).
23 Remove the facia complete, as described in Chapter 11.
24 On turbocharged models, remove the air cooling gallery by disconnecting the wiring plug and pulling the gallery from the brackets; place it to one side. Unscrew the mounting bolts, and remove the heat shield.
25 Unbolt and remove the rear heat shield, and if necessary, bend the lower attachment lugs forwards.

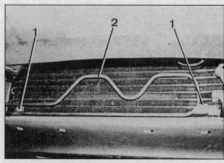

13.18 Power steering oil cooler pipe on the front of the condenser

1 Mounting nuts   *2 Oil cooler pipe*

26 Fit hose clamps to the heater hoses on the front of the bulkhead, then loosen the clips and pull the hoses from the heater matrix outlets. Some spillage of coolant is to be expected, and polythene sheeting and rags should be placed on the carpet to catch it. If hose clamps are not available, the cooling system can be drained with reference to Chapter 1.

27 Loosen the union nuts, and disconnect the refrigerant lines from the condenser; blank off the openings to prevent entry of foreign matter.

28 Unscrew and remove the heater mounting nuts from the front of the bulkhead. Pull off the plastic cover from over the heater motor entry, then unscrew the nut and remove the metal strap.

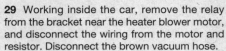

13.30 Air distribution unit removal

1 Mounting bolts *2 Resistor*

29 Working inside the car, remove the relay from the bracket near the heater blower motor, and disconnect the wiring from the motor and resistor. Disconnect the brown vacuum hose.

30 Unbolt and remove the air distribution unit **(see illustration)**.

31 If necessary, remove the heater blower motor, with reference to Section 10.

32 Remove the rubber grommet from the evaporator connections, and release the two clamps.

33 Unscrew and remove the bolts securing the two halves of the air distribution unit.

34 Disconnect the vacuum line and connecting rod on the left of the vacuum valve.

35 Lift off the upper half of the air distribution unit, and remove the evaporator **(see illustrations)**.

36 Refitting is a reversal of the removal procedure. If the evaporator is being renewed, calculate the quantity of fluid in the old unit by pouring it into a calibrated container, then pour the same quantity of new oil into the new unit. Blank off the openings until just prior to fitting the lines. Fit new O-rings to the unions, and smear them with compressor oil before connecting the unions. After fitting the evaporator, and before recharging the system, the drier should be renewed as follows.

37 Disconnect the wiring from the air mass meter, then loosen the unions and disconnect the refrigerant lines from the drier. Unscrew the mounting nuts and withdraw the drier from the engine compartment. Loosen the pinch-bolt and remove the drier from the bracket.

38 Calculate the quantity of oil in the old drier by pouring it into a calibrated container, then pour the same quantity of new oil into the new drier. Note that if the lines are being renewed at the same time, the quantity of fluid in them must be calculated as well, and the same quantity of new oil poured into the new lines.

39 Have the system recharged by a refrigeration specialist or Volvo dealer on completion.

3

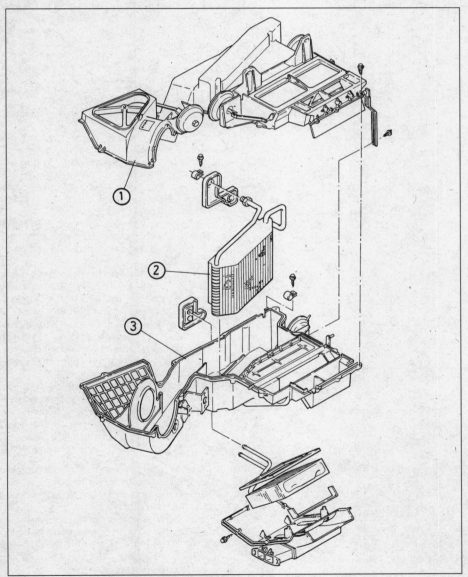

13.35a Evaporator and heater components

1 Upper housing   *2 Evaporator*   *3 Lower housing*

13.35b Removing the evaporator

Notes

Chapter 4 Part A:
Fuel system - carburettor engines

Contents

Degrees of difficulty

| Easy, suitable for novice with little experience | | Fairly easy, suitable for beginner with some experience | | Fairly difficult, suitable for competent DIY mechanic | 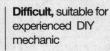 | Difficult, suitable for experienced DIY mechanic | | Very difficult, suitable for expert DIY or professional | |

Specifications

Fuel grade

Fuel octane requirement:

Models without a catalytic converter . . . . 98 RON leaded (4-star)*, 98 RON super unleaded, or 95 RON unleaded

Models with a catalytic converter . . . . 98 RON super unleaded or 95 RON unleaded only - **do not** use leaded 4-star

* Leaded petrol is being phased out in the UK market by January 2000 to be replaced by Lead Replacement Petrol (LRP). Cars which previously ran on leaded (4-star) petrol should run satisfactorily on LRP but, if in doubt, consult the vehicle manufacturer.

Fuel pump

Type	Mechanical, operated by eccentric on camshaft
Delivery pressure (measured at the same height as pump)	0.16 to 0.18 bar

Carburettor (general)

Type	Solex CISAC 28-34 Z10
Application	B18K, B18K(D), B18KP, B18KP(D) engines
Choke type	Manual

Carburettor data

Accelerator pump cam	36
Throttle butterfly opening in relation to choke	26° ± 30'
Needle valve	1.8
Float weight (without bronze bush in pivoting point)	6.1 grams ± 1 gram
Float height (measured with gasket)	33.8 mm
Fast idle adjustment screw-to-cam gap	2.0 mm
Float chamber vent opening	2.0 to 4.0 mm
Accelerator pump injector	35

	Primary	Secondary
Venturi diameter	20 mm	27 mm
Jet sizes:		
Main jet	97.5 ± 2.5	140.0 ± 2.5
Emulsion tube	DZ175 ± 5.0	EZ155 ± 5.0
Idle fuel jet	43 ± 3	-
Idle air jet	190	70

Torque wrench settings

	Nm	lbf ft
Carburettor	14	10
Fuel pump	14	10
Fuel tank (oiled threads)	23	17
Inlet and exhaust manifolds	20	15
Throttle linkage on inlet manifold	9	7

4A

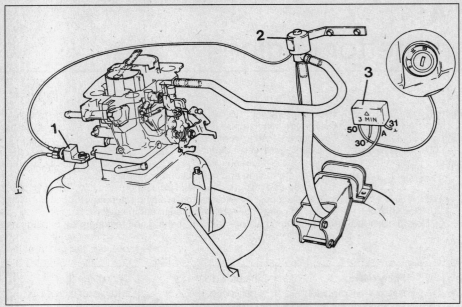

1.4 Carburettor float chamber ventilation system

1 *Thermal sensor*   2 *Electrically-operated air valve*   3 *Time delay relay*

1 General information and precautions

The fuel system consists of a fuel tank mounted under the car (just in front of the rear axle), a mechanical fuel pump and a Solex twin-choke downdraught carburettor. The mechanical fuel pump is operated by an eccentric on the camshaft, and is mounted on the rear right-hand end of the cylinder head.

A vapour separator is fitted in the fuel supply line to the carburettor, and a return line to the fuel tank is taken from the separator. A gauze fuel filter is located in the carburettor fuel delivery union.

A three-way catalytic converter (without a Lambda sensor) is fitted to some models - see Part C of this Chapter.

To improve hot starting, some models are fitted with a carburettor float chamber ventilation system **(see illustration)**. This system consists of a sensor located on the inlet manifold, an electronically-operated air valve, and a time-delay relay. The relay is engaged for 3 minutes when the engine is started. If the temperature sensed by the sensor is greater than 70°C, the air valve opens for a maximum period of three minutes; if the temperature is lower than 63°C, the relay is switched off.

A carburettor cooling system is also employed, to prevent the carburettor overheating immediately after switching off the engine **(see illustrations)**. The system is linked to the radiator cooling fan described in Chapter 3; carburettor cooling only occurs with the engine stopped. When the engine is running, a vacuum valve closes the air duct leading to the carburettor, in order to prevent accumulation of dust and insects when the car is in motion. On early models, the system uses the radiator cooling fan to blow air over the carburettor; later models are fitted with a separate fan, and air is taken from the left-hand side wheel housing.

⚠ **Warning: Many of the procedures in this Chapter require the removal of fuel lines and connections, which may result in some fuel spillage. Before carrying out any operation on the fuel system, refer to the precautions given in Safety first! at the beginning of this manual, and follow them implicitly. Petrol is a highly dangerous and volatile liquid, and the precautions necessary when handling it cannot be overstressed.**

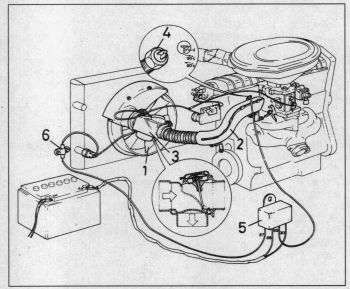

1.5a Carburettor cooling system fitted to early models

1 *Radiator cooling fan*   4 *Thermal switch*
2 *Air bypass*   5 *Relay*
3 *Vacuum valve*   6 *Resistor*

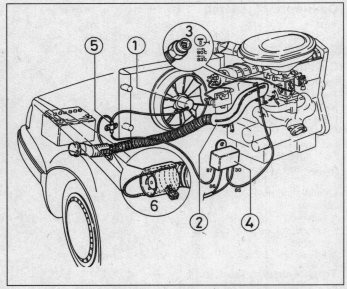

1.5b Carburettor cooling system fitted to later models

1 *Radiator cooling fan*   4 *Relay*
2 *Cooling air circuit*   5 *Resistor*
3 *Temperature sensor*   6 *Cooling air fan*

2 Air cleaner housing assembly - removal and refitting

Removal

1 With the bonnet open, disconnect the air inlet tube from the temperature control unit on the side of the air cleaner housing **(see illustration)**.

2 Unscrew and remove the three mounting nuts from the top of the housing **(see illustration)**.

3 Disconnect the pre-heating hose from the bottom of the temperature control unit **(see illustration)**.

4 Lift the housing from the three mounting studs on the carburettor, then disconnect the crankcase ventilation hose **(see illustration)**.

5 Withdraw the housing assembly from the engine compartment.

Refitting

6 Refitting is a reversal of the removal procedure.

2.1 Disconnecting the air inlet tube from the temperature control unit

3 Fuel pump - testing, removal and refitting

Note: *Refer to the warning note in Section 1 before proceeding.*

Testing

1 To test the fuel pump on the engine, temporarily disconnect the outlet pipe which

2.2 Removing the air cleaner housing assembly mounting nuts

leads to the vapour separator located on the right-hand side of the bulkhead.

2 Disable the ignition system by unplugging the flywheel sensor wiring connector.

3 Hold a wad of rag under the pump outlet while an assistant spins the engine on the starter. *This test should only be carried out with the engine cold, to lessen the risk of fire, but keep your hands away from the radiator cooling fan anyway.* Regular spurts of fuel should be ejected as the engine turns.

4 The pump can also be tested when it has been removed. With the pump outlet pipe disconnected but the inlet pipe still connected, hold the wad of rag by the outlet. Operate the pump by depressing the plunger - this is best achieved by pressing the pump and plunger onto a hard surface. If the pump is in a satisfactory condition, a strong jet of fuel should be ejected.

5 If a suitable pressure gauge is available, a more accurate test may be carried out. Connect up the pressure gauge to the pump outlet, and run the engine at 1000 rpm until the pressure stops rising. The gauge should be held at the same height as the fuel pump. Check that the pressure is within the tolerance given in the Specifications.

6 If the pressure is too high, it may be adjusted lower by inserting additional gaskets between the pump and the insulating flange.

7 If the pressure is too low, first check and if necessary clean the fuel lines and filter gauze. If the pressure is still too low, the pump is faulty, and should be renewed.

4A

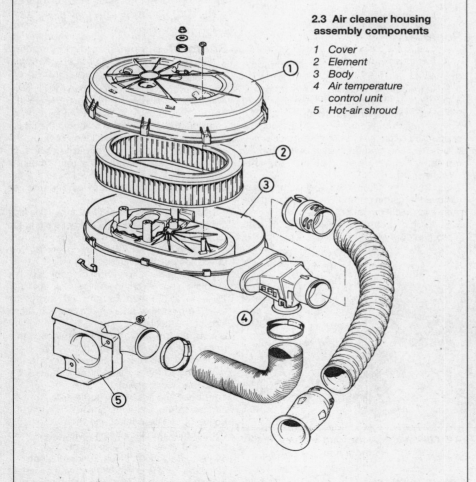

2.3 Air cleaner housing assembly components

1 Cover
2 Element
3 Body
4 Air temperature control unit
5 Hot-air shroud

2.4 Removing the air cleaner housing assembly - crankcase ventilation hose arrowed

3.9 Disconnecting the inlet and outlet hoses from the fuel pump

3.10a Removing the fuel pump from the cylinder head

3.10b View of the plunger and spring as the fuel pump is removed from the cylinder head

8 To check the return line, connect the pressure gauge to the vapour separator outlet line leading to the carburettor, and run the engine until the pressure stops rising. Note the pressure, then clamp the return hose from the vapour separator and check that the pressure now rises. If the pump is in good condition but the pressure does not rise, the return line may be blocked.

Removal

9 Identify the fuel pump inlet and outlet hoses for position, then disconnect and plug them **(see illustration)**.
10 Unscrew and remove the two nuts and washers, and remove the pump from the two studs on the cylinder head **(see illustrations)**.
11 Remove the gaskets and insulating block from the studs **(see illustration)**. Note the location and number of gaskets, as these determine the delivery pressure of the pump.

3.11 Removing the fuel pump gaskets and insulating block

4.4 Fuel gauge sender unit viewed through the rear floor aperture

Refitting

12 Refitting is a reversal of the removal procedure, but clean all traces of gasket from the mating surfaces, and fit new gaskets and a new insulating block if necessary.

4 Fuel gauge sender unit - removal and refitting

Note: *Refer to the warning note in Section 1 before proceeding.*

Removal

1 Disconnect the battery negative lead.
2 Remove the rear seat as described in Chapter 11.
3 Prise the plastic cover from the rear floor.
4 Disconnect the wiring plug from the top of the sender unit **(see illustration)**.
5 Unscrew the unions, and disconnect the supply and return lines from the sender unit.
6 Unscrew the securing collar and withdraw the sender unit from the fuel tank, together with the pump.
7 Remove the filter from the pump, then remove the clamping ring and disconnect the hose clip **(see illustration)**.
8 Slide the pump over the pipes, and disconnect the wiring from the fuel pump.

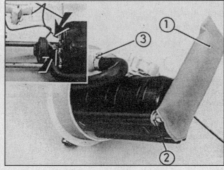

4.7 Fuel gauge sender unit and tank pump components

1 *Filter*   3 *Hose clip*
2 *Clamping ring*

Refitting

9 Refitting is a reversal of the removal procedure. Check the fuel line clips, and renew them if necessary. On models fitted with the electronic Information Centre, re-calibrate the digital readout as described in Chapter 12, Section 4.

5 Fuel tank - removal and refitting

Note: *Refer to the warning note in Section 1 before proceeding.*

Removal

1 A drain plug is not provided on the fuel tank, and it is therefore preferable to carry out the removal operation when the tank is nearly empty. Before proceeding, disconnect the battery negative lead, and then syphon or hand-pump the remaining fuel from the tank.
2 Chock the front wheels, then jack up the rear of the car and support on axle stands. To improve access, remove the rear wheels if required.
3 Remove the fuel gauge sender unit, as described in Section 4.
4 Loosen the clips on the fuel tank filler pipe connecting hose, and slide the hose along the pipe towards the tank.
5 Unscrew the filler pipe union on the fuel tank, then pull the pipe out of the tank.
6 Loosen the clip and disconnect the ventilation hose from the fuel tank.
7 Remove the screws and lift away the exhaust pipe heat shield from the right-hand side of the fuel tank.
8 Support the weight of the fuel tank with a trolley jack and block of wood.
9 Unscrew the rear bolts securing the fuel tank strap to the underbody, and unhook the strap **(see illustration)**.
10 Lower the fuel tank sufficiently to gain access to the ventilation hoses. Identify the hoses before disconnecting them, to ensure correct refitting; once this is done, disconnect them and lower the tank to the ground.
11 Withdraw the tank from under the car.
12 If the tank is contaminated with sediment or water, swill it out with clean fuel. If the tank

is damaged, or leaks, it should be repaired by a specialist, or alternatively renewed.

Refitting

13 Refitting is a reversal of the removal procedure, but make sure that the hoses are not trapped as the tank is lifted into place. Check all clips for damage, and renew them if necessary.

6 Accelerator cable - removal, refitting and adjustment

Removal

1 Remove the air cleaner assembly, as described in Section 2.
2 Remove the panel from under the facia, with reference to Chapter 11, Section 37.
3 Working under the facia, disconnect the inner cable from the top of the accelerator pedal.
4 Working in the engine compartment, note the position of the cable end ferrule adjustment in relation to the support bracket on the inlet manifold, then pull out the spring circlip (see illustration).
5 Unhook the inner cable from the intermediate lever sector, then withdraw the inner and outer cable through the ferrule support bracket (see illustration).
6 Turn the plastic nut in the bulkhead a quarter-turn, and withdraw the complete cable from the engine compartment.

Refitting

7 Refitting is a reversal of the removal procedure, making sure that there are no kinks in the cable.
8 Lightly grease the pivot points on the throttle linkage and accelerator pedal.
9 On completion, adjust the cable as described below.

Adjustment

10 The length of the rod connecting the intermediate lever to the carburettor should be 91 mm between centres - if necessary, adjust the rod by loosening the locknuts, turning the end sockets, then tightening the locknuts. The sockets must be at 90° to each other.

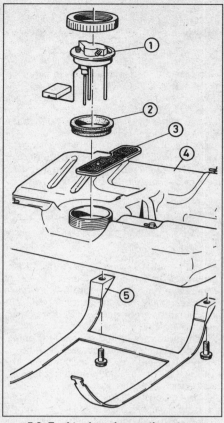

5.9 Fuel tank and mounting strap

1	Fuel gauge sender unit	3	Filter
2	Rubber gasket	4	Fuel tank
		5	Mounting strap

11 With the accelerator pedal fully released, check that there is a small amount of slack in the cable, with the carburettor throttle lever and the intermediate lever sector on their stops.
12 Have an assistant fully depress the accelerator pedal, then check that the throttle is in its fully-open position.
13 If adjustment is required, remove the spring clip from the adjustment ferrule, reposition the ferrule as necessary, then insert the clip in the next free groove on the ferrule.

6.4 Removing the accelerator cable ferrule spring clip

6.5 Unhooking the inner cable from the intermediate lever sector

7 Choke cable - removal, refitting and adjustment

Removal

1 Disconnect the battery negative lead.
2 Remove the air cleaner assembly, as described in Section 2.
3 Note the position of the choke cable on the carburettor support bracket, to aid refitting.
4 Release the spring clip from the bracket, then disconnect the inner cable from the choke lever on the carburettor (see illustrations).
5 Working inside the car, remove the spring clip from the top of the choke knob, then pull the knob from the cable end fitting (see illustrations).
6 Remove the lower trim panel from below the facia.

4A

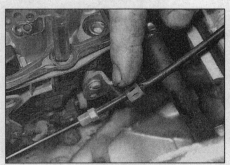

7.4a Release the spring clip . . .

7.4b . . . and disconnect the choke inner cable from the lever on the carburettor

7.5a Remove the spring clip - with needle-nose pliers . . .

7.5b . . . and pull the knob from the cable end fitting

7 Unscrew the nut and remove the choke cable from the facia, then disconnect the wiring for the choke warning light.
8 Withdraw the cable from inside the car, leaving the rubber grommet in position.

Refitting

9 Refitting is a reversal of the removal procedure. Adjust the cable as described below.

Adjustment

10 With the choke cable pulled out approximately 2.0 mm, and the choke lever on the carburettor in its rest position (ie choke fully open), fit the clip over the outer cable, and attach it to the support bracket.
11 Check that the choke lever on the carburettor is in its rest position with the knob pushed home, and fully closed (ie the choke valve is shut) with the knob pulled out.

8 Unleaded petrol - general information and usage

Models not fitted with a catalytic converter may use either 98 RON leaded (4-star), 98 RON super unleaded, or 95 RON unleaded fuel. **Note:** *Leaded petrol is being phased out in the UK market by January 2000; refer to the Specifications for more information.*

Models fitted with a catalytic converter may **only** use unleaded fuel, either 95 RON or 98 RON super; leaded 4-star must **not** be used, or the catalyst will be ruined.

9 Carburettor - general information

A twin-choke downdraught Solex CISAC carburettor is fitted. The carburettor is of progressive type; the primary throttle valve operates initially, and the secondary throttle valve operates progressively after the primary valve has opened.

A diaphragm-operated accelerator pump, for enriched mixture when accelerating, is fitted to the side of the carburettor. The additional fuel is injected through a small tube into the top of the primary barrel.

A pneumatic choke pull-down system opens up the choke valve slightly if full-throttle is used when the engine is warming up.

A further pneumatic full-load enrichment system is fitted, to provide additional fuel under full-throttle conditions.

Internal mixing of the fuel and air occurs in emulsion tubes, and the mixture is drawn into the engine through auxiliary venturis located in each barrel.

10 Carburettor - removal and refitting

Removal

1 Remove the air cleaner assembly, as described in Section 2.
2 Remove the air cleaner gasket from the top of the carburettor.
3 Disconnect the choke cable from the carburettor, with reference to Section 7.
4 Prise the intermediate rod from the throttle lever on the carburettor **(see illustration)**.
5 Disconnect the ignition module vacuum pipe from the carburettor **(see illustration)**.
6 Disconnect the crankcase ventilation hose from the carburettor flange.
7 Loosen the clip and disconnect the fuel inlet hose from the carburettor **(see illustration)**. Plug the hose with a suitable bolt.
8 Disconnect the wiring from the thermistor on the rear of the carburettor **(see illustration)**.
9 Using an Allen key, unscrew and remove the four carburettor mounting bolts **(see illustration)**.
10 Lift the carburettor from the inlet manifold and place it upright on the bench **(see illustration)**.
11 Remove the carburettor mounting gasket from the inlet manifold **(see illustration)**.

10.4 Disconnecting the intermediate rod from the throttle lever on the carburettor

10.5 Disconnecting the ignition module vacuum pipe from the carburettor

10.7 Disconnecting the fuel inlet hose from the carburettor

10.8 Disconnecting the thermistor wiring

10.9 Unscrewing the four carburettor mounting bolts (arrowed)

10.10 Lifting the carburettor from the inlet manifold

10.11 Carburettor mounting gasket on the inlet manifold

11.4 Insulating flange securing screw on the bottom of the carburettor - arrowed

11.6 Removing the filter from the fuel delivery union

11.7a Disconnecting the accelerator pump control rod (arrowed) from the throttle lever

11.7b Lifting the carburettor cover from the main body

11.7c View of the carburettor main body with the cover removed

Refitting

12 Refitting is a reversal of the removal procedure, noting the following points:
  a) *Make sure that the mating surfaces of the carburettor and inlet manifold are clean, and fit a new gasket.*
  b) *Adjust the accelerator and choke cables, as described in Sections 6 and 7.*
  c) *Adjust the idle speed and mixture with reference to Chapter 1.*

11 Carburettor -
fault finding, overhaul and adjustments

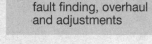

Fault finding

1 Faults with the carburettor are usually associated with dirt entering the float chamber and blocking the jets, causing a weak mixture or power failure within a certain engine speed range. If this is the case, then a thorough clean will normally cure the problem. If the carburettor is well worn, uneven running may be caused by air entering through the throttle valve spindle bearings.

Overhaul and adjustments

2 The following paragraphs describe cleaning and adjustment procedures which can be carried out by the home mechanic after the carburettor has been removed from the inlet manifold. If the carburettor is worn or damaged, it should either be renewed or overhauled by a specialist, who will be able to restore the carburettor to its original calibration.

3 Invert the carburettor, and allow the fuel contents to drain into a suitable container.

4 Remove the single screw and lift away the insulating flange from the bottom of the carburettor **(see illustration)**.

5 Scrape all traces of gasket from the carburettor, then clean the complete exterior with fuel or paraffin.

6 Unscrew the plug, and remove the filter from the fuel delivery union; recover the plug washer **(see illustration)**.

7 With the carburettor upright, disconnect the accelerator pump control rod from the throttle lever, then unscrew the five screws and lift the cover from the main body **(see illustrations)**.

8 Remove the O-ring seal from the calibrated orifice.

9 Using a thin drift, tap out the float spindle, and remove the float and gasket from the carburettor cover.

10 Remove the needle valve and idle jet from the carburettor cover.

11 Remove the screws and take off the pneumatic choke cover, then unhook the diaphragm operating rod from the eye **(see illustration)**.

12 If necessary, remove the accelerator pump from the main body; remove the four screws and lift off the cover, followed by the diaphragm and spring **(see illustration)**.

13 Carefully prise out the accelerator pump tube from the top of the main body **(see illustration)**.

14 Unscrew and remove both emulsion tubes, noting their locations.

15 Using a long thin screwdriver through the emulsion tube holes, unscrew and remove the main jets.

16 Clean the float chamber, main body and cover thoroughly, using petrol or (preferably) carburettor cleaner.

4A

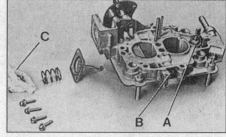

11.11 Carburettor cover components

A *Needle valve*
B *Idle air jet*
C *Pneumatic choke cover*

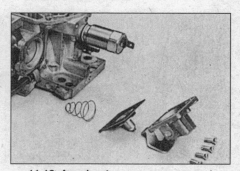

11.12 Accelerator pump component removal

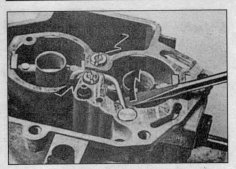

11.13 Removing the accelerator pump tube and emulsion tubes

17 When the carburettor has been completely dismantled (ie with all diaphragms and small components removed), blow through the carburettor internal channels and jets, using air from an air line or foot pump. *Wear eye protection if using compressed air.*

18 Examine all of the components for wear and damage, and renew as necessary. Check the floats for leakage - shake them, and listen for any fuel which may have got inside. Check the diaphragms for pin holes and deterioration.

19 Obtain a carburettor repair kit, which will contain all the new gaskets required.

20 Reassemble the carburettor using a reversal of the dismantling procedure, but do not fit the cover at this stage. When refitting the pneumatic choke cover, make sure that the bypass hole in the cover is correctly positioned in relation to the hole in the main body.

11.26 Using a drill (A) to check the fast idle setting

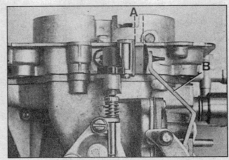

11.27 Float chamber ventilation opening dimension (A) and operating arm (B)

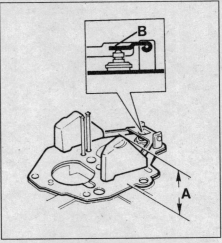

11.23a Checking the float height (A) - bend tag (B) to adjust

21 With the float assembly and gasket fitted to the cover, check the float height as follows.

22 Invert the cover, so that the floats are holding the needle valve shut; check also that the gasket is seated properly on the cover.

23 Using a steel rule or vernier calipers, check that the dimension from the gasket to the top of the floats is as given in the Specifications (see illustrations).

24 If adjustment is necessary, bend the tag on the float arm; repeat the check.

25 Reassemble the carburettor in the reverse order to the dismantling procedure.

26 With the choke valve fully open, use a 2.0 mm diameter drill to measure the distance between the fast idle adjustment screw and the cam on the throttle lever (see illustration). If necessary, turn the adjustment screw until the distance is correct.

27 Check that the float chamber ventilation valve closes when the throttle valve is opened. When the throttle valve is closed, the ventilation valve should be open by 2.0 to 4.0 mm - if necessary, bend the ventilation valve arm to correct the dimension (see illustration).

28 If necessary, the mixture adjustment screw may be set to its initial position as follows. Turn the screw in carefully until it just seats, then unscrew it by approximately two full turns.

12 Vacuum accumulator - removal, testing and refitting

Removal

1 Disconnect the vacuum line from the carburettor.

2 Prise the vacuum accumulator rubber grommet from the bulkhead (see illustration), then remove the accumulator from the grommet.

11.23b Checking the float height with a steel rule

Testing

3 Apply vacuum to the accumulator with a vacuum pump, and check that there is no leakage. Also check the vacuum hose for cracking and deterioration.

Refitting

4 Refitting is a reversal of the removal procedure.

13 Inlet and exhaust manifolds - removal and refitting

Removal

1 Remove the carburettor, as described in Section 10.

2 Apply the handbrake, then jack up the front of the car and support on axle stands.

3 Unscrew the nuts from the bottom of the bolts securing the exhaust downpipe to the exhaust manifold, and remove the springs. Disconnect the downpipe from the manifold, and remove the sealing ring (see illustrations).

4 For better access, unbolt the exhaust downpipe from the front silencer/catalytic converter (refer to Chapter 4C).

5 Unbolt and remove the carburettor cooling air duct.

6 Remove the throttle linkage and bracket from the top of the inlet manifold (see illustration).

12.2 Vacuum hose connection to the vacuum accumulator on the bulkhead

13.3a Exhaust downpipe-to-manifold bolts and springs

13.3b Removing the sealing ring from the exhaust manifold

13.6 Removing the throttle linkage and bracket from the top of the inlet manifold

13.7a Carburettor float chamber ventilation system thermal sensor on the inlet manifold heat shield

13.7b Removing the heat shield

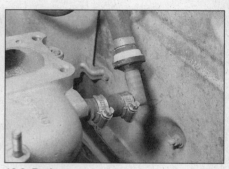

13.9 Brake servo vacuum hose connection to the inlet manifold

7 Unscrew the nuts, and remove the heat shield from the top of the inlet manifold. Note that one of the nuts also secures the carburettor float chamber ventilation system thermal sensor - this can be disconnected from the wiring, and placed to one side **(see illustrations)**.

8 Unclip and remove the crankcase ventilation hose.

9 Loosen the clip, and disconnect the brake servo vacuum hose from the inlet manifold **(see illustration)**.

10 Unbolt the hot-air shroud from the exhaust manifold **(see illustration)**.

11 Progressively unscrew the mounting nuts securing the inlet and exhaust manifolds to the cylinder head, then withdraw the assembly over the studs and remove from the engine compartment **(see illustration)**.

12 Remove the gasket from the cylinder head **(see illustration)**.

Refitting

13 Refitting is a reversal of the removal procedure, noting the following points:

a) Ensure that the cylinder head and

manifold mating faces are clean, and use a new gasket.

b) If necessary, unscrew the vacuum adaptor from the old inlet manifold, and transfer it to the new manifold.

c) Tighten the manifold nuts progressively to the specified torque, working from the central nuts outwards.

d) Renew the exhaust downpipe sealing ring (refer to Chapter 4C).

e) Refit the carburettor with reference to Section 10.

4A

13.10 Removing the hot-air shroud (arrowed) from the exhaust manifold

13.11 Removing the manifold assembly from the cylinder head

13.12 Removing the manifold gasket from the cylinder head

Chapter 4 Part B:
Fuel system - fuel injection engines

Contents

Degrees of difficulty

Easy, suitable for novice with little experience	**Fairly easy,** suitable for beginner with some experience	**Fairly difficult,** suitable for competent DIY mechanic	**Difficult,** suitable for experienced DIY mechanic	**Very difficult,** suitable for expert DIY or professional

Specifications

System types and applications

Engine codes B18E, B18ES, B18E(D)	Bendix/Fenix 1 or 3.2 engine management system
Engine codes B16F, B18EP, B18FP, B20F	Bendix/Fenix 3B engine management system
Engine codes B18F, B18FT, B18FT(M)	Bosch LH-Jetronic 2.2
Engine code B18U	Bosch/Siemens single-point injection and Fenix 3B engine management system

Fuel grade

Fuel octane requirement:

Models without a catalytic converter	98 RON leaded (4-star)*, 98 RON super unleaded, or 95 RON unleaded
Models with a catalytic converter	98 RON super unleaded or 95 RON unleaded only - **do not** use leaded 4-star

* *Leaded petrol is being phased out in the UK market by January 2000 to be replaced by Lead Replacement Petrol (LRP). Cars which previously ran on leaded (4-star) petrol should run satisfactorily on LRP but, if in doubt, consult the vehicle manufacturer.*

Idle speed and mixture settings

Idle speed:

B16F	850 to 950 rpm
B18E, B18ES, B18E(D)	750 to 850 rpm
B18EP	800 to 900 rpm
B18FP	850 to 950 rpm
B18F, B18FT, B18FT(M)	750 to 850 rpm
B18U	850 to 950 rpm
B20F	730 to 830 rpm

Idle mixture CO content:

B16F	0.2% to 1.0%
B18E, B18ES, B18E(D)	0.5% to 2.0%
B18EP	0.8% to 1.6%
B18FP	0.4% to 1.2%
B18F, B18FT, B18FT(M)	0.4% to 0.8%
B18U	0.3% to 1.1%
B20F	0.2% to 1.0%

4B

Fuel pump

Line pressure / residual pressure:
    B18E, B18ES, B18E(D) .... 2.5 bar/2.3 to 2.4 bar
    B16F, B18EP, B18FP, B18F, B18FT, B18FT(M) .... 3.5 bar/3.3 to 3.4 bar
    B18U .... 1.0 bar/0.85 to 0.90 bar
    B20F .... 3.0 bar/2.85 to 2.90 bar
Delivery (at 12 volts):
    B16F, all B18 engines except B18U .... 120 litres/hour
    B18U .... 92 litres/hour
    B20F .... 130 litres/hour
Diaphragm valve - B18EP, B18FP, B18F, B18FT, B18FT(M) .... 0.4 bar

Injector(s)

Colour / resistance at 20°C:
    Engine codes B18E, B18ES, B18E(D) .... Grey/2 to 3 ohms
    Engine codes B16F, B18EP, B18FP .... Black/14 to 15 ohms
    Engine code B18F, B20F .... Blue/16 to 17 ohms
    Engine code B18FT, B18FT(M) .... Brown/16 to 17 ohms
    Engine code B18U .... Blue/1.1 to 1.5 ohms

Injection system test data

Air pressure sensor:
    Resistance .... 1300 ohms
Air temperature transmitter (for injector cooling):
    Engages at .... 105 ± 2°C
    Disengages at .... 100 ± 2°C
Airflow meter (B18F, B18FT):
    Resistance between terminals 1 and 6 (basic setting) .... 382 ohms
    Resistance between terminals 6 and 7 .... 2.7 ohms
    Resistance between terminals 1 and 6 .... 0 to 1000 ohms
CO potentiometer (B18E, B18EP):
    Resistance .... 300 to 11 000 ohms
Coolant temperature sensor:
    Resistance at 20°C:
        Engine code B18E (Fenix 1) .... 290 ± 20 ohms
        All other engines .... 2500 ± 300 ohms
Flywheel sensor:
    Resistance .... 220 ± 60 ohms
Idle speed regulating valve:
    Resistance:
        Engine code B18E .... 44 ohms
        Engine codes B18EP, B18FP, B20F .... 8 ohms
        Engine codes B18F, B18FT .... 20 ohms
Inlet air temperature sensor:
    Resistance:
        Engine codes B18E, B18ES, B18E(D) .... 290 ± 20 ohms (black connector)
        All other engines .... 2500 ± 300 ohms (blue connector)
Oxygen sensor (B18F, B18FT, B18FP, B18U):
    Resistance in pre-heating resistor:
        Cold sensor (20°C) .... 3 ohms
        Hot sensor (350°C) .... 13 ohms

Torque wrench settings

	Nm	lbf ft
Air cleaner hose to body	30	22
Fuel tank (oiled threads)	23	17
Fuel injection manifold bolts	20	15
Fuel injection manifold nuts	10	7
Fuel pressure regulator	10	7
Inlet and exhaust manifolds	20	15
Inlet manifold studs/nuts	10	7
Knock sensor nut	20	15
Knock sensor stud	10	7
Oxygen sensor (oiled threads)	55	41
Single-point injector unit	9	7
Single-point injector	6	4
Temperature senders in cylinder head (oiled threads)	20	15
Throttle linkage	9	7
Throttle valve housing to inlet manifold	17	13

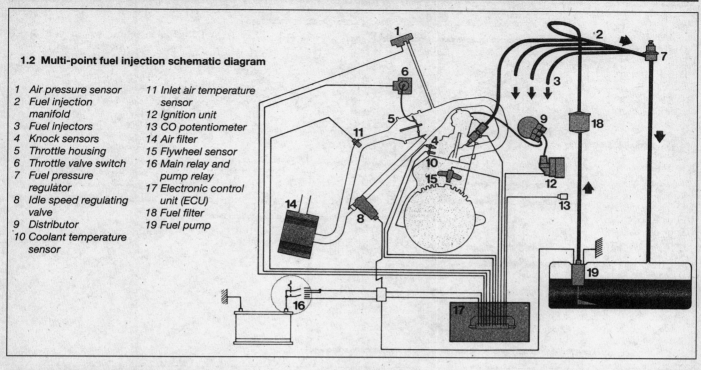

1.2 Multi-point fuel injection schematic diagram

1 Air pressure sensor
2 Fuel injection manifold
3 Fuel injectors
4 Knock sensors
5 Throttle housing
6 Throttle valve switch
7 Fuel pressure regulator
8 Idle speed regulating valve
9 Distributor
10 Coolant temperature sensor
11 Inlet air temperature sensor
12 Ignition unit
13 CO potentiometer
14 Air filter
15 Flywheel sensor
16 Main relay and pump relay
17 Electronic control unit (ECU)
18 Fuel filter
19 Fuel pump

1 General information and precautions

The fuel system consists of a fuel tank mounted under the car (just in front of the rear axle), an electric fuel pump which is incorporated in the fuel gauge sender unit in the fuel tank, and a fuel injection system.

B18F and B18FT engines are fitted with the LH-Jetronic system, which has separate electronic control units (ECUs) for the ignition and fuel injection systems. All other fuel injection engines have a full engine management system, where the ignition and fuel injection functions are controlled by a single electronic control unit (see illustration).

Engines other than the B18U engine are fitted with a multi-point injection system, where each cylinder has its own injector. The B18U engine is fitted with a single-point injection system - there is only one injector, housed in an injector unit mounted over the inlet manifold, in a similar position to a carburettor. An injector cooling system is fitted to some models (see illustrations).

A three-way catalytic converter is fitted to some models, and depending on model, this may incorporate a Lambda oxygen sensor for fine automatic control of the fuel mixture. An exhaust gas recirculation system is also fitted to some models.

4B

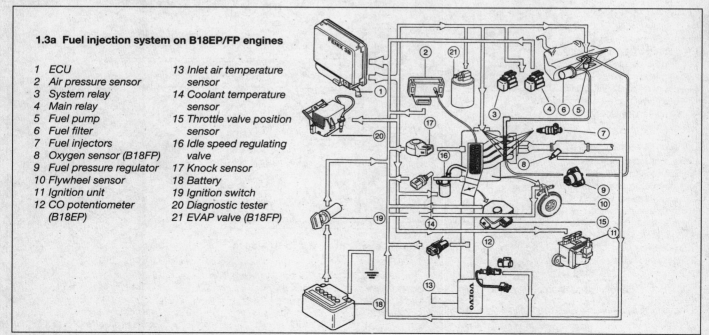

1.3a Fuel injection system on B18EP/FP engines

1 ECU
2 Air pressure sensor
3 System relay
4 Main relay
5 Fuel pump
6 Fuel filter
7 Fuel injectors
8 Oxygen sensor (B18FP)
9 Fuel pressure regulator
10 Flywheel sensor
11 Ignition unit
12 CO potentiometer (B18EP)
13 Inlet air temperature sensor
14 Coolant temperature sensor
15 Throttle valve position sensor
16 Idle speed regulating valve
17 Knock sensor
18 Battery
19 Ignition switch
20 Diagnostic tester
21 EVAP valve (B18FP)

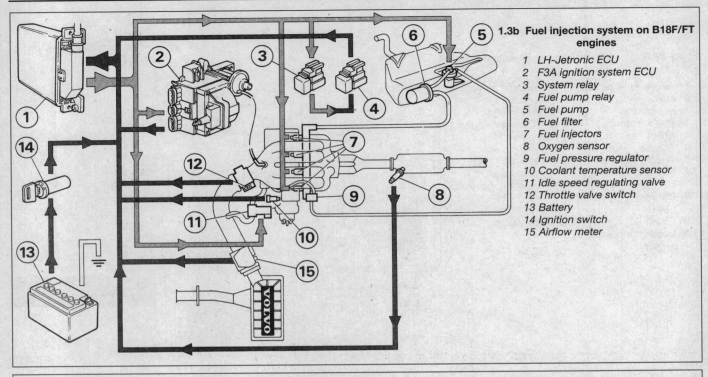

1.3b Fuel injection system on B18F/FT engines

1   LH-Jetronic ECU
2   F3A ignition system ECU
3   System relay
4   Fuel pump relay
5   Fuel pump
6   Fuel filter
7   Fuel injectors
8   Oxygen sensor
9   Fuel pressure regulator
10 Coolant temperature sensor
11 Idle speed regulating valve
12 Throttle valve switch
13 Battery
14 Ignition switch
15 Airflow meter

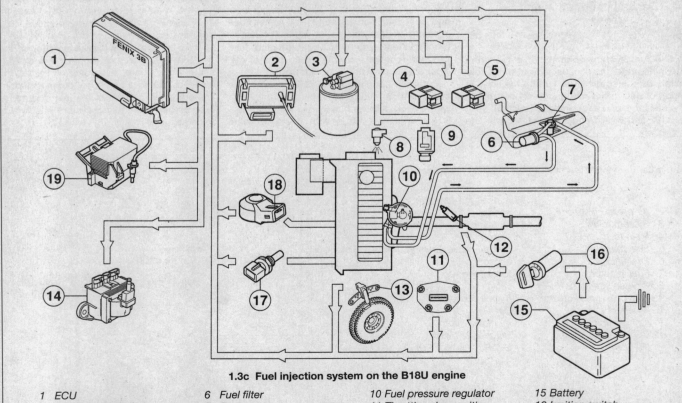

1.3c Fuel injection system on the B18U engine

1   ECU
2   Air pressure sensor
3   Solenoid valve, charcoal absorption canister
4   System relay
5   Main relay
6   Fuel filter
7   Fuel pump
8   Fuel injector with intake air temperature sensor
9   Idle speed regulating valve
10 Fuel pressure regulator
11 Throttle valve position sensor
12 Oxygen sensor
13 Flywheel sensor
14 Ignition unit
15 Battery
16 Ignition switch
17 Coolant temperature sensor
18 Knock sensor
19 Diagnostic tester

The B18U engine is fitted with a knock sensor, which temporarily retards the ignition timing to prevent pre-ignition (or 'pinking') when the engine loading exceeds a certain limit. This retarding of the ignition timing only occurs at engine speeds above 2970 rpm, and when the coolant temperature is higher than 80°C.

⚠️ *Warning: Many of the procedures in this Chapter require the removal of fuel lines and connections, which may result in some fuel spillage. Before carrying out any operation on the fuel system, refer to the precautions given in Safety first! at the beginning of this manual, and follow them implicitly. Petrol is a highly dangerous and volatile liquid, and the precautions necessary when handling it cannot be overstressed.*

⚠️ *Warning: On fuel injection engines, the fuel system operates at high pressure, meaning that any disconnection of the fuel lines could result in fuel spraying out uncontrollably. To avoid this possibility, always depressurise the system first, as described in Section 8.*

⚠️ *Warning: When working on the fuel injection system, it is recommended that, wherever possible, the battery negative lead is disconnected, and the lead moved away from the battery.*

2 Air cleaner housing assembly - removal and refitting

Removal

Except B18U engine

1 With the bonnet open, release the wire clips and lift the cover from the air cleaner housing **(see illustration)**.
2 Remove the air filter element.
3 Pull the housing from the rubber mountings, and loosen the bolts on the brackets **(see illustration)**.
4 Loosen the clip, and separate the housing from the inlet tube.
5 Withdraw the housing assembly from the engine compartment.
6 If necessary, the air inlet duct may be removed from the throttle housing, by loosening the clip and disconnecting the hoses from the idle speed regulating valve, Pulsair system (where fitted), and crankcase ventilation system. Where necessary, also disconnect the wiring from the CO potentiometer and air inlet temperature sensor **(see illustrations)**.

B18U engine

7 To remove the air cleaner housing, follow the procedure given in paragraphs 1 to 5. Air inlet duct removal is as follows.

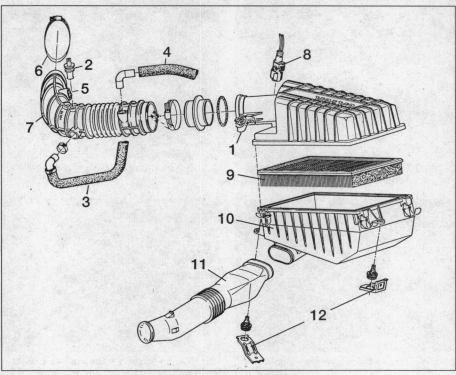

2.1 Air cleaner assembly

1 Cover	5 Crankcase ventilation	8 CO potentiometer
2 Air temperature sensor	hose connection	9 Air filter element
3 Idle speed regulating	6 Hose clip	10 Air filter housing
valve hose	7 Air inlet duct (except	11 Primary air inlet duct
4 Pulsair hose	B18U engine)	12 Mounting brackets

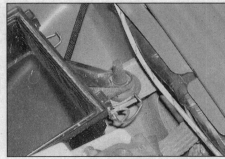

2.3 Air cleaner housing rubber mounting

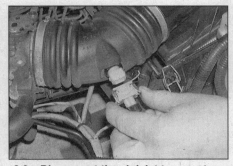

2.6a Disconnect the air inlet temperature sensor . . .

2.6b . . . then loosen the worm-drive clip . . .

2.6c . . . and detach the inlet tube, disconnecting the hose at the base

4B

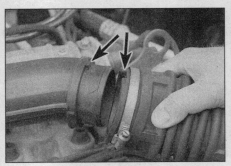

2.8 Detach the air inlet hose, noting its locating lug and recess (arrows)

2.9 Pull off the crankcase ventilation hose

2.10 Unscrew and remove the air inlet duct retaining bolts

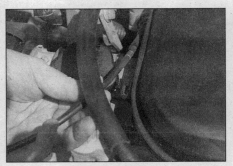

2.11a Unclip the accelerator cable . . .

2.11b . . . and the vacuum hoses from the clips at the sides of the duct

2.12 Lift up the air inlet duct, turning it over for access to the remaining hose connections

8 Loosen the clip securing the air inlet hose to the plastic duct, and detach the hose, noting its locating lug at the top **(see illustration)**.
9 Pull off the crankcase ventilation hose from

2.13a Unclip and pull off the hoses from the vacuum switch (arrowed) . . .

2.13b . . . and from the crankcase ventilation connection (arrowed)

the front of the air inlet duct **(see illustration)**.
10 Unscrew and remove the three inlet duct retaining bolts **(see illustration)**.
11 Unclip the accelerator cable and the vacuum hoses from the sides of the air inlet duct, noting their fitted positions **(see illustrations)**.
12 Carefully lift off the air inlet duct, bearing in mind there are still hoses connected to its base, and lay it to one side **(see illustration)**.
13 Noting their locations, disconnect the hoses from below the air inlet temperature control vacuum switch, and from the crankcase ventilation connection **(see illustrations)**. The air inlet duct can now be removed completely.

Refitting

14 Refitting is a reversal of the removal procedure.

---

3 Accelerator cable -
removal, refitting
and adjustment

Removal

1 Remove the panel from under the facia, with reference to Chapter 11, Section 37.
2 Disconnect the inner cable from the top of the accelerator pedal by removing the locking pin and clip **(see illustration)**.
Except B18U engine
3 Working in the engine compartment, open the throttle by hand to create some slack in

the inner cable, then pull the inner cable end fitting out of the throttle quadrant **(see illustration)**.
4 Note the position of the cable end ferrule adjustment in relation to the support bracket,

3.2 Accelerator cable components on non-B18U engines

3.3 Using pliers, pull the cable end fitting out of the throttle quadrant

3.4a Pull out the spring clip . . .

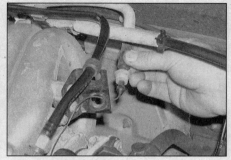

3.4b . . . and remove the cable outer from the support bracket

then pull out the spring circlip and remove the cable from the bracket on the upper inlet manifold section **(see illustrations)**.

B18U engine

5 Access to the accelerator cable is improved by removing the air inlet duct, as described in Section 2.

6 On early models, loosen the locknuts and disconnect the accelerator cable end fitting from the support bracket on the single-point injection unit. Unhook the cable from the throttle cam on the unit.

7 On later models, pull out the metal clip from the cable outer, then unhook the cable end fitting from the throttle cam **(see illustration)**. Pull off the small translucent cover from the end of the cable outer, then unscrew/slide the cable outer from the support bracket and remove the cable.

All engines

8 Turn the plastic cable end at the bulkhead a quarter-turn anti-clockwise, then withdraw the cable. Unclip and remove the cable from the engine compartment.

Refitting

9 Refitting is a reversal of the removal procedure, but make sure that there are no kinks in the cable. Lightly grease the pivot points on the throttle linkage and accelerator pedal.

10 On completion, adjust the cable as follows.

Adjustment

Except B18U engine

11 With the accelerator pedal fully released and the lever on the throttle housing also on its stop, check that there is a small amount of slack in the cable.

12 Have an assistant fully depress the accelerator pedal, then check that the throttle is in its fully-open position.

13 If adjustment is required, remove the spring clip from the adjustment ferrule, reposition the ferrule as necessary, then insert the clip in the next free groove on the ferrule. It must be possible to hear the throttle valve switch operating.

14 On later fuel injection engines, the spring clip at the cable end simply locates the end of the cable, and performs no adjustment function. Adjustment on these engines is carried out using a plastic nut and locknut at the cable end - loosen the locknut, then use the adjuster to take out excessive slack in the cable **(see illustration)**.

B18U engine

15 On early models, adjust the locknuts on the cable support bracket on the single-point injection unit so that all slack is eliminated, then turn the cable end fitting one complete turn and lock it in this position **(see illustration)**. This will give the inner cable the required slack.

16 On later models, use the metal hex fitting

on the cable outer to turn the cable outer in or out of the cable support bracket until all slack is eliminated from the cable. The metal clip should be inserted into the adjustment grooves, as close to the support bracket as possible, to lock the cable outer in position.

---

4 Idle speed and mixture settings - adjustment

1 Before making any adjustments, note the following points.

a) The engine should be in good condition, with balanced compressions, correct valve clearances, plugs clean and correctly gapped, and correct ignition timing.

b) The accelerator cable should be correctly adjusted, and all crankcase ventilation hoses should be clean.

c) The engine must be at normal operating temperature (indicated by the engine cooling fan having cut in and out - but see e below).

d) An exhaust gas analyser and tachometer will be required.

e) Adjustments must not be made while the electric cooling fan is in operation.

f) On models fitted with a catalytic converter, the CO content must be measured ahead of the catalytic converter by unscrewing the special plug and using

3.7 Removing the metal locking clip from the adjuster - cable end outer cover arrowed

3.14 On later engines, the adjuster nut (arrowed) is used to adjust the cable

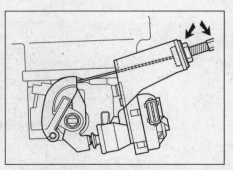

3.15 Accelerator cable adjustment points on B18U engines

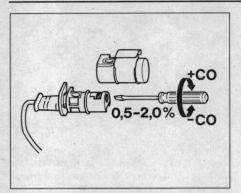

4.6 Adjusting the CO potentiometer on the B18E engine

an adaptor. Where an oxygen sensor is fitted, its wiring must be disconnected.

g) On models not fitted with a catalytic converter, the CO meter probe must be inserted at least 45 cm into the end of the exhaust tailpipe.

h) On models fitted with a Pulsair system, disconnect and plug the system hose while adjusting the CO content.

i) On automatic transmission models, select position N before adjustments are carried out.

j) On models with air conditioning, make sure that the air conditioning is switched off, unless otherwise stated.

B18E, B18ES and B18E(D) engines

2 Connect an exhaust gas analyser and tachometer to the engine, in accordance with the equipment manufacturer's instructions.

3 The idle speed is automatically controlled by the ECU, and cannot be adjusted. However, if the throttle valve switch is incorrectly adjusted, the idle speed may be affected. The idle speed should be checked to see if it is within the specified tolerance, and if not, the throttle valve switch should be checked with reference to Section 10.

4 The CO content must be checked with the engine hot, and with the electric cooling fan off. All other electrical accessories must also be switched off and the Pulsair system (where fitted) must be blanked off.

4.13 Throttle valve basic setting adjustment on B18EP and B18FP engines

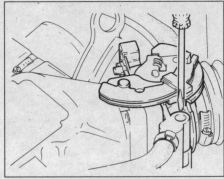

4.11 Adjusting the idle speed on B18EP and B18FP engines

5 Remove the CO potentiometer from the air cleaner, then remove the sealed cover for access to the adjustment screw. Remove the tamperproof cap if fitted.

6 With the engine idling, check that the CO content is as given in the Specifications. If it is not, turn the adjustment screw in the CO potentiometer until the correct reading is obtained **(see illustration)**. Wait a few seconds for the gases to reach the exhaust gas analyser before noting the CO reading.

7 Increase the engine speed to 2000 rpm for 30 seconds once every 3 minutes, to ensure that any excess fuel is cleared from the inlet manifold.

8 On completion, refit the cover and refit the potentiometer to the air cleaner.

B18EP and B18FP engines

9 Connect the exhaust gas analyser and tachometer to the engine in accordance with the equipment manufacturer's instructions.

10 Disconnect the wiring from the idle speed regulating valve, then start the engine and allow it to idle. Check that the idle speed is within the tolerance range given in the Specifications.

11 If adjustment is required, remove the tamperproof cap (where fitted) and turn the adjustment screw on the throttle housing until the speed is correct **(see illustration)**.

12 Should it not be possible to adjust the idle speed to the correct setting, the throttle housing should first be removed and cleaned

thoroughly, making sure that no solvent enters the throttle valve switch. Refit the throttle housing using a new gasket, then adjust the throttle valve basic setting as follows.

13 Release the locking clip from the basic setting adjustment screw, and unscrew the screw until the throttle valve is fully closed **(see illustration)**. Now tighten the screw until it just contacts the stop, then tighten it a further three quarters of a turn. Refit the locking clip, making sure that the adjustment screw is not moved. It should now be possible to adjust the idle speed as previously described.

14 Refit the tamperproof cap (where removed) and reconnect the wiring to the idle speed regulating valve.

B18FP engine

15 To check the CO content on the B18FP engine, unscrew and remove the plug from the front of the catalytic converter, and connect the exhaust gas analyser using an adaptor. Run the engine at idle speed, and check that the CO content is as given in the Specifications.

16 It is not possible to adjust the CO content on the B18FP engine, so if it is not within the specified tolerance, check the inlet and exhaust manifold gaskets and all inlet air hoses for damage and deterioration.

B18EP engine

17 To check the CO content on the B18EP engine, connect the exhaust gas analyser and allow the engine to idle. Check that the CO content is as given in the Specifications.

18 If adjustment is required, remove the CO potentiometer from the air cleaner, then remove the sealed cover for access to the adjustment screw. Remove the tamperproof cap if fitted.

19 Turn the adjustment screw in the CO potentiometer until the correct reading is obtained. Wait a few seconds for the gases to reach the exhaust gas analyser before noting the CO reading.

20 Increase the engine speed to 2000 rpm for 30 seconds once every 3 minutes, to ensure that any excess fuel is cleared from the inlet manifold.

21 On completion, refit the cover, and refit the potentiometer to the air cleaner.

B18F, B18FT and B18FT(M) engines

22 Connect an exhaust gas analyser and tachometer to the engine, in accordance with the equipment manufacturer's instructions.

23 Close the idle speed regulating valve by earthing the white cable located near the crankcase ventilation hose **(see illustration)** - attach a spare piece of wire, if necessary.

24 If applicable, switch off the air conditioning.

25 Start the engine, and allow it to idle. Check that the idle speed is within the tolerance given in the Specifications.

4.23 Earth the white cable located near the crankcase ventilation hose on B18F and B18FT engines

26 If adjustment is required, remove the tamperproof cap - where fitted - (we drilled two 2.0 mm diameter holes in the cap, and used circlip pliers) and turn the adjustment screw on the throttle housing until the speed is correct.

27 Should it not be possible to adjust the idle speed to the correct setting, the throttle housing should first be removed and cleaned thoroughly, making sure that no solvent enters the throttle valve switch. Refit the throttle housing using a new gasket, then adjust the throttle valve basic setting as follows.

28 Loosen the locknut and unscrew the basic setting adjustment screw until the throttle valve is fully closed. Now tighten the screw until it just contacts the stop, then tighten it a further quarter of a turn. Tighten the locknut, making sure that the adjustment screw is not moved. It should now be possible to adjust the idle speed as previously described.

29 Remove the earth connection from the white cable, and check that the idle speed increases to 800 ± 25 rpm.

30 Fit a new tamperproof cap on completion.

B16F, B18U and B20F engines

31 The idle speed is automatically controlled by the ECU, via the idle speed control motor on the front of the injection unit. The idle speed cannot be adjusted, but it should still be checked to see if it is within the specified tolerance.

32 Connect an exhaust gas analyser and tachometer to the engine, in accordance with the equipment manufacturer's instructions.

33 To check the CO content of the exhaust gas, first disconnect the wiring from the oxygen sensor (Lambda control sensor) to deactivate the closed-loop control system. If necessary, jack up the front of the car and support on axle stands to gain better access to the sensor.

34 Unscrew and remove the oxygen sensor from the catalytic converter.

 Warning: The catalytic converter may be very hot!

35 Using an adaptor, connect the exhaust gas analyser to the oxygen sensor hole in the catalytic converter (**see illustration**).

36 Disconnect the battery negative lead for approximately 1 minute, in order to allow the system to adjust the Lambda sensor control to its basic setting.

37 Start the engine and allow it to idle, then check that the CO content is as given in the Specifications.

38 The CO content cannot be adjusted, but if the reading is too high, check for excessive fuel pressure, fuel leakage, faulty injector, faulty evaporative emission system, or a blocked catalytic converter. If the reading is too low, an air leak is indicated, so check the manifold gaskets and inlet air hoses.

39 Refit the oxygen sensor and connect the lead. Remove the exhaust gas analyser and tachometer.

---

5 Unleaded petrol -
general information and usage

Refer to Chapter 4 Part A, Section 8.

6 Fuel gauge sender unit and fuel pump -
removal and refitting

Note: *Refer to the warning notes in Section 1 before proceeding.*

Removal

1 Disconnect the battery negative lead.

2 Remove the rear seats, as described in Chapter 11.

3 Where applicable, remove the rear console as described in Chapter 11, Section 35.

4 Prise the plastic cover from the rear floor.

5 Disconnect the wiring plug from the top of the sender unit.

6 Unscrew the unions, and disconnect the supply and return lines from the sender unit.

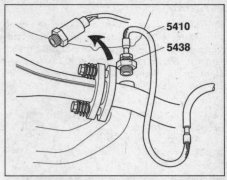

4.35 Volvo adaptor and hose for checking the CO content on B16F, B18U and B20F engines

7 Unscrew the securing collar and withdraw the sender unit from the fuel tank, together with the pump. Remove the rubber sealing ring from the tank (**see illustration**).

8 Remove the filter from the pump, then remove the clamping ring and disconnect the hose clip.

9 Slide the pump over the pipes, and disconnect the wiring from the fuel pump.

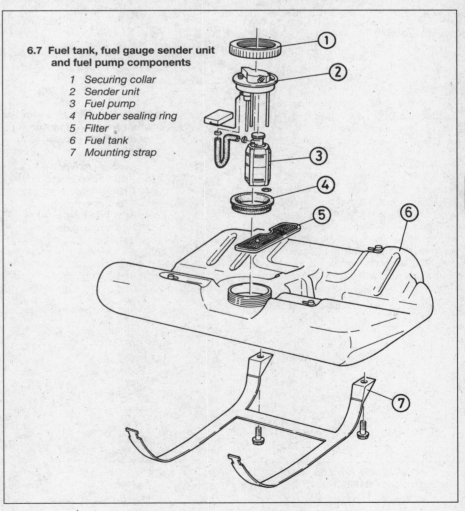

6.7 Fuel tank, fuel gauge sender unit and fuel pump components

1 Securing collar
2 Sender unit
3 Fuel pump
4 Rubber sealing ring
5 Filter
6 Fuel tank
7 Mounting strap

4B

Refitting

10 Refitting is a reversal of the removal procedure. Check the fuel line clips, and renew them if necessary. On models fitted with the electronic Information Centre, re-calibrate the digital readout as described in Chapter 12, Section 4.

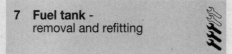

7 Fuel tank -
removal and refitting

Note: *Refer to the warning notes in Section 1 before proceeding.*

Removal

1 A drain plug is not provided on the fuel tank, and it is therefore preferable to carry out the removal operation when the tank is nearly empty. Before proceeding, disconnect the battery negative lead, and then syphon or hand-pump the remaining fuel from the tank.
2 Chock the front wheels, then jack up the rear of the car and support on axle stands. To improve access, remove the rear wheels if required.
3 Remove the fuel gauge sender unit, as described in Section 6.
4 Loosen the clips on the fuel tank filler pipe connecting hose, and slide the hose along the pipe towards the tank.
5 Unscrew the filler pipe union on the fuel tank, then pull the pipe rearwards out of the tank.
6 Loosen the clip, and disconnect the ventilation hose from the fuel tank.
7 Remove the screws, and lift away the exhaust pipe heat shield from the right-hand side of the fuel tank.

8 Where fitted, unbolt and remove the fuel strainer from its bracket.
9 Support the weight of the fuel tank with a trolley jack and block of wood.
10 Unscrew the rear bolts securing the fuel tank straps to the underbody, and unhook the straps.
11 Lower the fuel tank sufficiently to gain access to the ventilation hoses **(see illustration)**. Identify the hoses before disconnecting them, to ensure correct refitting; once this is done, disconnect them and lower the tank to the ground.
12 Withdraw the tank from under the car.
13 If the tank is contaminated with sediment or water, swill it out with clean fuel. If the tank is damaged, or leaks, it should be repaired by a specialist, or alternatively renewed.

Refitting

14 Refitting is a reversal of the removal procedure, but make sure that the hoses are not trapped as the tank is lifted into place. Check all clips for damage, and renew them if necessary.

8 Fuel system -
depressurisation

Note: *Refer to the warning notes in Section 1 before proceeding.*

⚠️ **Warning: The following procedure will merely relieve the pressure in the fuel system - remember that fuel will still be present in the system components, and take precautions accordingly before disconnecting any of them.**

1 The fuel system referred to in this Section is defined as the tank-mounted fuel pump, the fuel filter, the fuel injector(s), the fuel pressure regulator, and the metal pipes and flexible hoses of the fuel lines between these components. All these contain fuel, which will be under pressure while the engine is running and/or while the ignition is switched on. The pressure will remain for some time after the ignition has been switched off, and must be relieved before any of these components are disturbed for servicing work. Ideally, the engine should be allowed to cool completely before work commences.
2 Referring to Section 9, locate and remove the fuel pump relay. Alternatively, identify and remove the fuel pump fuse.
3 With the fuel pump disabled, crank the engine for about ten seconds. The engine may fire and run for a while, but let it continue running until it stops. The fuel injector(s) should have opened enough times during cranking to considerably reduce the line fuel pressure, and reduce the risk of fuel spraying out when a fuel line is disturbed.
4 Disconnect the battery negative lead, and move the lead away from the battery.

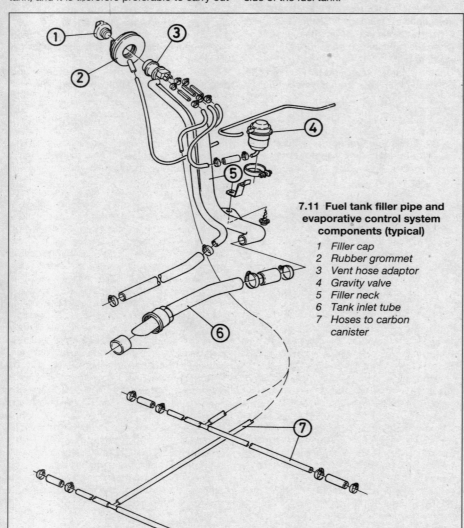

7.11 Fuel tank filler pipe and evaporative control system components (typical)

1 Filler cap
2 Rubber grommet
3 Vent hose adaptor
4 Gravity valve
5 Filler neck
6 Tank inlet tube
7 Hoses to carbon canister

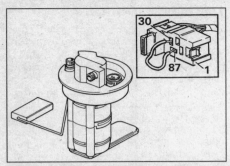

9.3 Bridging the fuel pump relay terminals to test the fuel pump

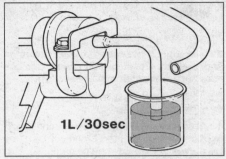

9.6a Checking the fuel pump delivery on non-B18U engines

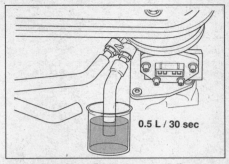

9.6b Checking the fuel pump delivery on B18U engines

5 Place a suitable container beneath the relevant connection/union to be disconnected, and have a large rag ready to soak up any escaping fuel not being caught by the container.

6 Slowly loosen the connection or union nut (as applicable) to avoid a sudden release of pressure, and position the rag around the connection to catch any fuel spray which may be expelled.

7 Once the pressure has been released, disconnect the fuel line. Insert plugs to minimise fuel loss and prevent the entry of dirt into the fuel system.

9 Fuel system pressure check

Note: *Refer to the warning notes in Section 1 before proceeding.*

1 Switch on the ignition, and check that the fuel pump runs for about three seconds - this will be heard as a buzzing noise beneath the rear seats. If the pump does not work, the problem will be found in the master relay or pump relay, or in the pump itself.

2 The injection system relays and fuel pump fuse are normally located behind the glovebox - on some models, they may be behind the right-hand side of the facia panel. Remove the facia lower trim panel and remove the two relays from the bracket, leaving them connected to the base.

3 Using a bridging wire, connect terminal 87 on the pump relay to terminal 30 **(see illustration)**. If the pump now operates, the pump relay may be faulty.

4 To check the master relay, switch on the ignition and connect a voltmeter between each of the terminals in turn and earth. Terminals 30, 86 and 89 should register 12 volts, but terminal 85 should produce a reading of zero to 1 volt.

5 To check the pump relay, connect the voltmeter between each of the terminals in turn and earth. Terminal 30 should register 12 volts. Terminal 85 should register zero to 1 volt for three seconds after switching on the ignition, then 12 volts. Terminal 86 should register 12 volts with the ignition switched on.

Terminal 87 should register 12 volts for three seconds after switching on the ignition, then approximately 1 volt.

6 If a suitable pressure gauge is available, first depressurise the fuel system as described in Section 8. Connect the gauge between the fuel inlet line and the injector manifold on all engines except the B18U; connect between the fuel inlet line and the single-point injection unit on the B18U engine **(see illustrations)**. A T-piece connector should be used, so that the fuel circulates back to the fuel tank.

7 Disconnect the flywheel sensor at the connector, then have an assistant crank the engine on the starter motor. Check that the line pressure rises to the specified amount, and that the volume of fuel delivered is correct. If the pressure is too high or too low, the fault may be in the pressure regulator, fuel pump, fuel lines, or there may be a fuel leak.

8 If the pressure is too high, disconnect the return line from the regulator, and blow into it. Clear any blockages found; if the return line is clear, renew the pressure regulator.

9 If the pressure is too low, first check the fuel level in the fuel tank (don't necessarily believe the fuel gauge), and check for leakage. If no faults are found, check the fuel pump as follows.

10 To check the fuel pressure, bridge terminals 30 and 87 at the pump relay, then briefly pinch the return line and check that the pressure immediately rises quickly - do not allow the pressure to rise above 6.0 bars. If the pressure rises but is still too low, renew the pressure regulator; if the pressure rises slowly, check for blockages in the fuel filter or fuel line, or for a possible loss of voltage at the pump.

11 To check the fuel delivery, disconnect the return line from the pressure regulator or single-point injection unit (according to model), and connect a hose from the regulator/single-point injection unit to a calibrated beaker. Bridge the terminals and run the pump, and check that 1 litre (except B18U engine) or 0.5 litre (B18U engine) of fuel is pumped out, in a maximum of 30 seconds.

12 If after making the above checks the pressure is still too low, renew the regulator. If the fuel delivery is insufficient, renew the pump.

10 Fuel injection system components - testing

General

1 The fuel injection and ignition systems should be checked at the same time. Refer to Chapter 5B for information on the ignition system. Before commencing work, check that the engine is in good condition; be sure that problems are not in fact due to worn spark plugs, faulty HT leads, or a blocked air cleaner element, etc. Disconnect the flywheel sensor and check the engine compressions, with reference to Chapter 2A. Also check the valve clearances, vacuum hoses, and accelerator cable operation.

2 Note that on B18E, B18F and B18FT engines, the complete fuel injection system may be tested using a special Volvo tester connected to the engine management or fuel injection system ECU multi-plug.

3 On B16F, B18EP, B18FP, B18U and B20F engines, the engine management ECU incorporates a fault code memory system, and by using a special Volvo test instrument, it is possible to extract the code and identify the faulty area of the fuel injection system.

4 For this reason, if a fault develops in the fuel injection system, it may save considerable time and expense if the car is taken to a Volvo dealer for the system to be checked with the special testers. The following information is given for those wishing to check the system themselves using more conventional equipment.

5 Check the battery condition and the fuel pump fuse, and check that all wiring connectors are sound; faulty connections are the cause of many problems.

6 Check that all of the inlet manifold bolts are tight, and also check the injector sealing O-rings (where applicable).

Fuel injectors (except B18U engine)

7 Run the engine at idle speed, then disconnect the wiring connectors from each injector in turn, and check that the engine speed momentarily drops. If the engine speed

4B

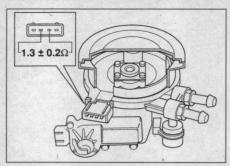

10.10 Checking the resistance of the single-point injector

does not drop on one of the injectors, then that injector is faulty.

8 If more than one injector is proved faulty, remove the connectors from the injectors, and check the resistances using an ohmmeter. If the resistance is not as specified, renew the injectors as necessary. If the resistance is correct, check the wiring for possible breaks.

Fuel injector (B18U engine)

9 Disconnect the wiring multi-plug from the single-point injection unit.
10 Connect an ohmmeter across the two middle terminals on the single-point injection unit, and check that the resistance of the injector is as given in the Specifications (see

illustration). If it is, check the wiring for possible breaks.

Flywheel sensor

11 Disconnect the wiring at the connector, and use an ohmmeter to check that the resistance of the sensor is as specified.

Inlet air and coolant temperature sensors

12 Disconnect the wiring at the connectors, and use an ohmmeter to check that the resistance across the sensor terminals is as given in the Specifications.

Air pressure sensor

13 The air pressure sensor terminals are numbered 17, 33 and 16, in that order, with terminal 16 nearest the sensor hose connection. Switch on the ignition, and connect a voltmeter between terminals 17 and 16; the voltage should be 5.0 volts. If not, check the wiring and the ECU.
14 If the voltage is correct, disconnect the vacuum hose from the inlet manifold, and connect a vacuum pump to it. Now measure the voltage between terminals 17 and 33, with and without vacuum. The voltage should vary between 5.0 volts without vacuum, up to 2.2 volts with vacuum. The resistance of the sensor windings may also be compared with the information given in the Specifications.

Throttle valve switch

15 Disconnect the wiring at the connector, and connect an ohmmeter across terminals 2 and 18 (except B18U engine) or 8 and 17 (B18U engine). With the throttle valve closed, zero resistance should be registered; with the valve open, infinity resistance should be registered (see illustrations).
16 On engines other than the B18U, connect the ohmmeter between terminals 3 and 18. With the throttle valve closed, infinity resistance should be registered; with the valve open, zero resistance should be registered. If necessary, adjust the throttle valve switch, and repeat the check. Renew the switch if the readings are still incorrect.

Idle speed regulating valve (except B18U engine)

17 Disconnect the wiring at the connector, and connect an ohmmeter across the two outer terminals; the resistance should be as given in the Specifications. If not, renew the valve.

Fuel system ECU

18 It is not possible to check the ECU, and on no account should any test instruments be connected to its terminals. It is possible to check the fuel injection system components by disconnecting the multi-plug from the ECU, then connecting an ohmmeter or

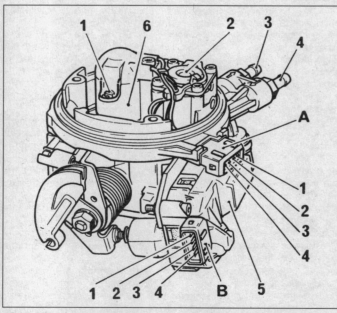

10.15a Single-point injection unit components - throttle lever side

1 Air temperature sensor	4 Fuel feed
2 Fuel pressure regulator	5 Idle speed control motor
3 Fuel return to tank	6 Single-point injector

Connector A
1 Air temperature sensor
2 Single-point injector (+)
3 Single-point injector (-)
4 Air temperature sensor

Connector B
1 Engine feed (+) or (-)
2 Engine feed (-) or (+)
3 Part-throttle switch
4 Part-throttle switch

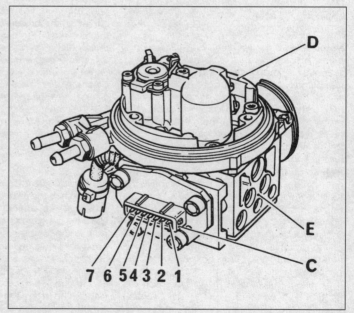

10.15b Single-point injection unit components - fuel inlet side

D Injector body	E Throttle valve body

Connector C
1 Automatic transmission track (+)
5 Automatic transmission track cursor
7 Automatic transmission track (-)

3 Injection track (-)
2 Injection track cursor
6 Injection track (+)
3 Full-load switch (-)
4 Full-load cursor
6 Full-load switch (+)

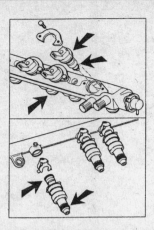

11.5 Removing the injectors from the injector manifold - B20F engine (top), all other engines (bottom)

Check the condition of the injector/manifold O-rings (arrowed)

voltmeter between the component terminals on the plug. However, this requires special probes and accurate instruments, and this work is best left to a specialist or Volvo dealer.

Injector cooling fan and switch (turbo models)

19 The cooling fan should engage at a temperature of 105°C and disengage at a temperature of 100°C. Checking the exact operating temperature may prove difficult without specialised equipment, but a rough check could be accomplished using a hairdryer and a thermometer. If the sensor switch is suspect, confirm by fitting a new one, and check if the fan then operates at the correct temperature.

---

11 Fuel injection system components (except B18U engine) - removal and refitting

Note: *Refer to the warning notes in Section 1 before proceeding.*

Fuel injectors

Removal

1 Depressurise the fuel injection system, then disconnect the fuel lines from the injection manifold.
2 If necessary, remove the upper section of the inlet manifold, with reference to Section 13 or 14.
3 Disconnect the vacuum line from the fuel pressure regulator.
4 Unscrew the two bolts or nuts, and pull the fuel injection manifold together with the injectors from the cylinder head.
5 On the B20F engine, remove the Torx bolts securing the injector retaining plates. On all other engines, pull out the spring clips. Remove the injectors from the manifold **(see illustration)**.

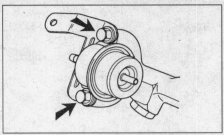

11.12a Fuel pressure regulator retaining bolts (arrowed) - engines except B20F . . .

6 Remove the rubber O-rings from the injectors.
7 Check the O-rings for damage and deterioration, and renew them if necessary.

Refitting

8 Refitting is a reversal of the removal procedure, but smear the rubber O-rings with a little petroleum jelly before fitting them to the injectors.

Fuel pressure regulator

Removal

9 Depressurise the fuel injection system, then disconnect the fuel lines from the injection manifold.
10 Disconnect the vacuum pipe from the pressure regulator.
11 On the B20F engine, remove the fuel injection manifold as described in paragraphs 1 to 4.
12 Remove the two securing bolts, take off the mounting collar (where applicable) and remove the pressure regulator from the injection manifold **(see illustrations)**.

Refitting

13 Refitting is a reversal of removal, but check the condition of the O-ring seals, and smear them with a little petroleum jelly to ease fitting.

Throttle valve switch

Removal

14 Disconnect the wiring from the throttle valve switch.
15 Note the position of the switch, then unscrew the two bolts and remove the switch from the throttle housing.

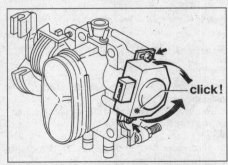

11.17 Adjusting the throttle valve switch

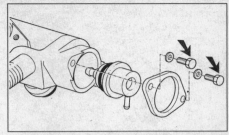

11.12b . . . and on the B20F engine - note mounting collar

Refitting

16 Refitting is a reversal of the removal procedure, but adjust the switch as follows before tightening the two bolts. First make sure that the accelerator cable is adjusted correctly.
17 Turn the throttle valve switch fully clockwise, then slowly turn it anti-clockwise until the internal contacts are heard to close **(see illustration)**. At this point, tighten the bolts. Do not over-tighten the bolts, otherwise the threads may be stripped in the alloy throttle housing.
18 Check the adjustment of the switch by slowly opening the throttle valve, checking that the internal switch is heard immediately after the throttle moves.

Throttle valve housing

Removal

19 Loosen the clip, and disconnect the air inlet hose from the throttle housing.
20 Use two hose clamps to clamp the coolant hoses leading to and from the throttle housing, then disconnect the two hoses.
21 Pull out the spring clip, and disconnect the accelerator cable from the throttle housing.
22 Unscrew the mounting bolts, and remove the throttle housing from the inlet manifold **(see illustration)**.
23 If necessary, remove the throttle valve switch.

4B

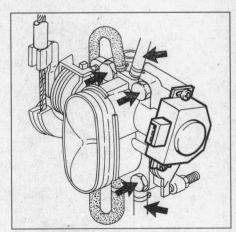

11.22 Throttle valve housing removal - mounting bolts and hoses arrowed

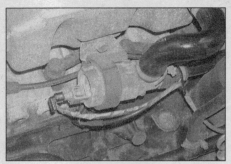

11.25 Idle speed regulating valve

Refitting

24 Refitting is a reversal of the removal procedure. If necessary, check and top-up the cooling system.

Idle speed regulating valve

Removal

25 Disconnect the wiring from the idle speed regulating valve **(see illustration)**.
26 Loosen the clips, and disconnect the hoses from the idle speed regulating valve.
27 Loosen the clamping ring bolt, and remove the valve from the engine compartment.

Refitting

28 Refitting is a reversal of the removal procedure.

Fuel system ECU

Removal

29 Remove the side trim panel from the inside of the passenger footwell.
30 Disconnect the wiring multi-plug from the ECU, then unscrew the mounting bolt and remove the ECU from inside the car.

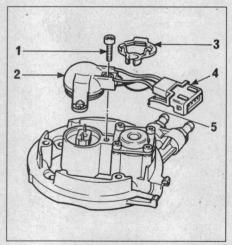

12.2 Removing the air temperature sensor on the single-point injector unit

1 Screw	4 Connector
2 Cover	5 Connector
3 Mounting	hooks

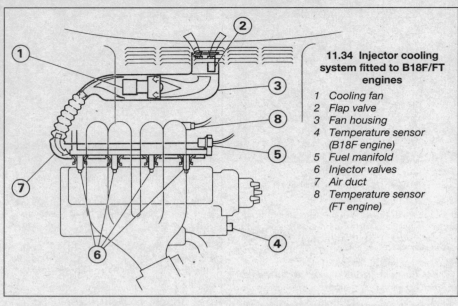

11.34 Injector cooling system fitted to B18F/FT engines

1 Cooling fan
2 Flap valve
3 Fan housing
4 Temperature sensor (B18F engine)
5 Fuel manifold
6 Injector valves
7 Air duct
8 Temperature sensor (FT engine)

Refitting

31 Refitting is a reversal of the removal procedure.

Injector cooling fan and switch (turbo models)

Removal

32 Disconnect the battery negative lead.
33 Disconnect the wiring from the injector cooling fan.
34 Disconnect the air duct bellows, then remove the fan assembly from the rubber mountings **(see illustration)**.
35 Unclip and remove the fan motor.
36 Remove the thermal switch from the inlet manifold.
37 Check and if necessary renew the roll-over valves.

Refitting

38 Refitting is a reversal of the removal procedure.

---

12 Fuel injection system components (B18U engine) - removal and refitting

Note: *Refer to the warning notes in Section 1 before proceeding.*

Fuel injector

Removal

1 Remove the air cleaner assembly, with reference to Section 2.
2 Remove the air temperature sensor by first removing the screw and lifting the sensor cover; disconnect the wiring leads from the special mounting, and release the connector plug **(see illustration)**.
3 Lift out the injector from the housing **(see illustration)**.

4 Carefully prise the O-ring seals from the injector.

Refitting

5 Refitting is a reversal of the removal procedure, but renew the O-ring seals, and lubricate them so that they easily enter the single-point injector unit.

Fuel pressure regulator

Removal

6 Remove the air cleaner inlet duct from the injection unit, with reference to Section 2.
7 Refer to Section 8 and depressurise the fuel system, then disconnect the battery negative lead and position it away from the terminal.
8 Refer to paragraph 2 and remove the air temperature sensor - the wiring can be left connected if preferred.

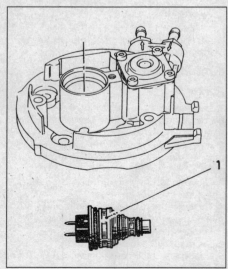

12.3 Injector (1) removed from the single-point injector unit

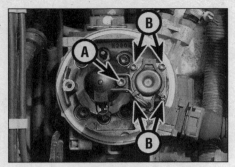

12.9 Air temperature sensor retaining screw (A) and pressure regulator frame screws (B)

9 Slacken and withdraw the four retaining screws and lift off the fuel pressure regulator retaining frame **(see illustration)**.
10 Lift out the upper cover, spring and membrane **(see illustration)**.
11 Clean all the components thoroughly, then inspect the membrane for cracks or splits.

Refitting

12 Refitting is a reversal of removal. Tighten the pressure regulator retaining frame screws securely.

Single-point injector unit

Removal

13 Remove the air cleaner assembly, with reference to Section 2.
14 Disconnect the three wiring plugs from the injector unit, noting their locations **(see illustration)**.
15 Loosen the clips, and disconnect the fuel inlet and return lines, noting their fitted positions are each denoted by a direction-of-flow arrow **(see illustration)**.

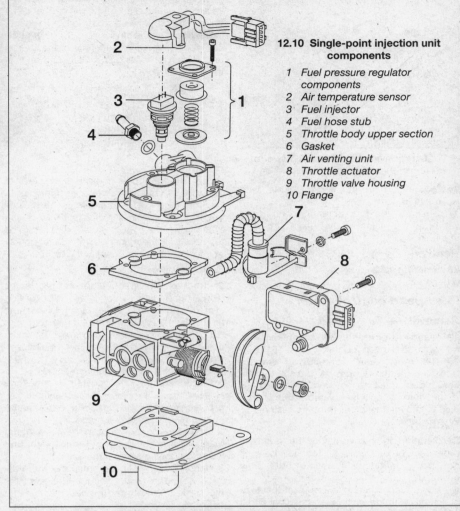

12.10 Single-point injection unit components

1 Fuel pressure regulator components
2 Air temperature sensor
3 Fuel injector
4 Fuel hose stub
5 Throttle body upper section
6 Gasket
7 Air venting unit
8 Throttle actuator
9 Throttle valve housing
10 Flange

4B

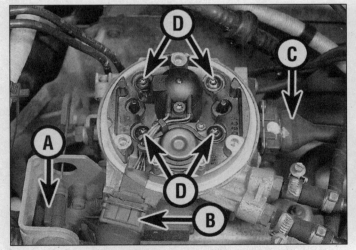

12.14 Single-point injector unit removal details

A Idle speed control motor wiring plug
B Fuel injector and air temperature sensor wiring plug
C Throttle valve position sensor wiring plug
D Mounting through-bolts

12.15 Fuel inlet (A) and return (B) connections - note direction-of-flow arrows

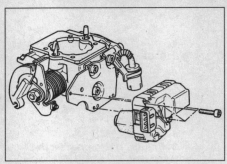

12.20 Removing the idle speed control motor on the single-point injector unit

16 Disconnect the accelerator cable, with reference to Section 3.

17 Unscrew the four mounting bolts, and withdraw the injector unit from the inlet manifold.

Refitting

18 Refitting is a reversal of the removal procedure.

Idle speed control motor

Removal

19 Remove the air cleaner assembly, with reference to Section 2.

20 The motor can be removed without removing the throttle casing, but the throttle casing bolts must be removed to gain access to the motor screws **(see illustration)**. Do not disconnect the fuel pipes from the casing.

Refitting

21 Refitting is a reversal of the removal procedure, but the motor switch must be in its no-load position with the throttle fully released.

22 Volvo technicians use a special tester to check this with the ignition switched on, and if necessary a shim is inserted between the motor and throttle switch. If there is any problem with the idle speed after fitting the motor, then a Volvo dealer should make this check.

Fuel system ECU

Removal

23 Remove the side trim panel from the inside of the passenger footwell.

24 Disconnect the wiring multi-plug from the ECU, then unscrew the mounting bolt and remove the ECU from inside the car.

Refitting

25 Refitting is a reversal of the removal procedure.

Air inlet temperature control vacuum switch

26 The switch is located inside the air inlet duct, and controls the blending of cold air and exhaust manifold-warmed air into the throttle body. First, remove the air inlet duct as described in Section 2.

27 Using a small flat-bladed screwdriver,

prise off the retaining plate from below the vacuum switch. The plate will probably be quite stiff, but work carefully, to avoid damaging the pipe stubs.

28 Working through the mouth of the air inlet duct, remove the vacuum switch, and recover the seal (if fitted).

13 Inlet and exhaust manifolds (except turbo models) - removal and refitting

Removal

1 Remove the throttle housing or single-point injector unit (as applicable), with reference to Section 11 or 12. Alternatively, the throttle housing/single-point injector unit may be left attached to the inlet manifold, and removed together with the manifold. If the latter course of action is taken, disconnect the air inlet duct.

B18U engine

2 Either clamp the coolant supply hoses using hose clamps, or drain the cooling system as described in Chapter 1. Disconnect the coolant hoses from the inlet manifold.

3 Loosen the clip, and disconnect the brake servo vacuum hose from the inlet manifold.

4 Unscrew the nuts, and remove the heat shield from the top of the inlet manifold.

5 Disconnect the hot-air duct, then unbolt the hot-air shroud from the exhaust manifold.

6 Unscrew the nuts securing the exhaust downpipe to the exhaust manifold.

7 Unscrew the bolt securing the exhaust manifold bracket to the cylinder block, and lower the downpipe from the manifold.

8 Unscrew the mounting nuts, and withdraw the inlet and exhaust manifold assembly from the studs on the cylinder head; remove the gaskets.

All other engines

9 Disconnect the vacuum hoses from the inlet manifold upper section.

10 Remove the idle speed regulator by disconnecting the wiring and hoses, and loosening the clamping ring.

11 Unscrew the bolts, and remove the inlet manifold upper section from the lower section **(see illustration)**.

13.11 Inlet manifold upper section retaining bolts (arrowed)

12 Apply the handbrake, then jack up the front of the car and support on axle stands.

13 Remove the engine compartment lower splash guard.

14 Unscrew the nuts securing the exhaust downpipe to the exhaust manifold.

15 Unscrew the bolt securing the exhaust manifold bracket to the cylinder block, and lower the downpipe from the manifold.

16 Unscrew the mounting nuts, and withdraw the inlet and exhaust manifold assembly from the studs on the cylinder head; remove the gaskets.

Refitting

17 Refitting is a reversal of the removal procedure, noting the following points:

a) Always use new gaskets.

b) Tighten the manifold-to-cylinder head nuts progressively to the specified torque, working from the central nuts outwards; tighten the exhaust downpipe-to-manifold nuts in the same manner.

c) If removed, refit the throttle housing or single-point injector unit (as applicable), as described in Section 11 or 12.

d) On models with the B18U engine, refill the cooling system (if drained) as described in Chapter 1.

14 Inlet and exhaust manifolds (turbo models) - removal and refitting

Removal

1 Disconnect the injector air cooling hose, then remove the throttle housing with reference to Section 11. Alternatively, the throttle housing may be left attached to the upper section of the inlet manifold, and removed together with the manifold. If the latter course of action is taken, disconnect the air inlet duct from the manifold.

2 Using a hose clamp, clamp the coolant pipe to the inlet manifold, then disconnect the pipe.

3 Disconnect the vacuum hose from the inlet manifold upper section.

4 Remove the idle speed regulator by disconnecting the wiring and hoses, and loosening the clamping ring.

5 Unscrew the bolts, and remove the inlet manifold upper section from the lower section.

6 Unclip the air cleaner top cover, then release the air inlet hose clips, and remove the top cover and airflow meter. Remove the remaining air ducts as necessary.

7 Remove the injector cooling fan assembly, with reference to Section 11.

8 Disconnect the crankcase ventilation hose at the valve cover.

9 Apply the handbrake, then jack up the front of the car and support on axle stands.

10 Remove the engine compartment lower splash guard.

11 Remove the heat shield from the driveshaft.

12 Drain the cooling system, with reference to Chapter 1.

13 Unscrew the nuts, and remove the exhaust downpipe from the turbocharger.

14 Unbolt the exhaust manifold bracket from the cylinder block, and remove the bolt from the bracket.

15 Unbolt the heat shield from the bulkhead.

16 Unscrew the bolts, and disconnect the exhaust downpipe from the catalytic converter. Remove the downpipe from under the car.

17 Disconnect the vacuum hose, and unbolt the wastegate from the turbocharger.

18 Unscrew the union bolts, and disconnect the coolant pipes from the turbocharger.

19 Unscrew the union nuts, and disconnect the turbocharger lubricating pipes.

20 Unbolt and remove the right-angled exhaust flange.

21 Disconnect the inlet and outlet hoses from the compressor.

22 Unscrew the mounting nuts, and remove the turbocharger from the exhaust manifold.

23 Unscrew the nuts, and withdraw the inlet and exhaust manifold assembly from the studs on the cylinder head; remove the gaskets **(see illustration)**.

24 Examine the flame rings for excessive wear, and renew them if necessary.

Refitting

25 Refitting is a reversal of the removal procedure, noting the following points:

a) *Always use new gaskets, and tighten all nuts and bolts to the specified torques.*

b) *Tighten the manifold-to-cylinder head nuts progressively to the specified torque, working from the central nuts outwards; tighten the exhaust downpipe-to-manifold nuts in the same manner.*

c) *Refit the throttle housing and injector cooling fan assembly as described in Section 11.*

d) *Refit the driveshaft heat shield, and refill the cooling system with reference to Chapter 1.*

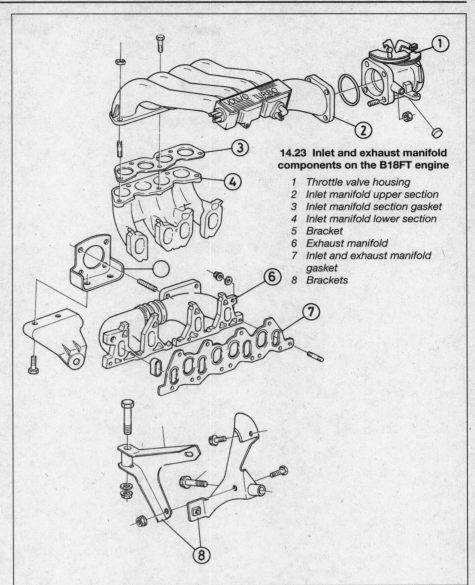

14.23 Inlet and exhaust manifold components on the B18FT engine

1 *Throttle valve housing*
2 *Inlet manifold upper section*
3 *Inlet manifold section gasket*
4 *Inlet manifold lower section*
5 *Bracket*
6 *Exhaust manifold*
7 *Inlet and exhaust manifold gasket*
8 *Brackets*

4B

Chapter 4 Part C:
Exhaust and emission control systems

Contents

Degrees of difficulty

Easy, suitable for novice with little experience		Fairly easy, suitable for beginner with some experience		Fairly difficult, suitable for competent DIY mechanic		Difficult, suitable for experienced DIY mechanic		Very difficult, suitable for expert DIY or professional	

Specifications

Turbocharger (B18FT, B18FT(M))

Type	Garrett T2
Boost pressure regulating valve resistance	29 ± 3 ohms

Torque wrench settings

	Nm	lbf ft
Catalytic converter to exhaust system	40	30
Exhaust clamps	25	18
Exhaust downpipe to manifold	25	18
Inlet and exhaust manifolds	20	15
Inlet manifold studs	13	10
Oxygen sensor	55	41
Turbocharger	38	28
Turbocharger banjo bolts	45	33
Turbocharger oil pipes:		
Upper	22	16
Lower	45	33
Turbocharger studs	21	15

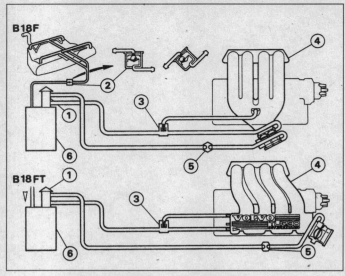

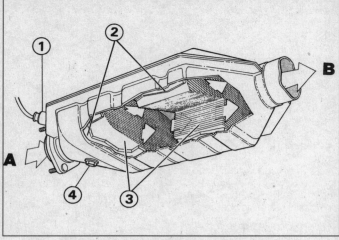

1.6 Sectional view of the catalytic converter

1.1 Fuel evaporative emission control system

1 Diaphragm valve
2 Gravity valve
3 Diaphragm valve
4 Inlet manifold
5 Temperature-sensitive valve
6 Carbon absorption canister

1 Oxygen sensor (early models)
2 Insulation
3 Catalyst elements
4 Emission test point (early models)

A Oxygen, hydrocarbon, carbon monoxide, nitrogen oxides in
B Water, carbon dioxide, nitrogen out

1 General information

Fuel evaporative emission control (EVAP)

Certain models are equipped with a fuel evaporative emission control system. This consists of a carbon absorption canister which absorbs fuel fumes from the fuel tank when the engine is stopped, thus preventing the fumes from escaping to the atmosphere. When the engine is started, the fumes are drawn into the engine for normal combustion **(see illustration)**.

Crankcase emission control

A positive crankcase ventilation system is fitted; the blow-by gases inside the engine do not escape to atmosphere, but are drawn into the inlet manifold for combustion. Oil suspended in the gases is collected in an oil separator and returned to the sump.

On fuel injection models, the system differs between non-turbo and turbo engines.

On some non-turbo engines, a thermistor is fitted, and the crankcase ventilation hose is connected to the inlet manifold, to heat the gases while the engine is warming up - this prevents ice forming in the system. Under closed-throttle conditions, the gases pass through a calibrated orifice to the inlet manifold, but with the throttle open, the gases pass to the inlet manifold via the throttle valve.

On turbo models, the system incorporates a vacuum control valve, which prevents oil from the oil separator being drawn into the inlet manifold.

Exhaust emission control

To minimise the amount of pollutants which escape into the atmosphere, most models are fitted with a catalytic converter in the exhaust system. One type of catalyst control system is described as 'open-loop', and has no feedback from the converter to the fuel system - this is employed on carburettor models, and no oxygen sensor is fitted. With the 'closed-loop' control system, the lambda/oxygen sensor in the exhaust system provides the fuel injection/ignition system ECU with constant feedback, enabling the ECU to adjust the fuel mixture for optimum combustion **(see illustration)**.

Some models may be fitted with an exhaust gas recirculation system (EGR), which prevents the occurrence of peak temperatures in the combustion chambers,

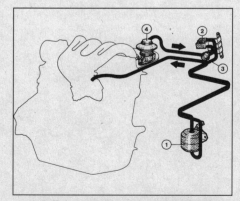

1.7 Exhaust gas recirculation (EGR) system

1 Vacuum reservoir
2 Modulation valve
3 Pressure regulator
4 EGR valve

and reduces emissions of harmful nitrous oxides. The system recycles a proportion of the exhaust gases during part-load conditions, and is operational only when the engine is at normal operating temperature **(see illustration)**.

Pulsair system

The Pulsair system is also part of the emission control package fitted to B18ES engines. It uses fluctuations in pressure in the exhaust manifold to draw in pulses of air from the air cleaner housing. The air provides oxygen which combines with unburnt hydrocarbons to reduce exhaust pollution.

The components of the system are an air distribution manifold, two non-return valves, a shut-off valve and associated pipework. The shut-off valve is controlled by inlet manifold vacuum and stops air flowing to the exhaust manifold for a couple of seconds at the beginning of deceleration, so preventing backfiring. The non-return valves prevent exhaust gas from arriving in the air cleaner.

Exhaust system

Refer to Section 2.

2 Exhaust system - general information and component renewal

1 The exhaust system consists of three sections on models without a catalytic converter, and four sections on models with a catalytic converter (except models with the B20F engine - see paragraph 11) **(see illustration)**.

2 Both the front pipe and tail pipe can be removed separately, leaving the rest of the

exhaust system in position. However, to remove the intermediate section, it is recommended that the tailpipe is removed first, then the intermediate section disconnected from the front pipe.

3 After disconnecting the intermediate section from the front downpipe and freeing the rubber mountings, the exhaust must be removed forwards and its rear end lifted over the rear axle. The catalytic converter (where fitted) can be removed separately from the rest of the system.

4 To remove the system (or part of the system), apply the handbrake and/or chock the front wheels, then jack up the front or rear of the car and support on axle stands. Alternatively, position the car over an inspection pit or on car ramps.

Front downpipe

5 To remove front downpipe which has an oxygen sensor fitted, either trace the wiring back from the sensor and disconnect it, or unscrew the sensor from the pipe (see Section 5).

6 Unscrew the bolts securing the downpipe to the front silencer or catalytic converter; remove the springs (where fitted).

7 Unscrew the nuts securing the downpipe to the exhaust manifold, and remove the springs. Withdraw the downpipe from under the car.

Front silencer or catalytic converter

8 To remove the front silencer or catalytic converter, wait until the exhaust system is cold, then spray a little penetrating oil on the joint bolts.

2.10 Exhaust front pipe connection to the catalytic converter

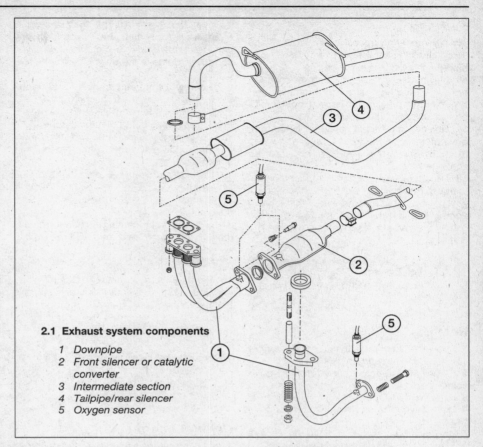

2.1 Exhaust system components

1 *Downpipe*
2 *Front silencer or catalytic converter*
3 *Intermediate section*
4 *Tailpipe/rear silencer*
5 *Oxygen sensor*

9 Where applicable, remove the oxygen sensor from the catalytic converter before removing it, referring to Section 5.

10 Support the silencer/converter, then unscrew the joint bolts (recover the springs, where fitted) and lower the section to the floor **(see illustration)**. When removing a catalytic converter, remember that the unit can be damaged if roughly handled. Recover the gasket normally fitted to the front connection, and discard it.

11 On B20F engine models, the catalytic converter is part of the intermediate section, and cannot be removed separately - refer to the following sub-section for details on removing the intermediate section.

Intermediate section

12 Unscrew the joint clamp bolts at the front and rear of the section, and release the rubber mountings from the underbody **(see illustration)**.

13 To free the intermediate section, tap around the joints with a hammer until the rust is dislodged, then twist the pipes if necessary. Lower the section from under the car.

Tailpipe

14 To remove the tailpipe, loosen the clamp bolt securing the tailpipe to the intermediate section, and release the rear rubber mountings from the underbody **(see illustrations)**.

4C

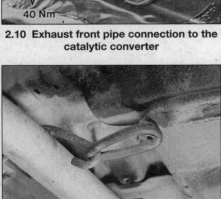

2.12 Exhaust intermediate section rubber mounting

2.14a Exhaust tailpipe-to-intermediate section joint

2.14b Exhaust tailpipe rubber mounting

Refitting

15 When refitting the exhaust system, make sure that all the sections are correctly aligned before tightening the joint bolts.

16 On models fitted with a compensating bellows to the rear exhaust system, support the exhaust pipe in its normal position to prevent stressing the bellows.

17 Use new gaskets at each end of the front downpipe, or at the front connection when refitting the front silencer or catalytic converter.

18 Use an exhaust jointing compound on the joint to the tailpipe section, to ensure a gastight seal. It is recommended that jointing compound is not used upstream of the catalytic converter, as this may damage the catalyst.

3 Turbocharger - removal and refitting

Removal

1 Apply the handbrake, then jack up the front of the car and support on axle stands.
2 Remove the engine compartment lower splash guard.
3 Remove the heat shield from the driveshaft.
4 Drain the cooling system, with reference to Chapter 1.
5 Unscrew the nuts, and remove the exhaust downpipe from the turbocharger.
6 Unbolt the exhaust manifold bracket from the cylinder block, and remove the bolt from the bracket.

7 Unbolt the heat shield from the bulkhead.
8 Unscrew the bolts, and disconnect the exhaust downpipe from the catalytic converter. Remove the downpipe from under the car.
9 Disconnect the vacuum hose, and unbolt the wastegate from the turbocharger.
10 Unscrew the union bolts, and disconnect the coolant pipes from the turbocharger.
11 Unscrew the union nuts, and disconnect the turbocharger lubricating pipes **(see illustration)**.
12 Unbolt and remove the right-angled exhaust flange.
13 Disconnect the inlet and outlet hoses from the compressor.
14 Unscrew the mounting nuts, and remove the turbocharger from the exhaust manifold.

Refitting

15 Refitting is a reversal of the removal procedure, but always use new gaskets, and tighten all nuts and bolts to the specified torques. If removed, refit the turbocharger bypass valve.

4 Intercooler - general information, removal and refitting

General information

1 An intercooler was fitted to all turbocharged engines. The intercooler is effectively an 'air radiator', used to cool the pressurised inlet air before it enters the engine.

2 When the turbocharger compresses the inlet air, one side-effect is that the air is heated, causing the air to expand. If the inlet air can be cooled, a greater effective volume of air will be inducted, and the engine will produce more power.

3 The compressed air from the turbocharger, which would normally be fed straight into the inlet manifold, is instead ducted to the base of the intercooler. The intercooler is mounted at the front of the engine compartment, in the air flow. The heated air entering the base of the unit rises upwards, and is cooled by the air flow over the intercooler fins, much as with the radiator. When it reaches the top of the intercooler, the cooled air is then ducted into the inlet manifold **(see illustration)**.

Removal

4 On 480 models, refer to Chapter 3 and remove the radiator.
5 The intercooler is mounted in front of the radiator, and is secured in position by a bolt and retaining clip at the top.
6 Disconnect the upper and lower hoses from the intercooler, then release the upper fasteners and lift the unit out of its lower locating bush.

Refitting

7 Refitting is a reversal of removal, noting the following points:
a) *Clean the intercooler fins of any debris before refitting, taking care not to cut your fingers - the fin edges are sharp.*
b) *Tighten the hose clips securely, to prevent air leaks.*

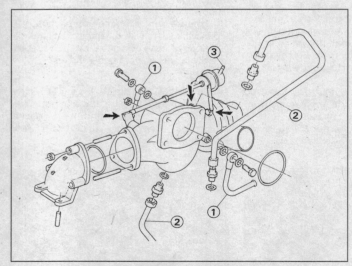

3.11 Turbocharger removal

1 Coolant pipes	*3 Vacuum hose connection*
2 Lubrication oil pipes	

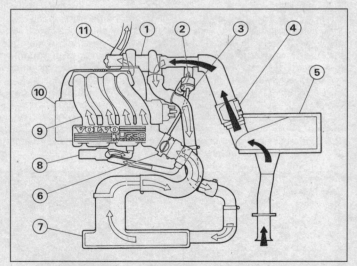

4.3 Diagram showing air flow on turbo models

1 Turbo unit	*7 Intercooler*
2 Vacuum operated bypass	*8 Idle speed regulator*
3 Vacuum sensing hose	*9 Inlet manifold*
4 Airflow meter	*10 Cylinder head*
5 Air cleaner assembly	*11 Exhaust system*
6 Throttle valve housing	

5 Emission control system components - testing and renewal

Fuel evaporative emission control

1 The fuel evaporative emission carbon canister is located under the right-hand front wheel arch. To improve access, jack up the front of the car and remove the right-hand front wheel. On 480 models, release the screws and other fasteners, and remove the right-hand front wheel arch liner for access.

2 Identify all hoses to the canister, then loosen the clips and disconnect them.

3 Unscrew the mounting nuts and bolts, and remove the canister together with the bracket.

4 Unscrew the clamp bolt, and release the canister from the bracket.

5 Shake the canister, and listen for loose carbon particles inside. Invert the canister to see if any carbon particles fall out; if there are any carbon particles, the canister should be renewed.

6 Refitting is a reversal of the removal procedure, but make sure that the canister is fitted in an upright position.

Crankcase emission control

7 To check the crankcase ventilation thermistor heating element fitted to some non-turbo models, disconnect the wiring at the connector, and connect an ohmmeter across the two terminals. With the engine cold, the resistance should be between 5 and 9 ohms; with the engine hot, it should be between 20 and 700 ohms.

8 To check the crankcase ventilation vacuum control valve on turbo models, first remove the valve by disconnecting the two hoses and pulling the valve off of the oil separator. Clean the stub connection, and blow into the valve - the valve should snap closed, and it should not be possible to blow through it. It should be possible, however, to suck through the valve.

9 The diaphragm valve can be checked as follows. Plug the connection to the oil separator, then connect a hose to the stub connection and apply strong suction - the valve should snap shut, and airflow should only be heard through the calibrated orifice. Refit the valve using a reversal of the removal procedure.

Exhaust gas recirculation system (where fitted)

10 Check that all of the vacuum lines to the EGR valve, pressure regulator, modulation valve and vacuum reservoir are in good condition and secured correctly.

11 Disconnect the vacuum hoses from the EGR valve, then start the engine.

12 With the engine cold, no suction should be felt. If suction is felt, check the modulation valve and the coolant temperature sensor.

13 With the engine warm, suction should be felt between engine speeds of 1400 and 3150 rpm. If suction is felt, reconnect the hose to the EGR valve, and check visually that the valve opens; if not, the EGR valve is defective. If suction is not felt, check the modulation valve and the coolant temperature sensor.

14 To check the modulation valve, disconnect the input hose while, or immediately after, switching off the engine; check that vacuum is clearly felt. If vacuum is felt, check the modulation valve, regulating valve and the wiring. If vacuum is not felt, check the vacuum hoses or the vacuum reservoir.

Pulsair system (where fitted)

15 Disconnect the hoses from the Pulsair non-return valves, then start the engine.

16 Place your hand carefully over the valves (they may be hot), and check that air is being sucked into them. If not, the valves are faulty, and should be renewed.

17 To remove the valves, unscrew the nut from the mounting clamp, and remove the clamp. Unscrew the unions, and remove the valves from the engine.

18 Refitting is a reversal of the removal procedure.

Catalytic converter (where fitted)

19 Testing the catalytic converter can only be made using an exhaust gas analyser, so any faults will normally only be apparent at an MOT test, when the exhaust gas content is checked.

Catalytic converter oxygen sensor

Testing

20 An accurate voltmeter is required to test the oxygen sensor.

21 Apply the handbrake, then jack up the front of the car and support on axle stands.

22 Run the engine to normal operating temperature, and check that the thermostat has opened (indicated when the radiator top hose gets hot).

23 Carry out the following check in as short a time as possible, to prevent damage to the catalytic converter.

24 Trace the wiring back from the oxygen sensor, and disconnect it at the wiring plug. Connect a voltmeter to the two terminals.

25 Increase the engine speed several times, and check that the voltmeter registers between 0.5 and 0.7 volts. If the voltage is incorrect, renew the oxygen sensor.

Removal

26 Apply the handbrake, then jack up the front of the car and support on axle stands.

27 Trace the wiring back from the oxygen sensor, and disconnect it at the wiring plug.

28 Unscrew and remove the sensor (see illustration). If it is tight, apply some penetrating oil to the threads first.

Refitting

29 Refitting is a reversal of the removal procedure. Apply anti-seize liquid to the threads of the sensor before inserting and tightening it to the specified torque. Do not allow any of the liquid to contact the sensor body or sensing element.

6 Catalytic converter - general information and precautions

The catalytic converter is a reliable and simple device which needs no maintenance in itself, but there are some facts of which an owner should be aware if the converter is to function properly for its full service life.

a) DO NOT use leaded petrol in a car equipped with a catalytic converter - the lead will coat the precious metals, reducing their converting efficiency and will eventually destroy the converter.

b) Always keep the ignition and fuel systems well-maintained in accordance with the manufacturer's schedule (Chapter 1) - particularly, ensure that the air cleaner filter element, the fuel filter and the spark plugs are renewed at the correct interval - if the intake air/fuel mixture is allowed to become too rich due to neglect, the unburned surplus will enter and burn in the catalytic converter, overheating the element and eventually destroying the converter.

c) If the engine develops a misfire, do not drive the car at all (or at least as little as possible) until the fault is cured - the misfire will allow unburned fuel to enter the converter, which will result in its overheating, as noted above.

d) DO NOT push- or tow-start the car - this

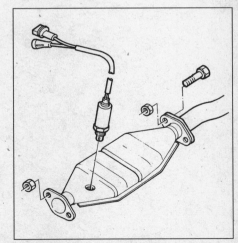

5.28 Catalytic converter oxygen sensor removal

Early models have the sensor fitted to the catalytic converter, as shown - on later models, the sensor is fitted to the downpipe

will soak the catalytic converter in unburned fuel, causing it to overheat when the engine does start - see b above.

e) DO NOT switch off the ignition at high engine speeds - i.e. do not blip the throttle immediately before switching off. If the ignition is switched off at anything above idle speed, unburned fuel will enter the (very hot) catalytic converter, with the possible risk of its igniting on the element and damaging the converter.

f) DO NOT use fuel or engine oil additives - these may contain substances harmful to the catalytic converter.

g) DO NOT continue to use the car if the engine burns oil to the extent of leaving a visible trail of blue smoke - the unburned carbon deposits will clog the converter passages and reduce its efficiency; in severe cases the element will overheat.

h) Remember that the catalytic converter operates at very high temperatures - hence the heat shields on the car's underbody - and the casing will become hot enough to ignite combustible materials which brush against it. DO NOT, therefore, park the car in dry undergrowth, over long grass or piles of dead leaves.

i) Remember that the catalytic converter is FRAGILE - do not strike it with tools during servicing work, take great care when working on the exhaust system, ensure that the converter is well clear of any jacks or other lifting gear used to raise the car and do not drive the car over rough ground, road humps, etc in such a way as to 'ground' the exhaust system.

j) In some cases, particularly when the car is new and/or is used for stop/start driving, a sulphurous smell (like that of rotten eggs) may be noticed from the exhaust. This is common to many catalytic converter-equipped cars and seems to be due to the small amount of sulphur found in some petrols reacting with hydrogen in the exhaust to produce hydrogen sulphide (H_2S) gas; while this gas is toxic, it is not produced in sufficient amounts to be a problem. Once the car has covered a few thousand miles the problem should disappear - in the meanwhile a change of driving style or of the brand of petrol used may effect a solution.

k) The catalytic converter, used on a well-maintained and well-driven car, should last for between 50 000 and 100 000 miles - from this point on, careful checks should be made at all specified service intervals of the CO level to ensure that the converter is still operating efficiently - if the converter is no longer effective it must be renewed.

Chapter 5 Part A:
Starting and charging systems

Contents

Degrees of difficulty

| Easy, suitable for novice with little experience | | Fairly easy, suitable for beginner with some experience | | Fairly difficult, suitable for competent DIY mechanic | | Difficult, suitable for experienced DIY mechanic | | Very difficult, suitable for expert DIY or professional | |

Specifications

System type .... 12-volt, negative earth

Battery
Capacity .... 55 Ah

Alternator
Type .... Bosch, Paris-Rhone or Valeo
Output:
  Bosch/Valeo .... 70 amps
  Paris-Rhone .... 63 or 72 amps
Minimum brush length:
  Bosch/Valeo .... 7.0 mm
  Paris-Rhone .... 8.0 mm
Voltage regulator control voltage:
  Unloaded .... 13.5 to 15.0 volts
  Loaded with 30 amps .... 14.0 to 15.0 volts

Starter motor
Type .... Bosch or Paris-Rhone
Rating .... 0.85, 0.95 or 1.36 kW
Commutator minimum thickness (Paris-Rhone) .... 2.0 mm
Commutator minimum diameter (Bosch) .... 33.5 mm
Brush minimum length:
  Paris-Rhone .... 6.0 mm
  Bosch .... 9.0 mm

Torque wrench settings	Nm	lbf ft
Alternator mounting bolt	40	30
Alternator pulley nut:		
Paris-Rhone	50	37
Bosch	45	33
Alternator sliding link to block	32	24
Alternator to sliding link	13	10

5A

1 General information and precautions

⚠️ **Warning: Before carrying out any work on the electrical system, read through the precautions given in Safety first! at the beginning of this manual.**

The engine electrical system consists mainly of the charging and starting systems. Because of their engine-related functions, these are covered separately from the body electrical devices such as the lights, instruments, etc (which are covered in Chapter 12). Refer to Part B of this Chapter for information on the ignition system.

The electrical system is of the 12-volt negative earth type, and consists of a 12-volt battery, an alternator with integral voltage regulator, a starter motor, and related electrical accessories, components and wiring.

The battery is charged by the alternator, which is belt-driven from a crankshaft-mounted pulley.

The starter motor is of the pre-engaged type, incorporating an integral solenoid. On starting, the solenoid moves the drive pinion into engagement with the flywheel ring gear before the starter motor is energised. Once the engine has started, a one-way clutch prevents the motor armature being driven by the engine.

Further details of the various systems are given in the relevant Sections of this Chapter. While some repair procedures are given, the usual course of action is to renew the component concerned. The owner whose interest extends beyond mere component renewal should obtain a copy of the *Automobile Electrical & Electronic Systems Manual*, available from the publishers of this manual.

Precautions

⚠️ **Warning: It is necessary to take extra care when working on the electrical system to avoid damage to semi-conductor devices (diodes and transistors), and to avoid the risk of personal injury. In addition to the precautions given in Safety first!, observe the following when working on the system:**

Always remove rings, watches, etc before working on the electrical system. Even with the battery disconnected, capacitive discharge could occur if a component's live terminal is earthed through a metal object. This could cause a shock or nasty burn.

Do not reverse the battery connections. Components such as the alternator, electronic control units, or any other components having semi-conductor circuitry could be irreparably damaged.

Never disconnect the battery terminals, the alternator, any electrical wiring or any test instruments when the engine is running.

Do not allow the engine to turn the alternator when the alternator is not connected.

Never test for alternator output by 'flashing' the output lead to earth.

Always ensure that the battery negative lead is disconnected when working on the electrical system.

If the engine is being started using jump leads and a slave battery, connect the batteries **positive-to-positive** and **negative-to-negative** (see *Booster battery (jump) starting*). This also applies when connecting a battery charger.

Never use an ohmmeter of the type incorporating a hand-cranked generator for circuit or continuity testing.

Before using electric-arc welding equipment on the car, **disconnect the battery, alternator and components such as the electronic control units** (where applicable) to protect them from the risk of damage.

Caution: Certain radio/cassettes fitted as standard equipment by Volvo have a built-in security code to deter thieves. If the power source to the unit is cut, the anti-theft system will activate. Even if the power source is immediately reconnected, the radio/cassette unit will not function until the correct security code has been entered. Therefore, if you do not know the correct security code for the radio/cassette unit, do not disconnect the battery negative terminal or remove the radio/cassette unit from the vehicle. Refer to your Volvo dealer for further information on whether the unit fitted to your car has a security code.

2 Electrical fault finding - general information

Refer to the information in Chapter 12.

3 Battery - testing and charging

Conventional and low-maintenance battery - testing

1 If the vehicle covers a small annual mileage, it is worthwhile checking the specific gravity of the electrolyte every three months to determine the state of charge of the battery. Use a hydrometer to make the check, and compare the results with the following table. Note that the specific gravity readings assume an electrolyte temperature of 15°C (60°F); for every 10°C (18°F) below 15°C (60°F) subtract 0.007. For every 10°C (18°F) above 15°C (60°F) add 0.007.

	Above 25°C	Below 25°C
Charged	1.210 to 1.230	1.270 to 1.290
70% charged	1.170 to 1.190	1.230 to 1.250
Discharged	1.050 to 1.070	1.110 to 1.130

2 If the battery condition is suspect, first check the specific gravity of electrolyte in each cell. A variation of 0.040 or more between any cells indicates loss of electrolyte or deterioration of the internal plates.

3 If the specific gravity variation is 0.040 or more, the battery should be renewed. If the cell variation is satisfactory but the battery is discharged, it should be charged as described later in this Section.

Maintenance-free battery - testing

4 In cases where a sealed for life maintenance-free battery is fitted, topping-up and testing of the electrolyte in each cell is not possible. The condition of the battery can therefore only be tested using a battery condition indicator or a voltmeter.

5 Certain models my be fitted with a maintenance-free battery, with a built-in charge condition indicator. The indicator is located in the top of the battery casing, and indicates the condition of the battery from its colour. If the indicator shows green, then the battery is in a good state of charge. If the indicator turns darker, eventually to black, then the battery requires charging, as described later in this Section. If the indicator shows clear/yellow, then the electrolyte level in the battery is too low to allow further use, and the battery should be renewed. **Do not** attempt to charge, load or jump start a battery when the indicator shows clear/yellow.

6 If testing the battery using a voltmeter, connect the voltmeter across the battery and note the voltage. The test is only accurate if the battery has not been subjected to any kind of charge for the previous six hours. If this is not the case, switch on the headlights for 30 seconds, then wait four to five minutes before testing the battery after switching off the headlights. All other electrical circuits must be switched off, so check that the doors and tailgate are fully shut when making the test.

7 If the voltage reading is less than 12.2 volts, then the battery is discharged, whilst a reading of 12.2 to 12.4 volts indicates a partially discharged condition.

8 If the battery is to be charged, remove it from the vehicle and charge it as described later in this Section.

Conventional and low maintenance battery - charging

Note: *The following is intended as a guide only. Always refer to the manufacturer's recommendations (often printed on a label attached to the battery) before charging a battery.*

9 Charge the battery at a rate equivalent to 10% of the battery capacity (eg for a 45 Ah battery charge at 4.5 A) and continue to charge the battery at this rate until no further rise in specific gravity is noted over a four-hour period.

10 Alternatively, a trickle charger charging at the rate of 1.5 amps can safely be used overnight.

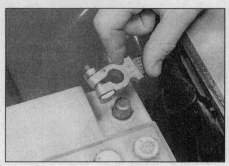

4.2 Disconnecting the battery negative terminal clamp

4.3 Lift the plastic cover for access to the positive terminal

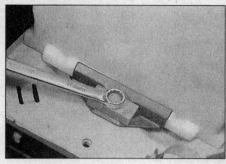

4.4 Unscrewing the battery clamp bolt

11 Specially rapid boost charges which are claimed to restore the power of the battery in 1 to 2 hours are not recommended, as they can cause serious damage to the battery plates through overheating. If the battery is completely flat, Volvo recommend that recharging should take at least 24 hours.

12 While charging the battery, note that the temperature of the electrolyte should never exceed 37.8°C (100°F).

Maintenance-free battery - charging

Note: *The following is intended as a guide only. Always refer to the manufacturer's recommendations (often printed on a label attached to the battery) before charging a battery.*

13 This battery type takes considerably longer to fully recharge than the conventional type, the time taken being dependent on the extent of discharge, but it can take anything up to three days.

14 A constant voltage type charger is required, to be set, when connected, to 13.9 to 14.9 volts with a charger current below 25 amps. Using this method, the battery should be useable within three hours, giving a voltage reading of 12.5 volts, but this is for a partially-discharged battery and, as mentioned, full charging can take far longer.

15 If the battery is to be charged from a fully-discharged state (condition reading less than 12.2 volts), have it recharged by your Volvo dealer or local automotive electrician, as the charge rate is higher and constant supervision during charging is necessary.

4 Battery - removal and refitting

Removal

1 The battery is located in the left-hand front corner of the engine compartment. First check that all electrical components are switched off, in order to avoid a spark occurring as the negative lead is disconnected. Note also that if the radio has a security coding, it will be necessary to insert this code when the battery is re-connected.

2 Loosen the nut on the negative terminal clamp, then remove the clamp and lead from the terminal, and place it to one side away from the battery **(see illustration)**.

3 Lift the plastic cover over the positive terminal **(see illustration)**, then loosen the nut, remove the clamp and lead from the terminal, and place it to one side away from the battery.

4 Unscrew the clamp bolt, and remove the clamp from the side of the battery **(see illustration)**.

5 Lift the battery from the tray, keeping it upright and taking care not to let it come into contact with your clothing.

6 If necessary, unscrew the four bolts and remove the battery tray from the engine compartment.

7 Clean the battery terminal posts, clamps, tray and battery casing. If the tray or surrounding body panels are rusted as a result of battery acid spilling onto them, clean them thoroughly and re-paint.

Refitting

8 Refitting is a reversal of removal, but always connect the positive terminal clamp first, and the negative terminal clamp last.

5 Charging system - testing

1 If the charge warning light fails to light when the ignition is switched on, first check the alternator wiring connections for security. If satisfactory, check that the warning light bulb has not blown and is secure in its holder (see Chapter 12). If the light still fails to light, check the continuity of the warning light feed wire from the alternator to the bulbholder. If all is satisfactory, the alternator is at fault, and should be renewed or taken to an auto-electrician for testing and repair.

2 If the ignition warning light lights when the engine is running, stop the engine, and check that the drivebelt is correctly tensioned (Chapter 1) and that the alternator connections are secure. If all is so far satisfactory, the alternator brushes and commutator will have to be checked (Section 7). If the fault persists,

the alternator should be renewed, or taken to an auto-electrician for testing and repair.

3 If the alternator output is suspect (even if the warning light functions correctly), the regulated voltage may be checked as follows.

4 Connect a voltmeter across the battery terminals, and start the engine.

5 Increase the engine speed until the voltmeter reading remains steady at approximately 13.5 to 15 volts.

6 Switch on as many electrical accessories (eg the headlights, heated rear window and heater blower) as possible, and check that the alternator maintains the regulated voltage at around 14 to 15 volts.

7 If the regulated voltage is not as stated, the fault may be due to worn brushes, weak brush springs, a faulty voltage regulator, a faulty diode, a severed phase winding, or a worn or damaged commutator. The brushes and commutator may be checked (Section 7), but if the fault persists, the alternator should be renewed or taken to an auto-electrician for testing and repair.

6 Alternator - removal and refitting

Removal

1 Disconnect the battery negative terminal.

2 Unscrew the nuts, and disconnect the battery positive and B- cables from the terminals on the rear of the alternator. Also disconnect the charge warning light wire **(see illustration)**.

6.2 Wiring connections to the rear of the Valeo alternator

1 Battery positive   *2 Charge warning*
3 B-   *light*

5A

6.5 Removing the alternator from the engine

7.2a Prise off the plastic guard . . .

7.2b . . . and disconnect the regulator wiring

3 Loosen the alternator pivot and link mounting bolts, then back off the tension adjustment nut so that the alternator swivels in towards the engine.
4 Remove the drivebelt from the alternator pulley.
5 Remove the pivot and link mounting bolts completely, and lift the alternator from the engine **(see illustration)**.

Refitting

6 Refitting is a reversal of the removal procedure. Tension the drivebelt with reference to Chapter 1.

7 Alternator brushes and regulator - checking and renewal

1 Remove the alternator with reference to Section 6.
2 On Paris-Rhone and Valeo alternators, prise off the plastic guard from the rear of the alternator using a screwdriver, and pull the regulator wire from the spade terminal on the diode carrier **(see illustrations)**.
3 Unscrew the mounting bolts, and lift the regulator and brush assembly from the alternator. As it is being removed, tilt it slightly to prevent damage to the brushes **(see illustration)**.

4 Measure the length of each brush, from the end of the holder to the top of the brush **(see illustration)**. If either brush is worn below the specified minimum amount, obtain and fit a new regulator and brush assembly. If the brushes are still serviceable, clean them with a petrol-moistened cloth.
5 Check that the brush spring pressure is equal for both brushes, and gives reasonable tension. If in doubt about the condition of the brushes and springs, compare them with new parts at a Volvo parts dealer.
6 Clean the slip rings with a petrol-moistened cloth, then check for signs of scoring, burning or severe pitting. If evident, the slip rings should be attended to by an automobile electrician.
7 Fit the regulator and brush assembly using a reversal of the removal procedure.

8 Starting system - testing

1 If the starter motor fails to operate, first check the condition of the battery by switching on the headlights. If they glow brightly, then gradually dim after a few seconds, the battery is in a discharged condition.

2 If the battery is satisfactory, check the starter motor main terminal and the engine earth cable for security. Check the terminal connections on the solenoid, located on the starter motor.
3 If the starter still fails to turn, use a voltmeter, or 12-volt test light and leads, to ensure that there is battery voltage at the solenoid main terminal (ie the cable from the battery positive terminal).
4 With the ignition switched on and the ignition key in the 'start' position, check that voltage is reaching the solenoid terminal with the spade connector, and also the starter main terminal beneath the end cover.
5 If there is no voltage reaching the spade connector, there is a wiring or ignition switch fault. If voltage is available, but the starter does not operate, then the starter or solenoid is likely to be at fault.

9 Starter motor - removal and refitting

Removal

1 Disconnect the battery negative terminal. On the B18FT(M) engine, remove the battery and battery tray complete.

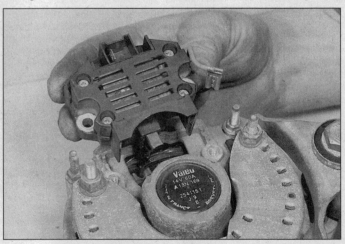

7.3 Removing the regulator and brush assembly from the Valeo alternator

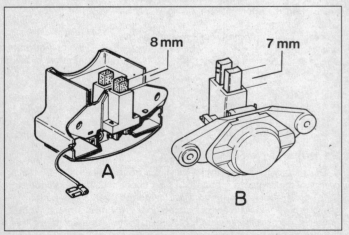

7.4 Alternator minimum brush length dimensions

A Paris-Rhone   B Bosch/Valeo

9.9a Upper view of the starter motor solenoid terminals

9.9b Lower view of the starter motor solenoid terminals

9.10 Starter motor rear mounting bracket

2 Apply the handbrake, then jack up the front of the car and support on axle stands.

3 Refer to Chapter 4A or 4B, and remove the air cleaner assembly on carburettor engines; remove the air cleaner assembly and airflow meter on fuel injection engines.

4 Where applicable, unscrew and remove the bolt from the Pulsair line clamp bracket.

5 Unscrew and remove the mounting bolts attaching the starter motor to the transmission.

6 Where applicable, unscrew and remove the starter motor upper heat shield bolt. Note that the heat shield mounting was modified in early 1991, and on certain later models the shield is attached to the exhaust manifold by a nut.

7 Working under the engine compartment,

remove the engine splash guard. On engines fitted with the Pulsair system, detach the exhaust downpipe from the exhaust manifold, with reference to Chapter 4C.

8 Unscrew the lower starter motor heat shield bolt, and remove the heat shield. Also unbolt the right-hand driveshaft heat shield.

9 Unscrew the nut, and disconnect the battery positive supply cable from the starter motor solenoid, then disconnect the trigger wire (see illustrations).

10 Unscrew the mounting bolt attaching the rear of the starter motor to the bracket, and remove the bracket (see illustration). On 480 models, one of the bracket bolts must be removed and the remaining one loosened only; on 440 models, a nut must be unscrewed.

11 The starter motor may now be withdrawn from below the engine.

Refitting

12 Refitting is a reversal of the removal procedure. On models where the exhaust downpipe was removed, check the gasket and renew it if necessary.

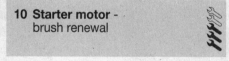

10 Starter motor - brush renewal

Paris-Rhone

1 Unscrew the nuts and remove the bracket from the end of the starter.

2 Remove the pinion pivot pin from the starter motor housing.

3 Unscrew the two nuts, and remove the front end shield (see illustration).

4 Unscrew the two bolts, and remove the dust excluder.

5 Hold the shaft stationary, and unscrew the bolt from the end of the shaft; remove the shims.

6 Remove the rear end shield from the yoke.

7 Remove the brushes from their guides, and remove the brush holder.

8 Measure the length of the brushes, and compare with the minimum dimension given in the Specifications. If either brush is worn to or below this figure, renew all of the brushes.

9 Clean the brush holder assembly, and wipe the commutator with a petrol-moistened cloth. If the commutator is dirty, it may be cleaned with fine glass paper, then wiped with the cloth.

10 Fit the new brushes using a reversal of the removal procedure, but make sure that they move freely in their holders.

Bosch

11 Unscrew the two bolts, and remove the dust excluder from the end of the starter motor. Remove the thrustwashers and shims (see illustrations).

12 Unscrew the two long through-bolts, and remove the rear end shield (see illustration).

13 Remove the intermediate plate, and release the brush mounting brackets from the holder (see illustrations). Move the holder to one side.

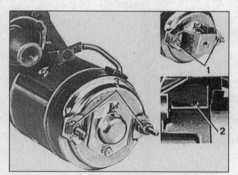

10.3 Starter motor brush renewal on the Paris-Rhone starter

1 Bracket nuts
2 Pivot pin
3 Front end shield nuts

10.11a Removing the dust excluder . . .

10.11b . . . thrustwasher . . .

10.11c . . . and shims from the starter motor

5A

10.12 Removing the through-bolts and rear end shield

10.13a Intermediate plate removal

10.13b Releasing the brush mounting brackets

14 Measure the length of the brushes, and compare with the minimum dimension given in the Specifications **(see illustration)**. If either brush is worn to or below this figure, renew all of the brushes.

15 Clean the brush holder assembly, and wipe the commutator with a petrol-moistened cloth. If the commutator is dirty, it may be cleaned with fine glass paper, then wiped with the cloth.

16 Fit the new brushes using a reversal of the removal procedure, but make sure that they move freely in their holders.

10.13c Removing the brush holder assembly

10.14 Measuring the length of the starter motor brushes

Chapter 5 Part B:
Ignition system

Contents

Degrees of difficulty

Easy, suitable for novice with little experience	Fairly easy, suitable for beginner with some experience	Fairly difficult, suitable for competent DIY mechanic	Difficult, suitable for experienced DIY mechanic	Very difficult, suitable for expert DIY or professional

Specifications

General

System type	Electronic computer control unit with position/speed sensor, ignition coil and basic distributor

Application:

Engine codes B18K/B18K(D)/B18KP/B18KP(D)	Bendix 417A
Engine code B18F	Fenix 3A (F3A)
Engine code B18E/B18E(D)/B18ES	Fenix 1 or 3.2
Engine codes B16F, B18EP/FP, B18U, B20F	Fenix 3B
Engine codes B18FT/FT(M)	Bosch EZ210K
Firing order	1-3-4-2
Location of No 1 cylinder	Flywheel/transmission end

Distributor

Type	Cap and rotor arm only, rotor arm attached to end of camshaft
Direction of rotor arm rotation	Anti-clockwise

Ignition system test data

Ignition coil:

Primary winding resistance	0.4 to 0.8 ohms
Secondary winding resistance:	
Except engine codes B18FT/B18FT(M)	2500 to 5500 ohms (typical)
Engine codes B18FT/B18FT(M)	7200 ohms
Flywheel position/speed sensor:	
Resistance	160 to 280 ohms
Knock sensor:	
Resistance	Greater than 1 000 000 ohms

Torque wrench settings

	Nm	lbf ft
Knock sensor	17	13
Oil temperature sensor	25	18

5B

1 General information and precautions

The electronic ignition system operates on an advanced principle, whereby most functions of the distributor are replaced by a computer module. On non-turbo fuel injection models, the fuel and ignition systems are inter-related, and more information on this can be found in Chapter 4B.

The ignition system consists of three major components - the computer module or ECU, the distributor, and the flywheel position/ speed sensor. The computer module (fitted to all carburettor engines, and to the B18F engine) incorporates an ignition coil and a vacuum advance unit. The electronic control unit (ECU) fitted to fuel injection engines (except the B18F) controls all the ignition functions internally. The distributor merely directs the HT voltage received from the coil to the appropriate spark plug, and is a very simple component compared to a conventional unit. The angular position/speed sensor is mounted above the edge of the flywheel, and determines the position and speed of the crankshaft by sensing special teeth on the flywheel periphery.

The computer module on carburettor and B18F engines receives information on crankshaft position relative to TDC and BDC, and also on engine speed, from the angular position/speed sensor; engine load information comes from the vacuum advance unit. From these constantly-changing variables, the computer calculates the precise instant at which HT voltage should be supplied, and triggers the coil accordingly (see illustration).

On fuel injection engines except the B18F, the ECU receives information on engine speed, temperature and throttle opening, and from these variables determines the most efficient timing according to programmed co-ordinates retained in the ECU memory. The ECU triggers the coil accordingly, and the voltage then passes from the coil to the appropriate spark plug, via the distributor, in the conventional way.

The functions of the centrifugal and vacuum advance mechanisms, as well as the contact breaker points normally associated with a distributor, are all catered for by the computer module or ECU, so that the sole purpose of the distributor is to direct the HT voltage from the coil to the appropriate spark plug.

Depending on model, the module/ECU also receives information on the engine coolant and oil temperatures, and this information is then collated together with the other factors to control the ignition advance as required.

On all fuel injection models, a knock sensor is fitted on the cylinder head. In the event of pre-ignition ('pinking'), the ignition timing is retarded by the ECU to compensate.

On turbo models, a boost pressure regulator is fitted, allowing the ignition ECU control over the boost pressure, to provide a more rapid response to changing boost pressures in the engine than would be possible with just a conventional wastegate system (see illustration).

Precautions

⚠️ **Warning: Due to the sophisticated nature of the electronic ignition system, the following precautions must be observed, to prevent damage to the components and to reduce the risk of personal injury.**

Ensure that the *ignition is switched off* before disconnecting any of the ignition wiring.

Ensure that the *ignition is switched off* before connecting or disconnecting any ignition test equipment, such as a timing light.

Do not connect a suppression condenser or test light to the ignition coil negative terminal.

Do not connect any test appliance or stroboscopic timing light requiring a 12-volt supply to the ignition coil positive terminal.

Do not allow an HT lead to short out or spark against the module/ECU body.

2 Ignition system (except EZ210K type) - testing

1 Before commencing the test procedure, check that the earth wire from the computer module is connected to earth securely.

Flywheel sensor

2 Disconnect the wiring plug leading to the sensor on the left-hand side of the engine.
3 Connect an ohmmeter across the two contacts in the wiring plug, and check that the resistance is as specified (see illustration).

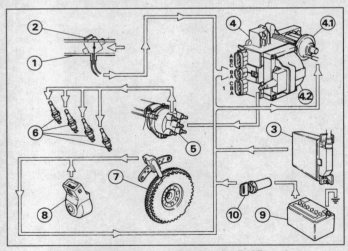

1.3 F3A ignition system fitted to the B18F engine

1	Inlet manifold	6	Spark plugs
2	Throttle valve switch	7	Flywheel and position/ speed sensor
3	LH-Jetronic ECU		
4	F3A ignition system	8	Knock sensor
4.1	Vacuum diaphragm unit	9	Battery
4.2	Ignition coil	10	Ignition switch
5	Distributor		

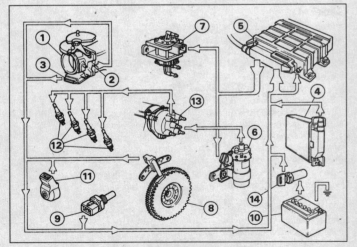

1.8 EZ210K ignition and boost pressure control system fitted to the B18FT engine

1	Throttle valve housing	8	Flywheel and position/speed sensor
2	Intake load sensor		
3	Throttle valve position switch	9	Coolant temperature sensor
4	LH-Jetronic ECU	10	Battery
5	Ignition ECU	11	Knock sensor
6	Ignition coil	12	Spark plugs
7	Boost pressure regulating valve	13	Distributor
		14	Ignition switch

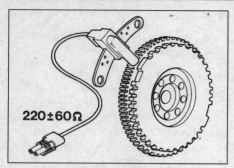

2.3 Checking the flywheel sensor

4 If the resistance is higher or lower, the sensor should be renewed. If the resistance is within the required range, remove the sensor and clean it thoroughly before refitting.

Oil temperature sensor (B18KP)

5 Disconnect the wiring at connector III on the computer module.

6 Connect an ohmmeter between terminal 6 on the connector and earth (see illustration).

7 When the engine oil temperature is less than 15°C or greater than 70°C, the resistance should be zero; between 15°C and 70°C, the resistance should be infinity. If the resistance is not correct, renew the temperature sensor.

Module vacuum unit (B18KP, B18F)

8 Connect a tachometer to the engine, in accordance with the equipment manufacturer's instructions.

9 Disconnect the vacuum hose from the vacuum unit, and connect a vacuum pump to it.

10 Start the engine, and run it at a constant speed of 2500 rpm.

11 Using the vacuum pump, apply a vacuum of 0.3 to 0.4 bars, and check that the ignition advances by 10°. If the ignition does not advance by the correct amount, renew the computer module unit complete.

Power supply

12 Disconnect the wiring at connector I as shown (see illustration). Switch on the ignition.

13 Connect a voltmeter between terminal A and earth, then operate the starter motor, and check that the voltage reading is at least

2.6 Checking the temperature sensor on the B18KP engine

6 Temperature sensor plug on the computer module
III Plug retaining clip

9.5 volts. If there is no voltage, check the supply from the ignition switch to the computer module. If the voltage is too low, check the battery voltage.

Earth connection

14 Connect an ohmmeter between terminal B of connector I and earth, and check that the resistance is zero. If the resistance is higher, check the security of the earth connection.

Ignition signal (B18E)

15 Disconnect the wiring plug II from the module (see illustration).

16 Connect a voltmeter between terminal B of the connector plug and earth.

17 Have an assistant spin the engine on the starter motor, and check that the voltage is between 300 and 400 millivolts. The pointer should vibrate as the engine is turning. If this is not the case, check the wiring to the electronic control unit.

Ignition signal (except B18E)

18 Disconnect the wiring plug II from the module.

19 Connect an LED tester between terminal B of the connector plug and earth.

20 Have an assistant spin the engine on the starter motor, and check that the LED tester flashes. If this is not the case, check the wiring to the electronic control unit.

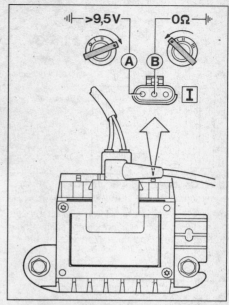

2.12 Checking the power supply and earth connection on the computer module

I Connector

Computer module ignition coil output

21 Disconnect the HT lead from the ignition coil, and remove the coil as described in Section 6.

22 With the coil removed, check the low tension terminals for corrosion, and clean them if necessary.

23 Connect an ohmmeter between terminals A and 1 as shown (see illustration); check that the resistance is zero. If the resistance is higher, renew the computer module with reference to Section 7.

24 Reconnect the wiring after making the check.

Ignition coil power supply

25 Reconnect all the wiring as applicable, then switch on the ignition and connect a 12-volt test light with a minimum rating of 4 watts between terminals 1 and 2 of the computer module (see illustration).

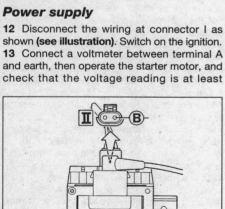

2.15 Checking the ignition signal on the B18E engine

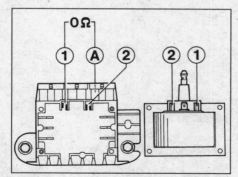

2.23 Checking the ignition coil output of the computer module

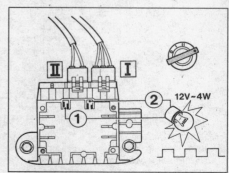

2.25 Checking the power supply to the ignition coil

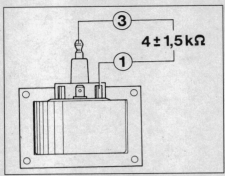

2.27 Checking the ignition coil secondary windings

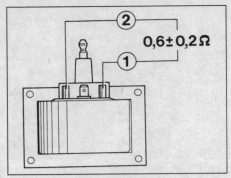

2.28 Checking the ignition coil primary windings

26 Operate the starter motor, and check that the test light flashes. If it does not flash, renew the computer module and make the check again.

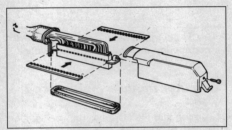

3.2 EZ210K ignition ECU multi-plug cap and strips

Ignition coil secondary windings

27 Connect an ohmmeter across terminals 1 and 3 of the ignition coil **(see illustration)**; check that the resistance is as given in the Specifications. If the resistance is higher or lower, renew the ignition coil.

Ignition coil primary windings

28 Connect an ohmmeter across terminals 1 and 2 of the ignition coil **(see illustration)**, and check that the resistance is as given in the Specifications If the resistance is higher or lower, renew the ignition coil.

Computer module

29 Disconnect the ignition coil HT lead from the distributor cap, and hold it (using insulated pliers) about 2 cm away from the cylinder block.

30 Have an assistant operate the starter motor, and check that there is a continuous stream of sparks onto the cylinder block. Make sure that the sparks do not come near the computer module, and that the lead is held no more than 2 cm away from the block, otherwise damage will be done. The module is proved to be working correctly if the sparks are regular.

Distributor cap and rotor arm

31 Check the distributor cap and rotor arm as described in Chapter 1.

---

3 Ignition system (EZ210K) - testing

Note: *The EZ210K ignition system incorporates a special diagnostic test point, which is used by Volvo technicians to diagnose faults quickly. In certain circumstances, it may be better to let a Volvo garage check the ignition system rather than carry out the following procedure.*

1 With the ignition switched off, remove the panel from the right-hand side of the centre console and disconnect the multi-plug from the ECU by pressing the retaining tab outwards.

2 Remove the cap and strips from the multi-plug for access to the rear of the pins **(see illustration)**. Do not attempt to test the pins from the end which enters the ECU, as they may be damaged. The pins are numbered on the side of the connector.

3 Connect a voltmeter between terminal 5 and earth, and check that the battery voltage is present (battery voltage is the reading obtained when the voltmeter is connected straight across the car battery terminals) **(see illustration)**.

4 Connect the voltmeter between terminal 6 and earth, and switch on the ignition; battery voltage should be present. Now operate the starter motor, and check that the voltage does not drop below 9 volts. If it does, check the battery.

5 Connect an ohmmeter across terminals 20 and 4, and check that the resistance does not exceed 0.1 ohms. A greater resistance indicates that the earth connection is faulty.

6 Connect the ohmmeter between terminal 2 and earth to check the engine coolant temperature sensor. When the coolant is at 20°C, the resistance should be 2500 ohms, and at 95°C, the resistance should be 160 ohms.

7 Connect the ohmmeter between terminal 7 and earth to check the throttle valve switch. With the accelerator pedal fully released (idle position), the resistance should be zero; with the pedal fully depressed, the resistance should be 1300 ohms.

8 Check the throttle valve switch acceleration and full-load signals as follows. Connect the ohmmeter between terminals 22 and 25. With the accelerator pedal fully released, the resistance should be 3700 ohms; with it fully depressed, the resistance should be 350 ohms.

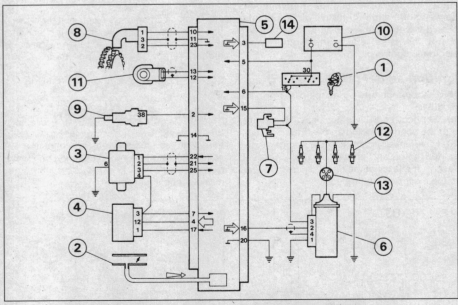

3.3 ECU terminal connections for the EZ210K ignition system

1 Ignition switch	6 Ignition coil	10 Battery
2 Intake load sensor	7 Boost pressure regulating valve	11 Knock sensor
3 Throttle valve position switch	8 Flywheel position/speed sensor	12 Spark plugs
4 LH-Jetronic ECU	9 Coolant temperature sensor	13 Distributor
5 Ignition ECU		14 Diagnostic test point

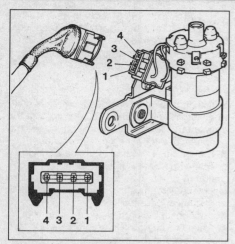

3.15 Ignition coil multi-plug terminals on the EZ210K ignition system

9 To check the throttle valve position signal, connect the ohmmeter between terminals 21 and 25. With the accelerator pedal fully released, the resistance should be 520 ohms; when the pedal is depressed slowly, the resistance should rise from 520 ohms to 3900 ohms.
10 To check the flywheel speed/position sensor, connect the ohmmeter between terminals 10 and 23; the resistance should be 220 ± 60 ohms.
11 Visually check the earth connections to terminals 11, 12, 20 and 21.
12 To check the knock sensor, disconnect the sensor wiring at the connector, and connect a bridging wire between the two

5.2a Distributor cap showing the earth lead (arrowed)

terminals. Now connect the ohmmeter between terminals 12 and 13, and check that the resistance is zero.
13 To check the boost pressure regulating valve, connect the ohmmeter between terminals 6 and 15; the resistance should be approximately 30 ohms.
14 Carefully refit the multi-plug to the ECU (ignition off), and refit the centre console panel.
15 Check the ignition coil by disconnecting the multi-plug and connecting a voltmeter between terminal 3 on the plug and earth **(see illustration)**. Check that battery voltage is present with the ignition switched on; if not, check the power feed to the ECU.
16 Connect the ohmmeter between terminal 2 on the coil socket and earth, to check the coil secondary windings. The resistance should not exceed 0.1 ohms; if it is higher than this, check the earth connections.
17 Connect an LED tester between terminal 4 and earth, then have an assistant spin the engine on the starter motor, and check that the LED flashes. If it does not flash, check the wiring.
18 Remove the plastic cover from the ignition coil, and disconnect both wires from the low tension terminals **(see illustration)**. If necessary, identify the wires for position to ensure correct refitting.
19 Connect an ohmmeter between the two low tension terminals, and check that the resistance is between 0.4 and 0.8 ohms.
20 Connect the ohmmeter between terminals 1 and 3, and between terminals 2 and 3, and check that the resistance is 7200 ohms.
21 If the previous procedure fails to find a fault, the ECU should be renewed.

4 Ignition timing - general information

The ignition timing is automatically adjusted by the computer module/ECU according to the engine temperature and load, and it is not possible to adjust it manually. If it is felt that engine performance is unsatisfactory which may be resulting from incorrect ignition advance, the system should be checked as described in Section 2 or 3.

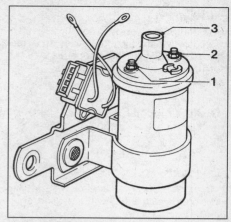

3.18 Ignition coil terminals on the EZ210K ignition system

1 & 2 Low tension (LT) terminals
3 High tension (HT) terminal

5 Distributor - removal and refitting

Removal

1 On all models, the distributor simply comprises a rotor arm driven from the end of the camshaft, and a distributor cap attached to the end face of the cylinder head.
2 To remove the distributor cap, unscrew the retaining screws, and withdraw it together with the HT leads (note that an earth lead is connected to one of the screws). If necessary, disconnect the HT leads from the spark plugs **(see illustrations)**. If the HT leads are being removed altogether, mark them for position as described in Chapter 1.
3 The rotor arm and shield can now be pulled free and removed **(see illustration)**.
4 Wipe clean the cap and leads, and check that the spring-tensioned carbon brush in the centre of the cap is in good condition. If the camshaft oil seal requires renewal, refer to Chapter 2A.
5 Carefully inspect the HT leads and cap for signs of deterioration as described in Chapter 1.

5B

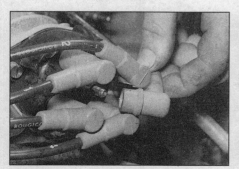

5.2b Disconnecting the coil HT lead from the distributor cap

5.2c Removing the distributor cap from the engine

5.3 Removing the rotor arm and shield

Refitting

6 Refitting is a reversal of the removal procedure. When fitting the rotor arm, ensure that its single inner tooth engages with the slot in the end of the camshaft.

6 Ignition coil - removal and refitting

Removal

1 The ignition coil is located on the left-hand side of the bulkhead in the engine compartment.
2 With the ignition switched off, disconnect the low tension (LT) wiring plug(s) from the computer module unit. Either one or two plugs will be present, depending on model.
3 Disconnect the HT lead from the ignition coil **(see illustration)**.
4 Remove the mounting bolts, and lift away the ignition coil.

Refitting

5 Refitting is a reversal of the removal procedure.

6.3 Disconnecting the HT lead from the ignition coil

7 Ignition computer module (carburettor and B18F engine models) - removal and refitting

Removal

1 The ignition computer module is located on the left-hand side of the bulkhead in the engine compartment; the ignition coil is attached to it.
2 To remove the module, first disconnect the battery negative lead.
3 Note the routing of the wiring harness leading to the module.
4 Disconnect the low tension (LT) wiring plug.
5 Disconnect the high tension (HT) lead from the ignition coil.
6 Disconnect the vacuum hose from the advance unit capsule on the module **(see illustration)**.
7 Remove the mounting bolts, and withdraw the module from the bulkhead **(see illustration)**.
8 If required, the ignition coil can be separated from the unit; do not attempt to remove the vacuum unit.

Refitting

9 Refitting is a reversal of the removal procedure.

7.6 Disconnect the vacuum hose (arrowed) . . .

8 Flywheel position/ speed sensor - removal and refitting

Removal

1 The angular position/speed sensor is used to monitor the TDC and BDC positions of the crankshaft, from the tooth gaps on the periphery of the flywheel (or driveplate).
2 The sensor is secured to the bellhousing by special shouldered bolts, and its position is preset in production to provide the required clearance. No adjustment of this clearance is necessary or possible.
3 Disconnect the battery negative terminal.
4 Trace the wiring back from the sensor, and disconnect it at the wiring plug.
5 Unscrew and remove the two mounting bolts securing the sensor to the top of the clutch bellhousing, and lift off the sensor. Note that the two retaining bolts are of the shouldered type, and must not be replaced with ordinary bolts. When handling the sensor, take care not to damage it.

Refitting

6 Refitting is a reversal of the removal procedure. If the old sensor is being refitted, clean any oil or dirt from it first.

7.7 . . . then unplug the connectors, remove the mounting bolts (arrowed) and remove the ignition computer module

Chapter 6
Clutch

Contents

Degrees of difficulty

Easy, suitable for novice with little experience		Fairly easy, suitable for beginner with some experience		Fairly difficult, suitable for competent DIY mechanic		Difficult, suitable for experienced DIY mechanic		Very difficult, suitable for expert DIY or professional	

Specifications

Type . . . . /	Single dry plate, with diaphragm spring, cable-operated

Clutch disc

Diameter	200 mm
Lining thickness (new, in compressed position)	7.7 ± 0.3 mm
Lining thickness (minimum)	6.4 ± 0.3 mm

Pressure plate

Maximum distortion (measured at the inner circumference)	0.2 mm

Torque wrench settings	Nm	lbf ft
Clutch cover	22	16
Gearbox-to-engine bolts	50	37
Pedal pivot bolt	20	15
Vibration damper	10	7

1 General information

All manual transmission models are equipped with a cable-operated, single dry plate diaphragm spring clutch assembly. The unit consists of a steel cover, which is dowelled and bolted to the rear face of the flywheel, containing the pressure plate and diaphragm spring **(see illustration)**.

The clutch disc is free to slide along the splined gearbox input shaft, and is held in position between the flywheel and the pressure plate by the pressure of the diaphragm spring. Friction lining material is riveted to the clutch disc, which has a spring-cushioned hub to absorb transmission shocks and help ensure a smooth take-up of the drive.

The clutch is actuated by a cable controlled by the clutch pedal. The clutch release mechanism consists of a release arm and bearing, which are in permanent contact with the fingers of the diaphragm spring.

Depressing the clutch pedal actuates the release arm by means of the cable. The arm pushes the release bearing against the diaphragm fingers, so moving the centre of the diaphragm spring inwards. As the centre of the spring is pushed in, the outside of the spring pivots out, so moving the pressure plate backwards and disengaging its grip on the clutch disc.

When the pedal is released, the diaphragm spring forces the pressure plate into contact with the friction linings on the clutch disc. The disc is now firmly sandwiched between the pressure plate and the flywheel, thus transmitting engine power to the gearbox.

Wear of the friction material on the clutch disc causes the normal rest position of the clutch pedal to gradually rise, and it is therefore necessary to adjust the pedal position at the specified service interval (see Chapter 1).

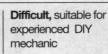

1.1 Clutch components

1 Gearbox input shaft bearing and clutch guide tube
2 Release bearing
3 Diaphragm spring
4 Pressure plate/cover assembly
5 Friction disc

6

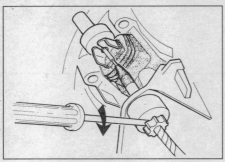

2.3 Using a screwdriver to release the plastic adjuster nut on the clutch cable

2.4a Clutch cable connection at the gearbox end

2.4b Removing the components from the end of the clutch cable

2 Clutch cable - removal and refitting

Removal

1 Disconnect the battery negative terminal.

2 Working in the engine compartment at the gearbox end of the cable, detach the vibration damper (where fitted).

3 On models where a plastic adjuster nut is fitted to the outer clutch cable near the gearbox bracket, insert a screwdriver between the adjuster nut and the plastic casing on the outer cable (see illustration). Turn the screwdriver clockwise, so that the adjuster nut turns as well and is released from its locked position. Continue to release the nut by hand until the inner cable is slack.

4 On models where the adjuster nut is on the end of the clutch inner cable, loosen the locknut, then unscrew and remove both the locknut and the adjuster nut (see illustrations). Where applicable, remove the vibration damper.

5 Unhook the end of the cable from the release fork.

6 Pull the cable, together with the plastic casing and grommet (where fitted), out of the gearbox mounting bracket; release the grommet from the bulkhead.

7 Release the cable from the attachment clamp on the bulkhead at the rear of the engine compartment (see illustration).

8 Working inside the car, remove the trim panels from the bottom of the facia for access to the clutch pedal.

9 Pull the inner cable towards the pedal, then release it from the plastic fitting.

10 Moving to the engine compartment again, pull the cable out of the bulkhead, and withdraw it completely. On turbo models, remove the damper (where fitted) from the end of the cable (see illustration).

Refitting

11 Before fitting the clutch cable, check if the two arrowed washers shown in the accompanying illustration are fitted (see illustration). If they are, check the chassis number of your car (refer to *Vehicle identification numbers* at the end of this manual) - if this is between numbers 503958 and 504778, the washers must **not** be refitted.

12 Thread the new cable through the bulkhead from the engine side, and route it so that there are no sharp bends or kinks. On 480 models, make sure that the cable is located correctly in the bulkhead opening.

13 The damper should be fitted on turbo models with a chassis number of 521204 onwards.

14 Inside the car, attach the inner cable to the plastic fitting on the pedal, making sure that it is engaged fully.

15 On models from chassis number 521204 onwards, fit the rubber grommet to the hole in the bulkhead.

16 Refit the trim panels to the bottom of the facia.

17 In the engine compartment, smear the grommet in the plastic casing with a little

soapy water or petroleum jelly, then insert the end of the cable through the mounting bracket on the gearbox and press in the plastic casing.

18 Engage the end of the inner cable with the release fork.

19 Where applicable, slide the vibration damper as far as possible onto the cable and tighten its screw.

20 Fit the cable to the attachment clamp on the bulkhead at the rear of the engine compartment.

21 Depress the clutch pedal several times to set the cable.

22 Finally, adjust the cable as described in Chapter 1, and reconnect the battery negative terminal.

3 Clutch pedal - removal and refitting

Removal

1 Working inside the car, remove the trim panels from the bottom of the facia for access to the clutch pedal.

2 Unhook the return springs from the clutch and brake pedals (see illustration).

3 Pull out the spring clip, and remove the clevis pin attaching the brake servo pushrod to the brake pedal.

4 Unscrew and remove the pivot bolt to release the clutch pedal, then disengage the inner cable from the plastic fitting on the end of the pedal (see illustration).

2.7 Clutch cable attachment clamp on the bulkhead (arrowed)

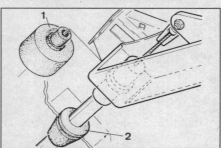

2.10 Clutch cable damper (1) and bulkhead grommet (2) - not fitted to all models

2.11 Two washers (arrowed) fitted to the end of the clutch cable on some models

3.2 Clutch and brake pedal return spring disconnection points, and pedal pivot bolt (arrowed)

3.4 Disconnecting the clutch inner cable from the plastic fitting on the end of the pedal

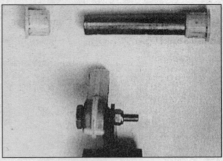

3.8 Clutch pedal steel shaft and nylon bushes, and plastic fitting for inner cable

Overhaul

5 Remove the nylon bushes, and take out the steel shaft.

6 Unbolt and remove the plastic cable fitting, and prise the rubber pad off the pedal.

7 Examine all the components for wear or damage, and renew as necessary.

8 Smear a little grease over the steel shaft, then fit the shaft and nylon bushes to the pedal, making sure that the bushes are the correct way round and pressed fully into the pedal **(see illustration)**.

9 Fit the plastic cable fitting with its open side facing to the left, to facilitate easy disconnection of the inner cable; tighten the nut.

10 Fit the new pedal rubber.

Refitting

11 Engage the end of the inner cable with the plastic fitting on the pedal.

12 Offer the pedal onto the pedal bracket, then insert the pivot bolt and tighten it to the specified torque. Check that both pedals move freely.

13 Reconnect the return springs to the clutch and brake pedals.

14 Locate the brake servo pushrod on the brake pedal, then insert the clevis pin and insert the spring clip.

15 Refit the trim panels to the bottom of the facia.

16 Check and if necessary adjust the pedal height/stroke, as described in Chapter 1.

4.8 Clutch cover retaining bolts

4 Clutch assembly - removal, inspection and refitting

> **Warning: Dust created by clutch wear and deposited on the clutch components may contain asbestos, which is a health hazard. DO NOT blow it out with compressed air or inhale any of it. DO NOT use petrol or petroleum-based solvents to clean off the dust. Brake system cleaner or methylated spirit should be used to flush the dust into a suitable receptacle. After the clutch components are wiped clean with rags, dispose of the contaminated rags and cleaner in a sealed, marked container.**

Removal

1 Access to the clutch may be gained in one of two ways. Either the engine/transmission unit can be removed as described in Chapter 2B, and the transmission separated from the engine, or the engine may be left in the car, and the transmission unit partially removed with reference to Chapter 7A. If the latter method is used, note the differences listed below, carry out the procedure described in Chapter 7A, then follow the procedure given here from paragraph 2 onwards. If the former method is used, follow the procedure given here from paragraph 8 onwards after separating the gearbox from the engine.

  a) Do not drain the gearbox oil.

  b) Do not remove the left-hand driveshaft from the gearbox; disconnect the stub axle and wishbone as described.

  c) Do not remove the steering gear heat shield.

  d) Do not remove the speedometer sensor on models with an electronic speedometer.

  e) Do not release the steering column lower universal joint or unscrew the subframe nuts.

  f) Do not disconnect the reversing light switch wiring at the gearbox.

2 Turn the steering wheel on full right-hand lock.

3 On B18E/F engines, push the starter motor heat shield as far to one side as possible.

4 Slide the right-hand driveshaft off its splines.

5 Support the weight of the gearbox on a trolley jack.

6 Separate the gearbox from the engine, and locate it between the chassis side member and the subframe. Note that the left-hand driveshaft must remain in the gearbox.

7 To prevent the top of the gearbox from falling back against the engine, insert a block of wood between them.

8 Having separated the gearbox from the engine, unscrew and remove the clutch cover retaining bolts, working in a diagonal sequence and slackening the bolts only a few turns at a time **(see illustration)**. Hold the flywheel stationary by placing a screwdriver over the front location dowel on the cylinder block and engaging it with the starter ring gear.

9 Ease the clutch cover off its locating dowels, and be prepared to catch the clutch disc which will drop out as the cover is removed **(see illustration)**. Note which way round the disc is fitted.

Inspection

10 With the clutch assembly removed, clean off all traces of dust using a dry cloth. This is best done outside or in a well-ventilated area, as the dust may contain asbestos, which is harmful and must not be inhaled. The clutch disc fitted as original equipment has friction linings which do not contain asbestos, but if the car has completed a moderate mileage, there is no guarantee that the original disc (or an asbestos-free replacement) is fitted.

6

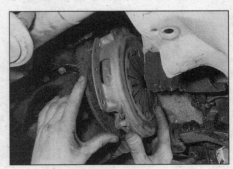

4.9 Removing the clutch cover and disc from the engine

4.16 Flywheel side markings on the clutch disc

4.22a Clutch alignment tool set

4.22b Using a clutch alignment tool to centralise the clutch disc

11 Examine the linings of the clutch disc for wear and loose rivets, and the disc itself for distortion, cracks, broken torsion springs and worn splines. The surface of the friction linings may be highly glazed, but, as long as the friction material pattern can be clearly seen, this is satisfactory. The disc must also be renewed if the lining thickness has worn down to, or just above, the level of the rivet heads.

12 If there is any sign of oil contamination, indicated by a continuous (or patchy) shiny black discolouration, the disc must be renewed, and the source of the contamination traced and rectified. This will be either a leaking crankshaft oil seal or gearbox input shaft oil seal, or both.

13 Check the machined faces of the flywheel and pressure plate. If either is grooved, or heavily scored, renewal is necessary. The pressure plate must also be renewed if any cracks are apparent, or if the diaphragm spring is damaged or its pressure suspect.

14 With the gearbox removed, it is advisable to check the condition of the release bearing, as described in Section 5.

 HAYNES HiNT *It is common practice to renew the release bearing as a matter of course whenever a new friction disc is fitted. Not to do so is false economy, since later renewal will mean taking everything out/apart again!*

Refitting

15 It is important that no oil or grease is

4.23 Tightening the clutch cover bolts

allowed to come into contact with the friction material of the clutch disc or the pressure plate and flywheel faces. It is advisable to refit the clutch assembly with clean hands, and to wipe down the pressure plate and flywheel faces with a clean, dry rag before assembly begins.

16 Begin reassembly by placing the clutch disc against the flywheel, with the side having the larger offset facing away from the flywheel. The flywheel side of a genuine Volvo disc should be marked as shown **(see illustration)**.

17 Place the clutch cover over the dowels. Refit the retaining bolts, and tighten them finger-tight so that the clutch disc is gripped, but can still be moved.

18 The clutch disc must now be centralised so that, when the engine and transmission are mated, the splines of the gearbox input shaft will pass through the splines in the centre of the clutch disc hub.

19 Centralisation can be carried out quite easily by inserting a round bar through the hole in the centre of the clutch disc, so that the end of the bar rests in the hole in the end of the crankshaft.

20 Moving the bar sideways (or up or down) will move the clutch disc in whichever direction is necessary to achieve centralisation.

21 Centralisation is easily judged by removing the bar and viewing the clutch disc hub in relation to the hole in the crankshaft. When the hole appears exactly in the centre of the clutch disc hub, all is correct.

22 An alternative (and more accurate) method of centralisation is to use a

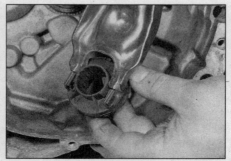

5.6 Connecting the release bearing to the release fork

commercially-available clutch aligning tool, obtainable from most motor accessory shops **(see illustrations)**.

23 Once the clutch is centralised, progressively tighten the cover bolts in a diagonal sequence to the torque setting given in the Specifications **(see illustration)**.

24 The transmission can now be refitted to the engine by reversing the removal procedure, referring to Chapter 2B or 7A as applicable.

---

5 Clutch release bearing - removal, inspection and refitting

Removal

1 To gain access to the release bearing, it is necessary to separate the engine and transmission, using one of the methods described in Section 4.

2 With the transmission removed from the engine, tilt the release fork, and slide the bearing assembly off the gearbox input shaft guide tube.

3 It may be possible to remove the bearing from its holder by releasing the four tags of the spring retainer, then lifting off the retainer and removing the bearing.

4 To remove the release fork, disengage the rubber cover, and then pull the fork upwards to release it from its ball pivot stud.

Inspection

5 Check the bearing for smoothness of operation, and renew it if there is any roughness or harshness as the bearing is spun. If the bearing is being inspected at the same time as a new friction disc is being fitted, fit a new release bearing as a matter of course.

Refitting

6 Refitting the release fork and release bearing is the reverse sequence to removal, but note the following points **(see illustration)**:
 a) *Lubricate the release fork pivot ball stud and the release bearing-to-diaphragm spring contact areas sparingly with molybdenum disulphide grease.*
 b) *Ensure that the release fork spring retainer locates behind the flat shoulder of the ball pivot stud.*

Chapter 7 Part A:
Manual gearbox

Contents

Degrees of difficulty

Easy, suitable for novice with little experience		**Fairly easy,** suitable for beginner with some experience		**Fairly difficult,** suitable for competent DIY mechanic		**Difficult,** suitable for experienced DIY mechanic		**Very difficult,** suitable for expert DIY or professional	

Specifications

Type . . . . Five forward speeds and reverse. All forward speeds with synchromesh. Final drive differential unit integral with main gearbox

Identification
Gearbox code number . . . . M50 series

Ratios (typical)
Final drive . . . . 4.07 : 1
1st . . . . 3.09 : 1
2nd . . . . 1.84 : 1
3rd . . . . 1.32 : 1
4th . . . . 0.97 : 1
5th . . . . 0.79 : 1
Reverse . . . . 3.55 : 1

Torque wrench settings

	Nm	lbf ft
ABS wheel sensor	11	8
Allen screw in gear lever	10	7
Filler/level plug	22	16
Gearbox drain plug	35	26
Gearbox/engine mountings	40	30
Gearbox-to-engine bolts	50	37
Gearchange control rod clamp bolt	20	15
Gearchange control rod to lever	20	15
Lower flywheel cover	27	20
Rear gearbox bracket	40	30
Rear gearbox-to-engine mounting	40	30
Reversing light switch	25	18
Speedometer sensor	25	18
Subframe nuts	90	66

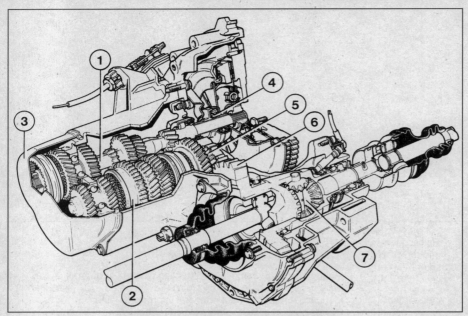

1.1 Cutaway view of the manual gearbox

1	Input (primary) shaft	3	End cover for 5th speed gear	5	Pinion gear
2	Output (secondary) shaft	4	Release bearing	6	Crown wheel
				7	Differential unit

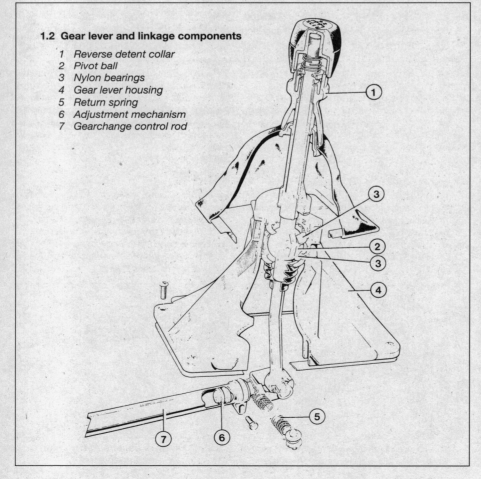

1.2 Gear lever and linkage components

1   Reverse detent collar
2   Pivot ball
3   Nylon bearings
4   Gear lever housing
5   Return spring
6   Adjustment mechanism
7   Gearchange control rod

1 General information

The manual gearbox is of five-speed type, with one reverse gear. Baulk ring synchromesh gear engagement is used on all the forward gears. The final drive (differential) unit is integral with the main gearbox, and is located at the rear of the gearbox casing (see illustration). The gearbox and differential both share the same lubricating oil.

Gear selection is by means of a floor-mounted lever, connected by a remote control housing and gearchange rod to the gearbox fork contact shaft (see illustration).

2 Gearchange linkage/mechanism - adjustment

Models up to chassis number 518449

1 To adjust the gearchange linkage accurately, it will be necessary to make up a tool to the dimensions shown (see illustration).
2 Apply the handbrake, then jack up the front of the car and support it on axle stands.
3 Loosen the clamp bolt on the gearchange rod at the bottom of the gear lever, and disconnect the return spring.
4 Inside the car, select second gear, and have an assistant hold it there. Move under the car, and place the gear lever on the gearbox in the second gear position. This can be found by moving the lever so that the gearbox shaft is pressed forwards until it is level with the resistance pin.
5 Locate the tool as shown in illustration 2.1, then position the gear lever in the special cut-out. Tighten the clamp bolt with the levers held in this position.
6 Remove the tool and reconnect the return spring.
7 Check that all gears can be selected easily.

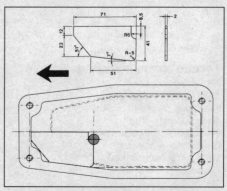

2.1 Tool for adjusting the gearchange linkage/mechanism on models up to chassis number 518449

Dimensions in mm

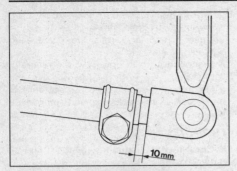

2.12 Gearchange linkage adjustment dimension for models from chassis number 518450

8 Lower the car to the ground.

Models from chassis number 518450

9 Apply the handbrake, then jack up the front of the car and support it on axle stands.
10 Loosen the clamp bolt on the gearchange rod at the bottom of the gear lever, and disconnect the return spring.
11 Inside the car, select first gear, and have an assistant hold it there. Move under the car, and place the gear lever on the gearbox in the first gear position. This can be found by moving the lever so that the gearbox shaft is pressed rearwards until it is level with the resistance pin.
12 Check that the dimension between the gearchange rod and the gear lever end fitting is as shown **(see illustration)**. If not, move the rod to its correct position.

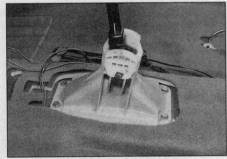

3.7 Gear lever assembly inside the car

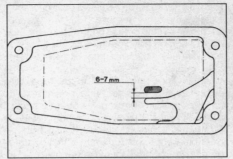

2.14 Interlock dimension for models from chassis number 518450

13 Lightly tighten the clamp bolt on the gearchange rod, making sure that the levers are not moved from their positions.
14 Release the gear lever, then move it to the right (ie towards the interlock). Check that the distance between the gear lever and interlock is between 6.0 and 7.0 mm **(see illustration)**.
15 Make any slight adjustments as necessary, then tighten the clamp bolt fully.
16 Check that all gears can be selected easily.
17 Lower the car to the ground.

---

3 Gearchange linkage/mechanism - removal, overhaul and refitting

Removal

1 Apply the handbrake, then jack up the front of the car and support on axle stands.
2 At the front end of the gearchange rod, pull the rubber dust cover forwards to give access to the bolt. Unscrew and remove the bolt, and recover the sleeve and nylon cover.
3 Disconnect the linkage from the lever, and move it to one side.
4 Where fitted, disconnect the return spring from the bottom of the gear lever.
5 Using an Allen key, remove the screw from the bottom of the gear lever **(see illustration)**. Remove the pin and remote control rod.
6 Unscrew the clamp bolt, and disconnect the remote control rod from the gear lever pivot joint. Remove the rod from under the car.

3.5 Gear linkage at the bottom of the gear lever - note Allen screw (arrowed)

7 Working inside the car, prise the gear lever boot from the centre console, and move the boot as far as possible up the gear lever **(see illustration)**.
8 Using circlip pliers, extract the circlip from the top of the plastic casing **(see illustration)**, then lift out the gear lever and remove from inside the car.

Overhaul

9 Mount the lower part of the gear lever in a vice, with the upper part facing downwards at an angle of about 45°.
10 Position a 28 mm open-ended spanner on the gear lever against the knob, then tap off the knob with a hammer **(see illustration)**. The gear lever boot can now be removed, followed by the other components. Note the position of the components for correct reassembly.
11 Clean all the components, and examine them for wear and damage.
12 Position the removed components and the boot on the gear lever in the correct order.
13 The knob must be positioned as shown **(see illustration)**. Prise out the gear position plate, then use a 20 mm drift to drive the knob onto the lever. Refit the plate.

Refitting

14 Refitting is a reversal of the removal procedure, noting the following points.
   a) *Lubricate the ball of the gear lever with a little petroleum jelly.*
   b) *Before fitting the Allen screw to the bottom of the gear lever, coat its threads with a little locking fluid.*

7A

3.8 Using circlip pliers to remove the circlip from the top of the plastic casing

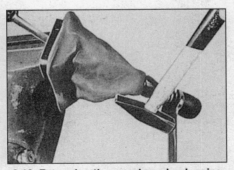

3.10 Removing the gear lever knob using an open-ended spanner and hammer

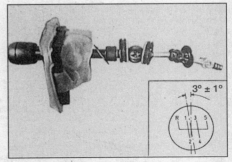

3.13 Gear lever assembly, showing knob setting diagram

c) Smear the sleeve and nylon cover with a little grease before fitting them.
d) The bolt securing the gearchange rod to the gearbox lever must be inserted from the top, and the nut tightened to the specified torque.
e) Before tightening the pinch-bolt on the rod, adjust the rod as described in Section 2.

4 Differential output oil seal (right-hand side) - renewal

1 Apply the handbrake, then jack up the front of the car and support it on axle stands. Remove the roadwheel on the appropriate side.
2 Remove the engine splash guard.
3 Position a suitable container beneath the gearbox, then unscrew the drain plug and allow the oil to drain. When most of the oil has drained, clean and refit the drain plug, tightening it securely. If necessary, renew the gasket on the drain plug.
4 Using a suitable punch, drive out the double roll pins securing the inner end of the right-hand driveshaft to the splined differential side gear.
5 On models with ABS, detach the wheel sensor wiring from the bracket.
6 Loosen the lower bolt securing the stub axle carrier to the bottom of the suspension strut. Unscrew and remove the upper bolt, then tilt the stub axle carrier, and disconnect the inner end of the driveshaft from the differential side gear. Take care not to damage the driveshaft rubber bellows or the flexible brake hydraulic hose. If necessary, loosen the clip and disconnect the brake hose from the bracket. Tie the driveshaft to one side.
7 Remove the driveshaft heat shield. On early models, it is retained by three bolts, but on later models with the larger heat shield, it is only necessary to loosen the top left-hand bolt and remove the other two bolts.
8 Wipe clean around the old oil seal, and measure its fitted depth below the casing edge. This is necessary to determine the correct fitted position of the new oil seal (if the special Volvo fitting tool is not available). Remove the O-ring from the side gear, then remove the old oil seal by first using a small drift to tap the outer edge of the seal inwards, so that the opposite edge of the seal tilts out of the casing. A pair of pliers or grips can then be used to pull the oil seal out of the casing. Take care not to damage the splines of the differential side gear.
9 Wipe clean the oil seal seating in the casing.
10 Before fitting the new oil seal, it is necessary to cover the splines on the side gear, to prevent damage to the oil seal lips. Ideally, a close-fitting plastic cap should be located on the splines, but if this is not available, wrap some adhesive tape over them to serve the same purpose.
11 Smear a little grease on the lips of the new oil seal and on the protective cap or tape.
12 Carefully locate the new oil seal over the side gear, and enter it squarely into the casing. Using a piece of metal tube or a socket, tap the oil seal into position to its correct depth, as previously noted. Volvo use a special tool to ensure that the oil seal is fitted to the correct depth, and it may be possible to hire this tool from a Volvo garage or tool hire shop **(see illustration)**.
13 Remove the plastic cap or adhesive tape, and apply a little grease to the splines of the side gear.
14 Locate a new O-ring on the side gear.
15 Engage the driveshaft with the splines on the side gear, so that the roll pin holes are correctly aligned. Tilt the stub axle carrier, and slide the driveshaft onto the side gear, making sure that it enters the oil seal centrally.
16 With the holes aligned, tap the double roll pins into position to secure. Seal the ends of the roll pins with a suitable sealant.
17 Refit the upper bolt securing the stub axle carrier to the bottom of the suspension strut, then tighten both upper and lower bolts to the specified torque (see Chapter 10).
18 Refit the driveshaft heat shield, and tighten the bolts.
19 Where applicable, refit the brake hydraulic hose to the bracket.
20 On models with ABS, refit the wheel sensor wiring to the bracket.
21 Refill the gearbox with the correct quantity and grade of oil, with reference to Chapter 1.
22 Refit the engine splash guard.
23 Refit the roadwheel, and lower the car to the ground.

5 Reversing light switch - removal and refitting

Removal

1 Apply the handbrake, then jack up the front of the car and support it on axle stands.
2 Remove the engine splash guard.
3 Position a suitable container beneath the

4.12 Using the Volvo tool (5316) to drive the oil seal into the gearbox casing

gearbox, then unscrew the drain plug and allow the oil to drain. When all of the oil has drained, clean and refit the drain plug, tightening it securely.
4 Disconnect the wiring from the reversing light switch.
5 Unscrew the switch from the bottom left-hand side of the gearbox, and remove the washer.

Refitting

6 Clean the location in the gearbox, and the threads of the switch.
7 Insert the switch (with a new washer) and tighten it fully.
8 Reconnect the wiring, and check the switch operation.
9 Refill the gearbox with the correct quantity and grade of oil, with reference to Chapter 1.
10 Refit the engine splash guard.
11 Lower the car to the ground.

6 Manual gearbox - removal and refitting (without subframe)

Note: This method of removing the gearbox should be used if the coolant hose from the radiator to the cylinder block at the bottom right-hand side of the engine compartment is routed under the subframe. The gearbox is removed from the left-hand side of the car between the subframe and the body.

Removal

1 The manual gearbox is removed from the left-hand side of the car, after disconnecting it from the engine. It will be necessary to have some form of lifting equipment available (such as an engine crane or suitable hoist) to lift the engine and retain it in this position while the gearbox is being removed. The gearbox itself is quite heavy, and because it is removed from the side of the car between the subframe and body, it is recommended that an assistant is available, as it will not be possible to attach a hoist to the gearbox or (initially) to place a trolley jack underneath it.
2 Loosen the left-hand front wheel bolts. Apply the handbrake, then jack up the front of the car and support it on axle stands. Remove the front left-hand roadwheel.
3 Turn the steering to the straight-ahead position, and engage the steering lock by removing the ignition key.
4 Where possible, open the bonnet to the service (fully-upright) position, which will allow better access to the engine compartment **(see illustration)**. On models with a separate bonnet stay, open the bonnet fully and attach a spring between the stay and the body.
5 Remove the engine splash guard.
6 Disconnect the battery negative and positive leads.
7 Unbolt and remove the battery clamp, then remove the battery from the car.

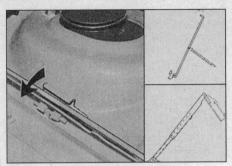

6.4 Opening the bonnet to the service position

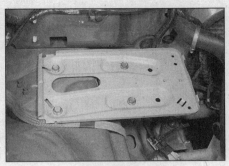

6.8 Battery tray

6.11a Disconnect the vacuum hose . . .

6.11b . . . loosen the clips, disconnect the control unit from the radiator ducting . . .

6.11c . . . and remove the control unit

6.18 Removing the flywheel speed/ position sensor from the top of the gearbox

8 Unscrew the four bolts and remove the battery tray from the engine compartment **(see illustration)**.

9 On turbo models, disconnect the wiring from the airflow meter at the connector, and disconnect the air duct from the airflow meter at the turbocharger end.

10 On all fuel injection models, remove the air cleaner assembly as described in Chapter 4B, together with the air inlet duct.

11 On B18K engines, remove the air inlet duct. Where fitted, disconnect and remove the carburettor cooling ducting and control unit **(see illustrations)**.

12 The starter motor must now be removed. Unbolt the clamp for the Pulsair lines (where fitted).

13 On B18E/F engines without a turbocharger, unscrew the bolt from the heat shield.

14 Unscrew and remove the three starter motor mounting bolts.

15 On B18E/F engines, cut the plastic cable-tie holding the speed sensor cable.

16 Remove the starter motor from the engine.

17 On models with a mechanical (non-electronic) speedometer, clean the area on the gearbox around the speedometer cable. Unhook the retaining pin behind the bracket, then remove the clip. Pull the speedometer cable carefully upwards, and remove it from the gearbox. Cover the hole with masking tape.

18 Unbolt the flywheel speed/position sensor from its location on the top of the gearbox, and suspend to one side **(see illustration)**.

19 Unscrew and remove the three uppermost bolts securing the gearbox to the engine **(see illustration)**. Note that the one nearest to the clutch release arm is shorter than the rest, and is coloured black on models from chassis number 505000 onwards.

20 Disconnect the clutch cable from the

gearbox, with reference to Chapter 6.

21 Attach a suitable hoist to the engine front and rear lifting eyes, and take the weight of the engine **(see illustration)**.

22 Position a suitable container beneath the gearbox, then unscrew the drain plug, and allow the oil to drain. When all of the oil has drained, clean and refit the drain plug, tightening it securely.

23 On models with ABS, unbolt the wheel sensor mounting bolt, and remove the sensor from the stub axle carrier by rotating it **(see illustration)**. Tie it to one side, out of the way.

24 Remove the front left-hand brake caliper, with reference to Chapter 9, but do not disconnect the brake hydraulic hose. Suspend the caliper from the front suspension strut with wire, making sure that the hose is not twisted or strained.

25 Where a side shield is fitted, unscrew the two screws and remove the shield.

7A

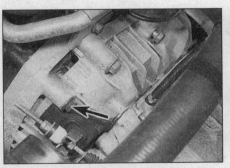

6.19 Gearbox-to-engine upper retaining bolts - shorter (black) bolt arrowed

6.21 Beam-type hoist fitted to the engine lifting eye (arrowed)

6.23 Front wheel sensor (arrowed) on models with ABS

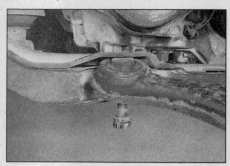

6.29a Unbolting the inner ends of the front suspension lower wishbone

6.29b Withdrawing the stub axle carrier assembly and driveshaft

6.31 Disconnecting the gearchange rod from the gearbox lever

26 Unscrew and remove the three bolts securing the left-hand driveshaft seal assembly to the gearbox, and pull out the assembly.

27 Unscrew and remove the two bolts securing the stub axle carrier to the left-hand front suspension strut.

28 Disconnect the steering tie-rod end from the steering arm on the stub axle carrier, with reference to Chapter 10.

29 Unbolt the inner ends of the front suspension lower arm from the subframe, and withdraw the stub axle carrier assembly from the car while supporting the inner end of the driveshaft **(see illustrations)**.

30 To prevent dust and dirt entering the gearbox, cover the driveshaft aperture with rags.

31 Disconnect the gearchange rod from the gearbox lever, by pulling back the rubber boot and unscrewing the bolt **(see illustration)**. Recover the sleeve and nylon cover, and tie the rod to one side.

32 Unbolt and remove the bracket between

the engine and gearbox; there are two bolts on the engine, and one bolt on the gearbox.

33 Unbolt and remove the lower cover from the bottom of the gearbox.

34 Remove the driveshaft heat shield. On early models, there are three bolts; on later models with a larger shield, it is only necessary to loosen the upper left-hand bolt and remove the two remaining bolts.

35 Remove the steering gear heat shield by unscrewing the mounting bolts located behind the exhaust system downpipes **(see illustration)**.

36 Working on the right-hand side driveshaft, use a suitable punch to drive out the roll pins. Slide the driveshaft outwards from the differential side gear as far as possible.

37 On models with an electronic speedometer, use an Allen key to unscrew the sensor mounting plate bolts on the gearbox **(see illustration)**. Carefully pull out the sensor, and place it to one side. Cover the

aperture in the gearbox with masking tape, to prevent dust and dirt entering.

38 On turbo models, unscrew the union nut and disconnect the turbocharger oil return line, then lower the engine sufficiently to unscrew the upper bolt from the starter motor heat shield **(see illustration)**. Now unscrew the bolt at the rear end, and pivot the heat shield to one side.

39 Disconnect the wiring from the starter motor by removing the nut and washer, and disconnecting the wiring at the connector. With all the wiring disconnected, pass the wiring through the eye on the gearbox, and place it to one side. On models with an electronic speedometer, also pass the speedometer sensor wiring through the eye.

40 Release the steering column universal joint from the pinion shaft on the steering gear, by unscrewing and removing the clamp bolt. If this bolt is rusted, apply some penetrating oil to it, and leave it to soak for some time. With the bolt removed, push the universal joint upwards as far as possible.

41 Unscrew the nut from the bottom of the left-hand front engine mounting, then unscrew the subframe nuts as far as possible.

480 models to chassis number 521500

42 Unscrew the two bolts securing the left-hand front engine mounting to the top of the subframe.

All other models

43 Unscrew the two bolts securing the left-hand rear engine mounting to the pad on the subframe **(see illustrations)**. It will be necessary to lower the engine to do this.

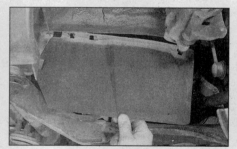

6.35 Removing the steering gear heat shield

6.37 Electronic speedometer sensor and mounting bolts

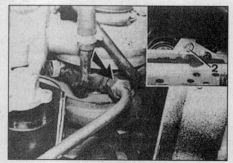

6.38 Oil return line union nut (arrowed), and heat shield (2) on turbo models

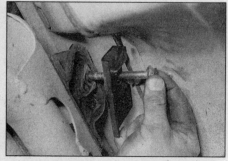

6.43a Removing the engine left-hand rear mounting bolts

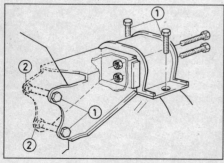

6.43b Gearbox-to-subframe mounting showing bolts (1) and nuts (2)

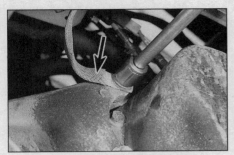

6.44 Unscrewing the engine left-hand front mounting bolts - note the earth strap (arrowed)

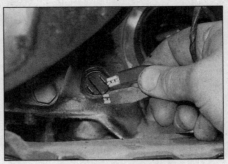

6.45 Disconnecting the wiring from the reversing light switch

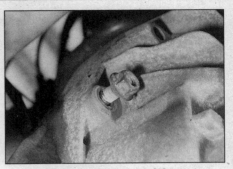

6.46 Gearbox front retaining nut

44 Unscrew the nut from the bottom of the front left-hand gearbox mounting, then raise the engine slightly, and unscrew the four bolts securing the mounting assembly to the gearbox. Note the location of the earth strap on one of the upper bolts **(see illustration)**. Remove the assembly.

45 Disconnect the wiring from the reversing light switch, and detach it from the clip on the gearbox **(see illustration)**.

46 Lift the rear of the engine a little, then unscrew and remove the nut or bolt securing the gearbox to the engine at the rear. Now unscrew and remove the bolt or nut located at the front of the engine **(see illustration)**.

480 models to chassis number 521500

47 Lift the engine slightly, then unscrew and remove the two bolts securing the gearbox mounting to the gearbox. Move the mounting to one side.

All models

48 Unscrew and remove the two nuts and washers from the subframe at the left-hand side of the engine.

49 Release the steering column universal joint from the steering gear pinion shaft.

50 The help of an assistant will now be required. If possible, place a trolley jack or axle stands to the left-hand side of the subframe, to act as further support for the gearbox when it is removed.

51 Check that the height of the engine is such that the gearbox can be withdrawn to the left, between the subframe and the body.

52 Separate the gearbox from the engine, at the same time pulling the right-hand driveshaft from the differential side gear **(see illustration)**. The careful use of a wide-bladed screwdriver may be necessary to release the gearbox from the dowels, but take care not to damage the mating face of the gearbox. With the gearbox separated from the engine, rest it on the subframe, then lift the gearbox out completely and place it on the floor.

Refitting

53 Refitting is a reversal of the removal procedure, but note the following additional points:

a) Apply a little high melting-point grease to the splines of the gearbox input shaft. Do not apply too much, however, otherwise there is the possibility of the grease contaminating the clutch friction disc. Make sure that the clutch release bearing is correctly located on the release arm.

b) When engaging the right-hand side driveshaft with the differential side gear, make sure that the roll pin holes are correctly aligned.

c) Fit new roll pins to the right-hand driveshaft, and seal the ends using a suitable sealant.

d) When refitting the starter motor heat shield to turbo models, first unscrew the bolt at the rear end of the starter, then fit the heat shield and tighten the rear bolt last.

e) When attaching the mountings to the subframe, make sure that the raised pin engages with the special hole in the subframe **(see illustration)**.

f) When refitting the sensor for the electronic speedometer, check the O-ring, and renew it if necessary.

g) When refitting the lower suspension arm bolts, make sure that the spacer sleeves are located in the subframe. The lower arm should be fitted first at the front, pressing the strut to the right and engaging the driveshaft with the differential sun gear; the rear mounting should then be fitted. Renew the two bolts securing the stub axle carrier to the strut. Delay tightening the lower arm bolts until the full weight of the car is on the suspension.

h) On models with ABS, smear a little grease

on the wheel sensor before fitting it to the stub axle carrier, and apply a little locking fluid to the threads of the retaining bolt before tightening it.

i) Refit and tighten the brake caliper mounting bolts with reference to Chapter 9.

j) Refill the gearbox with oil, and check the level, with reference to Chapter 1.

k) Adjust the clutch pedal/cable with reference to Chapter 1.

l) Tighten all nuts and bolts to the specified torque.

m) Check that all gears can be selected easily, and that the reversing light operates correctly.

7 Manual gearbox - removal and refitting (with subframe)

Note: *This method of removing the gearbox should be used if the coolant hose from the radiator to the cylinder block at the bottom right-hand side of the engine compartment is routed over the subframe. The gearbox is lowered to the ground, not withdrawn from the side of the car as in the previous Section.*

Removal

1 The manual gearbox is removed from under the car, after disconnecting it from the engine. It will be necessary to have some form of lifting equipment available (such as an engine crane or suitable hoist) to lift the engine and retain it in this position while the gearbox is being removed. The gearbox itself is quite

6.52 Removing the gearbox from the engine

6.53 Note the raised pin on the subframe mountings which must locate in the special hole

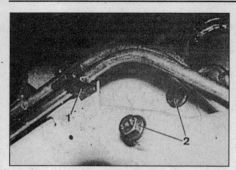

7.37 Power steering hydraulic fluid line clip (1) and steering gear mounting bolts (2) on the subframe

heavy, and a trolley jack or additional hoist will be required to lower it to the ground. It is also recommended that an assistant is available.

2 Apply the handbrake, then jack up the front of the car and support it on axle stands. Remove the front left-hand roadwheel.

3 Turn the steering to the straight-ahead position, and engage the steering lock by removing the ignition key.

4 Where possible, open the bonnet to the service (fully-upright) position, which will allow better access to the engine compartment. On models with a separate bonnet stay, open the bonnet fully, and attach a spring between the stay and the body.

5 Remove the engine splash guard.

6 Disconnect the battery negative and positive leads.

7 Unbolt and remove the battery clamp, then remove the battery from the car.

8 Unscrew the four bolts and remove the battery tray from the engine compartment.

9 On turbo models, disconnect the wiring from the airflow meter at the connector, and disconnect the air duct from the airflow meter at the turbocharger end.

10 On all fuel injection models, remove the air cleaner assembly as described in Chapter 4B, together with the air inlet duct.

11 On B18K engines, remove the air inlet duct. Where fitted, disconnect and remove the carburettor cooling ducting and control unit.

12 The starter motor must now be removed. Unbolt the clamp for the Pulsair lines (where fitted).

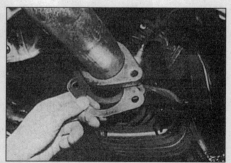

7.40 Disconnecting the front exhaust downpipe and removing the gasket on models with a catalytic converter

13 On engines without a turbocharger, unscrew the bolt from the heat shield.

14 Unscrew and remove the three starter motor mounting bolts.

15 Where applicable, cut the plastic cable-tie holding the speed sensor cable.

16 Remove the starter motor from the engine.

17 On models with a mechanical (non-electronic) speedometer, clean the area on the gearbox around the speedometer cable. Unhook the retaining pin behind the bracket, then remove the clip. Pull the speedometer cable carefully upwards, and remove it from the gearbox. Cover the hole with masking tape.

18 Unbolt the flywheel speed/position sensor from its location on the top of the gearbox, and suspend to one side.

19 Unscrew and remove the three uppermost bolts securing the gearbox to the engine. Note that the one nearest to the clutch release arm is shorter than the rest, and is coloured black on models from chassis number 505000 onwards.

20 Disconnect the clutch cable from the gearbox, with reference to Chapter 6.

21 Attach a suitable hoist to the engine front and rear lifting eyes, and take the weight of the engine.

22 Position a suitable container beneath the gearbox, then unscrew the drain plug and allow the oil to drain. When all of the oil has drained, clean and refit the drain plug, tightening it securely.

23 Where a side shield is fitted, unscrew the two screws and remove the shield.

24 On models with ABS, detach the wheel sensor wiring from the bracket.

25 Disconnect the gearchange rod from the gearbox lever, by pulling back the rubber boot and unscrewing the bolt. Recover the sleeve and nylon cover, and tie the rod to one side.

26 Unbolt and remove the bracket between the engine and gearbox; there are two bolts on the engine, and one bolt on the gearbox.

27 Unbolt and remove the lower cover from the bottom of the gearbox.

28 Remove the driveshaft heat shield. On early models, there are three bolts; on later models with a larger shield, it is only necessary to loosen the upper left-hand bolt and remove the two remaining bolts.

29 At the front of the subframe, cut through the plastic cable-ties holding the horn wiring, then unscrew the horn mounting bolts, and tie the horns to one side away from the subframe.

30 With the steering still straight-ahead, mark the position of the steering gear, so that it can be refitted in the same place. The rubber gaiters on each end of the steering gear should be equal in length.

31 Unscrew and remove the clamp bolt securing the steering column to the pinion shaft on the steering gear.

32 Unbolt the heat shield from the steering gear, then unscrew the four mounting bolts holding the steering gear to the subframe.

33 On models without power steering, remove the mounting brackets.

34 On power steering models, release the hydraulic fluid lines from the clips on the rear of the subframe.

35 Withdraw the steering gear, release the pinion shaft from the steering column universal joint, then remove it from the subframe.

36 Unscrew the engine-to-gearbox front mounting nuts, and also unbolt the earth lead.

37 On power steering models, release the hydraulic fluid lines from the clips on the subframe **(see illustration)**.

38 Unscrew the four subframe mounting nuts until there are just a few threads left on the studs.

39 Unscrew and remove the rear subframe-to-gearbox mounting bolts, taking care not to damage the brake lines which are in close proximity to them.

40 On models with a catalytic converter, disconnect the front exhaust downpipe by unscrewing the bolts and separating the flange. Remove the gasket (where fitted) **(see illustration)**.

41 On models without a catalytic converter, disconnect the front exhaust downpipe by unscrewing the clamp and tapping it to the rear. Unhook the rubber mounting straps, then tap the exhaust free and withdraw it from the front downpipe. Tie the exhaust pipe to one side.

42 Unscrew the four nuts attaching both front suspension lower arms to the subframe.

43 The subframe must now be removed. Remove the four nuts and washers from the subframe, and pull the subframe downwards. Remove the lower arm mounting bolts, then prise the lower arms from the subframe. The subframe can now be withdrawn over the front exhaust downpipe, and placed to one side.

44 Working on the right-hand side driveshaft, use a suitable punch to drive out the roll pins. Slide the driveshaft outwards from the differential side gear as far as possible. Do not support the driveshaft on the power steering hydraulic fluid lines.

45 On models with an electronic speedometer, use an Allen key to unscrew the sensor mounting plate bolts on the gearbox. Carefully pull out the sensor, and place it to one side. Cover the aperture in the gearbox with masking tape, to prevent dust and dirt entering.

46 On turbo models, unscrew the union nut and disconnect the turbocharger oil return line, then lower the engine sufficiently to unscrew the upper bolt from the starter motor heat shield. Now unscrew the bolt at the rear end, and pivot the heat shield to one side.

47 Disconnect the wiring from the starter motor by removing the nut and washer, and disconnecting the wiring at the connector. With all the wiring disconnected, pass the wiring through the eye on the gearbox, and

place it to one side. On models with an electronic speedometer, also pass the speedometer sensor wiring through the eye.

48 Disconnect the wiring from the reversing light switch, and detach it from the clip on the gearbox.

49 Unscrew and remove the three bolts securing the left-hand driveshaft seal assembly to the gearbox, and pull out the assembly.

50 Lift the rear of the engine a little, then unscrew and remove the nut or bolt securing the gearbox to the engine at the rear. Now unscrew and remove the bolt located below the starter motor at the front of the engine.

51 The help of an assistant will now be required. First place a trolley jack under the gearbox, and take its weight. Ideally, some form of cradle should be used, to hold the gearbox firmly and prevent any damage to the casing.

52 Separate the gearbox from the engine, at the same time pulling the right-hand driveshaft from the differential side gear. The careful use of a wide-bladed screwdriver may be necessary to release the gearbox from the dowels, but take care not to damage the mating face of the gearbox. Tie the right-hand driveshaft to one side, but (where applicable) do not support it on the power steering hydraulic fluid lines.

53 Lower the gearbox from the engine compartment, then move it under the engine and disconnect the left-hand driveshaft, taking care not to damage the driveshaft joint. Tie the driveshaft to one side, or support it on an axle stand. To prevent dust and dirt entering the gearbox, cover the driveshaft aperture with rags. Withdraw the gearbox from under the car.

Refitting

54 Refitting is a reversal of the removal procedure, but note the following additional points.

a) Apply a little high melting-point grease to the splines of the gearbox input shaft. Do not apply too much, however, otherwise there is the possibility of the grease contaminating the clutch friction disc. Make sure that the clutch release bearing is correctly located on the release arm.

b) When engaging the right-hand side driveshaft with the differential side gear, make sure that the roll pin holes are correctly aligned.

c) Fit new roll pins to the right-hand driveshaft, and seal the ends using a suitable sealant.

d) When refitting the starter motor heat shield to turbo models, first unscrew the bolt at the rear end of the starter, then fit the heat shield and tighten the rear bolt last.

e) When attaching the mountings to the subframe, make sure that the raised pin engages with the special hole in the subframe.

f) When refitting the sensor for the electronic speedometer, check the O-ring, and renew it if necessary.

g) When refitting the subframe, first locate it over the exhaust downpipe. On power steering models, lift the lines over the rear mounting pad. Locate the lower arms on the subframe, and insert the bolts loosely. With the rear engine mounting fitted to the subframe, tighten the subframe bolts, but make sure that there are no lines between the subframe and the body at the front right-hand mounting.

h) On models with a catalytic converter, renew the gasket at the flange if necessary. The exhaust clamp must be located in the middle of the slot before tightening the bolts.

i) Refit the horn wiring to the subframe, using new plastic cable-ties.

j) Delay tightening the lower arm bolts until the full weight of the car is on the suspension.

k) Refill the gearbox with oil, and check the level, with reference to Chapter 1.

l) Adjust the clutch pedal/cable with reference to Chapter 1.

m) Tighten all nuts and bolts to the specified torque.

n) Check that all gears can be selected easily, and that the reversing light operates correctly. If necessary, adjust the gearchange linkage as described in Section 2.

8 Manual gearbox overhaul - general information

Overhauling a manual gearbox is a difficult and involved job for the DIY home mechanic. In addition to dismantling and reassembling many small parts, clearances must be precisely measured and, if necessary, changed by selecting shims and spacers. Gearbox internal components are also often difficult to obtain, and in many instances, extremely expensive. Because of this, if the gearbox develops a fault or becomes noisy, the best course of action is to have the unit overhauled by a specialist repairer, or to obtain an exchange reconditioned unit.

Nevertheless, it is not impossible for the more experienced mechanic to overhaul a gearbox, if the special tools are available and the job is done in a deliberate step-by-step manner so that nothing is overlooked.

The tools necessary for an overhaul include internal and external circlip pliers, bearing pullers, a slide hammer, a set of pin punches, a dial test indicator, and possibly a hydraulic press. In addition, a large, sturdy workbench and a vice will be required.

During dismantling of the gearbox, refer to the accompanying illustrations, and make careful notes of how each component is fitted, to make reassembly easier and more accurate.

Before dismantling the gearbox, it will help if you have some idea what area of the unit is malfunctioning. Certain problems can be closely related to specific areas in the gearbox, which can make component examination and replacement easier. Refer to *Fault finding* at the end of this manual for more information.

7A

Chapter 7 Part B:
Automatic transmission

Contents

Degrees of difficulty

Easy, suitable for novice with little experience	Fairly easy, suitable for beginner with some experience	Fairly difficult, suitable for competent DIY mechanic	Difficult, suitable for experienced DIY mechanic	Very difficult, suitable for expert DIY or professional

Specifications

General

Type . . . . Four forward speeds and reverse. Final drive differential integral with transmission

Designation . . . . ZF 4 HP 14Q

Ratios

1st . . . . 2.41 : 1
2nd . . . . 1.37 : 1
3rd . . . . 1.00 : 1 (40% hydraulic, 60% mechanical)
4th . . . . 0.74 : 1 (100% mechanical)
Reverse . . . . 2.83 : 1
Final drive:
  B18FT . . . . 4.225 : 1
  All other models . . . . 4.405 : 1

Torque wrench settings

	Nm	lbf ft
ABS wheel sensor	11	8
Dipstick tube threaded sleeve	90	66
Dipstick tube union	50	37
Drain plugs	15	11
Driveplate	50	37
Fluid cooler	50	37
Oil pan	10	7
Speedometer sensor	25	18
Starter inhibitor/reversing light switch	40	30
Torque converter	21	15
Torque converter cover plate	27	20
Transmission front mounting	40	30
Transmission mounting bolts/nuts	50	37
Valve body bolts	10	7

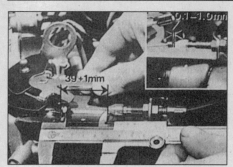

2.6 Kickdown cable adjustment

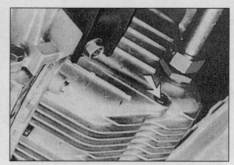

3.10 Transmission fluid drain plug

3.12 Dipstick tube mounting nut (4) and union nut (5)

1 General information

A four-speed fully-automatic transmission is available as an option on certain models. The transmission consists of a torque converter, an epicyclic geartrain, and hydraulically-operated brake bands.

The torque converter provides a fluid coupling between the engine and transmission, and acts as an automatic clutch. It also provides a degree of torque multiplication when accelerating.

The epicyclic geartrain provides the four forward and one reverse gear ratios, according to which of its component parts are held stationary or allowed to turn. The components of the geartrain are held or released by brake bands, which are activated by a hydraulic control unit. A pump within the transmission provides the necessary hydraulic pressure to operate the transmission brakes and clutches.

Due to the complexity of the automatic transmission, any repair or overhaul work must be left to a Volvo dealer with the necessary special equipment for fault diagnosis and repair. Refer to *Fault finding* at the end of this manual for more information.

2 Kickdown cable - adjustment

1 First check that the throttle cable and linkage is in good condition, and operating correctly. The accelerator cable should be in its rest (idle) position.
2 Using vernier calipers, check the distance between the end of the kickdown outer cable and the stop on the inner cable - this should be between 0.1 and 1.0 mm.
3 Open the throttle valve operating cam until slight resistance is felt - this is the kickdown point. Holding the cam in this position, measure the distance between the end of the outer cable and the stop on the inner cable - this should be 39.0 ± 1.0 mm.
4 If the distance measured in paragraph 2

was incorrect, loosen the locknut on the outer cable, and reposition the outer cable as necessary to bring the distance within the correct tolerance. Tighten the locknut after making an adjustment.
5 If the distance measured in paragraph 3 was incorrect, the stop on the inner cable must be renewed, and a new one located in the correct position. First remove the stop, taking care not to damage the inner cable.
6 Loosely locate the new stop on the inner cable, then turn the throttle valve operating cam until the slight resistance is felt (indicating the kickdown point). Hold the cam at this position without moving it, then position the stop at a distance of 39.0 ± 1.0 mm from the end of the outer cable **(see illustration)**. Tighten the stop on to the inner cable in this position.
7 With the throttle cam fully released, check and if necessary adjust the distance between the end of the kickdown outer cable and the stop on the inner cable, as described in paragraph 4.

3 Kickdown cable - removal and refitting

Removal

1 Due the risk of introducing dust and dirt into the hydraulic system of the automatic transmission, it is recommended that the engine compartment is thoroughly cleaned before removing the transmission oil pan.

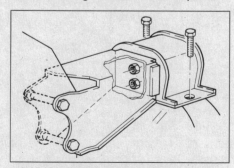

3.13 Automatic transmission mounting bracket and bolts

2 Turn the front wheels to the straight-ahead position, and remove the ignition key to engage the steering lock.
3 Remove the battery and battery tray, with reference to Chapter 5A.
4 Remove the air cleaner assembly, with reference to Chapter 4A or 4B, as applicable.
5 Attach a suitable hoist to the engine, and take its weight.
6 Disconnect the front left-hand mounting from the gearbox, by unscrewing the nut at the top and the two middle bolts on top of the oil pan.
7 Apply the handbrake, then jack up the front of the car and support on axle stands.
8 Remove the engine splash guard.
9 Remove the two screws, and pull the left-hand side shield away from the body.
10 Position a suitable container beneath the transmission oil pan, then unscrew the drain plug, and allow the fluid to drain completely **(see illustration)**.

 Warning: If the engine/ transmission is still warm, take precautions against scalding, as the fluid may still be very hot.

11 With all the fluid drained, refit and tighten the drain plug. Renew the sealing washer if necessary.
12 Unscrew and remove the bolt securing the dipstick tube to the cylinder block. Unscrew the union nut securing the dipstick tube to the oil pan, and remove the tube **(see illustration)**. Use two spanners to do this, using one to hold the sleeve stationary.
13 Unscrew the two bolts securing the transmission mounting to the subframe **(see illustration)**.
14 The steering gear must now be detached from the subframe. To do this, first remove the heat shield, and unscrew the four nuts and bolts. On models without power steering, remove the brackets.
15 At the rear of the subframe, release the steering fluid pipes from the clips **(see illustration)**.
16 Detach the steering gear from the subframe, making sure that the pinion shaft is not disconnected from the steering column. Tie the steering gear to one side.
17 Cut the two plastic cable-ties retaining the horn wiring to the subframe.

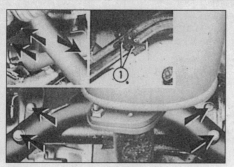

3.15 Steering gear mounting bolts and line clips (1)

3.23 Oil pan bolt locations

A 35 mm   B 25 mm   C 20 mm

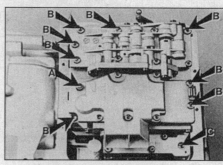

3.25 Valve body bolt locations

A 80 mm   B 75 mm   C 35 mm

18 Unscrew the mounting bolt for the right-hand horn, and pivot the horn towards the front panel.

19 Unscrew the bottom nut securing the engine mounting to the subframe.

20 Unscrew the subframe right-hand rear mounting nut until it is held by just a few threads. Unscrew the three remaining nuts, and remove the retaining plates.

21 Pull the subframe downwards at the front left-hand side. Recover the shims from the mountings, and put them in a safe place.

22 Unscrew the bottom nut, and remove the gearbox mounting from the subframe.

23 Unscrew and remove the bolts from the oil pan, then tap the side of the pan to release it from the transmission. Note there are three lengths of bolt - record their positions carefully for refitting **(see illustration)**. Withdraw the oil pan to the centre, then downwards, and place it to one side.

24 Move the selector lever inside the car to position P, then depress the accelerator pedal to its middle position, and retain it by suitable means.

25 Using a Torx key, unscrew the ten bolts securing the valve body, then remove the body assembly. Note that the bolts are of three different sizes - record their positions carefully for refitting **(see illustration)**.

26 Rotate the kickdown cam half a turn, and disengage the cable end. Pull the outer cable plastic sleeve out of the casing **(see illustration)**.

27 At the engine end of the cable, loosen the locknut on the outer cable adjustment, and disconnect the cable from the support bracket. Release the inner cable from the cam **(see illustration)**.

28 Remove the cable from the engine compartment.

Refitting

29 Refitting is a reversal of the removal procedure, but note the following additional points:

a) When fitting the outer cable to the transmission, check that the O-ring is correctly located on the plastic sleeve.

b) Ensure that the transmission end of the inner cable remains on its cam during the fitting of the cable. Pull the engine-end inner cable out, and retain it in this position with a pair of grips, taking care not to damage the inner cable.

c) When fitting the valve body, make sure that the mating faces are perfectly clean. Pull the selector lever valve out of the valve body, and hold it in this position with a length of welding wire. Locate the valve body so that the lever valve is over the lug of the gear selector disc **(see illustration)**. With the valve body in position, remove the welding rod, and insert two bolts to hold it. Move the gear selector disc backwards and forwards through the gear selector positions, and check whether the selector lever valve

moves with it. If all is correct, insert and tighten the remaining bolts in a diagonal and progressive sequence.

d) Always fit a new gasket to the oil pan.

e) Tighten all nuts and bolts to the specified torque.

f) Adjust the kickdown cable as described in Section 2.

g) Fill the transmission with the correct quantity of fluid, with reference to Chapter 1.

4   Selector cable -
adjustment

1 Select position P, then release the handbrake and check that the transmission is locked by attempting to push the car.

2 Apply the handbrake, then jack up the front of the car and support on axle stands.

3 Remove the battery and battery tray, with reference to Chapter 5A.

4 Prise the selector cable end fitting off the lever on the transmission.

5 Press the transmission lever forwards as far as possible, so that it is in its P position.

6 With the selector lever inside the car still at position P, check that the cable end fitting locates exactly over the ball on the lever. If it

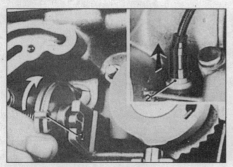

3.26 Disconnecting the kickdown cable at the transmission end

1 Cable end fitting
2 Cable plastic sleeve

3.27 Disconnecting the kickdown cable at the throttle housing end

1 Locknut   2 Bracket   3 Cam

3.29 Selector lever valve (1) and lug (2)

7B

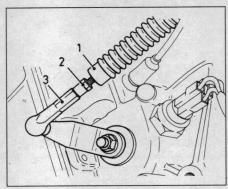

4.7 Selector cable adjustment

1   Rubber gaiter   3   End fitting
2   Locknut

does, then the cable is adjusted correctly, and the end fitting may be pressed on to the lever again.

7 If the end fitting is not exactly over the ball, then the cable must be adjusted as follows. Pull back the rubber gaiter for access to the adjustment nut, then release the locknut and adjust the nut as required until the end fitting is located over the ball. Tighten the locknut, and refit the rubber gaiter **(see illustration)**.

8 Press the end fitting on to the lever ball after making the adjustment.

9 Refit the battery tray and battery.

10 Lower the car to the ground, and check that all positions can be selected easily.

---

5   Selector cable -
removal and refitting

Removal

1 Remove the battery and battery tray, with reference to Chapter 5A.

2 Remove the air cleaner assembly, with reference to Chapter 4A or 4B, as applicable.

3 Move the selector lever to position P.

4 Apply the handbrake, then jack up the front of the car and support on axle stands.

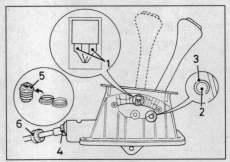

5.8 Selector cable attachment at the lever end

1   Operating pin   4   Nut
2   Pin   5   Sleeve
3   Opening   6   Rubber grommet

---

5 Pull the end fitting on the selector cable from the ball on the transmission lever.

6 At the support bracket on the transmission, loosen the locknut and disconnect the cable from the bracket.

7 Working inside the car, remove the front and rear centre console sections, with reference to Chapter 11.

8 Remove the operating pin by depressing its two ends **(see illustration)**.

9 Move the selector lever to position 1.

10 Using a suitable drift through the hole in the selector lever housing, press the pin out of the lever, and remove the locking pawl.

11 At the front of the housing, loosen the nut and withdraw the cable from the selector lever housing.

12 Remove the sleeve from the left-hand air duct pipe.

13 Press the cable grommet from the bulkhead, then pull the cable into the passenger compartment and withdraw it from the car.

Refitting

14 Refitting is a reversal of the removal procedure, but note the following additional points:

 a) Move the selector lever to position N before refitting the sleeve to the left-hand air duct pipe.
 b) Adjust the cable with reference to Section 4.

---

6   Selector assembly -
removal and refitting

Removal

1 Working inside the car, remove the front and rear centre console sections, with reference to Chapter 11.

2 Refer to illustration 5.8, and remove the operating pin by depressing its two ends.

3 Move the selector lever to position 1.

4 Using a suitable drift through the hole in the selector lever housing, press the pin out of the lever, and remove the locking pawl.

5 At the front of the housing, loosen the nut and withdraw the cable from the selector lever housing.

7.1 Starter inhibitor/reversing light switch location

---

6 Disconnect the wiring for the selector illumination, then unbolt and remove the selector lever housing from the floor.

Refitting

7 Refitting is a reversal of the removal procedure, but adjust the selector cable as described in Section 4.

---

7   Starter inhibitor/reversing
light switch - removal,
refitting and adjustment

Removal

1 The starter inhibitor/reversing light switch is located next to the selector lever on the side of the automatic transmission **(see illustration)**. First remove the battery and battery tray, as described in Chapter 5A.

2 Remove the air cleaner assembly, as described in Chapter 4A or 4B, as applicable.

3 Disconnect the two wires from the switch, then unscrew the switch from the transmission casing; recover the shim.

Refitting and adjustment

4 Refitting is a reversal of the removal procedure, but refit the shim, tighten the switch to the correct torque wrench setting, and check the adjustment as follows.

5 With position P or N selected, the switch contacts should be closed. Connect an ohmmeter across terminals A and B on the switch **(see illustration)**. If the resistance is infinite, the internal contacts are open, and a thicker shim should be fitted. If the resistance is zero, the internal contacts are closed, and the shim thickness is correct. Select both P and N positions in turn when making the check.

6 Refit the air cleaner assembly and the battery.

7 The following check should be made with the automatic transmission at its normal working temperature, and the car on level ground.

8 Depress the brake pedal and release the handbrake, then select position D. Turn the ignition key to the starting position, and hold it there.

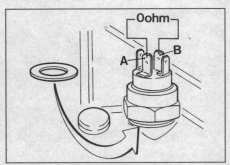

7.5 Starter inhibitor/reversing light switch terminals A and B, and adjustment shim location

9 Move the selector lever slowly to position N until the engine starts, then release the ignition key and let the engine idle. Release the footbrake, and check whether the car creeps forward.

10 Repeat paragraphs 8 and 9, but this time start from position R.

11 If the car creeps, carry out the switch adjustment procedure again.

8 Oil seals - renewal

Differential side (driveshaft) oil seals

1 Loosen the front wheel bolts. Apply the handbrake, then jack up the front of the car and support on axle stands. Remove the front wheels.

2 Remove the splash guard from under the engine.

3 Position a suitable container beneath the transmission, then unscrew the drain plug and drain the fluid. Refit and tighten the drain plug on completion.

 Warning: Take suitable precautions to prevent scalding, as the fluid may be very hot.

4 If renewing the right-hand oil seal, unbolt and remove the heat shield above the right-hand side driveshaft **(see illustration)**.

5 Disconnect the right-hand side driveshaft from the transmission by careful levering; Volvo technicians use a special tool to do this **(see illustration)**, but a similar tool can be made up to serve the same purpose. Do not attempt to pull the driveshaft out of the transmission.

6 If renewing the left-hand oil seal, disconnect the left-hand side driveshaft from the transmission, levering carefully, using the same method as described in the previous paragraph (the lever should be located on the stiffened rib on the transmission casing). If the driveshaft fails to release with moderate pressure, it can be driven out from the right-hand side of the differential after removing the right-hand driveshaft.

7 On models fitted with ABS, remove the wheel sensor from the stub axle carrier by unscrewing the bolt.

8 Disconnect the tie-rod end from the stub axle carrier, with reference to Chapter 10.

9 Unscrew and remove the two bolts securing the stub axle carrier to the front suspension strut. Also unscrew and remove the two bolts securing the lower suspension balljoint to the lower arm. Support the stub axle and driveshaft on an axle stand.

10 Position a drip tray beneath the transmission. Pull the driveshaft from the transmission, and rest it on the subframe. Take care not to strain the flexible brake hydraulic fluid hose or the driveshaft rubber boots.

11 Wipe clean around the old oil seal, and

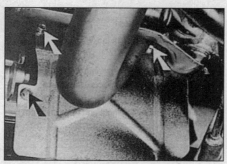

8.4 Heat shield mounting bolts over the right-hand driveshaft

measure its fitted depth below the casing edge. This is necessary to determine the correct fitted position of the new oil seal (if the special Volvo fitting tool is not available).

12 Remove the old oil seal by first using a small drift to tap the outer edge of the seal inwards, so that the opposite edge of the seal tilts out of the casing. A pair of pliers or grips can then be used to pull the oil seal out of the casing. Take care not to damage the splines of the differential side gear.

13 Wipe clean the oil seal seating in the casing.

14 Smear a little grease on the lips of the new oil seal, then enter it squarely into the casing. Using a piece of metal tube or a socket, tap the oil seal into position to its correct depth, as previously noted. Volvo use a special tool to ensure that the oil seal is fitted to the correct depth, and it may be possible to hire this tool from a Volvo garage or tool hire shop.

15 To ensure effective locking of the driveshaft to the differential side gear, it is recommended that the circlip is always renewed after removing the driveshaft.

16 Insert the driveshaft into the differential, taking care not to damage the oil seal lips. Press it in fully, to ensure that the circlip engages with the groove.

17 Locate the lower suspension balljoint on the lower arm, then insert the bolts and tighten to the specified torque (Chapter 10).

18 Refit the stub axle carrier to the front suspension strut, and tighten the bolts to the specified torque (the bolts should be renewed, as a safety precaution) (Chapter 10).

19 Connect the tie-rod end to the stub axle

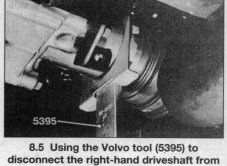

8.5 Using the Volvo tool (5395) to disconnect the right-hand driveshaft from the transmission

carrier, with reference to Chapter 10.

20 On models fitted with ABS, smear a little grease on the wheel sensor, and press it into the stub axle carrier. Apply some locking fluid to the threads of the bolt, then insert and tighten it to the specified torque (Chapter 9).

21 Locate the flexible brake hose in the special recess in the front suspension strut.

22 Refit the front roadwheels.

23 On the right-hand side, refit the heat shield and tighten the bolts.

24 Refit the splash guard under the engine.

25 Lower the car to the ground.

26 Fill the automatic transmission with the correct amount of fluid, with reference to Chapter 1.

Input shaft (torque converter) oil seal

27 Remove the transmission with reference to Section 10.

28 Position the transmission on its left-hand end, so that the torque converter is uppermost and horizontal.

29 Where fitted, remove the torque converter retaining plate. Insert two bolts in diagonally-opposite holes in the torque converter, and use these to pull the torque converter out of the transmission casing **(see illustration)**. Keep the torque converter horizontal while removing it, then pour out the fluid into a suitable container.

30 Note the fitted position of the old oil seal, so that the new one can be fitted the same way.

31 Using a hooked instrument, extract the old oil seal from the centre of the transmission bellhousing **(see illustration)**.

8.29 Insert two bolts in diagonally-opposite holes, and pull out the torque converter

8.31 Hooking out the old seal using the special Volvo tool (5919)

7B

10.12 Fluid cooler mounting bolt (9)

32 Wipe clean the oil seal location in the casing, then smear a little grease on the lips of the new oil seal, and press it in using a metal tube to keep it square.

33 Wipe clean the oil seal bearing surface of the torque converter, and make sure that there are no traces of dirt which may find its way into the hydraulic system.

34 Lower the torque converter into the bellhousing and onto the input shafts, twisting it as necessary until it engages with the splines.

35 Fit the retaining plate to hold the torque converter in the bellhousing.

9 Fluid cooler - general information

A fluid cooler is located on the top of the automatic transmission bellhousing, towards the front. It is of canister type, and is connected to the engine cooling system by two hoses. The cooler transfers heat from the transmission hydraulic fluid to the engine coolant.

10 Automatic transmission - removal and refitting

Removal

1 Due the risk of introducing dust and dirt into the hydraulic system of the automatic

10.15 Upper bolts securing the automatic transmission to the engine (arrowed)

10.14 Flywheel speed/position sensor bolts (arrowed)

transmission, it is recommended that the engine compartment is thoroughly cleaned before commencing work.

2 Remove the battery and battery tray, with reference to Chapter 5A.

3 Remove the air cleaner assembly, with reference to Chapter 4A or 4B, as applicable.

4 Pull out the automatic transmission fluid level dipstick.

5 Loosen the adjustment nut on the kickdown cable ferrule, remove the cable from the support bracket, then release the inner cable from the cam.

6 Move the selector lever to position P.

7 Disconnect the end of the selector cable from the balljoint on the transmission lever, then unscrew the locknut and release the cable from the bracket on the side of the transmission.

8 Unscrew the earth cable bolt.

9 Unscrew the two bolts securing the wiring harness bracket to the transmission, and move the bracket to one side.

10 On models where the lower coolant hose is routed below the subframe, drain the cooling system with reference to Chapter 1, then disconnect the bottom hose from the radiator.

11 On models where the lower coolant hose is routed above the subframe, use hose clamps to clamp the two coolant hoses near the transmission fluid cooler.

12 Loosen the fluid cooler mounting bolt one full turn **(see illustration)**. Release the hose clips, and disconnect the two hoses from the fluid cooler.

13 Disconnect the two wires from the starter/inhibitor switch.

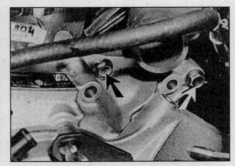

10.16 Starter motor upper mounting bolts (arrowed)

14 Unscrew the two bolts securing the flywheel speed/position sensor to the top of the transmission **(see illustration)**, and move the sensor to one side.

15 Unscrew and remove the two top bolts securing the transmission to the engine **(see illustration)**. The bolt located by the fluid cooler can only be loosened - it is not possible to remove this bolt at this stage, as the fluid cooler is in the way.

16 Unscrew and remove the two starter motor upper bolts **(see illustration)**.

17 Loosen the left-hand front wheel bolts. Apply the handbrake firmly, then jack up the front of the car and support on axle stands.

18 Remove the engine splash guard.

19 Attach a suitable hoist to the engine, and take its weight.

20 Remove the left-hand front roadwheel, then unbolt and remove the side shield from under the wheel arch.

21 Position a suitable container beneath the transmission, then unscrew the drain plug and drain the fluid. Refit and tighten the drain plug on completion.

 Warning: Take suitable precautions to prevent scalding, as the fluid may be very hot.

22 Unscrew and remove the three bolts, and remove the heat shield from above the right-hand driveshaft.

23 Remove the heat shield from the steering gear. Unscrew the four bolts securing the steering gear to the subframe; on models without power steering, remove the brackets. Disconnect the hydraulic pipes from the clips at the rear of the subframe. Remove the steering gear from the subframe, making sure that the two sections of the steering column are not separated; tie the steering gear to one side.

24 Disconnect both driveshafts from the transmission, with reference to Section 8.

25 Cut the two plastic cable-ties securing the horn wiring to the subframe. Unscrew the right-hand horn mounting bolt, and swivel the horn towards the front panel.

26 Unscrew and remove the mounting nuts from the two front engine mountings.

27 Unscrew the four subframe mounting nuts until they are held by just a few threads.

28 On power steering models, disconnect the hydraulic pipes from the clips at the rear of the subframe.

29 Unscrew the two bolts securing the transmission mounting to the subframe, then unscrew the two bolts securing the mounting to the transmission. Do not remove the mounting at this stage.

30 Disconnect the exhaust downpipe from the intermediate section, with reference to Chapter 4C.

31 Unscrew the nuts securing the inner ends of the front suspension lower arms to the subframe.

32 Unscrew the nuts from the subframe mounting bolts, and recover the washers. Pull the subframe downwards, making sure that

10.37 Torque converter cover plate bolts (arrowed)

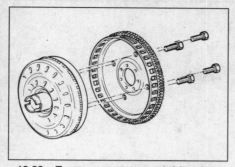

10.38a Torque converter and driveplate

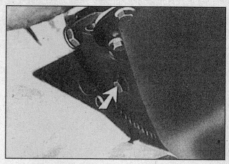

10.38b One of the torque converter-to-driveplate mounting bolts (arrowed)

the sleeve remains in position on the left-hand rear stud. Note the location of any shims on the engine mountings.

33 Remove the transmission mounting bracket, then remove the lower arm inner mounting bolts, and prise the lower arms out of the subframe.

34 Pull the subframe off the four studs, lowering the engine slightly at the same time. Withdraw the subframe over the front exhaust pipe, and remove it from under the car.

35 Remove the engine-to-transmission support bar by unscrewing the bolts.

36 Unscrew the bolt securing the transmission dipstick tube to the cylinder block, then unscrew the union nut from the transmission, and remove the dipstick tube.

37 Unbolt the torque converter cover plate from the transmission bellhousing (see illustration).

38 The four bolts securing the torque converter to the driveplate must now be removed. It will be necessary to turn the engine in order to bring each bolt into view (see illustrations). Hold the driveplate stationary using a wide-bladed screwdriver engaged with the starter ring gear, then unscrew and remove the bolts.

39 Remove the subframe mounting from the transmission (see illustration).

40 Unscrew the lower bolt securing the starter motor to the transmission.

41 Support the weight of the transmission on a trolley jack, preferably using wooden blocks or some form of cradle to hold the transmission firm. From this point onwards, an assistant should be available to help support the transmission as it is removed.

42 Unscrew the mounting nut from the rear end of the transmission under the starter motor.

43 Unscrew the mounting nut from the front end of the transmission.

44 Tie the left-hand driveshaft to one side.

45 On models with an electronic speedometer, unscrew the bolt and pull the sensor from the transmission. Remove the O-ring from the sensor.

46 On models with a mechanical speedometer (non-electronic type), release the clip and pull the speedometer cable out of the transmission.

47 Carefully remove the transmission from the engine. When the transmission comes away, take great care that the torque converter does not fall out - it should remain fully engaged with the transmission oil pump. Volvo technicians use a metal plate to hold the torque converter in position, and a similar plate can be made easily (see illustration).

48 As the transmission is removed, disconnect the right-hand driveshaft, and tie it to one side.

49 Withdraw the transmission from under the car.

Refitting

50 Refitting is a reversal of the removal procedure, but note the following additional points:

a) To ensure effective locking, it is recommended that the driveshaft circlips are renewed.

b) Take care not to damage the driveshaft oil seals.

c) Renew the O-ring on the electronic speedometer sensor.

d) Tighten all nuts and bolts to the specified torque wrench settings.

e) Make doubly sure that the torque converter is fully engaged with the transmission oil pump before refitting and tightening the engine-to-transmission bolts. If this is not done, the oil pump may be permanently damaged.

f) Press the driveshafts fully into engagement with the differential side

gears, until the circlips are heard to snap into place.

g) When tightening the subframe mounting bolts, make sure that there are no fluid lines trapped between the subframe and body at the front right-hand mounting.

h) Delay fully tightening the front suspension lower arm inner mounting bolts until the full weight of the car is on the suspension.

i) If necessary, renew the fluid cooler-to-transmission gasket.

j) Adjust the selector cable and kickdown cables, with reference to Sections 2 and 4.

k) Fill the transmission with the correct amount of fluid, with reference to Chapter 1.

l) Fill or top-up the cooling system (as applicable), with reference to Chapter 1.

11 Automatic transmission overhaul - general information

In the event of a fault occurring on the transmission, it is first necessary to determine whether it is of an electrical, mechanical or hydraulic nature, and to do this, special test equipment is required. It is therefore essential to have the work carried out by a Volvo dealer if a transmission fault is suspected.

Do not remove the transmission from the car for possible repair before professional fault diagnosis has been carried out, since most tests require the transmission to be in the vehicle.

7B

10.39 Automatic transmission mounting

10.47 Plate (arrowed) used to hold the torque converter in the transmission

Chapter 8
Driveshafts

Contents

Degrees of difficulty

Easy, suitable for novice with little experience	**Fairly easy,** suitable for beginner with some experience	**Fairly difficult,** suitable for competent DIY mechanic	**Difficult,** suitable for experienced DIY mechanic	**Very difficult,** suitable for expert DIY or professional

Specifications

Type . . . . Solid or hollow driveshafts, with spider-and-yoke or six-ball constant velocity joints

Lubrication
CV joint lubricant type/specification . . . . Volvo part number 1161029-2
Lubricant quantity . . . . 80 grams

Torque wrench settings

	Nm	lbf ft
Driveshaft heat shield	11	8
Driveshaft nut (use a new nut):		
Automatic transmission	230	170
Manual gearbox	220	162
Left-hand driveshaft inner boot retainer	25	18

1 General information

Drive is transmitted from the differential to the front wheels by means of two driveshafts. The left-hand driveshaft is solid, while the right-hand driveshaft may be either solid or hollow, depending on model.

Both driveshafts have constant velocity joints at their outer ends, and tripod spider joints at their inner ends.

On manual gearbox models, the right-hand inner joint has a female stub splined to the sun gear; on the left-hand side, the tripod spider is splined to the driveshaft, with the joint housing forming part of the sun gear.

On automatic transmission models, the driveshafts on both sides have a male stub splined to the sun gear.

2 Driveshaft (manual gearbox models) - removal and refitting

Removal

1 Remove the wheel cover or centre cover from the appropriate wheel, to expose the central driveshaft nut.

2 With the handbrake firmly applied, loosen the driveshaft nut two or three turns. This nut is very tight, and it may be necessary to slip a metal tube (such as a length of scaffold pole) over the socket handle to get enough leverage. If the car moves, have an assistant depress the footbrake as well.

3 Loosen the wheel bolts, then jack up the front of the car and support it on axle stands. Remove the appropriate roadwheel.

4 Unbolt and remove the engine splash guard.

Right-hand driveshaft

5 Where necessary, remove the heat shield. Using a parallel pin punch, drive out the double roll pin securing the inner joint yoke to the differential sun wheel stub shaft. Drive out the small inner roll pin first, then drive out the outer roll pin. Access to the roll pin is gained from under the car, and the driveshaft must be turned until the roll pin is visible (see illustrations).

Left-hand driveshaft

6 Drain the gearbox oil with reference to Chapter 1.

2.5a **Removing the heat shield**

2.5b **Driving out the double roll pin from the right-hand driveshaft**

8

2.7 Unbolting the left-hand driveshaft from the side of the gearbox

7 Unscrew the three bolts securing the rubber boot retaining plate to the side of the gearbox **(see illustration)**.

Both driveshafts

8 Remove the front brake caliper with reference to Chapter 9, but leave the hydraulic hose connected. Unclip the flexible brake hose from the front suspension strut, then tie the caliper to the front suspension coil spring with wire or string, taking care not to strain the hose.
9 Remove the screw and take off the brake disc.
10 On models with ABS, release the wheel sensor wiring from the bracket.
11 Unscrew and remove the two bolts securing the stub axle carrier to the suspension strut (new bolts must be obtained for reassembly). Note that the nuts are on the brake caliper side.
12 Unscrew the nut from the outer end of the driveshaft, and remove the washer. Discard the nut once removed - a new nut must be obtained for reassembly.
13 Pull the top of the stub axle carrier outwards, until the inner end of the driveshaft is released from the sun wheel stub shaft (right-hand side) or from the yoke sun wheel (left-hand side). Take care not to dislodge the tripod rollers on the left-hand side. Remove the O-ring on the right-hand sun wheel stub shaft.
14 Separate the driveshaft from the hub, and withdraw it from under the car. If it is tight, use a puller (or alternatively, use a soft metal drift) **(see illustration)**.

Refitting

15 When refitting the driveshaft, care should be taken to prevent damage to the rubber boots. Even the slightest knock can puncture the boot, causing the entry of water or dirt at a later date, which may lead to the premature failure of the joint.
16 Clean the splines of the driveshaft.

Right-hand driveshaft

17 Fit a new O-ring to the sun wheel stub shaft, and apply a little molybdenum disulphide grease to the splines.
18 Engage the inner end of the driveshaft with the sun wheel stub shaft, making sure that the roll pin holes are in alignment. Slide

2.14 Using a puller to separate the driveshaft from the hub

the driveshaft onto the sun wheel until the roll pin holes are aligned with each other.
19 Drive in new roll pins with their slots 90° apart, then seal the ends of the pins with sealing compound. The holes in the sun wheel stub shaft are chamfered to assist the fitting of new roll pins.
20 Refit the heat shield where applicable.

Left-hand driveshaft

21 Insert the tripod spider into the differential yoke sun wheel.
22 Wipe clean the side of the gearbox, then insert the three bolts securing the rubber boot retaining plate, and tighten to the specified torque. Make sure that the boot is not twisted during this procedure.
23 Refill the gearbox with oil, with reference to Chapter 1.

Both driveshafts

24 Apply locking fluid to the splines on the driveshaft outer joint stub axle.
25 Move the top of the stub axle carrier inwards, and at the same time engage the end of the driveshaft with the hub splines. Slide the hub fully onto the splines, then fit the washer and a new nut, screwing the nut on by just a few threads. If the splines are tight, carefully tap the hub on from the outside.
26 Insert new stub axle carrier bolts the correct way round, and tighten them to the specified torque (Chapter 10).
27 On models with ABS, refit the wheel sensor wiring to the bracket.
28 Fit the brake disc, and secure with the screw.
29 Refit the front brake caliper with reference

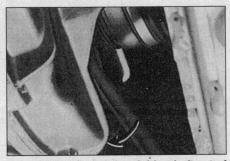

3.7 Levering the left-hand driveshaft out of the automatic transmission

to Chapter 9, then clip the flexible brake hose to the front suspension strut.
30 Fit and tighten the new driveshaft nut while holding the hub stationary, so that the driveshaft is pulled fully into the hub. Final tightening of the nut should be left until the car is on the ground.
31 Refit the engine splash guard.
32 Refit the wheel, and lower the car to the ground. Tighten the wheel bolts.
33 Fully tighten the driveshaft nut to the specified torque. Considerable force will be required - be sure that the handbrake is firmly applied, and have an assistant apply the footbrake should the car move.
34 Refit the wheel cover or centre cover to the wheel.

3 Driveshaft (automatic transmission models) - removal and refitting

Removal

1 Remove the wheel cover or centre cover from the appropriate wheel.
2 With the handbrake firmly applied, loosen the central driveshaft nut two or three turns. This nut is very tight, and it may be necessary to slip a metal tube (such as a length of scaffold pole) over the socket handle to get enough leverage. If the car moves, have an assistant depress the footbrake as well.
3 Loosen the wheel bolts, then jack up the front of the car and support it on axle stands. Remove the appropriate roadwheel.
4 Unbolt and remove the engine splash guard.
5 Drain the automatic transmission fluid with reference to Chapter 1.

Right-hand driveshaft

6 Disconnect the right-hand side driveshaft from the transmission by careful levering. Volvo technicians use a special tool to do this (shown in Chapter 7B, illustration 8.5) but a similar tool can be made up to serve the same purpose. Do not attempt to pull the driveshaft out of the transmission.

Left-hand driveshaft

7 Disconnect the left-hand side driveshaft from the transmission by careful levering, using the same method as described in the previous paragraph. The lever should be located on the stiffened rib on the transmission casing **(see illustration)**. If the driveshaft fails to release with moderate pressure, it can be driven out from the right-hand side of the differential after removing the right-hand driveshaft.

Both driveshafts

8 Remove the front brake caliper with reference to Chapter 9, but leave the hydraulic hose connected. Unclip the flexible brake hose from the front suspension strut, then tie the caliper to the front suspension coil spring

with wire or string, taking care not to strain the hose.

9 Remove the retaining screw, and take off the brake disc.

10 On models with ABS, release the wheel sensor wiring from the bracket.

11 Unscrew and remove the two bolts securing the stub axle carrier to the suspension strut (new bolts must be obtained for reassembly). Note that the nuts are on the brake caliper side.

12 Unscrew the nut from the outer end of the driveshaft, and remove the washer. Discard the nut once removed - a new nut must be obtained for reassembly.

13 Pull the top of the stub axle carrier outwards, and at the same time press the driveshaft through the hub. If it is tight, use a puller to press the driveshaft out of the hub (or alternatively, use a soft metal drift). While removing the driveshaft from the hub, make sure that it is not pressed back into the transmission, otherwise the circlip will lock it in position again.

14 Press the stub axle carrier downwards, and withdraw the driveshaft from the car.

Refitting

15 When refitting the driveshaft, care should be taken to prevent damage to the rubber boots. Even the slightest knock can puncture the boot, causing the entry of water or dirt at a later date, which may lead to the premature failure of the joint.

16 Clean the splines of the driveshaft.

17 Smear the lips of the oil seal in the transmission casing with a little grease.

18 Press the stub axle carrier downwards, then insert the driveshaft carefully into the transmission so that it engages with the differential sun gear. Take care to avoid any damage to the oil seal or driveshaft rubber boots. Press the driveshaft fully into the transmission until the circlip engages the groove.

19 Apply locking fluid to the splines on the driveshaft outer joint stub axle.

20 Engage the driveshaft splines with the hub, then press the stub axle carrier inwards until the washer and a new nut can be screwed onto the driveshaft. If the splines are tight, carefully tap on the hub from the outside. At this stage, only screw the nut on a few threads.

21 Insert new stub axle carrier bolts the correct way round, and tighten them to the specified torque (Chapter 10).

22 On models with ABS, refit the wheel sensor wiring to the bracket.

23 Fit the brake disc, and secure with the screw.

24 Refit the front brake caliper with reference to Chapter 9, then clip the flexible brake hose to the front suspension strut.

25 Fit and tighten the new driveshaft nut while holding the hub stationary, so that the driveshaft is pulled fully into the hub. Final

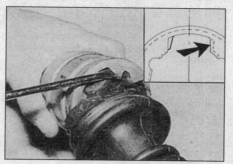

4.7 Bending out the inner joint housing locking lugs on the right-hand driveshaft - manual gearbox models

tightening of the nut can be left until the car is on the ground.

26 Refit the engine splash guard.

27 Refit the wheel, and lower the car to the ground. Tighten the wheel bolts.

28 Fully tighten the driveshaft nut to the specified torque. Considerable force will be required - be sure that the handbrake is firmly applied, and have an assistant apply the footbrake should the car move.

29 Refill the automatic transmission with fluid, with reference to Chapter 1.

30 Refit the wheel cover or centre cover to the wheel.

---

4 Driveshaft rubber boots - renewal

Right-hand driveshaft (manual gearbox)

Inner boot

1 Loosen the right-hand front wheel bolts. Apply the handbrake, then jack up the front of the car and support on axle stands. Remove the right-hand front roadwheel and the engine splash guard.

2 Unscrew and remove the upper bolt securing the stub axle carrier to the front suspension strut, noting which way round it is fitted. The lower bolt should only be loosened, not removed. Note that both bolts must be renewed on reassembly.

3 Unbolt and remove the driveshaft heat shield.

4 Using a parallel pin punch, drive out the double roll pin securing the inner joint yoke to the differential sun wheel stub shaft. Drive out the small inner roll pin first, then drive out the outer roll pin.

5 Pull the stub axle carrier outwards, and at the same time pull the inner driveshaft joint off the gearbox sun gear stub shaft splines.

6 Cut the large clip securing the boot to the inner joint, and pull back the boot.

7 Using a screwdriver, bend out the locking lugs of the inner joint housing, then disconnect the joint housing from the tripod

4.12 Chamfer (arrowed) on the right-hand driveshaft tripod spider - manual gearbox models

spider with a downwards twisting action. The screwdriver must be inserted under the projecting edge of the lugs, and care must be taken not to damage or remove the rollers (see illustration).

8 Using circlip pliers, extract the circlip from the groove in the driveshaft, then slide off the tripod spider. If it is tight, use a puller.

9 Cut the small clip, and pull the old rubber boot off the driveshaft.

10 If a metal clip is to be used, locate it on the driveshaft first.

11 Fit the new rubber boot on the driveshaft.

12 Slide the tripod spider onto the driveshaft, chamfered side first; if it is tight, use a suitable socket or metal tube. Refit the circlip (see illustration).

13 Remove all old grease, then pack the tripod spider and housing with 80 grams of new constant velocity joint grease.

14 Assemble the constant velocity joint housing to the tripod. Using a small hammer, tap the locking lugs back to their original position, making sure that they are not dented (see illustration).

15 Wipe clean the housing, and locate the large end of the rubber boot on it. Fit and tighten the clip.

16 Using a small screwdriver, lift the small end of the rubber boot to allow any trapped air to escape. Adjust the constant velocity joint so that the length of the rubber boot is 103.5 ± 2.0 mm, then remove the small screwdriver; fit and tighten the small clip (see illustration).

4.14 Tapping back the right-hand driveshaft locking lugs - manual gearbox models

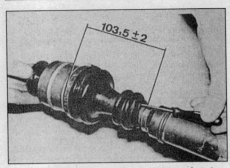

4.16 Right-hand driveshaft inner boot dimension - manual gearbox models

17 Apply a little grease to the splines of the sun gear stub shaft, then slide the driveshaft inner joint onto the stub shaft, making sure that the roll pin holes will be aligned with the holes in the shaft. Push in the stub axle carrier at the same time.

18 With the holes aligned, tap in new roll pins with their slots 90° apart, then seal their ends with sealing compound. The holes in the shaft are chamfered to assist fitting new roll pins.

19 Refit the driveshaft heat shield, and tighten the bolts.

20 Fit the new upper bolt securing the stub axle carrier to the front suspension strut, and tighten to the specified torque (Chapter 10). Now remove the lower bolt and discard it. Fit a new lower bolt, and tighten to the specified torque.

21 Refit the right-hand front roadwheel and the engine splash guard.

22 Lower the car to the ground.

Outer boot

23 Remove the driveshaft, as described in Section 2.

24 Mount the driveshaft horizontally in a vice.

25 Cut the two clips from the rubber boot, then pull the large end from the constant velocity joint and fold it inside out over the driveshaft.

26 Scoop away as much grease as possible from the joint.

27 Locate the ends of the circlip which holds the constant velocity joint onto the driveshaft. Using circlip pliers, open up the circlip until a 6.0 mm wide screwdriver or similar instrument

4.27 Expanding the circlip which retains the outer constant velocity joint on the driveshaft

can be inserted to keep the circlip in its open position **(see illustration)**.

28 Carefully tap the constant velocity joint off the end of the driveshaft, taking care not to drop it.

29 Pull off the old rubber boot.

30 Wipe clean the driveshaft. Where a metal clip is to be fitted, locate this on the driveshaft first. Locate the new rubber boot on the driveshaft.

31 Slide the constant velocity joint onto the driveshaft until the circlip is heard to snap into the groove.

32 Pack the joint with 80 grams of new constant velocity joint grease.

33 With the small end of the rubber boot located in its correct position, refit and tighten the clip.

34 Locate the large end of the rubber boot on the constant velocity joint.

Using a small screwdriver, lift the boot slightly to allow any trapped air to escape, then fit and tighten the clip.

35 Refit the driveshaft with reference to Section 2.

Left-hand driveshaft (manual gearbox)

Inner boot

36 Loosen the left-hand front wheel bolts. Apply the handbrake, then jack up the front of the car and support on axle stands.

37 Remove the engine splash guard.

38 Drain the oil from the gearbox with reference to Chapter 1, then refit and tighten the drain plug.

39 Remove the left-hand front roadwheel.

40 Unscrew the three bolts securing the rubber boot retaining plate to the side of the gearbox.

41 On models with ABS, unscrew the wheel sensor mounting bolt, then remove the sensor from the stub axle carrier, rotating it as it is withdrawn.

42 Remove the front brake caliper with reference to Chapter 9, but leave the hydraulic hose connected. Unclip the flexible brake hose from the front suspension strut, then tie the caliper to the front suspension coil spring with wire or string, taking care not to strain the hose.

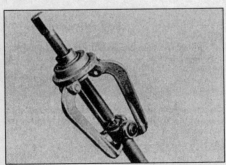

4.48 Using a puller to remove the tripod spider from the left-hand driveshaft - manual gearbox models

43 Unscrew the two mounting bolts securing the front suspension lower balljoint to the lower arm.

44 Unscrew and remove the two bolts securing the stub axle carrier to the suspension strut (new bolts must be obtained for reassembly). Note that the nuts are on the brake caliper side.

45 Disconnect the steering tie-rod end from the stub axle carrier, with reference to Chapter 10.

46 Withdraw the driveshaft and stub axle carrier together, taking care not to damage the inner tripod joint rollers.

47 Using circlip pliers, extract the circlip from the inner end of the driveshaft.

48 Slide the tripod spider from the splines on the driveshaft, using a puller if necessary **(see illustration)**.

49 Remove the clip or cable tie, then pull the rubber boot over the bearing on the driveshaft and withdraw it.

50 Where a metal clip is used, locate it over the bearing and onto the driveshaft.

51 Manipulate the new rubber boot over the bearing, and refit the clip to secure it to the bearing outer track.

52 Slide the tripod spider on the driveshaft, chamfered side first, then fit the circlip in the groove. Lightly oil the tripod rollers.

53 Locate the driveshaft and stub axle carrier assembly in position, and engage the inner tripod joint with the sun gear.

54 Fit the front suspension lower balljoint to the lower arm, then insert and tighten the two bolts to the specified torque (Chapter 10).

55 Refit the steering tie-rod end to the stub axle carrier, with reference to Chapter 10.

56 Refit the stub axle carrier to the suspension strut. Insert the new bolts the correct way round, and tighten to the specified torque (Chapter 10).

57 Refit the front brake caliper with reference to Chapter 9. Clip the flexible hose to the front suspension strut.

58 On models with ABS, smear the wheel sensor with a little grease, then push it into the stub axle carrier. Apply a little locking fluid to the threads of the mounting bolt, then refit and tighten it.

59 Wipe clean the side of the gearbox. Refit the rubber boot retaining plate, and tighten the bolts to the specified torque.

60 Refit the left-hand front roadwheel.

61 Refill the gearbox with oil, with reference to Chapter 1.

62 Refit the engine splash guard.

63 Lower the car to the ground, and tighten the wheel bolts.

Outer boot

64 If the driveshaft is removed as described in Section 2, the outer rubber boot may be renewed by removing the outer constant velocity joint; the following paragraphs describe its renewal after removal of the inner rubber boot.

65 Remove the clips securing the outer rubber

boot to the constant velocity joint and drive-shaft, then slide the boot along the driveshaft and over the bearing at the inner end.

66 Scoop the old grease from the constant velocity joint.

67 Slide the new rubber boot onto the driveshaft and over the bearing.

68 Pack the constant velocity joint with 80 grams of new constant velocity joint grease, then slide the rubber boot into position and onto the joint.

69 Fit and tighten the small clip. Using a screwdriver, carefully lift the larger end of the rubber boot to expel any trapped air, then locate it on the joint again and fit the large clip.

70 Refit the inner rubber boot as described previously.

Both driveshafts (automatic transmission)

Outer boot

71 The procedure is the same as that for the right-hand driveshaft (manual gearbox), except that the removal and refitting of the driveshaft is described in Section 3.

Inner boot

72 The inner boot is removed after removing the outer boot. Cut the clips, then slide the boot along the driveshaft and off the outer end.

73 Scoop out the old grease from the inner joint, and pack it with 80 grams of new constant velocity joint grease before refitting the boot and tightening the clips.

5.3 Bearing fitting dimension on the left-hand driveshaft

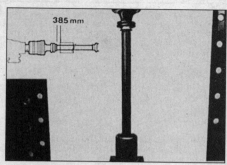

5.4 Vibration damper fitting dimension on the solid right-hand driveshaft

5 Driveshaft overhaul - general information

1 The inner and outer constant velocity joints may be renewed if necessary, but if the inner joint spider on the left-hand side is to be renewed, the sun gear yoke in the gearbox should be examined for wear.

Renewal of the sun gear yoke will require extensive gearbox repairs, which are best left to a specialist.

2 The procedure for removing the joints is the same as given in the rubber boot renewal procedure, covered in Section 4.

3 To renew the bearing on the left-hand driveshaft, first remove the driveshaft and remove the inner rubber boot. Using a puller or press, remove the bearing from the driveshaft. When fitting the new bearing, press it on so that the dimension from the inner end of the driveshaft to the nearest side of the bearing is 123.0 ± 0.3 mm **(see illustration)**.

4 To renew the vibration damper on the solid type right-hand driveshaft, first remove the driveshaft and remove the outer constant velocity joint and rubber boot. Apply some soapy water to the driveshaft, then using a puller or press, remove the vibration damper from the driveshaft. When fitting the new damper, apply the soapy water to the driveshaft first, and press the damper on until the distance from the inner rubber boot is 38.5 mm **(see illustration)**.

8

Chapter 9
Braking system

Contents

Degrees of difficulty

| Easy, suitable for novice with little experience | | Fairly easy, suitable for beginner with some experience | | Fairly difficult, suitable for competent DIY mechanic | | Difficult, suitable for experienced DIY mechanic | | Very difficult, suitable for expert DIY or professional | |

Specifications

System type .... Dual hydraulic circuit, split diagonally on non-ABS models, and front-to-rear on ABS models. Disc front brakes. Disc or drum rear brakes (all ABS models have disc rear brakes). Vacuum servo assistance on non-ABS models. Cable-operated handbrake on rear brakes

Front brakes

Type	Disc, solid or ventilated type
Disc diameter:	
Solid disc	260 mm
Ventilated disc	256 mm
Disc thickness:	
Solid disc:	
New	12.0 mm
Minimum thickness after machining	11.0 mm
Minimum service thickness	10.35 mm
Ventilated disc:	
New	22.0 mm
Minimum thickness after machining	20.0 mm
Minimum service thickness	19.30 mm
Maximum disc thickness variation	0.02 mm
Disc run-out (warpage) limit	0.05 mm

9

Rear brakes

Type . . . . Disc or drum
Drum brakes:
  Make . . . . Girling
  Drum inside diameter:
    New . . . . 203.0 mm
    Maximum diameter after machining . . . . 204.2 mm
    Maximum service diameter . . . . 204.7 mm
Disc brakes:
  Make . . . . Girling
  Disc diameter . . . . 228.0 mm
  Disc thickness:
    New . . . . 9.0 mm
    Minimum thickness after machining . . . . 8.5 mm
    Minimum service thickness . . . . 7.5 mm
  Maximum disc thickness variation . . . . 0.02 mm
  Disc run-out (warpage) limit . . . . 0.05 mm

Anti-lock braking system

Make . . . . ATE
Hydraulic operating pressure . . . . 140 to 180 bars
Wheel sensor resistance . . . . 400 to 1800 ohms
Motor relay resistance . . . . 70 ohms
Main relay resistance . . . . 70 ohms

Torque wrench settings

	Nm	lbf ft
ABS hydraulic accumulator	40	30
ABS hydraulic unit	27	20
ABS pressure/warning switch	23	17
ABS pump unit:		
M6 (8.8 mm)	8	6
M6 (10.9 mm)	11	8
ABS wheel sensor	11	8
Brake pedal bracket	25	18
Brake pedal pivot bolt	18	13
Disc retaining screw	10	7
Flexible brake hose to caliper	18	13
Front caliper guide pin bolt	27	20
Front caliper mounting bolt	110	81
Hydraulic brake line union nut	14	10
Master cylinder mounting nuts (non-ABS)	24	18
Rear brake disc/hub nut	180	133
Rear brake pressure regulating valve	25	18
Rear caliper guide pin bolt	27	20
Rear caliper mounting bolt	70	52
Rear wheel cylinder	7	5
Wheel bolts	110	81

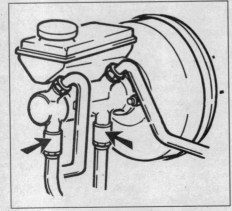

1.3 Location of the rear brake compensators on models with rear disc brakes

1 General information

The braking system is of dual hydraulic circuit type, comprising a master cylinder (or hydraulic unit on ABS models) and front disc calipers, with either rear disc calipers, or rear drum brakes and wheel cylinders. A dual-circuit hydraulic system is fitted on all models. Under normal conditions, both circuits operate in unison; in the event of failure of one circuit, the remaining circuit will provide adequate braking to stop the car in an emergency. On all non-ABS (anti-lock braking system) models, the circuit is split diagonally, whereas on ABS models, the circuit is split front to rear. A diagonally-split system leaves both front brakes, and one rear brake, working. If the system is split front to rear, either the front or the rear brakes will be available in an emergency.

Disc brakes are fitted to the front wheels, which may be either solid type or ventilated. Disc brakes are also fitted to the rear wheels, except on some carburettor 440 models where drum brakes are fitted. All models with ABS are fitted with rear disc brakes.

Rear brake compensators to prevent rear wheel lock-up during emergency braking are incorporated in the rear hydraulic circuits, and these regulate the hydraulic pressure to the rear brakes (see illustration). The system takes account of the loading of the car - the rear wheels are less likely to lock up when the car is fully-loaded, and more likely to when just the driver is in the car. On models with rear disc brakes, the compensators are located on the master cylinder, but on models

2.1 View of the brake and clutch pedals with lower facia panel removed

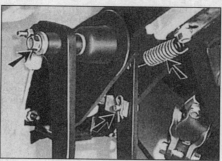

2.3 Brake pedal removal - pivot bolt, split pin and return spring arrowed

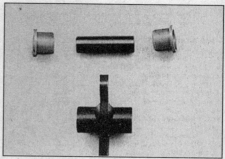

2.6 Brake pedal bushes and spacer

with rear drum brakes, they are located in the wheel cylinders themselves.

On non-ABS models, the master cylinder and vacuum servo unit are located on the right-hand side of the engine compartment. On ABS models, the ABS unit is located on the left-hand side of the engine compartment, and a control rod connects the brake pedal to the unit.

The cable-operated handbrake operates independently on the rear wheels. A vacuum servo unit is fitted to non-ABS models; on ABS models, pedal pressure assistance is provided automatically through the hydraulic unit and high-pressure pump.

Note: *When servicing any part of the system, work carefully and methodically; also observe scrupulous cleanliness when overhauling any part of the hydraulic system. Always renew components (in axle sets, where applicable) if in doubt about their condition, and use only genuine Volvo replacement parts, or at least those of known good quality. Note the warnings given in Safety first! and at relevant points in this Chapter concerning the dangers of asbestos dust and hydraulic fluid.*

2 Brake pedal - removal and refitting

Removal

1 Working inside the car, remove the lower facia panel beneath the steering column **(see illustration)**.
2 Unscrew the nut from the end of the pedal pivot bolt.
3 Extract the split pin, washer and clevis pin securing the servo unit pushrod to the brake pedal **(see illustration)**.
4 Unhook the brake pedal return spring.
5 Slide out the pivot bolt until the brake pedal can be withdrawn.
6 Prise the bushes and spacer out of the pedal **(see illustration)**.
7 Examine the bushes for wear, and renew them if necessary. If the pivot bolt is worn excessively, the clutch pedal will have to be removed (as described in Chapter 6), and the bolt renewed.

Refitting

8 Refitting is a reversal of the removal procedure, but lubricate the bushes, pivot bolt and pushrod clevis pin with molybdenum disulphide grease, and tighten the pivot bolt to the specified torque. If necessary, adjust the setting of the brake stop-light switch (Section 22).

3 Vacuum servo unit - removal and refitting

Removal

1 Disconnect the battery negative terminal.
2 Refer to Section 8 and remove the master cylinder.
3 Disconnect the non-return valve together with the vacuum hose from the servo unit.
4 Working inside the car, remove the lower facia panel from beneath the steering column.
5 Extract the split pin, washer and clevis pin securing the servo unit pushrod to the brake pedal.
6 Unscrew the four nuts (and recover the washers) securing the servo unit to the bulkhead, and withdraw the unit into the engine compartment.
7 Remove the O-ring from the joint face of the servo unit.
8 Note that the servo unit cannot be dismantled for repair or overhaul and, if faulty, must be renewed.

4.1 Disconnecting the vacuum servo hose and non-return valve from the inlet manifold

Refitting

9 Refitting is a reversal of the removal procedure, but renew the O-ring, and tighten the mounting bolts securely. Refer to Section 8 when refitting the master cylinder.

4 Vacuum servo unit non-return valve - removal, testing and refitting

Note: *The non-return valve can only be renewed together with the vacuum hose.*

Removal

1 Prise the vacuum non-return valve from the servo unit with a screwdriver, then disconnect the hose from the inlet manifold **(see illustration)**.

Testing

2 Examine the non-return valve and rubber sealing grommet for damage and signs of deterioration, and renew if necessary. The valve may be tested by trying to blow through it in both directions - it should only be possible to blow from the servo end to the manifold end.

Refitting

3 Refitting is a reversal of the removal procedure.

5 Vacuum servo unit air filter - renewal

1 Working inside the car, remove the lower facia panel from beneath the steering column.
2 Ease the convoluted rubber cover off the rear of the servo unit, and move it up the pushrod. Move the plastic cap back to gain access to the air filter elements **(see illustration)**.
3 Using a screwdriver or scriber, hook out the old air filter elements, and remove them from the servo. If the original ones are refitted, it will be necessary to cut them free.
4 Cut the new filter elements, then fit them over the pushrod and press them into the end of the servo unit.

9

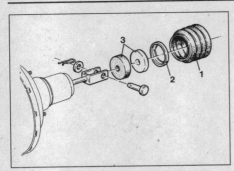

5.2 Vacuum servo unit air filter components

1 Convoluted rubber cover
2 Plastic cap
3 Air filter elements

5 Refit the plastic cap and rubber cover, then refit the lower facia panel beneath the steering column.

6 Hydraulic system - bleeding

⚠️ *Warning: Hydraulic fluid is poisonous; wash off immediately and thoroughly in the case of skin contact, and seek immediate medical advice if any fluid is swallowed or gets into the eyes. Certain types of hydraulic fluid are flammable, and may ignite when allowed into contact with hot components; when servicing any hydraulic system, it is safest to assume that the fluid IS flammable, and to take precautions against the risk of fire as though it is petrol that is being handled. Hydraulic fluid is also an effective paint stripper, and will attack plastics; if any is spilt, it should be washed off immediately, using copious quantities of fresh water. Finally, it is hygroscopic (it absorbs moisture from the air) - old fluid may be contaminated and unfit for further use. When topping-up or renewing the fluid, always use the recommended type, and ensure that it comes from a freshly-opened sealed container.*

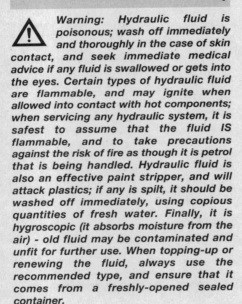

6.3 Using a one-man brake bleeding kit

Non-ABS models

1 If the master cylinder or brake pipes/hoses have been disconnected and reconnected, then the complete system (both circuits) must be bled. If a component of one circuit has been disturbed, then only that particular circuit need be bled.

2 Bleed the hydraulic system in the following order:
a) Left-hand rear brake.
b) Right-hand front brake.
c) Right-hand rear brake.
d) Left-hand front brake.

3 There are a variety of do-it-yourself brake bleeding kits available from motor accessory shops, and it is recommended that one of these kits is used wherever possible, as they greatly simplify the bleeding operation **(see illustration)**. Follow the kit manufacturer's instructions in conjunction with the following procedure.

4 During the bleeding operation, do not allow the brake fluid level in the reservoir to drop below the minimum mark, and only use new fluid for topping-up. Never re-use fluid bled from the system.

5 Before starting, check that all rigid pipes and flexible hoses are in good condition, and that all hydraulic unions are tight. Take great care not to allow hydraulic fluid to come into contact with the vehicle paintwork, otherwise the finish will be seriously damaged. Wash off any spilt fluid immediately with cold water.

6 If a brake bleeding kit is not being used, gather together a clean jar, a suitable length of clear plastic or rubber tubing which is a tight fit over the bleed screw, and a new tin of the specified brake fluid.

7 Clean the area around the bleed screw on the left-hand rear brake, and remove the dust cap. Connect one end of the tubing to the bleed screw, and immerse the other end in the jar containing sufficient brake fluid to keep the end of the tube submerged.

8 Open the bleed screw half a turn, and have an assistant depress the brake pedal to the floor and then slowly release it. Tighten the bleed screw at the end of each downstroke, to prevent the expelled air and fluid from being drawn back into the system. Continue this procedure until clean brake fluid, free from air bubbles, can be seen flowing into the jar, and then finally tighten the bleed screw.

9 Remove the tube, refit the dust cap, and repeat this procedure on the diagonally-opposite front brake caliper.

10 Repeat the procedure on the remaining circuit.

ABS models

Note: *Due to the complex nature of the ABS, it is strongly recommended that this work is carried out by a Volvo garage; the procedure is, however, given below for those wishing to attempt it.*

11 Both the front and rear brakes can be bled using the conventional mechanical method, but the only front brakes may be bled using the pressure method. The following paragraphs describe the mechanical method. Note that the rear brakes are bled using the high pressure of the ABS itself.

12 With the brake system at operating pressure (ie after having driven the car), top-up the brake fluid level in the reservoir to the MAX mark. Now with the engine switched off and the handbrake applied, depress the foot-brake pedal repeatedly until the operating pressure is eliminated and strong resistance is felt.

13 Bleed the hydraulic system in the following order:
a) Left-hand front brake.
b) Right-hand front brake.
c) Left-hand rear brake.
d) Right-hand rear brake.

14 There are a variety of do-it-yourself brake bleeding kits available from motor accessory shops, and it is recommended that one of these kits is used wherever possible, as they greatly simplify the bleeding operation. Follow the kit manufacturer's instructions in conjunction with the following procedure.

15 During the bleeding operation, do not allow the brake fluid level in the reservoir to drop below the minimum mark, and only use new fluid for topping-up. Never re-use fluid bled from the system.

16 Before starting, check that all rigid pipes and flexible hoses are in good condition, and that all hydraulic unions are tight. Take great care not to allow hydraulic fluid to come into contact with the vehicle paintwork, otherwise the finish will be seriously damaged. Wash off any spilt fluid immediately with cold water.

17 If a brake bleeding kit is not being used, gather together a clean jar, a suitable length of clear plastic or rubber tubing which is a tight fit over the bleed screw, and a new tin of the specified brake fluid.

18 Clean the area around the bleed screw on the left-hand front brake, and remove the dust cap. Connect one end of the tubing to the bleed screw, and immerse the other end in the jar containing sufficient brake fluid to keep the end of the tube submerged.

19 Open the bleed screw half a turn, and have an assistant depress the brake pedal to the floor and then slowly release it. Tighten the bleed screw at the end of each downstroke, to prevent the expelled air and fluid from being drawn back into the system. Continue this procedure until clean brake fluid, free from air bubbles, can be seen flowing into the jar, and then finally tighten the bleed screw.

20 Remove the tube, refit the dust cap, and repeat this procedure on the right-hand front brake.

21 The rear brakes must now be bled.

⚠️ *Warning: The rear brakes are bled using the high pressure of the ABS (180 bars), and special care should be taken to prevent personal injury. It is recommended that safety glasses and gloves are worn, at the very least.*

22 Top-up the brake fluid level if necessary.

23 Clean the area around the bleed screw on the left-hand rear brake, and remove the dust cap. Connect one end of the tubing to the bleed screw, and immerse the other end in the jar containing sufficient brake fluid to keep the end of the tube submerged.

24 Open the bleed screw half a turn.

25 Have an assistant depress the footbrake pedal and keep it down.

26 Have the assistant switch on the ignition for a maximum of 10 seconds, then tighten the bleed screw.

27 Release the footbrake pedal and top-up the hydraulic fluid level.

28 Repeat the bleeding procedure on the left-hand rear brake if necessary, until the brake fluid entering the jar is free of any air bubbles.

29 Refit the dust cap, and depressurise the hydraulic system by repeatedly depressing the footbrake pedal until resistance is felt.

30 Repeat the bleeding procedure on the right-hand rear brake.

31 Check if there is still any air in the brake hydraulic system, by quickly depressing the footbrake pedal several times as in an emergency stop. The pedal should feel hard, not spongy - if not satisfactory, bleed the brakes again.

32 After carrying out the bleeding procedure, check the footbrake pedal height as follows. First depressurise the hydraulic system by depressing the footbrake pedal until resistance is felt. Switch on the ignition to pressurise the system, then check that the distance from the floor to the pedal is between 150.0 and 160.0 mm **(see illustration)**.

7 Hydraulic pipes and hoses - removal and refitting

1 The hydraulic pipes, hoses, hose connections and pipe unions should be regularly examined.

2 First check for signs of leakage at the pipe unions, then examine the flexible hoses for signs of cracking, chafing and fraying.

3 The brake pipes should be examined carefully for signs of dents, corrosion or other damage. Corrosion should be scraped off, and if the depth of pitting is significant, the pipes must be renewed. This is particularly likely in those areas underneath the vehicle body where the pipes are exposed and unprotected.

4 If any section of pipe or hose is to be removed, the loss of fluid may be reduced by removing the hydraulic fluid reservoir filler cap, placing a piece of polythene over the filler neck, and securing it tightly with an elastic band. If a section of pipe is to be removed from the master cylinder, the reservoir should be emptied by syphoning out the fluid or by drawing the fluid out with a pipette.

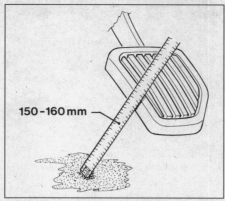

150 - 160 mm

6.32 Check the brake pedal height after bleeding the ABS hydraulic system

Removal

Note: *Refer to the warning at the start of Section 6 before proceeding.*

5 To remove a section of pipe, unscrew the union nuts at each end of the pipe, and release it from the clips attaching it to the body **(see illustration)**. Where the union nuts are exposed to the full force of the weather, they can sometimes be rusted and/or quite tight. If an open-ended spanner is used, burring of the flats on the nuts is not uncommon, and for this reason, it is preferable to use a special split-ring brake union spanner which will engage all the flats. If such a spanner is not available, self-locking grips may be used - though this is not recommended.

6 To remove a flexible hose, first clean the ends of the hose and the surrounding area, then unscrew the union nut(s) from the hose end(s) **(see illustration)**. Recover the spring clip, and withdraw the hose from the serrated mounting in the support bracket. Where applicable, unscrew the hose from the caliper.

7 Brake pipes with flared ends and union nuts in place can be obtained individually or in sets from Volvo dealers or accessory shops. The pipe is then bent to shape, using the old pipe as a guide, and is ready for fitting to the car.

Refitting

8 Refitting the pipes and hoses is a reversal of removal, noting the following points:

7.5 Brake pipe connection to the bracket at the front of the car

a) Make sure that brake pipes are securely supported in their clips, and ensure that the hoses are not kinked.

b) Check that the hoses are clear of all suspension components and underbody fittings, and will remain clear during movement of the suspension and steering.

c) On completion, remove the polythene from the reservoir, and bleed the brake hydraulic system as described in Section 6.

8 Master cylinder (non-ABS models) - removal, overhaul and refitting

Removal

Note: *Refer to the warning at the start of Section 6 before proceeding.*

1 Depress the brake pedal several times to dissipate the vacuum in the servo unit.

2 Remove the filler cap, syphon the brake fluid from the reservoir on top of the master cylinder, then refit the cap. Place a container beneath the master cylinder to catch any spilled fluid when the brake lines are disconnected.

3 Disconnect the wiring plug from the low fluid level switch on the filler cap.

4 As a safety precaution, identify the positions of the brake lines on the master cylinder.

5 For improved access on carburettor models, remove the air cleaner assembly, with reference to Chapter 4A.

6 Unbolt and remove the heat shield covering the master cylinder.

7 Unscrew the union nuts, and disconnect the two upper hydraulic lines; move them slightly to one side.

8 Remove the engine splash guard.

9 Unscrew the union nuts, and disconnect the two lower hydraulic lines.
Some loss of fluid will occur as the lines are disconnected.

10 Unscrew the two mounting nuts, and withdraw the master cylinder from the servo unit.

11 Where fitted, unscrew the two pressure-reducing valves from the two bottom ports of the master cylinder.

7.6 Flexible brake hose connection to the bracket at the rear of the car

9

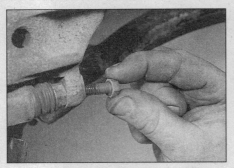

9.3a Removing the front brake caliper lower guide pin

12 Pull the reservoir from the master cylinder body, then prise out the two rubber grommets.

13 Swill out any sediment from the bottom of the reservoir, using only fresh brake fluid - **do not** use any other cleaning fluid.

14 It is not possible to obtain seals or internal components for the master cylinder, therefore if it is faulty, it should be renewed complete.

15 The reservoir locating seals may be renewed if necessary. The O-ring seal between the master cylinder and the vacuum servo should be renewed as a matter of course whenever the unit is removed, as a leak at this point will allow atmospheric pressure into the servo unit.

Refitting

16 Refitting is a reversal of the removal procedure, but note the following additional points:

9.4a Removing the outer brake pad from the carrier bracket

9.4b Removing the inner brake pad from the carrier bracket

9.3b Swivel the caliper upwards to remove the pads

a) Before refitting the pressure-reducing valves, make sure that the piston stop-pin is located correctly in the outlet aperture of the master cylinder.

b) Tighten the union nuts and master cylinder mounting nuts to the specified torque wrench settings.

c) Fill the reservoir with hydraulic brake fluid, and bleed the system with reference to Section 6.

d) Check the hydraulic lines for leakage.

---

9 Front brake pads - renewal

⚠️ **Warning: Disc brake pads must be renewed on both front wheels at the same time - never renew the pads on only one wheel, as uneven braking may result. Also, the dust created by wear of the pads may contain asbestos, which is a health hazard. Never blow it out with compressed air, and don't inhale any of it. An approved filtering mask should be worn when working on the brakes. DO NOT use petroleum-based solvents to clean brake parts - use brake cleaner or methylated spirit only.**

1 Loosen the front wheel bolts. Apply the handbrake, then jack up the front of the car and support it on axle stands. Remove the front roadwheels.

2 Detach the flexible brake hose mounting plate from the front suspension strut.

Models with solid brake discs

3 Unscrew the caliper lower guide pin bolt while holding the guide with an open-ended spanner, then swivel the caliper upwards **(see illustrations)**.

4 Withdraw the two brake pads from the carrier bracket **(see illustrations)**. If required, the thickness of the pads can be checked at this stage using a steel rule (refer to Chapter 1 Specifications for pad thicknesses).

5 Before fitting the pads, check that the guide pins are free to slide in the carrier bracket, and check that the rubber dust excluders around the guide pins are undamaged. Brush the dust and dirt from the caliper and piston, *but do not inhale it, as it is a health hazard.* Inspect

the dust excluder around the piston for damage, and inspect the piston for evidence of fluid leaks, corrosion or damage. If attention to any of these components is necessary, refer to Section 10.

6 Using a block of wood, press the piston back into the caliper as far as possible.

7 Smear a little copper brake grease on the backs of the pads, taking care not to allow any onto the friction material or the brake disc.

8 Locate the pads in the carrier bracket, and swivel the caliper down over them.

9 Refit the caliper lower guide pin bolt, and tighten it to the specified torque while holding the guide with an open-ended spanner.

Models with ventilated brake discs

10 Noting its fitted location, prise out the pad anti-rattle spring from the side of the caliper.

11 Prise off their dust covers, then unscrew the two guide pin bolts **(see illustration)**. It is recommended that the bolts are not removed completely, to avoid the risk of dirt contamination.

12 Remove the caliper and withdraw the pads. Do not allow the caliper to hang down by the flexible hose - either find something to rest it on, or tie it up so that the hose is not strained.

13 Before fitting the pads, check that the guide pins are free to slide in the carrier bracket - do not apply lubricant to the guide pins, however, as they slide in plastic sleeves. Brush the dust and dirt from the caliper and piston, *but do not inhale it, as it is a health hazard.* Inspect the dust excluder around the piston for damage, and inspect the piston for evidence of fluid leaks, corrosion or damage. If attention to any of these components is necessary, refer to Section 10.

14 Using a block of wood, press the piston back into the caliper as far as possible.

15 Smear a little copper brake grease on the backs of the pads, taking care not to allow any onto the friction material or the brake disc.

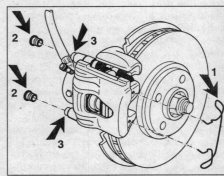

9.11 Brake pad renewal on models with ventilated discs

1 *Anti-rattle spring*
2 *Guide pin bolt dust covers*
3 *Guide pin bolts*

16 Locate the pads in the carrier bracket, then locate the caliper over them.

17 Insert and tighten the guide pin bolts to the specified torque, then refit the dust covers.

18 Finally, refit the pad anti-rattle spring, as noted on removal.

All models

19 Refit the flexible brake hose mounting plate to the front suspension strut.

20 Repeat the relevant procedure on the remaining front brake, then refit the roadwheels and lower the car to the ground. Tighten the wheel bolts to the specified torque.

21 Depress the brake pedal two or three times to bring the pads into contact with the disc. Check the hydraulic fluid level in the reservoir.

---

10 Front brake caliper - removal, overhaul and refitting

⚠️ **Warning: Hydraulic fluid is poisonous; wash off immediately and thoroughly in the case of skin contact, and seek immediate medical advice if any fluid is swallowed or gets into the eyes. Certain types of hydraulic fluid are flammable, and may ignite when allowed into contact with hot components; when servicing any hydraulic system, it is safest to assume that the fluid IS flammable, and to take precautions against the risk of fire as though it is petrol that is being handled. Hydraulic fluid is also an effective paint stripper, and will attack plastics; if any is spilt, it should be washed off immediately, using copious quantities of fresh water. Finally, it is hygroscopic (it absorbs moisture from the air) - old fluid may be contaminated and unfit for further use. When topping-up or renewing the fluid, always use the recommended type, and ensure that it comes from a freshly-opened sealed container.**

Note: *Refer to the warning on the dangers of asbestos dust at the start of Section 9 before proceeding.*

Removal

1 Loosen the wheel bolts, then apply the handbrake, jack up the front of the car and support it on axle stands. Remove the appropriate roadwheel.

2 Fit a brake hose clamp to the flexible brake hose leading to the front brake caliper **(see illustration)**. This will minimise brake fluid loss during subsequent operations.

3 Loosen (but do not remove) the union on the caliper end of the flexible brake hose.

4 Remove the brake pads as described in Section 9.

5 On models with solid brake discs, unscrew the upper guide pin bolt, and withdraw the caliper.

6 If the caliper is to be dismantled, temporarily release the brake hose clamp, and have an assistant slowly depress the footbrake pedal until the caliper piston has been ejected just over halfway out of its bore. Refit the clamp.

7 Unscrew the caliper from the brake hose, then plug or tape over the end of the hose to prevent dirt entry.

Overhaul

8 With the caliper on the bench, wipe away all traces of dust and dirt, but *avoid inhaling the dust, as it is a health hazard.*

9 Remove the guide pins and dust covers from the frame.

10 Withdraw the partially-ejected piston from the caliper body, and remove the dust cover.

11 Using a suitable blunt instrument such as a knitting needle or a thick feeler blade, carefully extract the piston seal from the caliper bore.

12 Unscrew and remove the bleed screw.

13 Clean all the parts in methylated spirit or clean brake fluid, and wipe dry using a lint-free cloth. Inspect the piston and caliper bore for signs of damage, scuffing or corrosion, and if these conditions are evident, renew the caliper body assembly.

14 Inspect the condition of the dust excluders over the guides (where applicable), and renew these too if there is any sign of damage or deterioration. Check the guide pins for damage or distortion, and renew if necessary **(see illustration)**.

15 If the components are in satisfactory condition, a repair kit consisting of new seals and dust excluders should be obtained. The guides are also obtainable as a separate kit.

16 Lubricate the caliper bore, piston and seal with the special grease supplied in the repair kit, or if necessary use fresh hydraulic fluid. Also smear the inside of the dust cover with grease or fluid.

17 Fit the seal in the groove in the caliper bore.

18 Fit the piston in the caliper bore. Press the piston into the bore, and locate the dust cover in the piston and caliper grooves.

19 Refit and tighten the bleed screw.

20 Smear the guides with high-melting-point grease, and locate them in the frame together with the seals.

Refitting

21 Hold the flexible brake hose, and screw the caliper body back onto the hose. Do not fully tighten the union at this stage.

22 On models with solid discs, locate the caliper on the frame; insert the upper guide pin bolt, and tighten it to the specified torque while holding the guide with an open-ended spanner.

23 Refit the brake pads with reference to Section 9.

10.2 Brake hose clamp fitted to a flexible brake hose

24 Tighten the flexible brake hose union on the caliper to the specified torque, making sure that the hose is not twisted. The hose has a white line on it to help determine if it is twisted. If necessary, re-position the hose by adjusting the bracket at the body end.

25 Remove the brake hose clamp.

26 Bleed the hydraulic system with reference to Section 6. It should only be necessary to bleed the front brake which has been disconnected, but on completion, check that the pedal is firm - if necessary, bleed the complete system.

27 Refit the roadwheel, and lower the car to the ground. Tighten the wheel bolts to the specified torque.

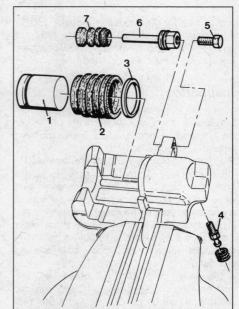

10.14 Front brake caliper components - solid-disc caliper shown

1 Piston	*5 Guide pin bolt*
2 Dust cover	*6 Guide pin*
3 Piston seal	*7 Dust cover*
4 Bleed screw	

9

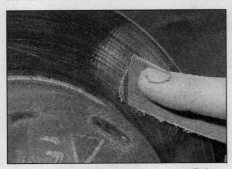

11.2 Using emery tape to remove light scoring from the disc

11.4a Checking the brake disc thickness with a micrometer

11.4b Checking the brake disc run-out with a dial test gauge

11.5 Suspending the front brake caliper from the coil spring with a length of wire

11.6a Unscrewing the front brake disc securing screw

11.6b Removing the front brake disc

11 Front brake disc -
inspection, removal and refitting

Note: *If either disc requires renewal, BOTH should be renewed at the same time, to ensure even and consistent braking. New brake pads should also be fitted.*

Inspection

1 Loosen the front wheel bolts. Apply the handbrake, then jack up the front of the car and support on axle stands. Remove the front wheels.

2 Rotate the disc by hand, and examine it for deep scoring, grooving or cracks. Light scoring is normal, and may be removed with emery tape, but, if excessive, the disc must be renewed **(see illustration)**.

3 Any loose rust and scale around the outer edge of the disc can be removed by lightly tapping it with a small hammer while rotating the disc.

4 Measure the disc thickness with a micrometer, if available. Disc run-out (warpage) can be checked using a dial test gauge; a less-accurate (but perhaps more accessible) method is to use a feeler gauge together with a metal base block **(see illustrations)**. Do not confuse disc warpage with wear in the hub bearings - the figures quoted by Volvo for disc run-out are for testing the discs when removed.

Removal

5 Unscrew the two bolts securing the brake caliper assembly to the stub axle carrier. Withdraw the caliper (complete with pads) off the disc, and suspend it from the front suspension coil spring **(see illustration)**. Avoid straining the flexible brake hose.

6 Using a Torx type socket bit or driver, or an Allen key (as applicable), remove the screw securing the disc to the hub, and withdraw the disc **(see illustrations)**. If it is tight, lightly tap its rear face with a hide or plastic mallet.

Refitting

7 Refitting is a reversal of the removal procedure, noting the following points:
  a) *If new discs are being fitted, first remove their protective coating.*
  b) *Ensure complete cleanliness of the hub*

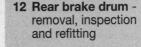

12.3 Rear brake drum removal

1 Drum holding screw
2 Black pin
3 White sleeve

and disc mating faces, and tighten the disc retaining screw to the specified torque.
  c) *Finally, depress the brake pedal two or three times to bring the pads into contact with the disc.*
  d) *Repeat the procedure on the remaining front wheel.*
  e) *Refit the roadwheels, and lower the car to the ground. Tighten the wheel bolts to the specified torque.*

12 Rear brake drum -
removal, inspection and refitting

Note: *Refer to the warning on the dangers of asbestos dust at the start of Section 9 before proceeding.*

Removal

1 Loosen the rear wheel bolts. Chock the front roadwheels, then jack up the rear of the car and support on axle stands. Remove the rear roadwheels.

2 Release the handbrake lever, then working on one side, remove the screw securing the brake drum to the hub.

3 By judicious tapping, release the drum from the hub and withdraw it over the brake shoes. If it is tight, pull the handbrake lever on as far as possible, so that the black pin on the rear of the backplate can be pressed in. This will release the white sleeve, which can then be taken out together with the black pin **(see illustration)**.

4 If the handbrake cable has stretched, it may be necessary to adjust the handbrake first so that it can be fully applied. When the handbrake is now released, it should be possible to remove the drum.

5 With the brake drum removed, brush or wipe the dust from the drum, brake shoes, wheel cylinder and backplate. *Take great care not to inhale the dust, as it is a health hazard. It is recommended that an approved filtering mask be worn during this operation.*

Inspection

6 Examine the internal surface of the brake drum for signs of scoring or cracks. If any deterioration of the surface finish is evident, the drum may be skimmed to the maximum diameter given in the Specifications; otherwise, renewal is necessary.

7 If the drum is to be skimmed, it will be necessary to have the work carried out on both rear drums, to maintain a consistent internal diameter on both sides.

Refitting

8 Locate the brake drum over the shoes, and align the securing screw hole with the hole in the hub. Insert and tighten the screw.

9 Where necessary, refit the black pin and white sleeve with the handbrake applied.

10 Depress the footbrake pedal several times to operate the self-adjusting mechanism.

11 The handbrake should now be adjusted as described in Chapter 1, or after removing the brake drum on the other side, if this is being done.

12 On completion, refit the roadwheel(s) and lower the car to the ground.

---

13 Pressure-regulating valve - removal and refitting

Note: *Refer to the warning on the dangers of hydraulic fluid at the start of Section 10 before proceeding.*

Removal

1 Chock the front roadwheels, then jack up the rear of the car and support on axle stands.

2 To reduce the loss of brake fluid, unscrew the cap from the fluid reservoir, then tighten

14.5a Self-adjusting mechanism and ratchet on the rear brakes

the cap down onto a piece of polythene sheet.

3 Working under the car, position a suitable container beneath the pressure-regulating valve to catch any spilled fluid.

4 Identify the four hydraulic lines for position, then unscrew the union nuts and disconnect them from the valve.

5 Unscrew and remove the mounting bolts, release the pull-off spring from the operating lever, and withdraw the pressure-regulating valve together with the pull-off spring.

Refitting

6 Refitting is a reversal of the removal procedure, but tighten the mounting bolts and union nuts to the specified torque. Remove the polythene sheet from the fluid reservoir, and bleed the system as described in Section 6. Ideally, the valve should be adjusted by a Volvo dealer - this work involves checking the rear axle loading, and using a spring balance to determine the correct position of the operating arm.

---

14 Rear brake shoes - renewal

⚠️ *Warning: Drum brake shoes must be renewed on both rear wheels at the same time - never renew the shoes on only one wheel, as uneven braking may result. Also, the dust created by wear of the shoes may contain asbestos, which is a health hazard. Never blow it out with compressed air, and don't*

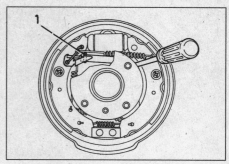

14.5b Checking movement of the self-adjusting mechanism ratchet (1)

inhale any of it. An approved filtering mask should be worn when working on the brakes. DO NOT use petroleum-based solvents to clean brake parts - use brake cleaner or methylated spirit only.

1 Remove both rear brake drums, with reference to Section 12.

2 Clean away the accumulated dust from the shoes and backplate, taking care not to inhale any of it - see the warning above.

3 Examine the brake shoes for wear; if either shoe is worn down to the specified minimum amount (Chapter 1), renew all the rear brake shoes as a set.

4 Check the wheel cylinder for leakage of fluid, and for seizure of the pistons.

> **HAYNES HINT** *When working on the rear brakes, only dismantle one side at a time - in this way, the other rear brake can be used as a guide to the fitted location of components.*

5 Before removing the shoes, use a screwdriver to lever the trailing shoe outwards, and check that the self-adjusting mechanism ratchet turns at the same time **(see illustrations)**.

6 Note the fitted positions of the shoes, springs and adjuster strut **(see illustrations)**.

7 Remove the shoe steady spring cups from both shoes by depressing and turning them through 90° **(see illustration)**. Remove the cups, springs and pins.

8 Using a pair of pliers, unhook and remove the upper return spring **(see illustration)**.

14.6a Rear brake shoes fitted to the backplate

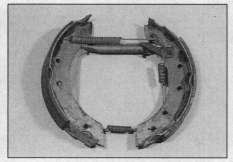

14.6b Rear brake shoes assembled on the bench

14.7 Removing the rear brake shoe steady spring cups

9

14.8 Upper return spring connection (arrowed) to the rear brake shoes

14.9 Using an adjustable spanner to lever the rear brake shoe from the bottom anchor

14.10 Disconnecting the handbrake cable from the trailing shoe

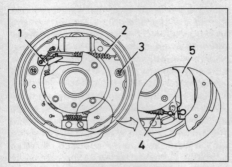

14.17 Rear brake shoes

1 *Self-adjusting mechanism*
2 *Upper shoe return spring*
3 *Shoe steady spring*
4 *Handbrake cable*
5 *Shoe handbrake lever*

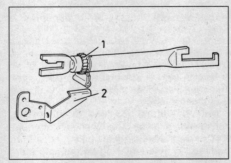

14.18a Rear brake shoe self-adjusting mechanism

1 *Ratchet*   2 *Arm*

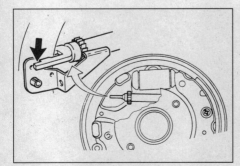

14.18b Self-adjusting mechanism location on the leading brake shoe

9 Using a screwdriver or adjustable spanner, lever the trailing shoe from the bottom anchor, and disconnect the lower return spring **(see illustration)**.
10 Pull the trailing shoe outwards, then disconnect the handbrake cable from the lever on the shoe **(see illustration)**.
11 Remove the leading brake shoe, together with the self-adjusting mechanism, from the backplate.
12 Unhook the spring, and disconnect the self-adjusting mechanism from the leading shoe.
13 Clean the self-adjusting mechanism, paying particular attention to the wheel and threads. Note that the left-hand and right-hand mechanisms are not interchangeable. Apply a little high-melting-point grease to the threads of the adjuster.
14 Clean the backplate, then apply a little high-melting-point grease to the shoe contact points on the backplate.
15 Transfer the self-adjusting mechanism to the new leading shoe, making sure that the spring is correctly fitted. Adjust the ratchet nut to the fork end of the strut, so that the strut is at its minimum length. Refit the spring to hold it in place.
16 If necessary, fit a new black pin and white sleeve to the backplate.
17 Attach the handbrake cable to the lever on the new trailing shoe, then locate the shoe on the backplate, making sure that its ends are located on the wheel cylinder piston and the bottom anchor. Refit the shoe steady spring to hold it in place **(see illustration)**.

15.3 Loosening the flexible brake hose union on the rear of the wheel cylinder

18 Connect the lower return spring to both shoes, then pull the leading shoe onto the lower anchor. Locate the self-adjusting mechanism between both shoes **(see illustrations)**. Fit the shoe steady spring to the leading shoe.
19 Refit the upper return spring.
20 Check that the shoes are located centrally on the backplate, and that the springs are in position.
21 Refit the rear brake drum, with reference to Section 12.

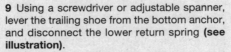

15 Rear wheel cylinder - removal and refitting

Note: *Refer to the warning on the dangers of hydraulic fluid at the start of Section 10 before proceeding.*

Removal

1 Remove the rear brake shoes, as described in Section 14.
2 Using a hose clamp, clamp the rear brake hose leading to the rear wheel cylinder.
3 Clean the area around the flexible brake hose union on the rear of the wheel cylinder, then loosen it a half turn **(see illustration)**.
4 Unscrew the two mounting bolts, and withdraw the wheel cylinder inwards from the backplate **(see illustrations)**.
5 Unscrew the wheel cylinder from the hose, and remove the seal **(see illustration)**.

15.4a Unscrew the mounting bolts . . .

15.4b ... and withdraw the wheel cylinder inwards from the backplate

Refitting

6 Wipe clean the backplate, and pull the flexible hydraulic hose through the wheel cylinder mounting hole.

7 Fit a new seal, and screw the wheel cylinder onto the flexible hydraulic hose. Do not fully tighten the union at this stage.

8 Insert the two mounting bolts, and tighten them to the specified torque.

9 Tighten the hose union to the specified torque. Make sure that the hose is not twisted - the hose has a white line on it to help in this respect. If the hose is twisted, re-position the mounting at the other end of the hose.

10 Refit the rear brake shoes, with reference to Section 14.

11 Remove the hose clamp, and bleed the hydraulic system as described in Section 6.

16 Rear wheel cylinder - overhaul

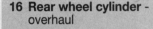

Note: *Refer to the warning on the dangers of hydraulic fluid at the start of Section 10 before proceeding.*

1 If the wheel cylinder seals are leaking, it may be possible to cure the problem by fitting new seals, provided that the wheel cylinder bore is not worn or corroded excessively.

16.6 Rear wheel cylinder pistons and seals

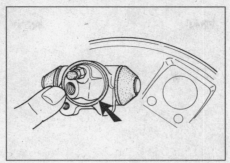

15.5 Rear wheel cylinder mounting seal location

Note, however, that if the wheel cylinders have seen extended service, it may be preferable (and perhaps no more expensive) to renew the wheel cylinders complete - check parts prices and availability.

2 First remove the brake shoes, as described in Section 14.

3 Using a hose clamp, clamp the hydraulic hose leading to the rear wheel cylinder.

4 Unscrew the bleed screw one turn.

5 Position cloth rags beneath the wheel cylinder, to catch any spilled fluid.

6 Prise both dust covers from the ends of the wheel cylinder, and pull out the pistons, followed by the return spring. Keep the pistons identified for position **(see illustration)**.

7 Prise the seals from the pistons.

8 Wipe the pistons and the inside of the wheel cylinder bore clean, and examine them for damage, wear and corrosion. If the surfaces of the bore or pistons are scored or deeply worn, the complete wheel cylinder should be renewed. If the surfaces are in good condition, the seals may be renewed as follows.

9 Lubricate the bore of the wheel cylinder and the pistons with the special grease supplied with the repair kit.

10 Using the fingers only (no tools), manipulate the seals onto the pistons, making sure that the sealing lips are located the correct way round. Fit the dust covers on the pistons as well.

11 Insert the first piston into the cylinder with a twisting motion, and locate the dust cover in the groove on the wheel cylinder.

12 Insert the return spring followed by the second piston, again using a twisting motion

17.2 Prising off the damping spring

and locating the dust cover in the groove on the wheel cylinder.

13 Tighten the bleed screw.

14 Remove the hose clamp, and refit the brake shoes with reference to Section 14.

15 Bleed the brake hydraulic system, with reference to Section 6.

16 Lower the car to the ground.

17 Rear brake pads - renewal

⚠ *Warning: Disc brake pads must be renewed on both rear wheels at the same time - never renew the pads on only one wheel, as uneven braking may result. Also, the dust created by wear of the pads may contain asbestos, which is a health hazard. Never blow it out with compressed air, and don't inhale any of it. An approved filtering mask should be worn when working on the brakes. DO NOT use petroleum-based solvents to clean brake parts - use brake cleaner or methylated spirit only.*

1 Loosen the rear wheel bolts. Chock the front roadwheels, then jack up the rear of the car and support on axle stands. Remove the rear roadwheels.

2 Noting its fitted location, use a screwdriver to prise off the damping spring **(see illustration)**.

3 Working on one side, prise out the rubber plug from the inner side of the caliper.

4 Insert a screwdriver between the outer brake pad and the hole in the caliper, and lever the caliper outwards to maintain pressure on the piston. Using an Allen key inserted through the plug hole in the caliper, turn the automatic adjuster anti-clockwise until no more resistance is felt **(see illustration)**. This action will return the automatic adjuster to its original position, to allow for new pads to be inserted. Do not attempt to unscrew the adjuster more than this, as damage may be caused.

5 Prise the two rubber caps from over the caliper guide pins, then use an Allen key or socket to unscrew the pins **(see illustrations)**. Leave the pins in their sleeves, to prevent entry of dust and dirt.

17.4 Turning the automatic adjuster using an Allen key

9

17.5a Prise off the rubber caps . . .

17.5b . . . then unscrew the guide pins using an Allen key

Overhaul

7 With the caliper on the bench, wipe away all traces of dust and dirt, but *avoid inhaling the dust as it is a health hazard*.

8 Using an Allen key through the special hole in the caliper, turn the automatic adjuster clockwise until the piston moves freely.

9 Prise the dust cover from the groove in the caliper, then pull the piston out of its bore. Remove the dust cover from the piston.

10 Using a suitable blunt instrument (such as a knitting needle or a thick feeler blade), carefully extract the piston seal from the caliper bore.

11 Unscrew the bleed screw, and remove the guide pins and sleeves.

12 Clean all the parts in methylated spirit or clean brake fluid, and wipe dry using a lint-free cloth. Inspect the piston and caliper bore for signs of damage, scuffing or corrosion; if these conditions are evident, renew the caliper body assembly. Inspect the condition of the dust excluders over the guide pins, and renew these too if there is any sign of damage or deterioration. Check the guide pins for damage or distortion, and renew if necessary **(see illustration)**.

13 If the components are in satisfactory condition, a repair kit consisting of new seals and dust excluders should be obtained. The guide pins and sleeves are also obtainable as a separate kit.

14 Lubricate the caliper bore, piston and seal with the special grease supplied in the repair kit, or if necessary use fresh hydraulic fluid.

6 Withdraw the caliper over the brake pads **(see illustration)**. Either rest the caliper on an axle stand, or alternatively suspend it with wire, taking care not to strain the flexible brake hose.

7 Withdraw the two brake pads from the carrier bracket. If required, the thickness of the pads can be checked at this stage using a steel rule (refer to Chapter 1 Specifications for pad thicknesses).

8 Before refitting the pads, check that the guide pins are free to move, and check that the rubber dust caps are undamaged. Brush the dust and dirt from the caliper and piston, but do not inhale it, as it is a health hazard. Inspect the dust excluder around the piston for damage, and inspect the piston for evidence of fluid leaks, corrosion or damage. If attention to any of these components is necessary, refer to Section 18.

9 Locate the pads in the carrier bracket, then position the caliper over them.

10 Insert the guide pins, and tighten them to the specified torque using a suitable Allen socket **(see illustration)**. **Do not** lubricate the pins or sleeves, as the sleeves are made of self-lubricating plastic.

11 Refit the guide pin rubber caps and the damping spring.

12 Using the Allen key inserted through the special hole in the caliper, turn the automatic adjuster clockwise until resistance is felt, then turn the adjuster anti-clockwise until the brake disc can be rotated freely. Refit the rubber plug.

13 Repeat the procedure on the remaining rear brake, then refit the roadwheels.

14 On completion, check the hydraulic fluid level in the reservoir; depress the brake pedal two or three times to bring the pads into contact with the disc, and lower the car to the ground.

15 Check the handbrake adjustment, with reference to Chapter 1.

18 Rear brake caliper - removal, overhaul and refitting

Note: *Refer to the warning on the dangers of hydraulic fluid at the start of Section 10 before proceeding.*

Removal

1 Loosen the rear wheel bolts. Chock the front roadwheels, then jack up the rear of the car and support on axle stands. Remove the appropriate roadwheel.

2 Fit a brake hose clamp to the flexible brake hose leading to the rear brake caliper - this will minimise brake fluid loss during subsequent operations.

3 Loosen (do not remove) the union on the caliper end of the flexible brake hose.

4 Remove the brake pads, as described in Section 17.

5 Unscrew the brake caliper from the flexible brake hose. Be prepared for some loss of fluid - place a container beneath the caliper.

6 Unhook the handbrake cable from the operating lever on the caliper, and withdraw the caliper. Pour out the remaining fluid.

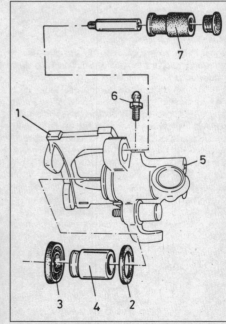

18.12 Rear brake caliper components

1 Caliper	5 Automatic
2 Piston seal	adjuster
3 Dust cover	6 Bleed screw
4 Piston	7 Dust cover

17.6 Withdraw the caliper over the brake pads

17.10 Tighten the guide pins to the specified torque

Also smear the inside of the dust cover with grease or fluid.

15 Fit the seal in the groove in the caliper bore.

16 Insert the piston in the caliper bore, and turn the automatic adjuster anti-clockwise until the piston is fully against the stop in the caliper.

17 Fit the dust cover to the grooves in the piston and caliper.

18 Refit the bleed screw, guide pins and sleeves.

Refitting

19 Screw the caliper fully onto the flexible brake hose, but do not tighten it at this stage.

20 Hook the handbrake cable onto the operating lever on the caliper.

21 Refit the brake pads, with reference to Section 17.

22 Fully tighten the flexible brake hose union to the specified torque.

23 Remove the brake hose clamp from the flexible brake hose.

24 Bleed the hydraulic system, with reference to Section 6. It should only be necessary to bleed the rear brake which has been disconnected. Check on completion, however, that the pedal is firm, and if necessary bleed the complete system.

25 Refit the roadwheel and lower the car to the ground.

---

19 Rear brake disc - inspection, removal and refitting

Note: *If either disc requires renewal, BOTH should be renewed at the same time, to ensure even and consistent braking. New brake pads should also be fitted.*

Inspection

1 Loosen the rear wheel bolts. Chock the front roadwheels, then jack up the rear of the car and support on axle stands. Remove the appropriate rear roadwheel.

2 Rotate the disc by hand, and examine it for deep scoring, grooving or cracks. Light scoring is normal, and may be removed with emery tape, but if excessive, the disc must be renewed.

3 Any loose rust and scale around the outer edge of the disc can be removed by lightly tapping it with a small hammer while rotating the disc.

4 Measure the disc thickness with a micrometer, if available. Disc run-out (warpage) can be checked using a dial test gauge, although a less-accurate (but perhaps more accessible) method is to use a feeler gauge together with a metal base block. Do not confuse disc warpage with wear in the hub bearings - the figures quoted by Volvo for disc run-out are for testing the discs when removed.

20.3 Handbrake cable adjuster and front ends of the handbrake cables

Removal

5 Prise out the rubber plug from the inner side of the caliper.

6 Insert an Allen key through the hole in the caliper, and turn the automatic adjuster anti-clockwise until the brake pads are clear of the disc.

7 Unscrew the two bolts securing the brake caliper assembly to the rear axle, and lift the assembly off of the brake disc. Either rest the caliper on an axle stand, or alternatively suspend it with wire, taking care not to strain the hydraulic hose.

8 Using a screwdriver or small chisel, tap the grease cap from the centre of the disc.

9 Unscrew the hub nut, and remove the washer.

10 Withdraw the hub and disc assembly off the stub axle.

11 If necessary, remove the bearing, with reference to Chapter 10, Section 9.

Refitting

12 Locate the hub and disc assembly onto the stub axle.

13 Fit the washer and a new hub nut, and tighten the nut to the specified torque.

14 Tap the grease cap onto the hub.

15 Refit the brake caliper assembly together with the brake pads over the disc. Insert the caliper mounting bolts, and tighten them to the specified torque.

16 Depress the footbrake pedal several times to set the pads in their normal position.

17 Check and if necessary adjust the handbrake, with reference to Chapter 1.

20.5 Base of the handbrake, showing the wiring (arrowed) to the warning light switch

---

20 Handbrake lever - removal, overhaul and refitting

Removal

1 Chock the front wheels, then jack up the rear of the car and support it on axle stands. Fully release the handbrake lever.

2 Working under the car, unbolt and remove the heat shield from the exhaust system.

3 Back off the cable adjuster until both handbrake cables are slack **(see illustration)**.

4 Working inside the car, remove the rear section of the centre console, with reference to Chapter 11.

5 Disconnect the wiring from the handbrake warning light switch **(see illustration)**.

6 Unscrew and remove the two handbrake lever mounting bolts.

7 Extract the spring clip, and withdraw the clevis pin securing the cable to the lever.

8 Withdraw the handbrake lever assembly from inside the car.

Overhaul

9 To renew the pushbutton operating rod and spring, or ratchet, first drill out the pivot pin.

10 Remove the pushbutton complete with the operating rod, spring and ratchet pawl, or remove the ratchet.

11 Fit the new components to the lever.

12 With the holes aligned, fit a new pivot pin, and stake it in position with a hammer and centre-punch.

Refitting

13 Refitting is a reversal of the removal procedure, but adjust the handbrake as described in Chapter 1.

---

21 Handbrake cable - removal and refitting

Primary

1 Chock the front wheels, then jack up the rear of the car and support it on axle stands. Fully release the handbrake lever.

2 Working under the car, unbolt and remove the heat shield from the exhaust system.

3 Unscrew and remove the nut on the cable adjuster, and remove the half-round stop.

4 If necessary, disconnect the equaliser from the secondary cables.

5 Working inside the car, remove the rear section of the centre console, with reference to Chapter 11.

6 Extract the spring clip and withdraw the clevis pin securing the cable to the handbrake lever.

7 Withdraw the primary cable from the car.

8 Refitting is a reversal of the removal procedure, but adjust the handbrake cable as described in Chapter 1.

9

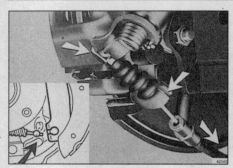

21.15 Disconnecting the handbrake cable from the rear brake disc caliper

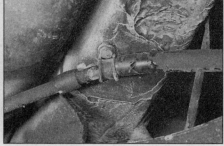

21.16a Handbrake cable support on the underbody

21.16b Handbrake cable support clip on the trailing arm

Secondary

9 Chock the front wheels, then jack up the rear of the car and support it on axle stands. Fully release the handbrake lever.

10 Working under the car, unbolt and remove the heat shield from the exhaust system.

11 Unscrew and remove the nut on the cable adjuster, and remove the half-round stop. Disconnect the equaliser from the secondary cables.

12 Disconnect the relevant handbrake cable from its front mounting by pulling out the clip.

13 Remove the relevant rear wheel.

14 On models with rear brake drums, remove the rear brake shoes as described in Section 14, then disconnect the cable from the rear brake backplate by tapping it free with a narrow punch.

15 On models with rear brake discs, pull the outer cable forwards from the caliper, and move the inner cable through the slot in the caliper bracket. Unhook the inner cable end fitting from the lever on the caliper **(see illustration)**.

16 Release the cable from the supports on the underbody, then unclip the cable from the trailing arm and withdraw the cable from under the car **(see illustrations)**.

17 Refitting is a reversal of the removal procedure, but adjust the handbrake cable as described in Chapter 1.

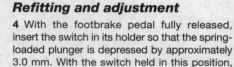

22 Stop-light switch - removal, refitting and adjustment

Removal

1 Working inside the car, remove the lower facia panel from under the steering column.

2 Disconnect the two wires from the switch terminals.

3 Turn the switch approximately 30° anti-clockwise, and withdraw it from the holder in the pedal bracket.

Refitting and adjustment

4 With the footbrake pedal fully released, insert the switch in its holder so that the spring-loaded plunger is depressed by approximately 3.0 mm. With the switch held in this position, turn it clockwise 30° to lock it in its holder.

5 Connect the two wires to the switch terminals.

6 With the ignition switched on, check that the brake stop-lights come on within a pedal stroke of 20.0 mm.

7 Refit the lower facia panel.

23 Anti-lock braking system (ABS) - general information

Two different generations of ABS have been fitted to the Volvo 400 range - models up to 1993 have an ATE Mark II system, and from 1993 onwards, a Teves Mark IV system is employed. There are detail differences between the two systems, but the principles of operation are the same.

The hydraulic components used are similar to those used in a conventional braking system, but the following additional items are fitted:

a) A speed sensor on each wheel, and a sensor gear mounted on each driveshaft and rear disc/hub, to monitor rotational speed.

b) An electronic computer comprising a self-monitoring system, a hydraulic unit which incorporates a pressure-regulating valve, and a high-pressure pump **(see illustrations)**.

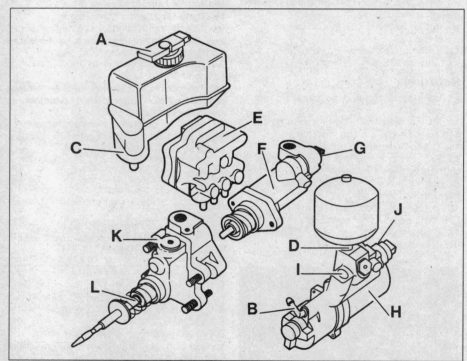

23.1a Anti-lock braking system (ABS) underbonnet components - early models

A Fluid reservoir filler cap	E Valve block	I Sealing screw
B Fluid return line	F Master cylinder	J Pressure/warning switch
C Fluid reservoir	G Main valve	K Sealing screw
D Hydraulic accumulator	H Pump unit motor	L Pushrod

Left-hand-drive version shown - right-hand-drive similar

c) *A warning light fitted to the instrument panel.*

d) *On models with the Mark IV system, a brake pedal position sensor is fitted to the base of the vacuum servo unit, which informs the system ECU how far the brake pedal has been depressed.*

The anti-lock braking system operates in the following way. As soon as the car's roadspeed exceeds 3 mph, the system becomes operational.

When the brakes are applied heavily, if a wheel starts to lock, the speed sensors detect the rapidly-falling speed of any roadwheel. The computer operates a regulator valve to reduce the hydraulic braking pressure to that wheel until the particular roadwheel deceleration ceases.

As soon as the abnormal deceleration ceases (and the danger of wheel lock-up is passed), a reverse phase begins and raises the hydraulic pressure to normal; the anti-lock cycle can be repeated up to ten times per second.

The warning light serves to indicate to the driver the fact that the system is not working. Should this happen, normal braking is still available, but the fault in the ABS must be repaired at the earliest opportunity.

If the warning light illuminates intermittently, check that the wheel sensor lead connections are clean and secure.

If a fault develops on the ABS system, it is recommended that the car be taken to a Volvo garage for diagnosis and for replacement of any components.

24 Anti-lock braking system components (Mark II ABS) - removal and refitting

Caution: As a safety precaution, the ABS should be given a comprehensive test by a qualified Volvo technician after removing and refitting any component. In the event of a fault in the system, before removing any components, have the system tested by a Volvo agent - special test equipment is required, and much time and trouble could be saved by professional diagnosis.

System ECU

1 The system ECU is located either in the rear left-hand corner of the engine compartment, under the passenger seat, or in the left-hand side of the luggage compartment, behind the side trim panel.

2 Disconnect the battery negative terminal.

Engine compartment

3 Carefully press in the ECU multi-plug retaining catch, and unplug the connector.

4 Depending on model, the ECU will be retained by a clip or a strap to its mounting bracket - release the retainer and remove the ECU.

Passenger seat

5 For easiest access, remove the passenger

23.1b Teves Mark IV ABS unit fitted to later models

seat as described in Chapter 11. If preferred, the ECU can be removed if the seat is slid forwards or backwards as necessary.

6 Remove the mounting bolts, and release the ECU from its floor mounting.

7 Carefully press in the ECU multi-plug retaining catch, and unplug the connector.

8 Remove the ECU from the car.

Luggage compartment

9 Open the tailgate or bootlid (as applicable).

10 Turn the catch, and open the ECU cover on the left-hand rear side of the luggage compartment.

11 Release the plastic strap and withdraw the ECU from its location, then press in the retaining clip and disconnect the wiring plug **(see illustration)**.

All locations

12 Refitting is a reversal of the removal procedure, but take care not to damage the terminal pins on the wiring plug as it is being reconnected.

Pressure/warning switch

Note: *Refer to the warning on the dangers of hydraulic fluid at the start of Section 10 before proceeding.*

13 Depressurise the brake hydraulic system by depressing the footbrake pedal several times until strong resistance is felt.

14 Place some cloth rags under the hydraulic unit to catch any spilled fluid.

15 With the ignition switched off, disconnect the wiring plug from the pressure/warning switch.

16 Using a thin-walled 36.0 mm box spanner,

24.11 Anti-lock braking system ECU removal

unscrew the pressure/warning switch until it is just held on by a few threads.

17 Fit a new O-ring seal to the new switch, then unscrew the old switch and fit the new switch as quickly as possible to prevent excessive loss of hydraulic fluid **(see illustration)**. Tighten the switch to the specified torque.

18 Top-up the fluid level in the reservoir, and remove the cloth rags. It is not necessary to bleed the hydraulic system.

19 Check that the switch is functioning correctly as follows. Depress the footbrake pedal and hold it down, then switch on the ignition and check that the pedal moves down slightly until resistance is felt. The ABS warning light should also go out at the same time. Switch off the ignition.

Hydraulic accumulator

Note: *Refer to the warning on the dangers of hydraulic fluid at the start of Section 10 before proceeding.*

20 Depressurise the brake hydraulic system by depressing the footbrake pedal several times until strong resistance is felt.

21 Place some cloth rags under the hydraulic unit to catch any spilled fluid.

22 Where necessary, remove the ignition coil or ignition unit, with reference to Chapter 5B.

23 Unscrew the hydraulic accumulator from the top of the pump unit, and remove the sealing O-ring.

24 To refit the accumulator, fit a new O-ring seal, then tighten the accumulator into the pump (to the specified torque).

25 Fit the ignition coil or ignition unit, if removed.

26 Top-up the fluid level in the reservoir, and remove the cloth rags. It is not necessary to bleed the hydraulic system.

27 Have the complete system checked by a Volvo agent as soon as possible (see caution at the start of the Section).

Pump unit

Note: *Refer to the warning on the dangers of hydraulic fluid at the start of Section 10 before proceeding.*

28 Depressurise the brake hydraulic system by depressing the footbrake pedal several times until strong resistance is felt.

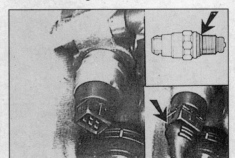

24.17 ABS pressure/warning switch removal

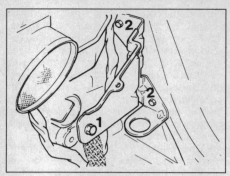

24.42 ABS bracket location on the inner wing

1 Earth lead
2 Bracket mounting bolts

29 Place some cloth rags under the hydraulic unit to catch any spilled fluid.
30 Blank off the inlet hose to the air metering unit and/or the turbocharging unit (as applicable).
31 Disconnect the wiring plugs from the pump unit.
32 Unscrew the union nut, and disconnect the hydraulic pipe from the master cylinder.
33 Unscrew the mounting bolt and remove the pump unit, noting the location of the sleeves.
34 Remove the clip, and withdraw the return hose with the right-angled nipple from the pump unit.
35 Clean the motor/pump unit assembly, then unscrew the pressure/warning switch, and remove the hydraulic accumulator from the pump.
36 Refitting is a reversal of the removal procedure, but renew the O-ring seals, and tighten the components to the specified torques. The retaining clip should be sealed with lacquer. The threads of the pump unit mounting bolt should be coated with locking fluid before inserting it and tightening to the specified torque. Do not run the pump unit with the brake fluid reservoir empty. Bleed the brake hydraulic system with reference to Section 6, and finally have the complete system checked by a Volvo agent (see caution at the start of the Section).

24.47a ABS cross-rod and brackets

1 Clevis pin removal hole in bracket

Hydraulic unit

Note: *Refer to the warning on the dangers of hydraulic fluid at the start of Section 10 before proceeding.*

37 On models fitted with air conditioning, remove the distributor cap, rotor arm, battery and battery tray, and air cleaner assembly. Blank off the inlet hose to the air metering unit and/or the turbocharging unit (as applicable).
38 Depressurise the brake hydraulic system by depressing the footbrake pedal several times until strong resistance is felt.
39 On models fitted with air conditioning, remove the drier and drier bracket from the support on the inner wing.
40 Place cloth rags beneath the hydraulic unit.
41 Unbolt the earth lead from the hydraulic unit.
42 Unscrew the mounting bolts, and remove the bracket from the inner wing **(see illustration)**.
43 Unscrew the union nuts, and disconnect the brake pipes.

Models with clevis removal hole in bracket

44 Have an assistant depress the brake pedal and hold it down.
45 Unscrew the four mounting nuts, and withdraw the hydraulic unit forwards from the bracket.
46 Disconnect the wiring connectors.
47 Extract the spring clip, and remove the clevis pin connecting the hydraulic unit to the cross-rod **(see illustrations)**.

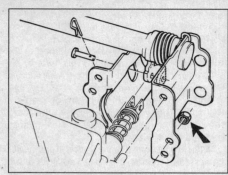

24.47b ABS hydraulic unit removal - bracket with hole

48 Withdraw the hydraulic unit from the engine compartment.

Models without clevis removal hole in bracket

49 Working inside the car, unscrew the four nuts securing the pedal bracket to the bulkhead **(see illustration)**.
50 Extract the spring clip, and disconnect the pushrod from the brake pedal.
51 Working in the engine compartment, withdraw the cross-rod bracket from the bulkhead, and recover any packing.
52 Unscrew the four mounting nuts, then raise the hydraulic unit slightly.
53 Disconnect the wiring connectors.
54 Extract the spring clip, then disconnect the cross-rod from the bracket. Note the return spring is still under tension, so be prepared to release it slowly **(see illustration)**.
55 Remove the clevis pin, and withdraw the hydraulic unit from the engine compartment.
56 If necessary, the brake pedal pushrod may now be removed. On models fitted with a turbocharger, first remove the ignition coil and modulation valve on the bulkhead.

All models

57 Clean the exterior of the hydraulic unit, and drain the fluid from the reservoir.
58 Unscrew the union nut, and disconnect the brake pipe from the hydraulic unit, then remove the brake fluid reservoir and pump unit.
59 Refitting is a reversal of the removal procedure, but renew the O-ring seals, and tighten each component to the specified torque. Check the pushrod for signs of damage or excessive wear. Bleed the brake hydraulic system with reference to Section 6, and finally have the complete system checked by a Volvo agent (see caution at the start of the Section).

Front wheel sensor

60 Apply the handbrake, then jack up the front of the car and support on axle stands. Remove the applicable front wheel.
61 In the engine compartment, pull the wiring connector from the clip on the inner wing, and disconnect the plug.

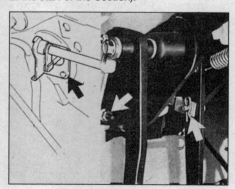

24.49 Brake pedal/cross-rod removal

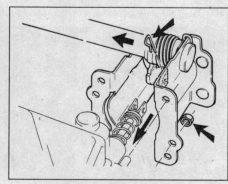

24.54 ABS hydraulic unit removal - bracket without hole

62 Prise out the rubber grommet, and pull the sensor wiring into the wheel arch **(see illustration)**.

63 Unscrew the mounting bolt, and remove the sensor from the hub carrier by turning it slightly.

64 Remove the sensor and wiring from the brackets - on the right-hand side, release the cable tie, and pull back the insulating sleeve on the cable.

65 Refitting is a reversal of the removal procedure. Smear the sensor with a little grease before refitting it. Apply a little locking fluid to the threads of the mounting bolt, and tighten the bolt to the specified torque.

Rear wheel sensor

66 Chock the front wheels, then jack up the rear of the car and support on axle stands.

67 Remove the rear light cluster unit bulbholder, with reference to Chapter 12, Section 7.

68 Remove the wiring connector from the clip, then disconnect the plug.

69 Prise the rubber grommet from the underbody, and pull the cable through **(see illustration)**. Disconnect the wiring from the brackets on the rear suspension radius arms.

70 Unscrew the mounting bolt, and remove the sensor form the stub axle by turning it slightly.

71 Refitting is a reversal of the removal procedure. Smear the sensor with a little grease before refitting it. Apply a little locking fluid to the threads of the mounting bolt, and tighten the bolt to the specified torque.

Sensor gears

72 The sensor gears are located on the front driveshafts and rear disc/hubs; although they may be removed separately, it is suggested that this work is entrusted to a Volvo dealer.

---

25 Anti-lock braking system components (Mark IV ABS) - removal and refitting

Caution: As a safety precaution, the ABS should be given a comprehensive test by a qualified Volvo technician after removing and refitting any component. In the event of a fault in the system, before removing any components, have the system tested by a Volvo agent - special test equipment is required, and much time and trouble could be saved by professional diagnosis.

System ECU

1 The system ECU is located in the engine compartment. Disconnect the battery negative terminal.

2 Unplug the upper connector from the ECU.

3 Unscrew and remove the three rubber-mounted nuts securing the hydraulic control unit, and slide the unit sideways and upwards out of its mounting bracket, taking care not to

24.62 ABS front wheel sensor removal

1 *Rubber grommet*
2 *Sensor mounting bolt*

strain the hydraulic pipes and hoses, nor the wiring to the relay **(see illustration)**.

4 Supporting the hydraulic unit, remove the socket-head screws securing the ECU to the unit, and remove the ECU from the car.

5 Refitting is a reversal of the removal procedure, tightening all mountings securely, and taking care not to damage the terminal pins on the wiring plug as it is being reconnected.

Brake pedal position sensor

6 The brake pedal position sensor can be removed from the vacuum servo without disturbing any of the other braking system components. However, access to the sensor is limited. Move aside as much of the wiring harness and hoses as can be achieved without disconnection.

7 Disconnect the wiring connector, then use a pair of circlip pliers to release the retaining circlip at the base of the sensor, and withdraw the sensor from the servo **(see illustration)**.

8 Refitting is a reversal of removal. If a new sensor is being fitted, use the same colour end fitting on the new sensor as the one removed.

System relay

9 The combination relay is located below the hydraulic unit, at the front. Disconnect the battery negative terminal.

10 Disconnect the two wiring plugs from the base of the relay, noting that the smaller grey connector is to the rear.

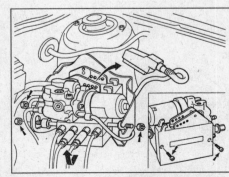

25.3 Removing the ABS hydraulic unit and ECU

24.69 ABS rear wheel sensor removal

1 *Rubber grommet*
2 *Sensor mounting bolt*

11 Unhook the relay from the mounting bracket, and remove it from the car.

12 Refitting is a reversal of removal, making sure that the wiring connections are securely made.

Hydraulic unit

Note: *On models with the Mark IV ABS unit (fitted from 1993 onwards), the unit cannot be dismantled - if any one of the components is faulty, a complete unit must be fitted.*

13 Disconnect the battery negative lead.

14 Depressurise the brake hydraulic system by depressing the footbrake pedal several times until strong resistance is felt.

15 On models fitted with air conditioning, remove the drier and drier bracket from the support on the inner wing, where applicable.

16 Disconnect the upper wiring connector to the ECU, and the smaller grey connector from the system relay at the base of the unit.

17 Place cloth rags beneath the hydraulic unit.

18 Noting their positions carefully (attach labels if necessary), disconnect the fluid supply and return hoses, and the six union connections, from the hydraulic unit **(see illustration)**.

19 Unscrew and remove the three rubber-mounted nuts securing the hydraulic control unit, and slide the unit sideways and upwards out of its mounting bracket.

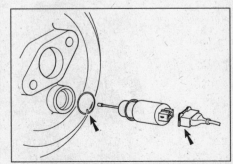

25.7 Removing the brake pedal position sensor - circlip and wiring connector arrowed

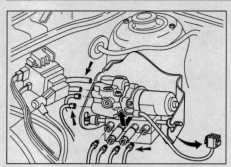

25.18 Disconnecting the fluid pipes, hoses and relay wiring when removing the ABS hydraulic unit

Wheel sensor components

20 Refer to the appropriate paragraphs of Section 24.

26 Traction control system - general information

On later turbo models, a traction control system is fitted as standard, and was available as an option on other models with ABS. The system is an additional part of the anti-lock braking system. When wheelspin is detected via the front wheel ABS sensors, an extra pair of valves on the ABS unit open to apply the front brakes until the spinning wheels are brought under control. As with ABS, any problems with the traction control system are best referred to a Volvo dealer in the first instance.

Chapter 10
Suspension and steering

Contents

Degrees of difficulty

Easy, suitable for novice with little experience	**Fairly easy,** suitable for beginner with some experience	**Fairly difficult,** suitable for competent DIY mechanic	**Difficult,** suitable for experienced DIY mechanic	**Very difficult,** suitable for expert DIY or professional

Specifications

Front suspension
Type . . . . Independent by MacPherson struts and coil springs, integral telescopic shock absorbers and anti-roll bar

Rear suspension
Type . . . . Independent Watt linkage with trailing arms and coil springs, constant-track beam axle, telescopic shock absorbers and anti-roll bar

Roadwheels
Type . . . . Pressed-steel or aluminium alloy, according to model
Size . . . . 5.5Jx14 or 6Jx14

Tyres
Size:
    5.5Jx14 pressed-steel wheels 175/65R14T
    5.5Jx14 pressed-steel wheels 165/70R14T
    5.5Jx14 alloy wheels 185/60HR14
    6Jx14 alloy wheels 185/60HR14
Pressures . . . . See end of Weekly checks

Steering
Type . . . . Rack-and-pinion, power-assisted on some models
Turns lock-to-lock:
    Manual steering 3.9
    Power steering 3.1

Wheel alignment settings

Camber angle (front wheels):
 440 and 460 models . . . . - 0° 24' ± 30'
 480 up to chassis number 520381 . . . . 0° ± 30'
 480 from chassis number 520382 . . . . - 0° 30' ± 30'
Castor angle (front wheels):
 440 and 460 models . . . . 4° 06' ± 30'
 480 up to chassis number 520381 . . . . 4° 16' ± 30'
 480 from chassis number 520382 . . . . 3° 20' ± 30'
Maximum castor variation between sides . . . . 0° 30'
Steering axis inclination (front wheels) . . . . 13° 15' ± 30'
Toe setting (front wheels):
 At wheel rim . . . . 0 to 1.0 mm toe-in
 Halfway between rim and outer edge of tyre . . . . 0 to 1.5 mm toe-in
 At outer edge of tyre . . . . 0 to 2.0 mm toe-in
Rear wheel toe setting (at wheel rim):
 440 and 460 models . . . . 2.0 to 4.0 mm toe-in
 480 up to chassis number 510749 . . . . 2.0 to 4.0 mm toe-in
 480 from chassis number 510750 . . . . 0 mm

Torque wrench settings

	Nm	lbf ft
Front suspension		
Anti-roll bar link	35	26
Anti-roll bar U-clamps	21	15
Front hub/driveshaft nut (use a new nut):		
Automatic transmission models	230	170
Manual gearbox models	220	162
Lower arm (use new nuts/bolts)	80	59
Lower arm balljoint (use new nuts/bolts)	45	33
Lower arm balljoint castellated nut (use new split pin)	55	41
Strut piston nut (use a new nut)	65	48
Strut upper mounting bolts	25	18
Stub axle carrier-to-suspension strut bolts (use new bolts)	100	74
Rear suspension		
Anti-roll bar link	30	22
Anti-roll bar U-clamps	21	15
Panhard rod to rear axle	100	74
Panhard rod to underbody	75	55
Radius arms	40	30
Rear axle mounting bolts	40	30
Rear hub nut	180	133
Rear stub axle	40	30
Shock absorber	52	38
Trailing arm	40	30
Steering		
Airbag module screws	8	6
Intermediate shaft pinch-bolt	18	13
Power steering high-pressure line banjo bolt	35	26
Power steering high-pressure line on pump	26	19
Power steering hydraulic line union nuts	33	24
Power steering pump mounting bolt	21	15
Power steering pump pivot bolt	40	30
Power steering unions in steering gear	41	30
Steering column	23	17
Steering column height adjustment pivot bolt	22	16
Steering column steady bracket	21	15
Steering gear	21	15
Steering wheel	60	44
Tie-rod end balljoint	55	41
Tie-rod end locknut	75	55
Tie-rod to rack	85	63
Roadwheels		
All models	110	81

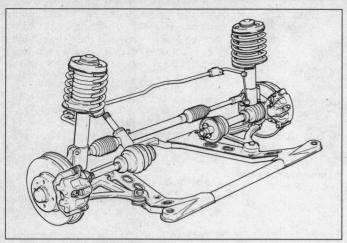

1.1 Front suspension and steering components

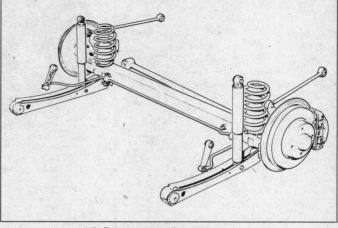

1.2 Rear suspension components

1 General information

The independent front suspension is of the MacPherson strut type, incorporating coil springs, integral telescopic shock absorbers, and an anti-roll bar. The struts are attached to stub axle carriers at their lower ends by two bolts, and the carriers are in turn attached to the lower suspension arm by balljoints. The anti-roll bar is attached to the bulkhead by rubber mountings, and is attached to the front suspension struts by vertical links (also incorporating rubber bearings) **(see illustration)**.

The independent rear suspension is of independent Watt linkage type, with trailing arms, constant-track beam axle, coil springs, shock absorbers, rear radius arms and an anti-roll bar. On models with a high performance specification, the shock absorbers are of pressurized gas type **(see illustration)**.

A rack-and-pinion steering gear is fitted, together with a standard or adjustable steering column and 'safety' intermediate shaft **(see illustration)**.

Power-assisted steering is available on some models. Variable-ratio steering is provided on both manual and power-assisted steering - with manual steering, the rack tooth spacing is calibrated to give less effort when parking; with power steering, progressively-increasing assistance occurs as the engine speed decreases **(see illustrations)**.

1.3 Steering column components

1 Steering gear	5 Lower nylon bearing	10 Nut
2 Lower universal joint	6 Inner column	11 Adjustable steering
3 Intermediate shaft	7 Upper bearing	column locking lever
4 Upper universal joint	8 Hub	12 Outer column
	9 Steering wheel	

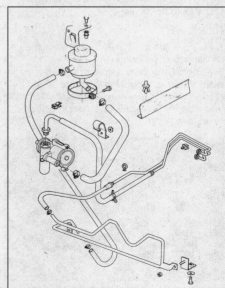

1.4a Power-assisted steering system with tubular cooler

10

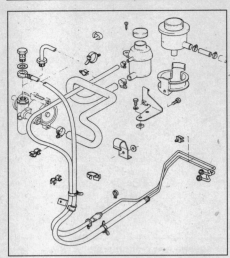

1.4b Power-assisted steering system without tubular cooler

2 Front hub bearings - checking, removal and refitting

Note: *The front hub bearings should only be removed from the stub axle carrier if they are to be renewed. The removal procedure renders the bearings unserviceable, and they must not be re-used.*

Checking

1 Wear in the front hub bearings can be checked by measuring the amount of side play present. To do this, a dial test indicator should be fixed so that its probe is in contact with the disc face of the hub. The play should be between 0 and 0.05 mm. If it is greater than this, the bearings are worn excessively, and should be renewed.

Removal

2 Remove the stub axle carrier from the car, as described in Section 3.
3 Support the stub axle carrier securely on blocks or in a vice. Using a tube of suitable diameter in contact with the inner end of the hub flange, drive the hub flange out of the bearing.

2.10 Stake the new dust cover to the stub axle carrier in three places

4 The bearing will come apart as the hub flange is removed, and one of the bearing inner races will remain on the hub flange. To remove it, support the flange in a vice, and use a two or three-legged puller.
5 Extract the bearing retaining circlip from the inner end of the stub axle carrier.
6 Support the stub axle carrier on blocks or in a vice, so that the side nearest the roadwheel is uppermost.
7 Place the previously-removed inner race back in position over the ball cage. Using a tube of suitable diameter in contact with the inner race, drive the complete bearing assembly out of the stub axle carrier.
8 Remove the dust cover from the outer side of the stub axle carrier.

Refitting

9 Clean the bearing location seating inside the hub.
10 Fit a new dust cover to the outer side of the stub axle carrier, and stake it in three places using a blunt chisel **(see illustration)**.
11 Fit the outer circlip in its groove in the stub axle carrier.
12 Support the stub axle carrier so that the side away from the roadwheel is uppermost, and place the new bearing squarely in position.
13 Using a tube of suitable diameter in contact with the bearing outer race, drive the bearing into the stub axle carrier until it contacts the circlip. Ensure that the bearing goes in completely square - if it tips at all, it will bind as it is being fitted.
14 Fit the inner circlip in its groove in the stub axle carrier.

15 Locate the stub axle carrier and bearing assembly over the hub flange, and drive the bearing inner races onto the flange using a tube in contact with the bearing's inner race.
16 Refit the stub axle carrier with reference to Section 3.

3 Front stub axle carrier - removal and refitting

Removal

1 Remove the wheel cover or centre cover from the appropriate wheel, to expose the central driveshaft nut.
2 With the handbrake firmly applied, loosen the driveshaft nut two or three turns. This nut is very tight, and it may be necessary to slip a metal tube (such as a length of scaffold pole) over the socket handle to get enough leverage. If the car moves, have an assistant depress the footbrake as well.
3 Loosen the wheel bolts, then jack up the front of the car and support it on axle stands. Remove the appropriate roadwheel.
4 Remove the front brake disc with reference to Chapter 9, then unbolt the brake caliper frame from the stub axle carrier.
5 Unscrew the nut from the outer end of the driveshaft, and remove the washer. Discard the nut once removed - a new nut must be obtained for reassembly.
6 Disconnect the steering tie-rod end balljoint from the stub axle carrier, with reference to Section 27.
7 Unscrew and remove the two bolts securing the stub axle carrier to the suspension strut. Note that the nuts are on the brake caliper side **(see illustrations)**. Discard these bolts once removed - new bolts must be obtained for reassembly.
8 Unscrew and remove the two bolts securing the lower balljoint to the front suspension lower arm.
9 Withdraw the stub axle carrier from the drive-shaft, and remove it from the car. If the driveshaft is a tight fit in the drive flange, tap it out using a plastic mallet, or use a suitable puller **(see illustration)**.

3.7a Unscrewing the nuts and bolts securing the suspension strut to the upper part of the stub axle carrier

3.7b The bolt heads are on the brake caliper side

3.9 Separating the stub axle carrier from the driveshaft with a puller

3.10 Applying thread-locking fluid to the front brake caliper mounting bolts

Refitting

10 Refitting is a reversal of the removal procedure, but observe the following points:

a) Apply thread-locking fluid to the splines on the driveshaft outer joint stub axle before inserting it into the drive flange.

b) Renew the driveshaft nut and the stub axle carrier-to-suspension strut bolts.

c) Apply thread-locking fluid to the threads of the front brake caliper mounting bolts **(see illustration)** before inserting and tightening them.

d) Tighten all nuts and bolts to the specified torque (refer also to Chapter 9 as necessary).

4.4 Front suspension strut removal

1 *Anti-roll bar link mounting on the strut*
2 *Flexible brake hose location through the bracket on early models (cut-out on later models)*
3 *Stub axle carrier-to-strut mounting nuts*

4.8 Unscrewing a suspension strut upper mounting bolt (remaining one arrowed) - do not remove strut piston nut located below dust cap

4 Front suspension strut - removal and refitting

Removal

1 Loosen the wheel bolts. Apply the handbrake, then jack up the front of the car and support it on axle stands. Remove the appropriate front roadwheel.

2 Unscrew and remove the two nuts and bolts securing the suspension strut to the upper part of the stub axle carrier. Note that the bolt heads are on the brake caliper side. Discard these bolts once removed - new bolts must be obtained for reassembly.

3 Unscrew the nut securing the front anti-roll bar link to the strut, and move the link to one side **(see illustration)**. This photograph also shows the slotted type strut bracket for the flexible brake hose; if the strut bracket on your car is slotted, pull the hose out and proceed to paragraph 8.

4 On early models, the flexible brake hose is routed through the strut bracket, and it is therefore necessary to disconnect the hose before removing the strut **(see illustration)**. Unscrew the filler cap from the brake hydraulic fluid reservoir, then tighten it down onto a piece of polythene sheet. This will prevent excessive loss of brake fluid in the subsequent procedure. Refer to the warning in Chapter 9, Section 6, about the dangers of hydraulic fluid.

5 Unscrew the union nut attaching the rigid brake pipe to the flexible hose end fitting at the bracket under the wheel arch. Plug the rigid pipe.

6 Detach the flexible hose end fitting from the bracket.

7 Remove the locating plate, and pull the flexible brake hose through the bracket on the strut.

8 Support the strut, then from within the engine compartment, unscrew the two bolts securing the strut upper mounting to the turret **(see illustration)**. Withdraw the strut from under the wheelarch.

Refitting

9 Refitting is a reversal of the removal pro-

5.2 Spring compressors fitted to the front coil spring

4.3 Anti-roll bar link connection to the front suspension strut. Note the slotted bracket for the brake hose (arrowed)

cedure, but note the following additional points:

a) Tighten all nuts and bolts to the specified torque wrench settings.

b) Apply a little locking fluid to the threads of the strut upper mounting bolts.

c) Bleed the brake hydraulic system, with reference to Chapter 9.

5 Front suspension strut - overhaul

Note: *Before attempting to dismantle the front suspension strut, a set of coil spring compressors and a new strut piston nut must be obtained.*

Dismantling

1 With the strut removed from the car, clean away all external dirt, then mount it upright in a vice.

2 Fit the spring compressors, and compress the coil spring until all tension is relieved from the upper mounting **(see illustration)**. Note that the compressors should be located directly opposite each other on the spring.

3 Withdraw the plastic cap over the strut piston nut, hold the strut piston with an Allen key, and unscrew the nut with a ring spanner **(see illustration)**. Discard the strut piston nut once removed - a new one must be obtained for reassembly.

4 Lift off the washer, upper mounting and spring seat assembly, followed by the spring

10

5.3 Unscrewing the front suspension strut piston nut

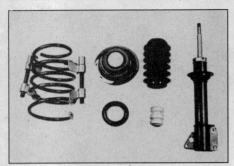

5.4 Front suspension strut components

6.2 Front anti-roll bar side link

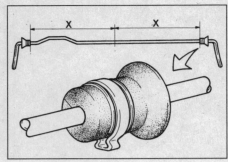

6.7 Flexible bush locations on the front anti-roll bar

X = 395.0 mm

with compressors still attached - do not remove the compressors from the spring, unless the spring is to be renewed. Finally, remove the bump stop, convoluted rubber cone, and the lower spring seat and bearing components **(see illustration)**.

Examination

5 With the strut assembly now completely dismantled, examine all the components for wear, damage or deformation, and check the bearings for smoothness of operation. Renew any of the components as necessary.
6 Examine the strut for signs of fluid leakage. Check the strut piston for signs of pitting along its entire length, and check the strut body for signs of damage or elongation of the mounting bolt holes.
7 To test the operation of the strut, hold it in an upright position; move the piston through a full stroke, and then through short strokes of 50 to 100 mm. In both cases, the resistance felt should be smooth and continuous. If the resistance is jerky, or uneven, or if there is any visible sign of wear or damage to the strut, renewal is necessary.

Reassembly

8 Reassembly is a reversal of dismantling, but make sure that the spring ends are correctly located in the upper and lower seats, and tighten the new piston nut to the specified torque.

6 Front anti-roll bar - removal and refitting

Removal

1 Apply the handbrake, then jack up the front of the car and support on axle stands.
2 Unscrew the nuts and disconnect the side links from the anti-roll bar. If required, the side links may be removed by unscrewing the lower nuts and disconnecting them from the front suspension struts **(see illustration)**.
3 Working from inside the engine compartment, unscrew the anti-roll bar mounting bolts, and remove the mounting brackets.
4 Cut through the clips, and remove the clamps and flexible bushes.

5 Withdraw the anti-roll bar from the side of the car.
6 Check the bar for damage, and the rubber bushes for wear and deterioration. Renew the bushes if necessary.

Refitting

7 Refitting is a reversal of the removal procedure, but delay fully tightening the mounting bolts until the unladen weight of the car is on the front suspension. The two flexible bushes should be located 395.0 mm from the centre of the bar before fitting the clips, and the crimped lugs of the clips must face downwards so that they locate in the mounting bracket recesses **(see illustration)**.

7 Front suspension lower arm - removal, overhaul and refitting

Removal

1 Apply the handbrake, then jack up the front of the car and support on axle stands.
2 Remove the engine splash guard.
3 Loosen the lower arm's two inner mounting nuts.
4 Unscrew and remove the two nuts securing the front suspension lower balljoint to the outer end of the lower arm **(see illustration)**. Discard the nuts and bolts once removed - new ones must be obtained for reassembly.
5 Unscrew the nuts from the inner mounting bolts, then remove the bolts. Discard the nuts

and bolts once removed - new ones must be obtained for reassembly.
6 Swing the front wheel out as far as possible, and disconnect the balljoint from the lower arm. If the left-hand lower arm is being removed, the left-hand driveshaft will be pulled out of the differential, and care must be taken to avoid damage to the rubber boot.
7 Withdraw the lower arm from under the car.

Overhaul

8 Ideally, a press is required to remove the bushes from the lower arm, but a removal tool can be made using a long bolt, nut, washers and a short length of metal tubing. Before removing the bushes, measure the distance between them so that the new bushes can be fitted correctly.
9 Before fitting the new bushes, grind off the lower edges of the locating lugs so that they are angled, and smear a little grease on them **(see illustration)**. Press in the bushes using the metal tubing and bolt, or by using the tubing and a vice, until the locating lugs engage the recesses.

Refitting

10 Refitting is a reversal of the removal procedure, but note the following additional points:
  a) *Smear the new inner mounting bolts with grease before inserting them.*
  b) *Tighten the new outer balljoint nuts to the specified torque, but delay tightening the*

7.4 The two nuts securing the front suspension lower balljoint to the outer end of the lower arm

7.9 Grind the bush locating lugs as shown in the inset before pressing the new bushes into the lower arm

9.3 Tap off the grease cap from the rear hub

9.4a Retaining nut on the rear hub

9.4b Removing the thrustwasher from the rear hub

inner mountings until the weight of the car is on the front suspension. Flex the front suspension several times and move the car forwards a short distance before tightening the bolts to the specified torque.

8 Front suspension balljoint - removal and refitting

Removal

1 Apply the handbrake, then jack up the front of the car and support on axle stands.
2 Unscrew and remove the two bolts securing the balljoint to the front suspension lower arm. Discard the nuts and bolts once removed - new ones must be obtained for reassembly.

9.5 Removing the rear hub assembly

3 Unscrew the balljoint nut. On early models, the nut may be castellated and have a split pin - a new split pin will be required for reassembly.
4 Using a balljoint separator tool, press the balljoint out of the stub axle carrier.

Refitting

5 Refitting is a reversal of the removal procedure, but tighten the mounting nuts to the specified torque. Where a castellated nut is fitted, if the split pin holes do not line up after tightening, the nut may be tightened by (up to) a further 60° angle - it should **never** be slackened in order to fit the split pin. A new split pin should be used.

9 Rear hub bearing - checking, removal and refitting

Checking

1 Loosen the rear wheel bolts. Chock the front wheels, then jack up the rear of the car and support it on axle stands. Remove the appropriate rear roadwheel, and fully release the handbrake.
2 Wear in the rear hub bearings can be checked by measuring the amount of side play present. To do this, a dial test indicator should be fixed so that its probe is in contact with the hub. The play should be between 0 and 0.03 mm. If it is greater than this, the bearings are worn excessively, and should be renewed.

Removal

Models with rear drum brakes

3 Remove the brake drum with reference to Chapter 9, then lever or tap off the grease cap from the centre of the hub **(see illustration)**.
4 Unscrew the hub nut, and remove the thrustwasher **(see illustrations)**. The nut is extremely tight - use only good-quality, close-fitting tools, and ensure that the car is adequately supported.
5 Pull the hub bearing assembly from the stub axle **(see illustration)**.

Models with rear disc brakes

6 Remove the disc/hub assembly with reference to Chapter 9.

All models

7 With the hub removed, extract the circlip and drive out the bearing, using a tube of suitable diameter inserted from the outside of the hub and in contact with the bearing outer race **(see illustrations)**.
8 Clean the bearing seating inside the hub.

Refitting

9 Place the bearing in the hub, and drive it fully home, again using a tube in contact with the bearing outer race **(see illustration)**. Take great care to keep the bearing square as it is installed, otherwise it may jam in the hub bore.
10 With the bearing in position, refit the retaining circlip.
11 Check that the bearing inner spacer/ thrustwasher is located on the stub axle.

9.7a Extract the circlip . . .

9.7b . . . then drive out the rear hub bearing with a metal tube

9.9 Driving the bearing into the rear hub

10

9.13 Tightening the rear hub nut

Smear a little grease onto the stub axle to help the bearing slide into position.

Models with rear drum brakes

12 Slide the hub onto the stub axle, and refit the thrustwasher and hub nut.

13 Noting the precautions in paragraph 4, tighten the hub nut to the specified torque **(see illustration)**, and then tap the grease cap into place.

Models with rear disc brakes

14 Refit the brake disc/hub assembly with reference to Chapter 9.

All models

15 Depress the footbrake several times. If necessary, adjust the handbrake as described in Chapter 1.

16 Refit the roadwheel, and lower the car to the ground. Tighten the wheel bolts to the specified torque.

10 Rear stub axle - removal and refitting
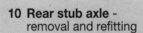

Removal

1 Remove the rear hub bearing, as described in Section 9.

2 Unscrew and remove the backplate/stub axle mounting bolts.

3 On models with rear brake discs, withdraw the backplate followed by the stub axle from the rear axle.

4 On models with rear brake drums, withdraw the backplate and suspend it with wire, taking

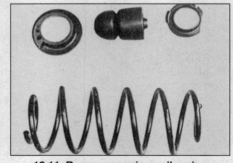
12.11 Rear suspension coil spring components

care not to strain the flexible brake hose, then remove the stub axle. If it is required to remove the backplate as well, the brake shoes and wheel cylinder will have to be removed, with reference to Chapter 9.

Refitting

5 Refitting is a reversal of the removal procedure, but tighten all nuts and bolts to the specified torque wrench settings (refer also to Chapter 9 as necessary). Refer to Section 9 when refitting the rear hub bearing, and to Chapter 9 when refitting the rear wheel cylinder on models with rear brake drums.

11 Rear anti-roll bar - removal and refitting

Removal

1 Chock the front wheels, then jack up the rear of the car and support on axle stands.

2 Disconnect the anti-roll bar from the side links by unscrewing the nuts and pulling out the links. If required, the side links may be removed by unscrewing the upper nuts and disconnecting them from the underbody.

3 Unscrew the anti-roll bar mounting bolts from the rear axle, and unhook the clamps from the rubber bushes. Withdraw the anti-roll bar from under the car.

4 Remove the flexible rubber bushes from the bar.

5 Check the bar for damage, and the rubber bushes for wear and deterioration. Renew the bushes if necessary **(see illustration)**.

Refitting

6 Refitting is a reversal of the removal procedure, but tighten the nuts to the specified torque.

12 Rear coil spring - removal and refitting

Removal

1 Chock the front wheels, then jack up the rear of the car and support on axle stands. Remove both rear wheels.

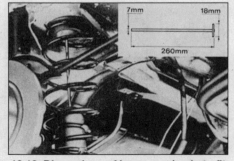
12.13 Dimensions of home-made pin to fit bump stop to rear axle

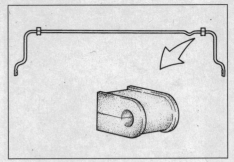
11.5 Rear anti-roll bar and flexible bushes

2 On models with rear brake discs, unbolt the brake calipers from the stub axles and suspend them with wire, taking care not to strain the flexible brake hoses.

3 On models with rear brake drums, either remove the wheel cylinders with reference to Chapter 9, or alternatively remove the stub axles with reference to Section 10, leaving the wheel cylinders connected to the hoses.

4 Unbolt the rear anti-roll bar from the rear axle, with reference to Section 11.

5 Support the rear axle centrally with a trolley jack.

6 Unscrew and remove the front mounting bolts for the trailing arms on both sides of the car.

7 Unscrew and remove the rear mounting bolts for the radius arms on both sides of the car.

8 Unscrew and remove the shock absorber lower mounting bolts from both sides of the car.

9 Lower the trolley jack until the coil springs are located loosely between the rear axle and underbody.

10 Prise the bump stop from the rear axle, then lift out the coil spring together with the bump stop and rubber cushion.

11 Clean and examine the coil spring, bump stop and rubber cushion for wear and damage, and renew them as necessary **(see illustration)**.

Refitting

12 Apply a little soapy water to the bottom of the bump stop, then locate the coil spring together with the bump stop and rubber cushion on the rear axle.

13 Make up a pin to the dimensions shown **(see illustration)**. Locate the pin on top of the bump stop, then press the bump stop firmly down into the rear axle. Remove the pin.

14 Raise the rear axle, making sure that the coil springs are correctly located.

15 Insert the shock absorber lower mounting bolts, and tighten the nuts to the specified torque.

16 Refit and tighten the rear mounting bolts for the radius arms.

17 Refit and tighten the front mounting bolts for the trailing arms.

18 Remove the trolley jack from under the rear axle.

13.2a Rear radius arm front mounting

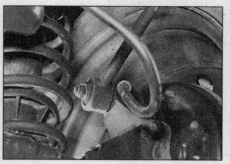

13.2b Inner view of the rear radius arm rear mounting

13.2c Outer view of the rear radius arm rear mounting

19 Refit the rear anti-roll bar to the rear axle, with reference to Section 11.
20 On models with rear brake drums, refit the stub axles with reference to Section 10, or refit the wheel cylinders with reference to Chapter 9.
21 On models with rear brake discs, refit the brake calipers to the stub axles, and tighten the bolts to the specified torque (Chapter 9).
22 Lower the car to the ground.

13 Rear radius arm - removal and refitting

Removal

1 Chock the front wheels, then jack up the rear of the car and support on axle stands.
2 Unscrew and remove the mounting nut

from the front of the radius arm, then unscrew and remove the rear mounting bolt (see illustrations).
3 On models with ABS, release the wheel sensor wiring from the radius arm.
4 Using a twisting action, remove the radius arm from the front mounting, then withdraw it from under the car. If necessary, raise the rear axle to allow the arm to pass the coil spring.

Refitting

5 Refitting is a reversal of the removal procedure. If the right-hand radius arm mounting bracket has a slot in it, loosen the right-hand mounting nut when refitting the left-hand radius arm. Delay fully tightening the radius arm mounting nut/bolt until the weight of the car is on the rear suspension.

14 Panhard rod - removal, overhaul and refitting

Removal

1 Chock the front wheels, then jack up the rear of the car and support on axle stands.
2 Unscrew and remove the Panhard rod upper mounting bolt, taking care not to damage the brake lines (see illustration).
3 Unscrew and remove the Panhard rod lower mounting bolt (see illustration).
4 Disconnect the attachment for the brake pressure-regulating valve, noting its precise position. Remove the Panhard rod from under the car.

Overhaul

5 Examine the rubber bushes, and if necessary renew them. They can be extracted using either a press, or a long bolt, nut, washers and a length of metal tubing. Once removed, the old bushes must not be re-used.

Refitting

6 Refitting is a reversal of the removal procedure, but note that the mounting bolts must be inserted from the front end. Tighten the nuts to the specified torque. The brake pressure-regulating valve should be checked and adjusted by a Volvo dealer.

15 Rear trailing arm - removal, overhaul and refitting

Removal

1 Chock the front wheels, then jack up the rear of the car and support on axle stands.
2 Disconnect the handbrake cable clip from the trailing arm.
3 Support the rear axle on an axle stand or trolley jack.
4 Unscrew and remove the appropriate rear shock absorber lower mounting bolt.
5 Unscrew and remove the rear mounting bolt securing the trailing arm to the rear axle (see illustration).
6 Unscrew and remove the front mounting bolt securing the trailing arm to the underbody (see illustration). Withdraw the trailing arm from under the car.

14.2 Panhard rod upper mounting

14.3 Panhard rod lower mounting on the rear axle

15.5 Rear suspension trailing arm connections to the rear axle and rear shock absorber

15.6 Rear suspension trailing arm connection to the underbody

10

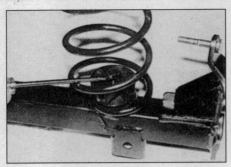

16.15 Push out the plastic locking pins with a screwdriver before removing the lower bump stops

16.16 Using a self-tapping screw to remove the upper bump stops

16.17 Fitting the upper bump stop with the arrow facing forwards

Overhaul

7 Examine the rubber bushes, and if necessary renew them. They can be extracted using either a press, or long bolt, nut, washers and a length of metal tubing. Once removed, the old bushes must not be re-used.

Refitting

8 Refitting is a reversal of the removal procedure, noting the following points:
  a) Smear the bolts with a little grease before inserting them.
  b) Delay fully tightening the bolts to the specified torque until the weight of the car is on the rear suspension.
  c) If the right-hand side radius arm mounting bracket has a slot in it, the rear axle must be aligned by loosening the right-hand radius arm bolt and allowing the arm to re-position itself, then tightening the bolt to the specified torque.

16 Rear axle - removal and refitting

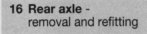

Removal

1 Loosen the rear wheel bolts. Chock the front wheels, then jack up the rear of the car and support on axle stands positioned beneath the underbody.
2 Loosen (do not remove) the nuts on the mounting bolts securing the trailing arms to the underbody and rear axle.
3 Remove the rear anti-roll bar, with reference to Section 11.
4 Unscrew and remove the Panhard rod mounting bolt on the rear axle.
5 Remove both rear wheels.
6 Disconnect both rear handbrake cable attachments from the trailing arms by pushing out the pins.
7 Remove both rear stub axles, with reference to Section 10.
8 Support the rear axle on a trolley jack or axle stands.
9 Unscrew the front mounting nuts, and disconnect the radius arms from the rear axle.
10 On models with rear disc brakes, locate

the handbrake cables over the rear axle.
11 Unscrew and remove the rear shock absorber lower mounting bolts, then lower the axle until the rear coil springs are loosely located between the axle and underbody.
12 Unscrew and remove completely the trailing arm rear mounting bolts.
13 Prise the axle away from the trailing arms, and lower it to the ground together with the coil springs.
14 On early models, remove the coil springs and bump stops by prising them out. Remove the washer plates.
15 On later models, use a screwdriver to push out the plastic locking pins from the lower bump stops, then remove the bump stops, coil springs and lower washer plates **(see illustration)**.
16 The upper bump stops may be removed from the underbody by screwing self-tapping screws into the locking pin, and pulling out the pins **(see illustration)**. The holder and bump stop may then be removed.

Refitting

17 Refitting is a reversal of the removal procedure, but note the following additional points:
  a) When fitting the upper bump stop on later models, make sure that the arrow faces towards the front of the car, and smear the plastic holder with a little grease **(see illustration)**.
  b) When fitting the bump stop on early models, use a 7.5 mm diameter metal rod inserted through the top of the coil spring

17.3 Rear shock absorber upper mounting

to press the bump stop firmly into the axle.
  c) Delay fully tightening the rear axle mounting bolts until the weight of the car is on the ground.
  d) Tighten all nuts and bolts to the specified torque.
  e) If the right-hand radius arm mounting bracket has a slot in it, loosen the right-hand mounting nut when refitting the left-hand radius arm.
  f) Refer to the appropriate Sections as given in the removal procedure when refitting the components.

17 Rear shock absorber - removal, testing and refitting

Removal

1 Loosen the rear wheel bolts. Chock the front wheels, then jack up the rear of the car and support it on axle stands. Remove the appropriate roadwheel.
2 Using a trolley jack, lift the trailing arm until the shock absorber is compressed slightly, then unscrew and remove the lower mounting bolt.
3 Unscrew and remove the upper mounting bolt from the underbody **(see illustration)**.
4 Withdraw the shock absorber from under the car.

Testing

5 Mount the shock absorber in a vice, and test it as described in Section 5 for the front suspension strut. Also check the mounting rubbers for damage and deterioration. Renew the complete unit if any damage or excessive wear is evident.

Refitting

6 Before refitting the shock absorber, mount it upright in the vice, and operate it fully through several strokes in order to prime it.
7 Refitting is a reversal of removal, but delay fully tightening the mounting bolts to the specified torque until the weight of the car is on the suspension.

18.3a Remove the horn pad from the steering wheel . . .

18.3b . . . for access to the retaining nut (arrowed)

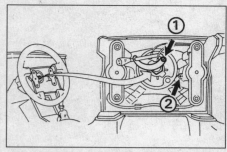

18.9 Airbag contact ring locking screw should be removed from storage hole (2) and inserted into fixing hole (1)

18 Steering wheel - removal and refitting

Warning: On models fitted with a driver's airbag (the steering wheel will typically be marked SRS), refer to Chapter 12 and remove the airbag module from the centre of the wheel. Failure to follow the instructions for removing the airbag module could well result in its accidental deployment.

Removal

1 Set the front wheels in the straight-ahead position, and release the steering lock by inserting the ignition key.
2 Disconnect the battery negative lead. On models with an airbag, wait 10 minutes before proceeding.

Models without a driver's airbag

3 Ease off the horn pad from the centre of the steering wheel, to gain access to the retaining nut **(see illustrations)**.
4 Using a socket, unscrew and remove the retaining nut.
5 Mark the steering wheel and steering column shaft in relation to each other, and withdraw the wheel from the shaft splines. If it is tight, tap it upwards near the centre, using the palm of your hand, or twist the steering wheel from side-to-side to release it from the splines.
6 If it is required to remove the slip ring and earth lead from the steering wheel, turn it over and use a screwdriver to depress the two locking tabs to remove the slip ring. The screwdriver may be used to remove the earth lead.

Models with a driver's airbag

7 Refer to Chapter 12 and remove the airbag module from the centre of the steering wheel.
8 Slacken, but do not remove, the steering wheel retaining nut.
9 Remove the locking screw from its storage hole, and insert it in the fixing hole, to lock the airbag contact ring in place **(see illustration)**.
10 Mark the steering wheel and steering column shaft in relation to each other, to ensure correct refitting.

11 The steering wheel nut can now be fully unscrewed, and the steering wheel pulled from the column. Do not turn the wheel as it is being removed.

Refitting

12 Refitting is a reversal of removal, noting the following points:
a) *On models without an airbag, make sure that the slip ring is firmly pressed into the steering wheel.*
b) *When refitting the steering wheel, align the previously-made marks.*
c) *On models with an airbag, hand-tighten the steering wheel nut, then unlock the contact ring by unscrewing the locking screw and returning it to its storage hole.*
d) *Tighten the steering wheel nut to the specified torque.*
e) *On models with an airbag, refit the airbag module to the steering wheel with reference to Chapter 12.*

19 Steering column - removal and refitting

Removal

1 Disconnect the battery negative lead, with reference to Chapter 5A.
2 Centralise the front wheels in the straight-ahead position, then remove the steering wheel as described in Section 18.

19.3 Removing the steering column surround

3 Remove the two upper screws and one lower screw securing the surround to the steering column. Using a small screwdriver, press in the two tabs located on each side of the surround, then remove the lower surround **(see illustration)**. Disconnect the wiring for the instrument lighting dimmer control, where applicable
4 On models not fitted with steering wheel height adjustment, bend out the tabs and remove the switch holder and stalks from the top of the steering column. Remove the upper surround.
5 On models with steering wheel height adjustment, move the steering wheel to its lowest position. Remove the upper surround, then bend out the tabs and remove the switch holder and stalks from the top of the steering column. Disconnect the wiring at the connector.
6 Remove the lower trim panel from under the steering column **(see illustration)**, then unscrew and remove the pinch-bolt securing the intermediate shaft universal joint to the bottom of the column.
7 Unscrew the four mounting bolts securing the steering column to the bulkhead **(see illustration)**. Where fitted, also unscrew the auxiliary steady bracket bolt.
8 Disconnect the wiring for the ignition switch at the connector, and the wiring for the ignition key illumination. On models with a driver's airbag, disconnect the orange wiring connector under the column.
9 Mark the steering column and intermediate shaft universal joint in relation to each other.

19.6 Removing the lower facia trim panel

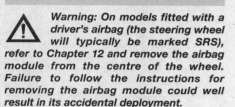

10

19.7 Steering column seen from driver's seat

Check that there is nothing else preventing removal of the column. Pull the steering column upwards, and disconnect it from the splines on the intermediate shaft universal joint.

Refitting

10 Engage the bottom of the steering column with the universal joint of the intermediate shaft, making sure that (where applicable) the previously-made marks are correctly aligned.

11 Insert the pinch-bolt, but do not tighten it at this stage.

12 Lift the steering column to the bulkhead, and insert the mounting bolts loosely. Where applicable, insert the auxiliary steady bracket bolt.

13 Press down on the steering column, and tighten the mounting bolts to the specified torque. Tighten the pinch-bolt and (where applicable) the auxiliary steady bracket bolt.

14 Connect the wiring for the ignition switch, ignition key illumination and airbag, as applicable.

15 Refit the lower trim panel under the steering column.

16 On models with steering wheel height adjustment, move the steering wheel to its lowest position. Fit the upper surround, making sure that the rubber seals are correctly located.

17 On models not fitted with steering wheel height adjustment, refit the upper surround, then press the switch holder and stalks onto the top of the steering column until the assembly is locked into position by the locking tabs.

18 Reconnect the wiring for the instrument lighting dimmer, where applicable. Refit the lower surround by pressing it firmly into the locking tabs, then insert and tighten the screws.

19 Refit the steering wheel, with reference to Section 18.

20 Connect the battery negative lead.

21 Check that the steering column lock only engages when the ignition key is fully removed from the switch.

20 Steering column - dismantling and reassembly

Dismantling

1 On models with steering column height adjustment, remove the spring, then unscrew the nut and take out the pivot bolt with the lever. Remove the adjusting mechanism from the steering column.

2 On models from chassis number 509329 onwards, remove the lever bearing assembly, by prising out the ring with a screwdriver and taking the pins out of the bores. Remove the ring on the other side, and take out the needle bearing **(see illustration)**.

3 Mount the steering column bracket in a vice, then slightly raise the column, and pull it out of the bracket. If necessary, use a soft-faced mallet to remove it.

4 Press in the plastic tabs, and remove the plastic sleeve from the bracket **(see illustration)**.

5 Mount the steering column in a vice, and drill out the ignition switch/lock mounting shear-bolts **(see illustration)**. If necessary, use a stud-extraction tool ('easy-out') to remove the bolts.

6 Remove the spacer sleeve from the top of the steering column, then extract the circlip (using circlip pliers) and press out the upper bearing by pushing the column upwards.

7 On adjustable-type columns, bend back the outer column bottom tube using a pair of pliers; remove the circlip on non-adjustable columns.

8 On early models, press the column downwards and out of the outer column, and remove the needle bearing together with the circlip. Press out the flexible bush with the column.

9 On later models, press out the flexible bush together with the needle bearing, using the column or by using a long drift. Take care not to damage the outer column.

10 Clean all of the components, and examine them for wear and damage. Renew them as necessary.

Reassembly

11 Tap the bearing into the top of the outer column, using a suitable socket, then refit the circlip.

12 Smear the inside surfaces of the outer column and the flexible bush with petroleum jelly (vaseline), then insert the inner column.

13 Pack the lower bearing with grease. The bearing must be fitted so that the numbers face into the outer column.

14 Insert the flexible bush and bearing into the column using a short screwdriver, taking care not to damage the bush.

15 Using a suitable drift, drive the bearing into the column until it is just under the locking opening on adjustable columns, or just under the circlip groove on non-adjustable columns.

16 Bend the outer column tube on adjustable columns, or fit the circlip on non-adjustable columns.

17 Insert the ignition key in the switch, and turn it to position 2. Using a small screwdriver through the small hole in the lock housing, depress the pin, then pull the lock cylinder out of the housing.

18 Locate the steering lock on the column, then insert and finger-tighten the shear-bolts. Check that the lock is positioned correctly.

19 Insert the lock cylinder with the ignition key in position 2, and check that the locking pin engages the small hole in the housing.

20 Check that the steering lock works correctly, then tighten the shear-bolts until their heads break off.

21 Mount the steering column bracket in a vice, and connect the spring so that its open end is on the bracket.

22 Insert the plastic sleeve in the bracket. Fit the column in the bracket.

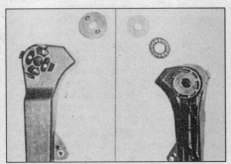

20.2 Height adjustment lever bearing assembly on models from chassis number 509329

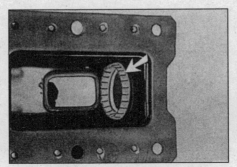

20.4 Plastic sleeve (arrowed) in the steering column mounting bracket

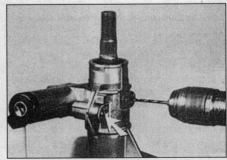

20.5 Drilling out the ignition switch/lock mounting shear-bolts

21.3a Using a small tool, depress the pin . . .

21.3b . . . then pull the lock cylinder out of its housing

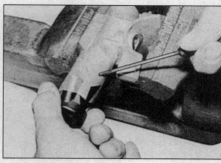

21.3c Removing the lock cylinder with the lock removed and mounted in a vice

23 On early models, fit the spring.

24 On models from chassis number 509329 onwards, refit the lever bearing assembly by packing the bores with grease, then locating the pins on the rings and pressing in the assembly until it locks into position. Fit the needle bearing and pack it with grease, then locate the ring on the bearing.

25 On models with adjustable columns, fit the adjustable mechanism. Apply a little grease to the locking shaft, lock washers and lever.

26 On the early type, fit the mechanism and pivot bolt, and tighten the pivot bolt until the threaded end protrudes by 5.0 mm out of the bracket at the lever side; fit and tighten the nut.

27 On the later type, fit the pivot bolt and locate the mechanism, then fit the nut on the pivot bolt, reconnect the spring, and tighten the nut.

28 Check that the mechanism operates correctly. Fit the spacer sleeve on the top of the column.

21 Steering lock -
removal and refitting

Note: *The lock cylinder may be removed from the lock without removing the steering column from the car. Remove the steering column shrouds for access, then follow the procedure from paragraphs 3 to 5 inclusive.*

Removal

1 Remove the steering column as described in Section 19.

2 Mount the steering column and bracket in a vice, then drill out the shear-bolts securing the lock to the housing. Use a stud-extraction tool ('easy-out') if necessary, to unscrew the remaining ends of the bolts from the housing.

3 Insert the ignition key, and turn it to position 2. Using a small screwdriver or similar tool, depress the pin through the small hole in the housing, and pull out the lock cylinder **(see illustrations)**.

Refitting

4 Locate the steering lock on the column, then insert and finger-tighten the shear-bolts. Check that the lock is positioned correctly.

5 Insert the lock cylinder with the ignition key in position 2, and check that the locking pin engages the small hole in the housing.

6 Check that the steering lock works correctly, then tighten the shear-bolts until their heads break off.

7 Refit the steering column, with reference to Section 19.

22 Steering column intermediate shaft -
removal and refitting

Removal

1 Working inside the car, remove the lower trim panel from under the steering column.

2 Centralise the front wheels in the straight-ahead position, then unscrew and remove the pinch-bolt securing the intermediate shaft universal joint to the bottom of the column.

3 Pull back the rubber boot from the bulkhead.

4 Working in the engine compartment, unscrew and remove the pinch-bolt securing the intermediate shaft universal joint to the steering gear pinion shaft.

5 If necessary, unscrew the steering column mounting bolts with reference to Section 19, and lift the column slightly.

6 Slide the intermediate shaft from the splines on the steering column and steering gear pinion shaft, and remove it from inside the car.

7 Check the shaft universal joints for excessive wear, and the shaft itself for any damage. Check the rubber boot, and if necessary renew it.

Refitting

8 Refitting is a reversal of the removal procedure, but tighten all nuts and bolts to the specified torque.

23 Steering gear rubber bellows - renewal

1 Remove the tie-rod end balljoint, as described in Section 27. Measure the distance from the locknut to the end of the tie-rod, to ensure correct refitting.

2 Release the two clips, and slide the rubber bellows off the rack-and-pinion housing and tie-rod.

3 Remove the grease from the old rubber bellows, and apply it to the tie-rod inner joint. Wipe clean the seating areas on the rack-and-pinion housing and tie-rod.

4 Slide the new rubber bellows onto the housing and tie-rod, and tighten the clips.

5 Refit the tie-rod end balljoint, as described in Section 27.

24 Steering gear - removal and refitting

Removal

1 Turn the front wheels to the straight-ahead position, and remove the ignition key to engage the steering lock.

2 Apply the handbrake, then jack up the front of the car and support on axle stands. Remove both front roadwheels.

3 Remove the heat shield for the right-hand side driveshaft. On early models, unscrew all of the bolts; on later models with the larger heat shield, it is not necessary to remove the top left bolt, as the heat shield is slotted.

4 Unbolt and remove the heat shield for the steering gear.

5 Unscrew and remove the pinch-bolt securing the intermediate shaft to the steering gear pinion shaft. Check if there are any alignment marks on the pinion shaft and steering gear housing, and if necessary make them to indicate the straight-ahead position.

6 Unscrew the nuts securing the tie-rod ends to the stub axle carriers on each side. On early models, it may be necessary to remove the split pins first (new split pins must be obtained for reassembly). Using a balljoint removal tool, separate the tie-rod ends from the stub axle carriers.

7 On models with power steering, position a container beneath the steering gear, then unscrew the union nuts and release the hydraulic lines **(see illustration)**. Plug the lines and apertures in the steering gear to prevent entry of dust and dirt.

10

24.7 Hydraulic fluid lines on the power-assisted steering gear

8 Loosen the right-hand rear subframe mounting nut as far as possible.

9 Unscrew and remove the steering gear mounting nuts and bolts, and remove the mounting brackets together with the heat shield **(see illustration)**.

10 Separate the steering column from the steering gear pinion shaft.

11 Unhook the two rubber mounting rings from the exhaust system, and pull the exhaust system down as far as possible. Use a block of wood to hold the exhaust system down.

12 Withdraw the steering gear, using a twisting motion.

Refitting

13 If a new steering gear is being fitted, determine the straight-ahead position of the pinion shaft as follows.

14 Disconnect the rubber bellows from one end, and turn the pinion fully to the right. Measure the distance from the steering gear housing to the end of the rack.

15 Move the rack to the halfway position, then mark the pinion shaft and housing in relation to each other.

16 Reconnect the rubber bellows.

17 Refitting is a reversal of the removal procedure, but note the following additional points:

a) *Use the alignment marks made to ensure the rack is fitted in the straight-ahead position.*

b) *Tighten all nuts and bolts to the specified torque.*

c) *Where applicable, fit a new split pin to the tie-rod end-to-stub axle carrier nut.*

25.11 Withdrawing the power steering pump (arrowed) from the front bracket

24.9 A steering gear mounting nut and bolt

d) *On models with power steering, bleed the hydraulic system with reference to Section 26.*

e) *Check and if necessary adjust the front wheel alignment, as described in Section 29.*

25 Power steering pump - removal and refitting

Removal

1 Open the bonnet so that it is in its service (fully-upright) position.

2 Disconnect the battery negative lead (refer to Chapter 5A if necessary).

3 Apply the handbrake, then jack up the front of the car and support on axle stands.

4 Remove the engine splash guard, and position a suitable container beneath the power steering pump.

5 Using brake hose clamps, clamp both the supply and return hoses leading from the pump.

6 Loosen the clip, and disconnect the supply hose from the pump; collect the escaping fluid in the container.

Models without air conditioning

7 Unscrew the union nut, and disconnect the high-pressure line from the pump.

8 Loosen the alternator adjustment and pivot bolts, and swivel the alternator towards the engine. Remove the drivebelt from the alternator, water pump and power steering pump pulleys.

9 Using a socket through the holes in the pulley, unscrew the three power steering pump mounting bolts.

10 Unscrew the three bolts securing the front brackets to the engine cylinder block.

11 Unscrew the mounting bolts securing the pump to the front bracket, and withdraw the pump from the engine compartment **(see illustration)**.

Models with air conditioning

12 Unscrew the banjo bolt, and disconnect the high-pressure line from the pump.

13 Remove the drivebelt guard, then unscrew and remove the adjusting and pivot

bolts. Remove the drivebelt from the water pump and power steering pump.

14 Withdraw the pump and brackets from the engine compartment.

All models

15 Examine the drivebelt for wear and damage, and renew it if necessary.

Refitting

16 Refitting is a reversal of the removal procedure, but note the following additional points:

a) *Tighten the mounting bolts gradually, so that no uneven forces are applied to the brackets or pump.*

b) *Tighten all nuts and bolts to the specified torque.*

c) *Tension the drivebelt with reference to Chapter 1, Section 5.*

d) *Check the condition of the high-pressure line sealing washer(s), and renew them if necessary.*

e) *Bleed the power steering hydraulic system, with reference to Section 26.*

26 Power steering system - bleeding

1 This will only be required if any part of the hydraulic system has been disconnected.

2 Remove the fluid reservoir filler cap, and top-up the fluid level to the maximum mark using the specified fluid. Refer to *Weekly checks* for fluid specifications and further details.

3 With the engine stopped, move the steering slowly from lock-to-lock several times to purge out the internal air, then top-up the level in the fluid reservoir.

4 Repeat this procedure with the engine running, and again top-up the level.

5 After refilling the system following a repair to the pump or steering gear, the hydraulic fluid may initially contain lots of minute air bubbles, which will cause the fluid to take on a milky appearance. Before continuing to bleed the system, wait for several minutes to allow the air to disperse.

27 Tie-rod end/balljoint - removal and refitting

Removal

1 Loosen the front wheel bolts. Apply the handbrake, then jack up the front of the car and support on axle stands. Remove the appropriate front roadwheel.

2 Count the number of exposed threads on the tie-rod next to the locknut, and record this figure.

3 Loosen the tie-rod end balljoint locknut on the tie-rod by a quarter of a turn. If necessary, hold the tie-rod stationary using a pair of grips.

4 Unscrew and remove the nut securing the balljoint to the stub axle carrier arm, and then release the tapered shank using a balljoint separator tool **(see illustration)**. On early models with a castellated nut, the split pin should be removed before unscrewing the nut (a new split pin must be obtained for reassembly).

5 Unscrew the tie-rod end from the tie-rod, counting the number of turns necessary to remove it.

6 If necessary, unscrew the locknut from the tie-rod.

Refitting

7 If removed, screw the locknut onto the tie-rod, and position it so that the same number of exposed threads are visible as was noted during removal, less a quarter-turn.

8 Screw the tie-rod end onto the tie-rod the number of turns noted during removal, until it just contacts the locknut. Now tighten the locknut while holding the track rod stationary.

9 Engage the shank of the balljoint with the stub axle carrier arm, and refit the locknut. Tighten the locknut to the specified torque.

10 If the balljoint shank turns while the locknut is being tightened, place a jack under the balljoint. The tapered fit of the shank will lock it, and prevent rotation as the nut is tightened.

11 On early models, after tightening the locknut, check the alignment of the split pin holes - if they are not aligned, the nut may be tightened by (up to) a further 60° angle, but it should **not** be loosened to align the holes. Fit a new split pin to the locknut.

12 Refit the roadwheel, and lower the car to the ground.

13 Finally check and if necessary adjust the front wheel alignment, with reference to Section 29.

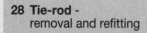

28 Tie-rod -
removal and refitting

Removal

1 Remove the steering gear, as described in Section 24.

2 Remove the steering gear rubber bellows, as described in Section 23.

3 Unscrew the inner balljoint from the steering gear rack while holding the rack stationary with a spanner, then withdraw the tie-rod. On models without power steering, the balljoint may be unscrewed using a spanner; on power steering models, grips must be used to turn the balljoint. Make sure that the rack is not turned within the steering gear housing, otherwise the rack teeth and pinion gear may be damaged.

Refitting

4 Refitting is a reversal of the removal procedure. After tightening the balljoint, lock it

27.4 Using a balljoint separator tool to release the tie-rod end tapered shank from the stub axle carrier arm

by staking onto the rack. Refit the rubber bellows and steering gear, with reference to Sections 23 and 24.

29 Wheel alignment and steering angles - general information

1 Accurate front wheel alignment is essential, to provide positive steering and prevent excessive tyre wear. Before considering the steering/suspension geometry, check that the tyres are correctly inflated, that the front wheels are not damaged, and that the steering linkage and suspension joints are in good order, without slackness or wear. In general, wheel alignment consists of the following four factors **(see illustration)**.

2 Camber is the angle at which the front wheels are set from the vertical, when viewed from the front of the car. Positive camber is the amount (in degrees) that the wheels are tilted outwards at the top of the vertical.

3 Castor is the angle between the steering axis and a vertical line, viewed from each side of the car. Positive castor is when the steering axis is inclined rearward at the top.

4 Steering axis inclination is the angle (when viewed from the front of the car) between the vertical and an imaginary line drawn through the suspension strut upper mounting and the lower suspension arm balljoint.

5 Toe setting is the amount by which the distance between the front inside edges of the roadwheels (measured at hub height) differs from the diametrically-opposite distance measured between the rear inside edges of the front roadwheels.

6 With the exception of the toe setting, all other steering angles are set during manufacture, and no adjustment is possible. It can be assumed, therefore, that unless the car has suffered accident damage, all the preset steering angles are correct. Should there be some doubt about their accuracy, it will be necessary to seek the help of a Volvo dealer, as special gauges are needed to check the steering angles.

7 Two methods are available to the home

mechanic for checking the toe setting. One method is to use a gauge to measure the distance between the front and rear inside edges of the roadwheels. The other method is to use a scuff plate, in which each front wheel is rolled across a movable plate which records any deviation, or scuff, of the tyre from the straight-ahead position as it moves across the plate. Relatively-inexpensive equipment of both types is available from accessory outlets to enable these checks, and subsequent adjustments, to be carried out at home.

8 If after checking the toe setting (using whichever method is preferable), it is found

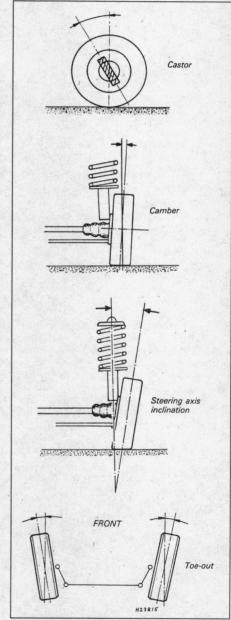

29.1 Wheel alignment and steering angles

that adjustment is necessary, proceed as follows.

9 Turn the steering wheel onto full-left lock, and record the number of exposed threads on the right-hand tie-rod end. Now turn the steering onto full-right lock, and record the number of threads on the left-hand side. If there are the same number of threads visible on both sides, then subsequent adjustment can be made equally on both sides. If there are more threads visible on one side than the other, it will be necessary to compensate for this during adjustment. *After adjustment, there must be the same number of threads visible on each tie-rod end. This is most important.*

10 To alter the toe setting, slacken the locknut on the tie-rod end, and turn the tie-rod using a self-grip wrench to achieve the desired setting. When viewed from the side of the car, turning the rod clockwise will increase the toe-in; turning it anti-clockwise will decrease the toe-out. Only turn the tie-rods by a quarter of a turn each time, and then recheck the setting using the gauges, or scuff plate.

11 After adjustment, tighten the locknuts, and reposition the steering gear rubber boots to remove any twist caused by turning the tie-rods.

Chapter 11
Bodywork and fittings

Contents

Degrees of difficulty

Easy, suitable for novice with little experience	**Fairly easy,** suitable for beginner with some experience	**Fairly difficult,** suitable for competent DIY mechanic	**Difficult,** suitable for experienced DIY mechanic	**Very difficult,** suitable for expert DIY or professional

Specifications

Torque wrench settings

	Nm	lbf ft
Seat belt mounting bolts	30	22
Tailgate hinges	20	15
Bonnet striker	9	7

1 General information

The bodyshell and underframe is of all-steel welded construction, incorporating progressive crumple zones at the front and rear, and a rigid centre safety cell. All body panels which are subject to extreme road exposure (or which are difficult to reach) are treated by zinc priming or by hot-dip galvanising.

The front and rear bumpers are of collapsible cellular construction, to minimise minor accident damage, and the front wings are bolted in position to facilitate accident damage repair. The plastic side panels are also designed to absorb light impact without damage, and from October 1993 onwards, the doors are strengthened with horizontal bars for additional resistance to side impact.

2 Maintenance - bodywork and underframe

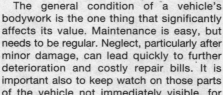

The general condition of a vehicle's bodywork is the one thing that significantly affects its value. Maintenance is easy, but needs to be regular. Neglect, particularly after minor damage, can lead quickly to further deterioration and costly repair bills. It is important also to keep watch on those parts of the vehicle not immediately visible, for instance the underside, inside all the wheel arches, and the lower part of the engine compartment.

The basic maintenance routine for the bodywork is washing - preferably with a lot of water, from a hose. This will remove all the loose solids which may have stuck to the vehicle. It is important to flush these off in such a way as to prevent grit from scratching the finish. The wheel arches and underframe need washing in the same way, to remove any accumulated mud, which will retain moisture and tend to encourage rust. Paradoxically enough, the best time to clean the underframe and wheel arches is in wet weather, when the mud is thoroughly wet and soft. In very wet weather, the underframe is usually cleaned of large accumulations automatically, and this is a good time for inspection.

Periodically, except on vehicles with a wax-based underbody protective coating, it is a good idea to have the whole of the underframe of the vehicle steam-cleaned, engine compartment included, so that a thorough inspection can be carried out to see what minor repairs and renovations are necessary. Steam-cleaning is available at many garages, and is necessary for the removal of the accumulation of oily grime, which sometimes

11

is allowed to become thick in certain areas. If steam-cleaning facilities are not available, there are some excellent grease solvents available which can be brush-applied; the dirt can then be simply hosed off. Note that these methods should not be used on vehicles with wax-based underbody protective coating, or the coating will be removed. Such vehicles should be inspected annually, preferably just prior to Winter, when the underbody should be washed down, and any damage to the wax coating repaired. Ideally, a completely fresh coat should be applied. It would also be worth considering the use of such wax-based protection for injection into door panels, sills, box sections, etc, as an additional safeguard against rust damage, where such protection is not provided by the vehicle manufacturer.

After washing paintwork, wipe off with a chamois leather to give an unspotted clear finish. A coat of clear protective wax polish will give added protection against chemical pollutants in the air. If the paintwork sheen has dulled or oxidised, use a cleaner/polisher combination to restore the brilliance of the shine. This requires a little effort, but such dulling is usually caused because regular washing has been neglected. Care needs to be taken with metallic paintwork, as special non-abrasive cleaner/polisher is required to avoid damage to the finish. Always check that the door and ventilator opening drain holes and pipes are completely clear, so that water can be drained out. Brightwork should be treated in the same way as paintwork. Windscreens and windows can be kept clear of the smeary film which often appears, by the use of proprietary glass cleaner. Never use any form of wax or other body or chromium polish on glass.

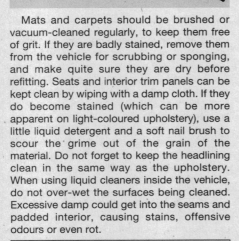

3 Maintenance - upholstery and carpets

Mats and carpets should be brushed or vacuum-cleaned regularly, to keep them free of grit. If they are badly stained, remove them from the vehicle for scrubbing or sponging, and make quite sure they are dry before refitting. Seats and interior trim panels can be kept clean by wiping with a damp cloth. If they do become stained (which can be more apparent on light-coloured upholstery), use a little liquid detergent and a soft nail brush to scour the grime out of the grain of the material. Do not forget to keep the headlining clean in the same way as the upholstery. When using liquid cleaners inside the vehicle, do not over-wet the surfaces being cleaned. Excessive damp could get into the seams and padded interior, causing stains, offensive odours or even rot.

HAYNES HINT *If the inside of the vehicle gets wet accidentally, it is worthwhile taking some*

trouble to dry it out properly, particularly where carpets are involved. Do not leave oil or electric heaters inside the vehicle for this purpose.

4 Minor body damage - repair

Repairs of minor scratches in bodywork

If the scratch is very superficial, and does not penetrate to the metal of the bodywork, repair is very simple. Lightly rub the area of the scratch with a paintwork renovator, or a very fine cutting paste, to remove loose paint from the scratch, and to clear the surrounding bodywork of wax polish. Rinse the area with clean water.

Apply touch-up paint to the scratch using a fine paint brush; continue to apply fine layers of paint until the surface of the paint in the scratch is level with the surrounding paintwork. Allow the new paint at least two weeks to harden, then blend it into the surrounding paintwork by rubbing the scratch area with a paintwork renovator or a very fine cutting paste. Finally, apply wax polish.

Where the scratch has penetrated right through to the metal of the bodywork, causing the metal to rust, a different repair technique is required. Remove any loose rust from the bottom of the scratch with a penknife, then apply rust-inhibiting paint to prevent the formation of rust in the future. Using a rubber or nylon applicator, fill the scratch with bodystopper paste. If required, this paste can be mixed with cellulose thinners to provide a very thin paste which is ideal for filling narrow scratches. Before the stopper-paste in the scratch hardens, wrap a piece of smooth cotton rag around the top of a finger. Dip the finger in cellulose thinners, and quickly sweep it across the surface of the stopper-paste in the scratch; this will ensure that the surface of the stopper-paste is slightly hollowed. The scratch can now be painted over as described earlier in this Section.

Repairs of dents in bodywork

When deep denting of the vehicle's bodywork has taken place, the first task is to pull the dent out, until the affected bodywork almost attains its original shape. There is little point in trying to restore the original shape completely, as the metal in the damaged area will have stretched on impact, and cannot be reshaped fully to its original contour. It is better to bring the level of the dent up to a point which is about 3 mm below the level of the surrounding bodywork. In cases where the dent is very shallow anyway, it is not worth trying to pull it out at all. If the underside of the dent is accessible, it can be hammered out gently from behind, using a mallet with a

wooden or plastic head. Whilst doing this, hold a suitable block of wood firmly against the outside of the panel, to absorb the impact from the hammer blows and thus prevent a large area of the bodywork from being 'belled-out'.

Should the dent be in a section of the bodywork which has a double skin, or some other factor making it inaccessible from behind, a different technique is called for. Drill several small holes through the metal inside the area - particularly in the deeper section. Then screw long self-tapping screws into the holes, just sufficiently for them to gain a good purchase in the metal. Now the dent can be pulled out by pulling on the protruding heads of the screws with a pair of pliers.

The next stage of the repair is the removal of the paint from the damaged area, and from an inch or so of the surrounding 'sound' bodywork. This is accomplished most easily by using a wire brush or abrasive pad on a power drill, although it can be done just as effectively by hand, using sheets of abrasive paper. To complete the preparation for filling, score the surface of the bare metal with a screwdriver or the tang of a file, or alternatively, drill small holes in the affected area. This will provide a really good 'key' for the filler paste.

To complete the repair, see the Section on filling and respraying.

Repairs of rust holes or gashes in bodywork

Remove all paint from the affected area, and from an inch or so of the surrounding 'sound' bodywork, using an abrasive pad or a wire brush on a power drill. If these are not available, a few sheets of abrasive paper will do the job most effectively. With the paint removed, you will be able to judge the severity of the corrosion, and therefore decide whether to renew the whole panel (if this is possible) or to repair the affected area. New body panels are not as expensive as most people think, and it is often quicker and more satisfactory to fit a new panel than to attempt to repair large areas of corrosion.

Remove all fittings from the affected area, except those which will act as a guide to the original shape of the damaged bodywork (eg headlight shells etc). Then, using tin snips or a hacksaw blade, remove all loose metal and any other metal badly affected by corrosion. Hammer the edges of the hole inwards, in order to create a slight depression for the filler paste.

Wire-brush the affected area to remove the powdery rust from the surface of the remaining metal. Paint the affected area with rust-inhibiting paint, if the back of the rusted area is accessible, treat this also.

Before filling can take place, it will be necessary to block the hole in some way. This can be achieved by the use of aluminium or plastic mesh, or aluminium tape.

Aluminium or plastic mesh, or glass-fibre matting, is probably the best material to use for a large hole. Cut a piece to the approximate size and shape of the hole to be filled, then position it in the hole so that its edges are below the level of the surrounding bodywork. It can be retained in position by several blobs of filler paste around its periphery.

Aluminium tape should be used for small or very narrow holes. Pull a piece off the roll, trim it to the approximate size and shape required, then pull off the backing paper (if used) and stick the tape over the hole; it can be overlapped if the thickness of one piece is insufficient. Burnish down the edges of the tape with the handle of a screwdriver or similar, to ensure that the tape is securely attached to the metal underneath.

Bodywork repairs - filling and respraying

Before using this Section, see the Sections on dent, deep scratch, rust holes and gash repairs.

Many types of bodyfiller are available, but generally speaking, those proprietary kits which contain a tin of filler paste and a tube of resin hardener are best for this type of repair. A wide, flexible plastic or nylon applicator will be found invaluable for imparting a smooth and well-contoured finish to the surface of the filler.

Mix up a little filler on a clean piece of card or board - measure the hardener carefully (follow the maker's instructions on the pack), otherwise the filler will set too rapidly or too slowly. Using the applicator, apply the filler paste to the prepared area; draw the applicator across the surface of the filler to achieve the correct contour and to level the surface. As soon as a contour that approximates to the correct one is achieved, stop working the paste - if you carry on too long, the paste will become sticky and begin to 'pick-up' on the applicator. Continue to add thin layers of filler paste at 20-minute intervals, until the level of the filler is just proud of the surrounding bodywork.

Once the filler has hardened, the excess can be removed using a metal plane or file. From then on, progressively-finer grades of abrasive paper should be used, starting with a 40-grade production paper, and finishing with a 400-grade wet-and-dry paper. Always wrap the abrasive paper around a flat rubber, cork, or wooden block - otherwise the surface of the filler will not be completely flat. During the smoothing of the filler surface, the wet-and-dry paper should be periodically rinsed in water. This will ensure that a very smooth finish is imparted to the filler at the final stage.

At this stage, the dent should be surrounded by a ring of bare metal, which in turn should be encircled by the finely 'feathered' edge of the good paintwork. Rinse the repair area with clean water, until all of the dust produced by the rubbing-down operation has gone.

Spray the whole area with a light coat of primer - this will show up any imperfections in the surface of the filler. Repair these imperfections with fresh filler paste or bodystopper, and once more smooth the surface with abrasive paper. Repeat this spray-and-repair procedure until you are satisfied that the surface of the filler, and the feathered edge of the paintwork, are perfect. Clean the repair area with clean water, and allow to dry fully.

 If bodystopper is used, it can be mixed with cellulose thinners to form a really thin paste which is ideal for filling small holes.

The repair area is now ready for final spraying. Paint spraying must be carried out in a warm, dry, windless and dust-free atmosphere. This condition can be created artificially if you have access to a large indoor working area, but if you are forced to work in the open, you will have to pick your day very carefully. If you are working indoors, dousing the floor in the work area with water will help to settle the dust which would otherwise be in the atmosphere. If the repair area is confined to one body panel, mask off the surrounding panels; this will help to minimise the effects of a slight mis-match in paint colours. Bodywork fittings (eg chrome strips, door handles etc) will also need to be masked off. Use genuine masking tape, and several thicknesses of newspaper, for the masking operations.

Before commencing to spray, agitate the aerosol can thoroughly, then spray a test area (an old tin, or similar) until the technique is mastered. Cover the repair area with a thick coat of primer; the thickness should be built up using several thin layers of paint, rather than one thick one. Using 400-grade wet-and-dry paper, rub down the surface of the primer until it is really smooth. While doing this, the work area should be thoroughly doused with water, and the wet-and-dry paper periodically rinsed in water. Allow to dry before spraying on more paint.

Spray on the top coat, again building up the thickness by using several thin layers of paint. Start spraying at one edge of the repair area, and then, using a side-to-side motion, work until the whole repair area and about 2 inches of the surrounding original paintwork is covered. Remove all masking material 10 to 15 minutes after spraying on the final coat of paint.

Allow the new paint at least two weeks to harden, then, using a paintwork renovator, or a very fine cutting paste, blend the edges of the paint into the existing paintwork. Finally, apply wax polish.

Plastic components

With the use of more and more plastic body components by the vehicle manufacturers (eg bumpers. spoilers, and in some cases major body panels), rectification of more serious damage to such items has become a matter of either entrusting repair work to a specialist in this field, or renewing complete components. Repair of such damage by the DIY owner is not really feasible, owing to the cost of the equipment and materials required for effecting such repairs. The basic technique involves making a groove along the line of the crack in the plastic, using a rotary burr in a power drill. The damaged part is then welded back together, using a hot-air gun to heat up and fuse a plastic filler rod into the groove. Any excess plastic is then removed, and the area rubbed down to a smooth finish. It is important that a filler rod of the correct plastic is used, as body components can be made of a variety of different types (eg polycarbonate, ABS, polypropylene).

Damage of a less serious nature (abrasions, minor cracks etc) can be repaired by the DIY owner using a two-part epoxy filler repair material. Once mixed in equal proportions, this is used in similar fashion to the bodywork filler used on metal panels. The filler is usually cured in twenty to thirty minutes, ready for sanding and painting.

If the owner is renewing a complete component himself, or if he has repaired it with epoxy filler, he will be left with the problem of finding a suitable paint for finishing which is compatible with the type of plastic used. At one time, the use of a universal paint was not possible, owing to the complex range of plastics encountered in body component applications. Standard paints, generally speaking, will not bond to plastic or rubber satisfactorily. However, it is now possible to obtain a plastic body parts finishing kit which consists of a pre-primer treatment, a primer and coloured top coat. Full instructions are normally supplied with a kit, but basically, the method of use is to first apply the pre-primer to the component concerned, and allow it to dry for up to 30 minutes. Then the primer is applied, and left to dry for about an hour before finally applying the special-coloured top coat. The result is a correctly-coloured component, where the paint will flex with the plastic or rubber, a property that standard paint does not normally possess.

5 Major body damage - repair

Where serious damage has occurred, or large areas need renewal due to neglect, it means that complete new panels will need welding in; this is best left to professionals. If the damage is due to impact, it will also be necessary to check completely the alignment of the bodyshell; this can only be carried out accurately by a Volvo dealer using special jigs. If the body is left misaligned, it is primarily dangerous (as the car will not handle properly) and secondly, uneven stresses will be imposed on the steering, suspension and possibly transmission, causing abnormal wear (particularly to the tyres) or complete failure.

11

6 Bumpers (except 480 models) - removal and refitting

Removal

Front bumper

1 On models up to 1994 model year, remove the radiator grille, as described in Section 8.

2 On models fitted with headlight washers, disconnect the washer tubing at the T-piece. On later models with headlight wash/wipe, this is not necessary.

3 Apply the handbrake, then jack up the front of the car and support on axle stands.

4 Remove the screws, and lower the splash guard from under the engine.

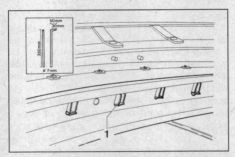

6.12 Removing the outer skin from the bumper beam

Inset shows tool dimensions
1 Attachment clips

6.17a Removing the rear trim from the luggage compartment

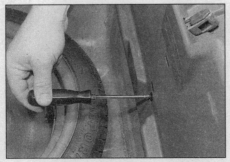

6.17b One of the rear bumper mounting nuts in the luggage compartment

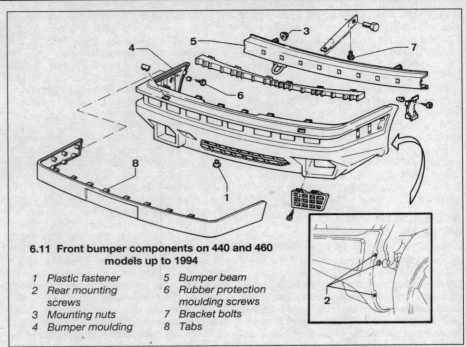

6.11 Front bumper components on 440 and 460 models up to 1994

1 Plastic fastener
2 Rear mounting screws
3 Mounting nuts
4 Bumper moulding
5 Bumper beam
6 Rubber protection moulding screws
7 Bracket bolts
8 Tabs

5 Using a screwdriver, remove the three lower plastic mounting screws.

6 Remove the three mounting screws on each side securing the rear ends of the bumper beneath the front wheel arches.

7 Unscrew the mounting nuts or bolts securing the bumper to the front panel.

8 Unbolt the central link rod.

9 Disconnect the wiring from the foglights and ambient air temperature sensor (as applicable).

10 Withdraw the bumper from the car.

11 If necessary, the bumper may be dismantled as follows **(see illustration)**. First remove the foglights or small grilles (as applicable), followed by the number plate and the headlight washer tubing (early models only) and guide brackets (where fitted).

12 To remove the outer skin from the bumper beam, make up a tool to the dimensions shown **(see illustration)**, and use the tool to press in and release the eight retaining clips.

13 Remove the rubber protection moulding retaining screws, then press in the tabs and remove the moulding.

14 On models up to 1994 model year with headlight washers, remove the hoods by pressing in the pins with a small screwdriver. Undo the screws and remove the washer nozzles.

Rear bumper

15 Working beneath each rear wheel arch in turn, remove the screws securing the liners (and the mudflaps, if fitted) to the rear bumper.

16 Unscrew the side mounting nuts from the underbody.

17 Working in the luggage compartment, remove the rear trim panel, then unscrew the two mounting nuts from the rear panel **(see illustrations)**.

18 Withdraw the bumper from the rear of the car.

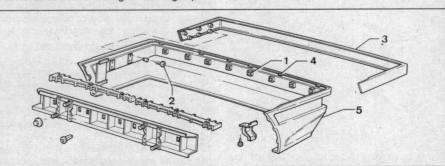

6.19 Rear bumper components on 440 and 460 models up to 1994

1 Attachment clips
2 Rubber protection moulding mounting screws
3 Rubber protection moulding
4 Tabs
5 Bumper moulding

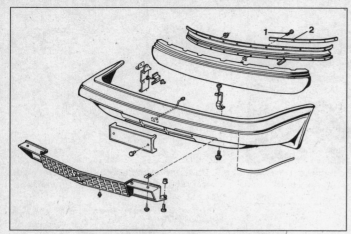

7.7 Front bumper components on 480 models

1 Rear end screws　　*2 Moulding strips*

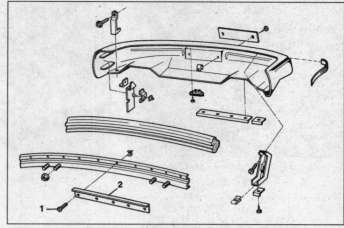

7.19 Rear bumper components on 480 models

1 Front end screws　　*2 Moulding strips*

19 If necessary, the bumper may be dismantled as follows (see illustration). First remove the outer skin from the bumper beam, using the tool described in paragraph 12.
20 Remove the rubber protection moulding retaining screws, then press in the tabs and remove the moulding.

Refitting

Front and rear bumpers

21 Refitting is a reversal of the removal procedure.

7 Bumpers (480 models) - removal and refitting

Removal

Front bumper (pre-1988 models)

1 Raise the headlights - switch them on, then release and open the bonnet, and switch them off.
2 Remove the direction indicators and long-range headlights, with reference to Chapter 12, Section 7.
3 Remove the self-tapping screws securing the lower edge of the bumper.
4 Unscrew and remove the mounting nuts, and withdraw the bumper forwards slightly from the front of the car.
5 Disconnect the wiring from the foglights, and remove the ambient air temperature sensor.
6 Withdraw the bumper from the car.
7 If necessary, the bumper may be dismantled as follows. Separate the skin from the beam, then unbolt the grille and number plate support (see illustration).

Front bumper (1988-on models)

8 Remove the direction indicator light units and long-range headlight units, with reference to Chapter 12, Section 7.
9 Remove the screws from the engine splash guard, then unscrew the bumper retaining nuts.

10 Disconnect the wiring for the foglights at the connector.
11 Where applicable, disconnect the wiring for the ambient air temperature sensor.
12 Withdraw the bumper from the front of the car.
13 To dismantle the bumper, remove the screws at the rear end, and remove the strips, taking note of their position for correct refitting. To remove the outer skin, first pull it over the steel beam at the top, and then at the bottom. Also remove the buffer block in the same manner.

Rear bumper (pre-1988 models)

14 Chock the front wheels, then jack up the rear of the car and support on axle stands.
15 Remove the screws and bolts, and remove the liners from the wheel arches on both sides.
16 Disconnect the wiring from the number plate light and rear foglights behind the spare wheel.
17 Unscrew the mounting nuts at the right and left-hand sides.
18 Unscrew the towing eye securing bolt from the bumper, and withdraw the bumper from the car.
19 To dismantle the bumper, unbolt the number plate panel, and remove the screws securing the strips (see illustration).

Rear bumper (1988-on models)

20 Chock the front wheels, then jack up the rear of the car and support on axle stands.
21 Loosen the mounting bracket bolts a few turns.
22 Remove the screws and bolts, and remove the liners from the wheel arches on both sides.
23 Disconnect the wiring from the number plate lights and rear foglights.
24 Unscrew the towing eye securing bolt from the bumper.
25 Unscrew the mounting nuts on the right and left-hand sides, then withdraw the bumper from the rear of the car.

26 To dismantle the bumper, remove the screws and strips, noting their positions. To remove the outer skin, first pull it over the steel beam at the bottom, then at the top. Pull the wiring for the number plate light through the opening in the rear beam. Remove the buffer block, and pull out the wiring for the lighting.

Refitting

Front and rear bumpers

27 Refitting is a reversal of the removal procedure. When refitting the rear bumper, make sure that the wiring for the number plate lighting is not trapped between the bumper and the body.

8 Radiator grille/panel - removal and refitting

Removal

440 and 460 models up to 1994

1 Press in the plastic lugs at the top corners, and pull the radiator grille forwards from the clips.
2 Lift the grille upwards from the bottom mountings (see illustration).

8.2 Removing the radiator grille (440 model shown)

11

8.4a Unbolt the safety catch/striker plate . . .

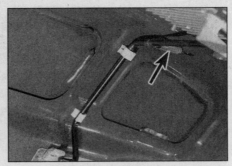

8.4b . . . then unclip the linkage from the bonnet - return spring arrowed

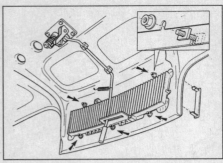

8.5 Radiator grille securing nuts (arrowed) - 440/460 models from 1994 onwards

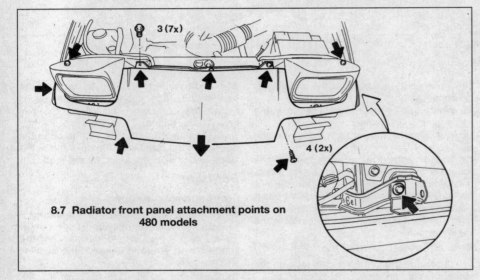

8.7 Radiator front panel attachment points on 480 models

440 and 460 models, 1994 onwards

3 On later models, the radiator grille is incorporated into the bonnet.

4 Unbolt the safety catch/striker plate from inside the bonnet, then unclip and release the safety catch operating linkage and return spring **(see illustrations)**.

5 Remove the five securing nuts, recover the rubber washers, and withdraw the grille from the bonnet aperture **(see illustration)**.

480 models

6 Remove the front direction indicator units and long-range headlights, with reference to Chapter 12, Section 7.

7 Unscrew the three upper mounting bolts and the two lower screws, then pull the panel forwards a little, and disconnect the headlight washer tubing at the T-piece. The panel can now be withdrawn forwards **(see illustration)**.

Refitting

8 Refitting is a reversal of the removal procedure. On models from 1994 onwards, check the alignment of the striker plate carefully before tightening the bolts.

9 Bonnet - removal, refitting and adjustment

Removal

1 Open the bonnet, and support it in the open position using the stay.

2 Where applicable, disconnect the battery negative lead, then disconnect the wiring for the engine compartment illumination. On 480 models, release the connector and wiring from the body.

3 Mark the outline of the hinges with a soft pencil, then loosen the four mounting bolts, two each side **(see illustration)** - on 480 models, refer to illustration 9.5b.

4 With the help of an assistant, release the stay, unscrew the four mounting bolts, and lift the bonnet from the car. Note that on 480 models, the bonnet is constructed of plastic material, and should therefore be handled carefully.

5 If necessary, the bonnet hinges may be unbolted from the body **(see illustrations)**. Remove the lid from the relay box, or move the wiring harness aside for access, as necessary.

9.3 Bonnet hinge - mounting bolts arrowed (440 model shown - hinge bolts are horizontal on 480 models)

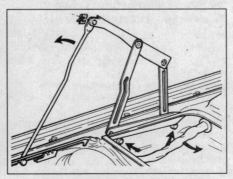

9.5a Bonnet hinge removal on 440 and 460 models

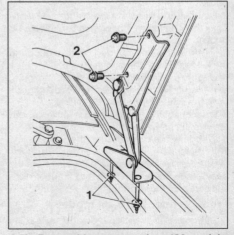

9.5b Bonnet hinge removal on 480 models

1 Mounting nuts on body
2 Mounting bolts on bonnet

**9.9 Bonnet striker -
pre-1994 model shown**

Refitting and adjustment

6 Refitting is a reversal of the removal procedure; position the bonnet hinges within the outline marks made during removal, and tighten the bolts. Check that there is a uniform gap all round the edge of the bonnet, and adjust its position if necessary.

7 On 440 and 460 models, adjustment is made on the bolts securing the hinges to the bonnet, but on 480 models it is made by loosening the nuts located beneath the front wheel arches, after removing the plastic liners.

8 To adjust the rear height of the bonnet on 440 and 460 models, loosen the bolts securing the hinges to the body, and adjust their position as required. On 480 models, rear height adjustment is made on the bolts attaching the hinges to the bonnet.

9 Adjustment of the front height of the bonnet is accomplished by screwing the rubber plugs on the front crossmember in or out, and by loosening the locknut on the bonnet striker, and turning the striker in or out **(see illustration)**.

10 Check also that the bonnet strikers enter the lock holes centrally.

10 Bonnet support strut - removal and refitting

Removal

1 Support the bonnet in its open position with a length of wood.

2 On 440 and 460 models up to 1994, pull out the special spring clip, and release the strut from the pin on the hinge. Where applicable, unbolt the front support, then release the strut using a twisting motion.

3 On 440 and 460 models from 1994 onwards, remove the special clip from the upper mounting, then lift the bonnet and push the strut forwards. Unbolt the lower mounting, and remove the strut.

4 On early 480 models, drill out the rivets securing the hinge clamp to the inner wing panel, and remove the screw securing the clip.

5 On later 480 models, pull out the spring pin and remove the washer, then extract the

clevis pin securing the top of the strut to the bonnet **(see illustration)**. Unscrew the two screws, and remove the strut from the lower mounting.

Refitting

6 Refitting is a reversal of the removal procedure. Apply a little grease to the pivot points. On early 480 models, it will be necessary to fit new rivets to the hinge clamp.

11 Bonnet release cable - removal, refitting and adjustment

Note: *The bonnet on 440 and 460 models is secured by two locks, whereas the 480 bonnet is secured by only one central lock.*

Removal

1 Support the bonnet in its open position.

2 Working inside the car, remove the knob from the release lever located at the foot of the door A-pillar.

3 Remove the trim panel to gain access to the release lever.

440 and 460 models

4 Working in the engine compartment, press in the spring, and unhook the bonnet release cable from the lock.

5 Release the cable clip from the front crossmember.

6 The cable is routed through the front wheel arch, and it is necessary to remove the plastic liner for access to the cable clips. Release the cable clips.

7 Unbolt the release lever from inside the car.

8 Prise the rubber grommet from the inner wing panel, then withdraw the cable from under the front wing **(see illustration)**.

480 models

9 Working in the engine compartment, release the sleeve, and remove the rubber grommet from the front crossmember.

10 The cable is routed through the front wheel arch, and it is necessary to remove the plastic liner for access to the cable clips. Release the cable clips.

11 Release the clip under the front wing, then unbolt the release lever from inside the car.

12 Release the cable from the lever and from the lock, then withdraw the cable together with the rubber grommet from under the front wing.

Refitting and adjustment

440 and 460 models

13 Refitting is a reversal of the removal procedure. Position the release lever centrally before tightening the mounting bolt.

14 To adjust the cable, first release the clip from the front crossmember, then use a 2.0 mm Allen key to loosen the grub screw in the nipple nearest the clip.

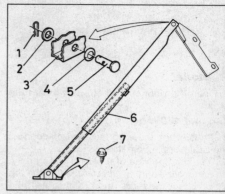

10.5 Bonnet support strut on 480 models

1 *Spring clip*	5 *Pin*
2 *Washer*	6 *Strut*
3 *Hinge*	7 *Mounting*
4 *Washer*	*screw*

15 Position the outer cable so that the outer nipple just contacts the spring, then clip the cable to the crossmember. Slide the inner nipple against the inner spring, then tighten the grub screw.

16 On 440 models up to and including VIN number 051613, check that the cable and catch operate freely without touching the coolant hose bleed screw, and if necessary, alter the position of the plastic cable tie to move the bleed screw away from the cable. Where necessary, the lever inside the car may be adjusted by first loosening the mounting bolt.

480 models

17 Refitting is a reversal of the removal procedure. With the release lever bolt loosened, adjust the outer cable so that the play is just taken up, then tighten the bolt.

All models

18 Check the cable operation, and if necessary, adjust the position of the bonnet as described in Section 9.

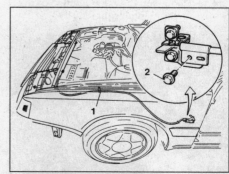

11.8 Bonnet release cable components

1 *Clip*
2 *Release lever mounting bolt*

11

12 Bonnet lock - removal and refitting

Removal

1 Open the bonnet, and support it with the strut.

440 and 460 models

2 Press in the inner spring, and disconnect the cable nipple from the spring.

3 The lock consists of a strong spring only. To remove the spring, first release it at the top by pulling it forwards, then release it at the bottom. The spring is under considerable tension, so extreme care should be exercised.

480 models

4 Unscrew and remove the lock mounting bolts.

5 Unscrew the three mounting bolts, and release the special stud fastener from the crossmember in order to lift the crossmember **(see illustration)**.

6 Remove the sleeve from the lock.

7 Disconnect the switch wiring at the connector.

8 Lift the crossmember slightly, and withdraw the lock together with the switch.

9 Unhook the cable from the lock.

Refitting

440 and 460 models

10 Refitting is a reversal of the removal procedure. To check the lock for adjustment, insert a 11.5 mm diameter drill, and try to push it past the spring. If the drill cannot be inserted

past the spring, the adjustment is correct. If the drill passes the spring, the cable should be adjusted as described in Section 11.

480 models

11 Refitting is a reversal of the removal procedure. Check the cable adjustment, referring to Section 11 if necessary.

13 Bonnet safety catch and lock striker - removal, refitting and adjustment

Removal

440 and 460 models

1 To remove the safety catch, unscrew the mounting bolts and remove the catch from the bonnet. On models from 1994 onwards, unclip and release the operating linkage.

2 To remove the lock striker, first support the bonnet in its open position using a length of wood, then unbolt the striker from the bonnet.

480 models

3 The safety catch and lock striker are incorporated in the same assembly. Unbolt the assembly from the bonnet.

Refitting and adjustment

4 Refitting is a reversal of the removal procedure, but apply a little locking fluid to the threads of the mounting bolts.

440 models

5 440 models with a VIN number up to and including 051613 may be fitted with a modified catch - refer to your local Volvo dealer. Before

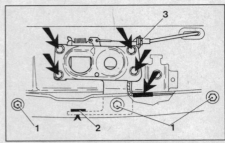

12.5 Bonnet lock components on 480 models

1 Crossmember mounting bolts
2 Special stud fastener
3 Sleeve

fully tightening the catch mounting bolts, check the operation of the bonnet catch as follows.

6 Lower the bonnet slowly, and check that the catch enters the opening correctly and fully. If necessary, the catch mounting bolt holes may be enlarged so that the catch enters the opening correctly.

480 models

7 The mounting bolts should be tightened to the exact torque setting specified - if the bolts are overtightened, the bonnet will be damaged, and if the bolts are not tightened to the correct torque, they might work loose.

All models

8 The striker may be adjusted by loosening the locknut and turning it so that it holds the bonnet at the correct height - the rubber buffers should also be adjusted at the same time.

14 Door inner trim panel - removal and refitting

Removal

440 and 460 models

1 On high-specification models, remove the outer section of the door grip by pulling or prising it out at the midway point, then unhook it at the front end. The inner section may be removed by unscrewing the top and bottom screws **(see illustrations)**.

14.1a Removing the outer section of the door grip

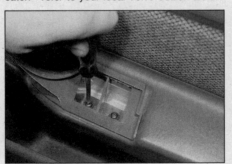

14.1b Remove the screws . . .

14.1c . . . and remove the inner section of the door grip

14.1d On later models, the door grip design has changed . . .

14.1e . . . but the removal method remains the same (upper screw only shown)

14.2 Removing the interior remote door handle

14.3a Remove the plastic cover from the manual window winder . . .

14.3b . . . and remove the retaining screw

14.4a Prise out the plastic cover . . .

14.4b . . . and remove the door grip

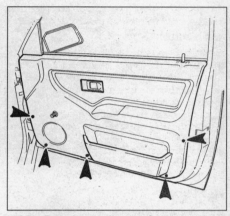

14.5a Door inner trim panel clip locations

2 Push the interior remote door handle surround forwards, then pull out the rear edge and remove the surround over the handle. The use of a screwdriver will be helpful **(see illustration)**.

3 Where a manual window winder is fitted, fully close the window, and note the position of the handle for correct refitting. Prise out the plastic cover and remove the screw, then remove the handle and spacer **(see illustrations)**.

4 On low-specification models (or on the rear doors), remove the plastic door grip by prising out the cover and removing the screw **(see illustrations)**.

5 The trim panel must now be prised away from the inner door. To avoid breaking the clip supports from the panel, it is important to lever the clips themselves away from the door, rather than lever the panel itself **(see illustrations)**. A wide-bladed screwdriver or fork-shaped lever should be used to prise the clips away. Where door speakers are fitted, disconnect the wiring from the speaker before fully withdrawing the panel.

6 If necessary, the plastic membrane may be removed by pulling it carefully away from the adhesive; alternatively, cut carefully through the bead of adhesive using a sharp knife **(see illustrations)**.

480 models

7 Remove the interior remote door handle surround by prising it out at the rear; push to the rear, then withdraw it over the handle.

8 Remove the upper trim panel over the hand grip by prising out the upper edge, then lifting the panel up from the hand grip.

9 Remove the screws, and lift off the hand grip.

10 Carefully prise off the lower trim panel and door bin, using a wide-bladed screwdriver or fork-shaped lever.

Refitting

11 Refitting is a reversal of the removal procedure. Check all the support clips, and renew any that are broken. Press the panel firmly over the clip positions until the clips snap into place.

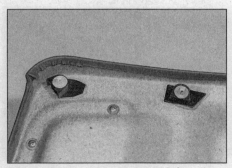

14.5b Clips on the rear of the inner door trim panel

14.6a Inner view of front door with membrane removed

14.6b Inner view of rear door with membrane removed

11

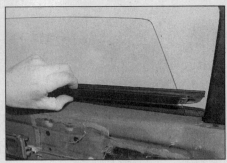

15.2 Removing the waistline weatherstrip from the inside of the glass

15.3a Unscrew the rear window channel mounting bolt . . .

15.3b . . . and remove the rear door rear window channel

15.5 Window glass bottom channel and mounting bolts

15.6 Removing the glass from the door

15 Door window glass - removal and refitting

Removal

1 Remove the door trim panel and membrane, as described in Section 14.

440 and 460 models

2 Remove the waistline weatherstrip from the inside of the glass **(see illustration)**.

3 On the rear door, remove the rear window channel **(see illustrations)**.

4 Open the window approximately halfway, so that the mounting bolts securing the bottom channel to the window are visible.

5 Support the window glass, then unscrew and remove the bottom channel mounting bolts **(see illustration)**.

6 Tilt the glass up at the rear edge, so that the top edge slides on the inside of the door, then

withdraw the glass from the door **(see illustration)**.

7 In necessary, carefully pull the channel from the bottom of the window.

480 models

8 Open the window so that the lower channel mounting bolts are visible through one of the cut-outs in the door.

9 Support the window glass, then unscrew and remove the bottom channel mounting bolts.

10 Remove the rubber grommet, then remove the screw securing the rear window channel to the door, and move the channel to one side.

11 Tilt the glass up at the rear edge, so that the top edge slides on the outside of the door, then withdraw the glass from the door.

Refitting

12 Where the lift channel has been removed from the old window, press it onto the new window in the position shown **(see illustrations)**.

440 and 460 models

13 If the old window is being refitted, the rest of refitting is a reversal of the removal procedure; if a new window is being fitted, carry out the following procedure.

14 Loosen the window regulator mounting nuts and bolts. Refit the window glass, and tighten the bottom channel bolts finger-tight. Fully close the window so that the upper edge is inserted in the top channel, then tighten the window regulator mounting nuts and bolts. Open and close the window two or three times, then open the window halfway and tighten the bottom mounting bolts.

480 models

15 Refitting is a reversal of the removal procedure.

16 Door window regulator - removal and refitting

Removal

1 Remove the door trim panel and membrane, with reference to Section 14.

2 Remove the waistline weatherstrip from the inside of the door glass.

3 Open the window halfway, so that the window glass bottom channel is visible through the door inner aperture. Support the glass, then mark the position of the bolts and unscrew them from the bottom channel **(see illustration)**. Raise the glass to its highest position, and support it.

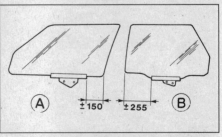

15.12a Window lift channel position dimensions (in mm) - 440 and 460 models

A Front window   *B Rear window*

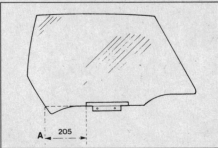

15.12b Window lift channel position dimension (A, in mm) - 480 models

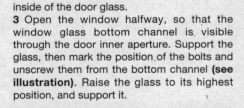

16.3 Marking the position of the window glass bottom channel

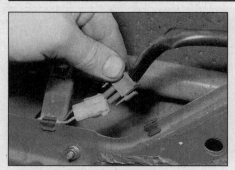

16.4 Disconnecting the electric window wiring

16.5a Window regulator lower mounting

16.5b Window regulator gear mounting on electric windows

16.5c Window regulator gear mounting on manual windows

16.5d Removing the manual window regulator from the door

17.4 Link rods connected to the door lock

4 Where electric windows are fitted, disconnect the wiring from the electric motor at the connector located on the bottom of the door **(see illustration)**.
5 Unscrew the window regulator mounting bolts, then withdraw the assembly from the opening in the door, rotating it as necessary to clear the surrounding components **(see illustrations)**.
6 Where applicable, the electric motor may be unbolted from the assembly. On 480 models, remove the cable retainer with the cable, and recover the three rubber bushes.

Refitting

7 Refitting is a reversal of the removal procedure. Initially, only finger-tighten the

mounting bolts; fully close the window, then tighten the regulator mounting bolts. Open and close the window two or three times, then open it halfway and tighten the bottom channel bolts.

---

17 Door lock, handles and lock cylinder - removal and refitting

Door lock (440 and 460 models)

1 Remove the door trim panel and membrane, as described in Section 14.
2 Fully close the window.

Front door

3 Unscrew and remove the rear window guide channel bottom mounting bolt, and move the channel to one side.
4 Reach into the door, and disconnect the four clips attaching the link rods to the lock **(see illustration)**.
5 Unscrew the three lock mounting screws from the rear edge of the door **(see illustration)**.
6 On the driver's door, release the retaining ring, and remove the microswitch from the lock **(see illustration)**.
7 Where central locking is fitted, disconnect the small link rod from the lock.
8 Withdraw the lock assembly through the opening in the inner door **(see illustration)**.

17.5 Front door lock mounting screws

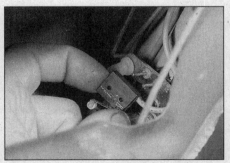

17.6 Removing the microswitch from the door lock

17.8 Removing the lock assembly from the front door

11

17.9 Unbolting the rear door rear window guide channel

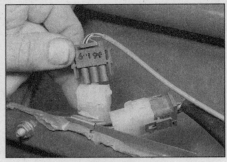

17.11 Disconnecting the wiring at the bottom of the door

17.12 Rear door lock mounting screws

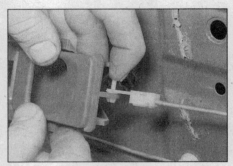

17.13a Pull out the plastic rod . . .

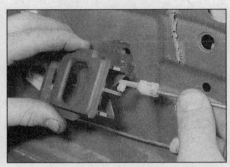

17.13b . . . and disconnect the inner remote door handle link rod

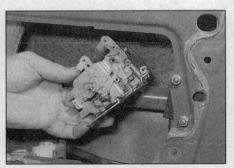

17.16 Removing the lock assembly from the rear door

Rear door - up to chassis number 318877

9 Unscrew the bolts securing the rear window guide channel to the door, and remove the channel **(see illustration)**.

10 Unscrew the lock lower mounting bolt.

11 Disconnect the wiring at the connector located at the bottom of the door **(see illustration)**.

12 Unscrew the lock mounting screws located on the rear edge of the door **(see illustration)**.

13 Disconnect the inner remote door handle link rod from the lock **(see illustrations)**.

14 Remove the screw from the inner door

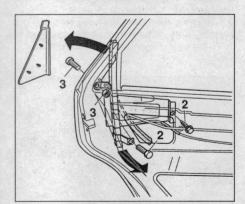

17.18 Removing the window guide channel

2 Guide channel/guard plate bolts
3 Socket-head bolt and nut

handle backing plate, and pull the plate forwards from the door.

15 Release the remote door handle rod from the clips.

16 Lower the lock, disconnect the remote control rod, then withdraw the lock assembly through the aperture in the inner door **(see illustration)**.

Rear door - from chassis number 318878

17 Prise off the triangular trim panel from the outside rear corner of the door frame. Unscrew and remove the socket-head bolt and nut beneath the trim panel.

18 From inside the door, remove the two bolts which secure the base of the window guide channel and the guard plate **(see illustration)**.

19 Twist the top of the window guide channel to the rear, and withdraw it from the door.

20 Disconnect the wiring at the connector located at the bottom of the door.

21 Unscrew the lock mounting screws located on the rear edge of the door.

22 Remove the screw from the inner door handle backing plate, and pull the plate forwards from the door.

23 Prise out the inner remote door handle link rod from the clip next to the handle.

24 Lower the lock assembly, and release the inner handle operating link rod from the lock.

25 Using a twisting motion, release the cable for the lock operating knob from the lock **(see illustration)**.

26 Withdraw the lock assembly through the lower aperture in the inner door.

Both doors

27 Refitting is a reversal of the removal procedure.

Door lock (480 models)

28 Remove the door trim panel and membrane, as described in Section 14.

29 Fully close the window.

30 Unscrew the bolt securing the rear window channel, and move the weatherstrip to one side.

31 Unbolt the connector bracket.

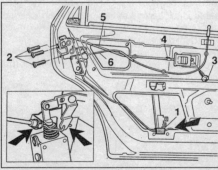

17.25 Rear door lock removal details

1 Wiring connector
2 Lock mounting screws
3 Inner handle securing screw
4 Inner handle link rod clip
5 Inner handle link rod
6 Lock operating knob cable
Inset shows lock operating knob cable disconnection

17.53 Removing the exterior door handle mounting screw

17.56 Releasing the rear end of the handle from the front door

17.57 Removing the outside handle from the front door

32 Disconnect the wiring at the connector, then prise out the rubber grommet.
33 Remove the remote control latch, and unclip the link rod.
34 Release the link rod from the exterior door handle.
35 Unscrew the three lock mounting bolts from the rear edge of the door.
36 Pull the lock forwards, and disconnect the small pin from the lock cylinder link rod.
37 Depress the plastic tabs, and remove the plastic unit from the lock.
38 Disconnect the remote control link rod, and withdraw the lock from the door aperture.
39 Refitting is a reversal of the removal procedure, but note that the lock cylinder link rod should be located in front of the door lock rod. The link rod for the exterior handle should be fitted, free of tension, with the clip pointing inwards.

Inside handle (440 and 460 models)

40 Remove the inner trim panel and membrane, with reference to Section 14.
41 Fully close the window, then remove the screw securing the inside handle to the inner door.
42 Slide the inside handle forwards to release it from the door.
43 Pull the handle out as far as possible, then disconnect it from the link rod by driving out the small pin with a small drift.
44 Refitting is a reversal of the removal procedure, but connect the link rod so that there is no play.

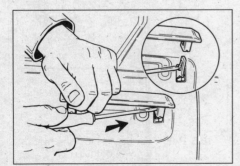

17.64 Use a screwdriver to depress the spring clip when removing the exterior handle on 480 models

Inside handle (480 models)

45 Remove the inner trim panel and membrane, with reference to Section 14.
46 Unscrew the mounting screws, then release the handle from the clips at the bottom, and slide it downwards out of the door.
47 Release the handle from the link rod, using a downwards twisting motion.
48 Refitting is a reversal of the removal procedure.

Exterior handle (440 and 460 models)

Front door

49 Remove the inner trim panel and membrane, with reference to Section 14.
50 Fully close the window, then pull the weatherstrip out of the window channel from inside the door.
51 Unscrew the mounting bolt, and pull the rear window channel downwards and out of the door.
52 Disconnect the link rods from the door lock.
53 Prise out the rubber plug from the inner panel, then unscrew and remove the exterior handle mounting screw (see illustration).
54 On models with central locking, disconnect the wiring from the exterior handle, and disconnect the wiring at the connector at the bottom of the door.
55 Unclip and remove the microswitch from the door lock.
56 Pull open the handle, and release the rear end of the handle from the door (see illustration).
57 Push the handle forwards slightly, then swivel it outwards at the rear, and disconnect the front end from the door (see illustration).
58 Withdraw the handle from the door, together with the link rods, taking care not to damage the rubber gasket.

Rear door

59 Remove the door lock, as described in Section 17.
60 Push the handle forwards slightly, then pull open the handle and release the rear end from the door.
61 Swivel the handle outwards from the door, and release the front end.

62 Withdraw the handle from the door, taking care not to damage the rubber gasket.
63 Refitting is a reversal of the removal procedure.

Exterior handle (480 models)

64 To remove the outer part of the exterior handle, first hold the handle in its open position, then use a small screwdriver to press in the spring clips through the special holes, and withdraw the handle from the door (see illustration).
65 To remove the inner part of the exterior handle, remove the inner door trim and membrane, as described in Section 14.
66 Remove the outer part as described above, then remove the weatherstrip from the window channel. Unscrew the mounting bolt, and pull out the window channel.
67 Unscrew the nuts, and take off the outer retaining plate.
68 Disconnect the link rod from the clip, and slide the inner part of the handle down and out of the door.
69 Refitting is a reversal of the removal procedure. When connecting the link rod, make sure that there is no free play.

Lock cylinder (440 and 460 models)

70 With the exterior handle removed as described in the previous paragraphs, insert the key in the lock cylinder.
71 Remove the screw from the inside of the handle, and remove the two plastic parts followed by the spring (see illustrations).

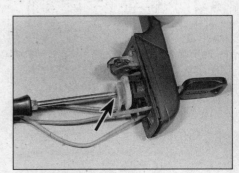

17.71a Remove the screw (arrowed) . . .

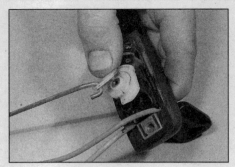

17.71b . . . and remove the plastic parts . . .

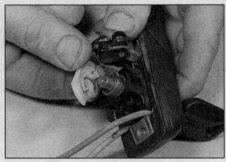

17.71c . . . and spring (arrowed)

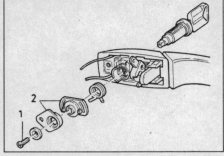

17.72a Lock cylinder components on the exterior handle - 440 and 460 models

1 Screw   *2 Plastic spacers*

17.72b Removing the lock cylinder and key from the handle

17.77 Lock cylinder removal on 480 models

1 Screw   *2 Nuts*

72 Remove the lock cylinder and key from the handle, noting which way round the cylinder is fitted **(see illustrations)**.
73 Refitting is a reversal of the removal procedure. If the special lock grease is available, smear the lock cylinder and component parts with it.

Lock cylinder (480 models)

74 Prise off the triangular cover plate from the inside of the door.
75 Remove the screw, pull the trim moulding loose at the front, then slide it to the rear off the flange.
76 Unscrew the two mounting nuts, withdraw the lock cylinder using a twisting motion, and release the lock from the link rod.

77 Unclip and remove the two switches. Also remove the lock illumination (where fitted) **(see illustration)**.
78 Prise off the C-clip and remove the plastic parts, noting their position.
79 Insert the key, and withdraw the cylinder.
80 Refitting is a reversal of the removal procedure. If the special lock grease is available, smear the lock cylinder and components parts with it.

---

18 Central locking components - removal and refitting

Door lock motors

1 Remove the door trim panel and membrane as described in Section 14.
2 Disconnect the motor wiring connector at the base of the inner door.
3 The lock motor is most easily removed once the lock mechanism has been completely removed, as described in Section 17, but if only the motor requires attention, support the lock and remove the three lock mounting screws.
4 Manoeuvre the lock assembly so that the two motor securing nuts or screws are accessible, and remove them **(see illustration)**.
5 Disconnect the motor link rod using a twisting motion, or slide the motor out of the clip on the operating arm, as applicable **(see illustration)**.

6 Refitting is a reversal of removal. Check the operation of the motor before refitting the door trim panel.

Lock microswitch (driver's door only)

7 Refer to Section 17, paragraphs 1 to 6.

Control unit(s)

Central locking control unit

8 Disconnect the battery negative lead, and position the lead away from the battery terminals.
9 The main central locking control unit is located inside the car, behind the glovebox; remove the glovebox as described in Section 36 for access. On some models, it may be possible to access the control unit by lowering the passenger-side under-facia trim.
10 Release the unit from its mountings, and carefully disconnect the wiring plug(s). Note that, on later models with an anti-theft alarm and immobiliser, the alarm and immobilising functions are incorporated into the central locking control unit.
11 Refitting is a reversal of removal.

Remote locking ultrasonic control unit

12 On later models with remote-control locking, the ultrasonic control unit is located in the passenger's footwell, behind the left-hand side carpeting/trim panel.

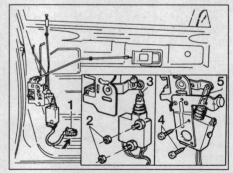

18.4 Central locking motor removal details

1 Wiring connector   *4 Motor securing*
2 Motor securing   *screws*
*   nuts*   *5 Motor operating*
3 Motor link rod   *arm*

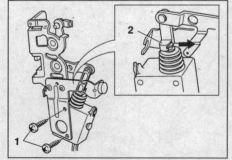

18.5 Rear door central locking motor removal details

1 Securing screws
2 Sliding the motor out of the operating arm clip

19.1 Disconnecting the wiring harness in the door pillar

19.2a Using a small drift to tap out the check pin (arrowed) . . .

19.2b . . . and disconnect the check link

13 Carefully release the carpet/trim panel securing clips, and gain access to the control unit.
14 Release the unit from its mountings, and carefully disconnect the wiring plug.
15 Refitting is a reversal of removal.

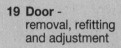 **19 Door -**
removal, refitting and adjustment

Removal

1 With the door open, carefully prise out the wiring harness rubber grommet from the door pillar, and separate the connectors **(see illustration)**. On the front door, it may be found that the wiring cannot be removed sufficiently to separate the connectors; in this case, the trim should be removed from the footwell for access to the connectors from inside the car.
2 Using a suitable drift, tap out the check pin from the bottom upwards, and disconnect the check link **(see illustrations)**.
3 Unscrew and remove the grub screws from both door hinges, and then lift off the door with the help of an assistant **(see illustrations)**.

Refitting and adjustment

4 Refitting is a reversal of the removal procedure, but do not overtighten the grub screws. On completion, check that the door engages the striker correctly, and if necessary

19.3a Unscrew the grub screws . . .

19.3b . . . and lift the door from the hinge brackets

adjust the striker by loosening the screws and repositioning it. The striker adjustment also determines the closed position of the rear edge of the door in relation to the surrounding bodywork.

 **20 Exterior mirror -**
removal and refitting

Mirror glass

⚠ *Warning: Wear thick gloves and eye protection when removing the mirror glass - even if the glass is not broken, it may break during removal*

1 Using a length of plastic, prise out the mirror glass at one side, so that it snaps out of the plastic holder **(see illustration)**. Take great care when removing the glass; do not

use excessive force, as the glass is easily broken.
2 Where applicable, disconnect the heater wiring from the glass **(see illustration)**.
3 On electrically-operated mirrors, the electric motors may be removed by unscrewing the mounting screws **(see illustration)**.
4 Refitting is a reversal of the removal procedure, but lightly grease the plastic holder to help in fitting the mirror.

Mirror assembly

5 On models with electric door mirrors, first remove the door inner trim panel and membrane as described in Section 14, then disconnect the wiring inside the door. Prise off the plastic cover **(see illustration)**.
6 On models with manually-operated door mirrors, remove the screw and pull off the control lever, then prise off the plastic cover.

20.1 Prising out the mirror glass

20.2 Heater wiring connections on the exterior mirror

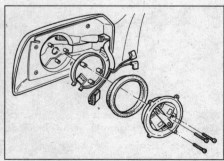

20.3 Electrically-operated exterior mirror components

11

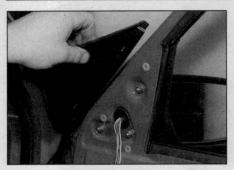

20.5 Removing the plastic cover from inside the door

20.7 Unscrewing the exterior mirror mounting nuts

7 Unscrew the nuts **(see illustration)** and withdraw the mirror from the outside of the door, together with the rubber seal.
8 Refitting is a reversal of the removal procedure.

21 Boot lid - removal, refitting and adjustment

Removal

1 Open the boot lid, and remove the trim panel by prising out the clips.
2 Separate the wiring connectors for the number plate lighting and central locking system, then remove the wiring and rubber grommet by feeding it through the hole in the boot lid.
3 Using a pencil, mark the position of the hinges on the boot lid so that they can be refitted correctly.
4 Have an assistant support the weight of the boot lid, then unscrew the mounting bolts on the hinges, and lift off the boot lid.

Refitting and adjustment

5 Refitting is a reversal of the removal procedure, but check that the boot lid is level with the surrounding bodywork. If adjustment is necessary, leave the mounting bolts finger-tight until the boot lid is aligned correctly, then fully tighten them.
6 The position of the striker also determines

the boot lid height, and it should be re-positioned if necessary. Access to the striker is gained by pulling back the weatherseal, and (on 440 models only) removing the trim panel.

22 Boot lid lock - removal and refitting

Removal

1 Open the boot lid, and remove the inner trim from the lid.
2 Unscrew the lock mounting bolts.
3 Unclip the control rod, and withdraw the lock from inside the boot lid.

Refitting

4 Refitting is a reversal of the removal procedure.

23 Boot lid private lock and cylinder - removal and refitting

Removal

1 Open the boot lid, and remove the inner trim from the lid.
2 Pull the spring plate from the inside of the lock.
3 Disconnect the control rods for the lock and central locking system.

4 Disconnect the small drain hose, then withdraw the lock from inside the boot lid.
5 To dismantle the lock, first drive out the roll pin, and remove the arm from the end of the cylinder.
6 Insert the key in the cylinder, and pull the cylinder assembly from the lock housing. Take care not to lose the ball and spring.

Refitting

7 Refitting is a reversal of the removal procedure, but smear a little lock grease on the moving components. The ball and spring can be inserted when the cylinder is being fitted, using a punch. The key should be rotated half a turn to fully insert the cylinder.

24 Tailgate - removal, refitting and adjustment

Removal

440 models

1 Remove the rear luggage compartment upper side trim panels, and pull the upper section of the weatherseal from the body aperture. Pull off the plastic strip.
2 Prise out the rubber grommets through which the tailgate wiring is inserted, then pull down the rear end of the headlining. Take care not to distort or damage the headlining.
3 Disconnect the rear washer tubes and wiring connectors.
4 Have an assistant support the tailgate, then disconnect the struts by pulling out the spring clips.
5 Mark the position of the tailgate on the hinges with a pencil, to ensure correct refitting.
6 Unbolt the tailgate from the hinges, and withdraw it from the car **(see illustration)**.

480 models

7 Open the tailgate, then pull the wiring out of the body until the connectors can be separated.
8 Have an assistant support the tailgate, then disconnect the struts.
9 Unscrew the mounting nuts located behind the headlining, and lift off the tailgate. Access to the nuts is difficult, and ideally, a cranked ring spanner should be used, as shown **(see illustration)**.

Refitting and adjustment

10 Refitting is a reversal of the removal procedure. Check that the tailgate is level with the surrounding bodywork, and if necessary adjust its position by moving within the elongated holes in the body. Check that the tailgate engages the striker correctly, and adjust if necessary. Also adjust the rubber buffers (where fitted) so that the tailgate is supported firmly.

24.6 Tailgate hinge and wiring tube

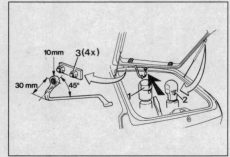

24.9 Spanner dimensions for unscrewing the tailgate mounting nuts on 480 models

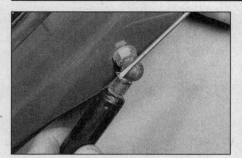

25.2 Prise out the spring clips from the support strut sockets with a small screwdriver

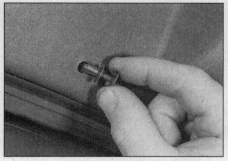

26.1a Removing a trim clip from the tailgate

26.1b Tailgate lock

25 Tailgate support strut -
removal and refitting

Removal

1 Support the tailgate in its open position.
2 Either prise out the spring clip, or drive out the plastic pin from the strut ball sockets (see illustration).
3 Pull off the strut ball sockets, and remove the strut.

Refitting

4 Refitting is a reversal of the removal procedure, but make sure that the strut is fitted the correct way round, with the piston rod end connected to the main body.

26 Tailgate lock -
removal and refitting

Removal

440 models

1 The procedure is similar to that for the boot lid lock - refer to Section 22 (see illustrations).

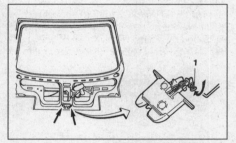

26.1c Removing the tailgate lock on 440 and 460 models

1 Clip

480 models

2 Remove the spare wheel and the side trim panels from the luggage compartment.
3 Remove the rear trim panel, and also release part of the weatherseal.
4 Unscrew the mounting bolts, and remove the lock. Disconnect the wiring and release cable as applicable (see illustration).

Refitting

5 Refitting is a reversal of the removal procedure.

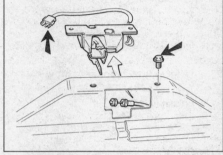

26.4 Removing the tailgate lock on 480 models

27 Tailgate private lock and cylinder -
removal and refitting

Removal

440 models

1 The procedure is similar to that for the boot lid, described in Section 23 (see illustrations).

480 models

2 Remove the spare wheel and the side trim panels from the rear luggage compartment.

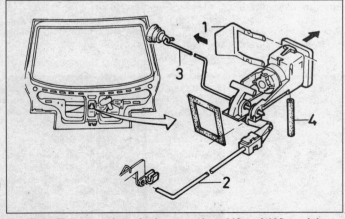

27.1a Tailgate private lock removal on 440 and 460 models

1 Clamping plate		*3 Central locking operating rod*	
2 Lock operating rod		*4 Drain hose*	

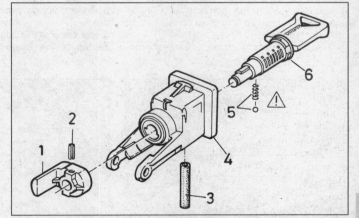

27.1b Tailgate lock cylinder components on 440 and 460 models

1 Carrier	*3 Drain hose*	*5 Ball and spring*
2 Roll pin	*4 Housing*	*6 Lock cylinder*

11

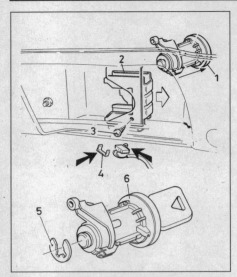

27.4 Tailgate lock cylinder components on 480 models

1 *Private lock assembly*	4 *Clip*
	5 *C-clip*
2 *U-shaped bracket*	6 *Private lock assembly*
3 *Screw*	

3 Remove the rear trim panel, and also release part of the weatherseal.

4 Remove the screw securing the U-shaped bracket to the rear panel, then push the bracket to the left-hand side **(see illustration)**.

5 Extract the clip, and disconnect the burglar alarm wiring.

6 Withdraw the tailgate private lock from the outside of the rear panel.

7 Remove the C-clip from the inner end of the private lock, and remove the various components.

8 Insert the key, then pull the cylinder from the housing, taking care not to lose the ball and spring.

Refitting

9 Refitting is a reversal of the removal procedure.

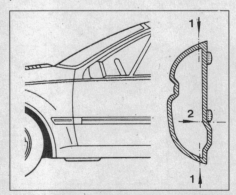

29.5 Cutting sequence when removing the side protection moulding on older 480 models

28 Windscreen and rear window/tailgate glass - general information

The windscreen and rear window/tailgate glass are bonded in place with special mastic; special tools are required to cut free the old units and fit replacements, as well as cleaning solutions and primers. It is therefore recommended that this work is entrusted to a Volvo dealer or windscreen replacement specialist.

On 480 models, the fixed rear side window and front door fixed quarterlight are fitted to the body with a rubber surround, and although it is possible to remove them without special tools, it is recommended that this work is entrusted to a Volvo dealer. The rubber surround is vulcanised to the glass.

29 Body exterior fittings/exterior trim panels - general information

1 The Volvo badges may be removed by levering carefully with a wooden spatula - the application of heat from a hairdryer will make removal easier. Take care not to damage the paintwork.

2 On 440 and 460 models, the rubber strip along the roof and A-pillar is removed by prising out the wide section first at the front, lifting the strip, and using a suitable tool to slide the clips from their bases. Use masking tape to protect the paintwork on each side of the strip.

3 On 480 models, the windscreen surround may be removed by pulling out part of the drip channel, and drilling out the rivets. Apply anti-rust liquid to the rivet holes before fitting the new surround. The roof trim moulding is removed by sliding it to the rear off the clips, and the B-pillar moulding is removed by pulling out the top edge.

4 On 440 and 460 models and newer 480 models, the side protection mouldings are removed with a wooden spatula, taking care not to damage the paintwork. Note the fitted position of the mouldings, to ensure correct refitting.

5 On older 480 models, the side protection mouldings are removed by first cutting them along the top and bottom edges, and removing the outer part of the moulding. Cut along the remaining moulding, about one-third of the width up from the bottom edge, and use a hot air gun or hairdryer when prising off the moulding **(see illustration)**. Note the fitted position of the mouldings, to ensure correct refitting.

6 To remove the sill mouldings, unscrew the retaining screws and remove the front and rear sections. Taking care not to scratch the paintwork, slide the middle section forwards, and remove the two screws from the rear of the mounting strip. Now slide the section to the rear, remove the remaining mounting strip screws, and remove the strip and middle section from the car.

7 The rear spoiler on 440 models is secured by five nuts - the central nut is visible once the tailgate inner trim panel is removed. The spoiler is also stuck to the bodywork with double-sided tape and/or adhesive - use heat to soften the adhesive.

8 The rear spoiler on 460 models is secured by two nuts in the centre, visible when the boot lid is open. The outer ends of the spoiler are stuck to the bodywork with double-sided tape and/or adhesive. When removing the spoiler, feed through the wiring for the high-level brake light (where fitted).

30 Seats - removal and refitting

Front seats

⚠️ *Warning: On models fitted with mechanical seat belt tensioners, refer to the information in Section 32. Do not remove the seat until the tensioner mechanism has been made safe.*

1 If necessary, unbolt the seat belt stalk from the seat **(see illustration)**.

2 Move the seat as far forwards as possible, then using a Torx key, unscrew the rear mounting bolts **(see illustration)**. Now move the seat rearwards, and unscrew the front mounting bolts.

30.1 Seat belt stalk on the front seat

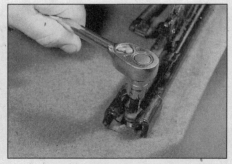

30.2 Unscrewing the front seat mounting bolts

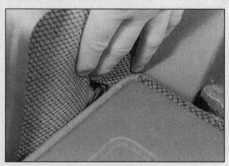

30.10a Tilt the backrest for access to the locking device

30.10b Locking device on the rear seat backrest

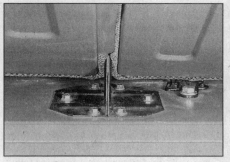

30.10c Centre bracket for the rear seat backrest

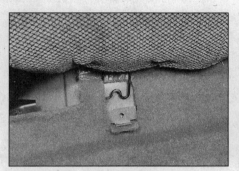

30.11a Lift up the outer end of the seat backrest . . .

30.11b . . . and disconnect the inner end from the pivot pin

30.12 Removing the rear seat side cushion

3 Tilt the seat backwards, and disconnect the wiring plug for the seat heating.
4 Lift the seat out from inside the car.
5 Refitting is a reversal of the removal procedure.

Rear seats

6 Where applicable, remove the trim panel from the side of the rear seat cushion.
7 Unscrew the mounting screws from the brackets on both sides, then use a screwdriver to prise the wire hooks from the front brackets. Lift out the rear seat cushion.
8 Working in the luggage compartment, loosen the rear seat belt stalk mounting bolts a few turns, and press out the wire hooks.
9 Remove the seat cushion while feeding the seat belts through.
10 Tilt the rear seat backrest forwards at an angle of approximately 45°, for access to the locking device located in the side bracket. Pull the locking device upwards, and at the same time, press in the plastic arms to release the device from the side bracket **(see illustrations)**.
11 Lift up the outer end of the seat backrest, and disconnect the inner end from the pivot pin. Withdraw the backrest from inside the car **(see illustrations)**.
12 If necessary, the side cushions may be unhooked from the trim panel **(see illustration)**.
13 Refitting is a reversal of the removal procedure.

---

31 Interior trim - general information

Interior trim panels

1 The interior trim panels are secured using either screws or various types of trim fasteners, usually studs or clips **(see illustration)**.
2 Check that there are no other panels overlapping the one to be removed; usually there is a sequence that has to be followed, and this will only become obvious on close inspection.
3 Remove all obvious fasteners, such as screws. If the panel will not come free, it is held by hidden clips or fasteners. These are usually situated around the edge of the panel, and can be prised up to release them; note, however that they can break quite easily so replacements should be available. The best way of releasing such clips without the correct type of tool, is to use a large flat-bladed screwdriver. Note in many cases that the adjacent sealing strip must be prised back to release a panel.
4 When removing a panel, **never** use excessive force or the panel may be damaged; always check carefully that all fasteners or other relevant components have been removed or released before attempting to withdraw a panel.

5 Refitting is the reverse of the removal procedure; secure the fasteners by pressing them firmly into place and ensure that all disturbed components are correctly secured to prevent rattles.

Headlining

6 The headlining is removed by removing the trim panels from the side pillars, followed by the removal of the interior light(s), grab handles and the sunroof switch (where fitted), weatherseal and control mechanism wiring. Pull the headlining forwards and out of the rear end cover, then remove it from the tailgate opening.
7 Note that headlining removal requires considerable skill and experience if it is to be carried out without damage, and is therefore best entrusted to an expert.

31.1 Removing the luggage compartment side trim panels

11

Carpets

8 The one-piece carpet is removed by removing the seats, centre console, side trim panels, and seat belt slide rails (480 models only); the wiring for the seat heating must also be disconnected. Removal and refitting is reasonably straightforward but very time-consuming.

32 Seat belt tensioner system - general information and precautions

General information

Models which are equipped with a driver's airbag (Supplementary Restraint System, or SRS) are also fitted with a front seat belt tensioner system. The system is designed to instantaneously take up any slack in the seat belt in the case of a sudden frontal impact, therefore reducing the possibility of injury to the front seat occupants. Each front seat is fitted with the system, and there are two different types of tensioner which may be used, depending on model.

On early models, the tensioners are of pyrotechnic (explosive gas) type, and are situated behind the B-pillar trim panel or rear side trim panel, with the seat belt inertia reel.

Later models have a mechanical (spring-loaded) type of tensioner, which is mounted next to the front seat. The mechanical tensioner can be identified by the cylindrical housing and round red button mounted next to the seat, but seek the advice of a Volvo dealer if in doubt.

The pyrotechnic seat belt tensioner is linked to the airbag system, and is triggered by a frontal impact above a pre-determined force. If an impact sufficient to deploy the airbag is sensed, the seat belt tensioners will also be triggered. Lesser impacts, including impacts from behind, will not trigger the system. When the system is triggered, the explosive gas in the tensioner mechanism causes a cable which acts on the inertia reel to retract and lock the seat belt. This prevents the seat belt moving and keeps the occupant firmly in position in the seat.

The mechanical type tensioner has its own impact sensor built into it, and when an impact of sufficient force is detected, the seat belt stalk is pulled downwards by a strong spring and cable, to take up any slack in the belt. The mechanical tensioner can act independently of the airbag system, although in practice it is unlikely to do so.

Once either type of tensioner has been triggered, the assembly must be renewed.

Precautions

There is a risk of injury if the system is triggered inadvertently when working on the vehicle, and it is therefore strongly recommended that any work which might involve the seat belt tensioner system is entrusted to a Volvo dealer. This is particularly the case where mechanical tensioners are fitted, as they must be made safe before being handled - if dropped, the mechanism could be triggered. Seek the advice of a Volvo dealer on how the tensioner may be made safe. Note the following warnings before contemplating any work on the front seat belts.

Warning: On models with pyrotechnic tensioners, disconnect the battery negative lead, position the lead away from the battery terminals, and wait for a period of at least 10 minutes before proceeding.

Do not expose the pyrotechnic tensioner to temperatures in excess of 100°C (212°F).

If the tensioner mechanism is dropped, it must be renewed, even it has suffered no apparent damage.

Do not allow any solvents to come into contact with the tensioner mechanism.

Do not attempt to open the tensioner mechanism, nor try to separate the tensioner from the inertia reel or belt stalk.

Pyrotechnic tensioners must be discharged before they are disposed of, but this task should be entrusted to a Volvo dealer.

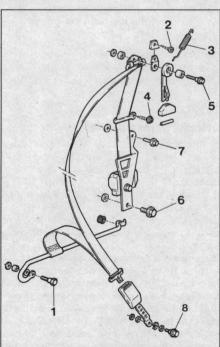

33.8 Front seat belt components on 480 models

1 Lower slide rail mounting bolt
2 Anchorage plate screw
3 Spring
4 Screw
5 Anchorage mounting bolt
6 Reel unit lower mounting bolt
7 Reel unit upper mounting bolt
8 Stalk mounting bolt

33 Seat belt components - removal and refitting

Warning: On models equipped with seat belt tensioners, refer to Section 32 before proceeding.

Removal

Front (440 and 460 models)

1 Unclip the front and rear sill trim panels.
2 Remove the screws, and pull off the B-pillar lower trim panel.
3 Unscrew the front seat belt upper anchorage bolt, then remove the screw located just below the anchorage, and pull off the upper trim panel. It may be necessary to pull out the weatherseal first, on some models.
4 Unbolt the seat belt anchorage and seat belt stalk from the sides of the front seat.
5 On models with pyrotechnic seat belt tensioners, disconnect the red wiring connector from the tensioner unit.
6 Unscrew the inertia reel unit mounting bolt, and remove the unit from the B-pillar.

Front (480 models)

7 Remove the trim panels from the B-pillar and from the side of the rear seat.
8 Unscrew the bolt securing the front end of the lower slide rail to the sill, and unhook the rear end from the body. Remove the rail from the seat belt **(see illustration)**.
9 Remove the screws, spring and bolts from the seat belt upper anchorage.
10 Unbolt the seat belt stalk from the seat.
11 On models with pyrotechnic seat belt tensioners, disconnect the red wiring connector from the tensioner unit.
12 Unscrew the inertia reel unit upper and lower mounting bolts, and remove the unit.

Rear (440 and 460 models)

13 Remove the parcel shelf and the carpet from the luggage compartment.
14 Fold the rear seat backrest forwards, and pull back the weatherseal from the side panel.
15 Remove the side trim panels from the luggage compartment.
16 Unscrew the seat belt upper anchorage bolt from the D-pillar, then unscrew the lower anchorage bolt from the wheel arch **(see illustrations)**.
17 Unscrew the inertia unit mounting bolt, and remove the unit **(see illustration)**.
18 Remove the rear seat backrest as described in Section 30, then unscrew the stalk mounting bolt and remove the stalk **(see illustration)**.

Rear (480 models)

19 Remove the side trim panel from the luggage compartment.
20 Remove the rear seat cushion and the side panel bin from alongside the rear seat.
21 Remove the trim panel from the C-pillar.

22 Carefully pull down the headlining at the rear end, and unscrew the seat belt upper anchorage mounting bolt.

23 Unhook the elastic from the side panel, and unscrew the inertia unit mounting bolts.

Refitting

24 Refitting is a reversal of the removal procedure, but tighten the mounting bolts to the specified torque.

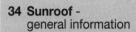

34 Sunroof -
general information

Sunroof glass

1 To remove the sunroof glass, open the sunroof to the tilted position, and remove the trim mouldings.

2 Loosen the three nuts on each side a few turns, then slide the glass out of the slotted holes, towards the rear.

3 Refitting is a reversal of the removal procedure, but adjust it as follows before refitting the trim mouldings.

4 Unscrew the vertical alignment bolts, apply locking fluid to their threads, then refit them and finger-tighten them.

5 Position the glass so that the front weatherseal is approximately 1.0 mm lower than the roof, and the rear weatherseal approximately 1.0 mm higher than the roof, then tighten the bolts.

6 Check that the glass is correctly aligned by inserting a piece of paper between the glass and roof - the resistance should be the same

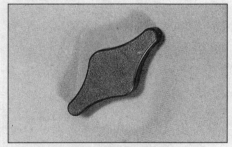

34.10 Manual key for operating the sunroof

35.1 Removing the storage tray

33.16a Rear seat belt upper anchorage

33.17 Rear seat belt inertia unit

as the paper is drawn around the glass.

7 Tighten the nuts, and check the operation of the sunroof.

Sunroof mechanism

8 The removal and refitting of the sunroof mechanism should be left to a Volvo dealer or sunroof specialist.

Manual operation

9 Should the sunroof fail to operate due to a flat battery or other electrical fault, it may be operated manually as follows.

10 Prise out the switch panel from the front of the headlining, and remove the manual override key **(see illustration)**.

11 Insert the key in the special hole in the headlining - on some models, it is located in the switch panel; on others, it is further back on the headlining, and it will be necessary to prise out a plug for access. Turn the key clockwise to close the sunroof, anti-clockwise to open it.

35.2 Removing the screw from the bottom of the ashtray

33.16b Rear seat belt lower anchorage

33.18 Rear seat belt stalks

35 Centre console -
removal and refitting

Removal

Front section

1 Prise out the two storage trays, using a small screwdriver to depress the plastic tabs **(see illustration)**.

2 On early models, remove the ashtray, then remove the screw located in the bottom of the housing **(see illustration)**. Remove the housing, and disconnect the wiring for the illumination and cigar lighter.

3 On later models, the ashtray surround is secured by a single screw, visible once the ashtray itself has been removed. Remove the ashtray surround, then remove the two bolts below **(see illustrations)**. Disconnect the wiring for the cigar lighter and its illumination bulb.

35.3a Remove the ashtray, then remove the single screw behind . . .

11

35.3b ... take out the ashtray surround ...

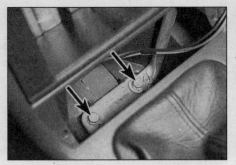

35.3c ... and remove the two bolts beneath

35.4 Gear lever gaiter removed from the console

4 Prise the gear lever gaiter from the console, and remove the screws **(see illustration)**.

5 Unscrew the mounting screws located at the front and rear of the console **(see illustration)**.

6 Press out and unhook the switch panel located at the front top of the console.

7 Prise out the side plugs, and remove the screws located beneath them **(see illustration)**.

8 Pull off the side carpets, and remove the vent mouldings **(see illustration)**.

9 Remove the front section of the console, feeding the gear lever gaiter through as the console is lifted out.

Rear section (440/460 models)

10 Move the front seats as far forwards as possible, then remove the screws from the rear lower corners of the centre console **(see illustration)**.

11 Prise out the trim cover from the tray under the handbrake lever, and remove the screw **(see illustration)**.

12 Remove the ashtray from the rear of the console **(see illustration)**.

35.5 Mounting screw located at the front of the console

13 Open the lid, and prise out the plastic cover from the front of the locker compartment. Remove the screws and lift out the locker, noting the location of the plastic spacers. Disconnect the wiring plug **(see illustrations)**.

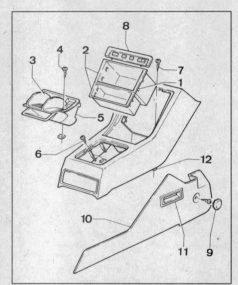

35.7 Centre console front section components

1	Tabs	7	Screw
2	Storage trays	8	Switch panel
3	Ashtray	9	Side plug
4	Screw	10	Side carpet
5	Locker	11	Vent mouldings
6	Screw	12	Console

35.8 Vent moulding on the side carpet

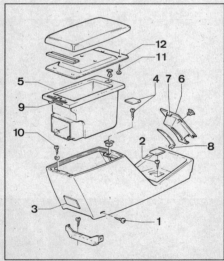

35.12 Centre console rear section components

1	Screw	7	Clip
2	Screw	8	Strip
3	Ashtray	9	Seat belt warning light
4	Screw and trim cover	10	Screw
5	Locker	11	Screw
6	Switch panel	12	Inner panel

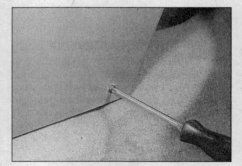

35.10 Removing the centre console rear mounting screws

35.11 Removing the centre mounting screw

35.13a Remove the plastic cover . . .

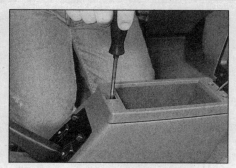

35.13b . . . unscrew the front screw . . .

35.13c . . . and rear screws . . .

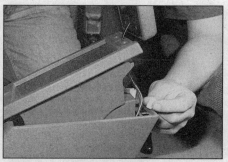

35.13d . . . and lift out the locker, noting the location of the plastic spacers

35.13e Disconnecting the wiring plug

35.15 Pulling the handbrake handle from the metal tubing

14 Carefully prise the switch panel from the top of the console by depressing the plastic tab.
15 Pull the handbrake handle from the metal tubing (see illustration). It is very tight, and the handbrake should be applied before attempting to pull off the plastic outer section.
16 Where applicable, disconnect the wiring for the switch panel.
17 If necessary, remove the handbrake lever blanking cover.
18 The locker may be removed from the console by unscrewing the screws and disconnecting the seat belt warning wiring. The inner panel may also be removed.
19 Release the bottom lugs, and withdraw the rear section of the console from inside the car (see illustration).

Rear seat console (480 models)

20 Remove the ashtray, then remove the screw below and remove the ashtray housing (see illustration).

21 Open the hinged cover, and remove the screws located inside the locker on the rear surface.
22 Unbolt and remove the rear seat belt anchorages from each side of the rear console.
23 Lift the rear console from inside the car.
24 Slide the catch from the front of the console.
25 Unhook the tension spring and remove the screw, then swivel the lid up and push out the hinge pin.
26 The lock may be removed from the lid by pushing it out from the inside.

Refitting

27 Refitting is a reversal of the removal procedure.

36 Glovebox -
removal and refitting

Removal

1 Open the glovebox, and unscrew the four mounting screws from the corners (see illustration).

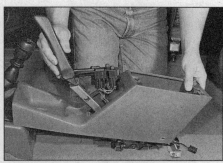

35.19 Removing the rear section of the centre console

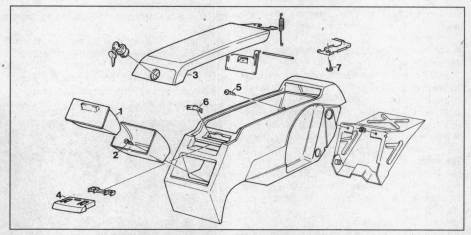

35.20 Rear seat console components on 480 models

1 Ashtray	3 Hinged cover	6 Leaf spring
2 Screw	4 Catch	7 Screw
	5 Screw	

11

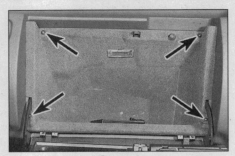

36.1 Glovebox and mounting screws (arrowed)

2 Pull the glovebox out of the facia sufficiently to disconnect the wiring from the glovebox light and switch, then remove the glovebox completely.

3 If necessary, the light, switch and lock may be removed from the glovebox.

Refitting

4 Refitting is a reversal of the removal procedure.

37 Facia - removal and refitting

Removal

1 Disconnect the battery negative lead, and position the lead away from the battery terminals. On models with a driver's airbag, wait 10 minutes before proceeding.

440 and 460 models

2 Remove the A-pillar upper and lower trim panels.

3 Remove the centre console (see Section 35).

4 Remove the steering wheel, with reference to Chapter 10. On models with a driver's airbag, disconnect the orange wiring connector under the steering column.

5 Remove the steering column combination switches, with reference to Chapter 12, Section 4.

6 Release the ignition switch wiring by cutting the plastic tie.

7 Prise out the fasteners, and remove the lower facia trim panels from both sides. Support the panels at the A-pillars.

8 Open the bonnet, and remove the fuse/relay box cover by unscrewing the two screws.

9 Press in the tabs (or remove the screws), and lower the fuse/relay box into the passenger compartment.

10 Referring to Chapter 12, Section 4, remove the switches to the right of instruments, and disconnect the wiring.

11 Remove the instrument panel, with reference to Chapter 12.

12 Unscrew the mounting screws, and withdraw the driver's-side section of the facia **(see illustrations)**.

13 Remove the heater control panel as described in Chapter 3.

14 If not already done, remove the heater blower switch, and disconnect the wiring.

15 Remove the radio/cassette player, as described in Chapter 12.

16 On models from 1994 onwards, remove the centrally-mounted switches from the facia panel as applicable, with reference to Chapter 12, Section 4.

17 On models with additional instruments in the centre of the facia, disconnect the wiring for the oil pressure gauge, turbo boost pressure gauge or voltmeter (as applicable).

18 If no additional instruments are fitted, prise out the oddments box fitted below the radio location, where applicable.

19 Remove the clock as described in Chapter 12

20 On models with an electronic information centre, disconnect the wiring for the channel selector from behind.

21 Remove the glovebox, as described in Section 36.

22 On later models, open the fusebox cover under the driver's side of the facia panel. Remove the mounting screws or clips, and detach the fusebox from the facia.

23 Unscrew the lower facia mounting screws.

24 Unscrew and remove all of the facia mounting screws. Two of the screws are located on each end of the facia; on some models, it is necessary to first prise out a plastic cover. There are also screws located under the facia and beneath the air vents.

25 With all of the mounting screws removed, pull out the facia sufficiently to disconnect the wiring. Note the location of each wire, and if necessary, identify them to ensure correct refitting. To save time when refitting, make a sketch of the wiring harness routing; also disconnect the earth leads.

26 Where applicable, disconnect the choke cable and knob from the facia.

480 models

27 Remove the trim panels from the A-pillars on each side of the car.

28 Remove the centre console, as described in Section 35.

29 Remove the steering wheel (Chapter 10) and the steering column combination switches (Chapter 12, Section 4). On models with a driver's airbag, disconnect the orange wiring connector under the steering column.

30 Remove the relay box cover in the engine compartment, then depress the tabs or remove the screws, and lower the relay box into the passenger compartment.

31 Remove the windscreen wiper blades and arms, as described in Chapter 1, Section 8.

32 Remove the four screws, and lift off the cover moulding from under the front of the windscreen.

33 Referring to Chapter 12, Section 4, remove the switches to the right of the instruments, and disconnect the wiring.

34 Remove the instrument panel, as described in Chapter 12.

35 Remove the radio/cassette player, as described in Chapter 12.

36 Remove the heater control panel as described in Chapter 3.

37 On models with additional instruments in the centre of the facia, disconnect the wiring for the oil pressure gauge, turbo boost pressure gauge or voltmeter (as applicable).

38 If no additional instruments are fitted, prise out the oddments box fitted below the radio location, where applicable.

39 If not already done, remove the heater blower switch, and disconnect the wiring.

40 Remove the clock and the centrally-mounted switches as described in Chapter 12, Sections 13 and 4.

41 On models with an electronic information centre, disconnect the wiring for the channel selector from behind.

42 Remove the glovebox as described in Section 36.

43 Open the fusebox cover under the driver's side of the facia panel. Remove the mounting screws or clips, and detach the fusebox from the facia.

44 Partly remove the weatherseals on both sides, then remove the two end panels and release the wiring harness from the clips.

45 With all of the mounting screws removed, pull out the facia sufficiently to disconnect the wiring. Note the location of each wire, and if necessary identify them to ensure correct refitting. To save time when refitting, make a sketch of the wiring harness routing.

46 Remove the screws, and take out the central electric module (CEM).

Refitting

47 Refitting is a reversal of the removal procedure.

37.12a Removing the driver's-side section of the facia . . .

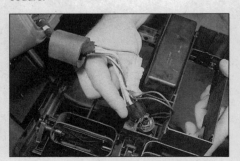

37.12b . . . and disconnecting the wiring - pre-1994 model shown

Chapter 12
Electrical system

Contents

Degrees of difficulty

Easy, suitable for novice with little experience	**Fairly easy,** suitable for beginner with some experience	**Fairly difficult,** suitable for competent DIY mechanic	**Difficult,** suitable for experienced DIY mechanic	**Very difficult,** suitable for expert DIY or professional 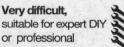

Specifications

System type .... 12-volt, negative earth

Fuses (440 and 460 models up to 1991)

Note: *Fuse number 2 is not used*

No	Rating (amps)	Circuit(s) protected
1	15	Courtesy lights, boot light, glove compartment and ignition switch lighting, cigar lighter
3	15	Central locking system, auxiliary water pump (fuel injection engines)
4	7.5	Instrument panel and information centre, auxiliary water pump relay, clock and radio
5	10	Rear foglight relay
6	20	Direction indicators, heated rear window, heated door mirrors, heater controls and clock illumination
7	30	Reversing lights, seat heating elements, courtesy light relay
8	15	Alternator, ignition unit, rev. counter, oil pressure gauge, indicator lights, clock and instrument illumination
9	7.5	Left-hand parking and tail lights, dashboard illumination
10	15	Right-hand parking and tail lights, number plate lights and rear wiper
11	10	Horn, air conditioning ventilator relay
12	10	Brake stop-lights
13	15	Hazard flasher unit
14	30	Headlight washer motor, air conditioning compressor relay
15	30	Heater blower, sunroof
16	15	Wiper motors, washer pumps
17	15	Electric windows, electric mirrors and radio aerial motor
18	7.5	Left-hand headlight, main beam
19	7.5	Right-hand headlight, main beam and indicator light
20	7.5	Right-hand headlight, dipped beam
21	7.5	Left-hand headlight, dipped beam
22	30	ABS relay
23	30	ABS pump
Behind glovebox, 10 amps		Fuel pump (fuel injection engines)
Behind glovebox, 10 amps		Oxygen sensor (Lambda sond) - B18FP and B18FT engines

Fuses (480 models up to 1991)

No	Rating (amps)	Circuit(s) protected
1	15	Courtesy lights, boot light, engine compartment light, glove compart-ment and ignition switch illumination, cigar lighter, clock and radio
2	20	Foglights, headlight flasher system
3	30	Heater blower (maximum speed)
4	30	Headlight retracting motors
5	15	Brake stop-lights, central locking system, fuel injector cooling fan (turbo models), auxiliary water pump (engine cooling), sunroof
6	7.5	Rear foglights
7	30	ABS relay
8	7.5	Left-hand headlight, main beam
9	7.5	Right-hand headlight, main beam and indicator light
10	7.5	Left-hand parking and tail lights, dashboard illumination, dim-dip beam rheostat
11	7.5	Right-hand parking and tail lights, number plate lights, radio illumination
12	7.5	Left-hand headlight, dipped beam
13	15	Right-hand headlight, dipped beam (and foglight switch on early models)
14	30	Air conditioning compressor and fan, brake stop-lights on later models
15	15	Heated rear window, heated door mirrors
16	20	Long-range headlights, horn, anti-theft alarm
17	15	Direction indicators, or starter motor relay and rear window wiper motor on later models
18	20	Headlight washing system, direction indicators on later models
19	7.5	Alternator, oil pressure gauge, clock illumination, instrument illumination and indicator lights
20	30	Reversing lights, heating controls, seat heater elements and relay, and auxiliary water pump or air conditioning compressor relay
21	3	ABS
22	15	Lighting switch, and belt lock illumination or day running lights
23	15	Wiper motors, washer pumps, sunroof
24	30	Electric windows, electric mirrors
25	20	Air conditioning and/or heater blower, radio
26	30 (special type - **do not** replace with normal type)	ABS pump
Mounted on fuel pump relay connector, 20 amps		Fuel pump
Mounted on oxygen sensor system relay, 20 amps		Oxygen sensor

Fuses (440 and 460 models 1992 on)

Note: *Fuse numbers 8, 9, 11 and 20 are not used*

No	Rating (amps)	Circuit(s) protected
1	25	Heating
2	15 (RHD 3A)	Radio power supply (RHD radio lighting)
3	30	Electric rear windows
4	30	Electric front windows and door mirrors
5	20	Heated rear window and door mirror heating
6	15	Wiper motors, washer pumps and seat heating
7	15	Headlight washers
10	7.5	Radio aerial motor, luggage compartment light and cigar lighter
12	10	Oxygen sensor
13	10	Fuel pump
14	7.5	Right-hand headlight, dipped beam
15	7.5	Left-hand headlight, dipped beam
16	5	Instrument panel warning lamps
17	7.5	Reversing lights, lights 'on' warning buzzer, compressor relay, crankcase heating and fuel injection diagnostic test point
18	7.5	Lighting switch illumination, rheostat, rear lights bulb failure detector, rear foglamp relay and interior time-delay relay
19	7.5	Direction indicators, oil pressure gauge and voltmeter
21	15	Central locking system, keyhole light, glovebox light, radio memory (RHD radio power supply) and clock
22	7.5	Ignition switch light, interior lighting, interior time-delay relay, clock (instrument panel), sun roof (15A) and ECU (B18FT)
23	-	Bridge
24	15	Air conditioning (compressor and cooling fan)
25	7.5	Brake stop-lights
26	10	Hazard warning lights
27	10	Horn and auxiliary water pump (B18FT)
28	7.5	Radio lighting, seat heating switch instrument panel, rheostat, left-hand parking lamp and warning lamp
29	15	Foglights, right-hand parking lamp, radio lighting and rear foglamp (RHD)
30	7.5	Left-hand headlight, main beam
31	7.5	Right-hand headlight, main beam and warning lamp
32	5	ABS

Fuses (480 models 1992 on)

Note: *Fuse numbers 3, 5 and 20 are not used*

No	Rating (amps)	Circuit(s) protected
1	25	Heating
2	10 (RHD 3A)	Radio power supply (RHD radio lighting)
4	3	Electric door mirrors
6	20	Wiper motors, CEM power supply and seat heating
7	30	Air conditioning relay, brake lights and diagnostic tester
8	20	Horn, auxiliary driving lights and central locking system
9	20	Start interlock and rear wiper
10	20	Headlight washers, direction indicators and Hazard warning lights
11	3	Rear foglamp (LHD)
12	10	Fuel pump
13	10	Oxygen sensor
14	7.5	Left-hand headlight, dipped beam
15	7.5	Right-hand headlight, dipped beam
16	5	Instrument panel warning lamps
17	7.5	CEM power supply, seat belt warning lamp, battery charge and oil pressure gauges, lighting switch illumination, rheostat and ECU (B18FT) (+15)
18	15	Air conditioning, reversing lights, rear lights bulb failure detector and crankcase heating
19	15	Lighting switch (day running lights) and dipped beam relay (RHD)
21	7.5	Cigar lighter, keyhole light, Electronic Information Centre, and radio memory (RHD radio power supply)
22	7.5	Clock, glovebox light, ignition switch light, car alarm LED and auxiliary water pump (B18FT)
23	-	Bridge
24	20	Foglights, boot light, main/dipped beam switch, radio aerial motor and interior light
25	20	Rear window and door mirror heating
26	30	Headlight motors
27	30	Electric front windows and tilting sunroof
28	7.5	Left-hand parking lamp and warning lamp, rear lights and dim-dip beam relay (RHD)
29	7.5	Right-hand parking lamp, radio lighting, foglights, rear lights, number plate light and rear foglamp (RHD)
30	7.5	Left-hand headlight, main beam
31	7.5	Right-hand headlight, main beam, warning lamp and auxiliary driving lights switch
32	5	ABS

Bulbs

	Wattage
Boot light	3
Burglar alarm switch	0.36
Courtesy light	5
Direction indicator side repeater	5
Direction indicators	21
Engine compartment light	15
Facia switch illumination	1.2
Front foglight	55
Glovebox and ignition switch lights	3
Hazard warning switch illumination	0.36
Headlight	60/55
Heater control panel	1.2
Heater fan switch illumination	1.2
High level stop-light	21
Information centre illumination	3
Instrument panel illumination	3
Instrument panel warning lights	1.2
Interior light	10
Reading lights (in grab handles)	3
Rear number plate light	5
Reversing light	21
Tail/stop-light	5/21

Torque wrench settings

	Nm	lbf ft
Airbag module retaining screws	8	6
Impact sensor mounting bolts	11	8

12

1 General information and precautions

⚠️ *Warning: Before carrying out any work on the electrical system, read through the precautions given in Safety first! at the beginning of this manual, and in Chapter 5A.*

The electrical system is of 12-volt negative earth type. Power for the lights and all electrical accessories is supplied by a lead/acid type battery which is charged by the alternator.

This Chapter covers repair and service procedures for the various electrical components not associated with the engine. Information on the battery, alternator and starter motor can be found in Chapter 5A.

It should be noted that prior to working on any component in the electrical system, the battery negative terminal should first be disconnected to prevent the possibility of electrical short-circuits and/or fires.

2 Electrical fault finding - general information

Note: *Refer to the precautions given in Safety first! and in Chapter 5A before starting work. The following tests relate to testing of the main electrical circuits, and should not be used to test delicate electronic circuits (such as engine management systems, anti-lock braking systems, etc), particularly where an electronic control module is used. No testing of any kind should be undertaken on the airbag system.*

General

1 A typical electrical circuit consists of an electrical component, any switches, relays, motors, fuses, fusible links or circuit breakers related to that component, and the wiring and connectors which link the component to both the battery and the chassis. To help to pinpoint a problem in an electrical circuit, wiring diagrams are included at the end of this Chapter.

2 Before attempting to diagnose an electrical fault, first study the appropriate wiring diagram to obtain a complete understanding of the components included in the particular circuit concerned. The possible sources of a fault can be narrowed down by noting if other components related to the circuit are operating properly. If several components or circuits fail at one time, the problem is likely to be related to a shared fuse or earth connection.

3 Electrical problems usually stem from simple causes, such as loose or corroded connections, a faulty earth connection, a blown fuse, a melted fusible link, or a faulty relay. Visually inspect the condition of all fuses, wires and connections in a problem circuit before testing the components. Use the wiring diagrams to determine which terminal connections will need to be checked, in order to pinpoint the trouble-spot.

4 The basic tools required for electrical fault-finding include a circuit tester or voltmeter (a 12-volt bulb with a set of test leads can also be used for certain tests); a self-powered test light (sometimes known as a continuity tester); an ohmmeter (to measure resistance); a battery and set of test leads; and a jumper wire, preferably with a circuit breaker or fuse incorporated, which can be used to bypass suspect wires or electrical components. Before attempting to locate a problem with test instruments, use the wiring diagram to determine where to make the connections.

5 To find the source of an intermittent wiring fault (usually due to a poor or dirty connection, or damaged wiring insulation), a wiggle test can be performed on the wiring. This involves wiggling the wiring by hand to see if the fault occurs as the wiring is moved. It should be possible to narrow down the source of the fault to a particular section of wiring. This method of testing can be used in conjunction with any of the tests described in the following sub-Sections.

6 Apart from problems due to poor connections, two basic types of fault can occur in an electrical circuit - open-circuit, or short-circuit.

7 Open-circuit faults are caused by a break somewhere in the circuit, which prevents current from flowing. An open-circuit fault will prevent a component from working, but will not cause the relevant circuit fuse to blow.

8 Short-circuit faults are caused by a short somewhere in the circuit, which allows the current flowing in the circuit to escape along an alternative route, usually to earth. Short-circuit faults are normally caused by a breakdown in wiring insulation, which allows a feed wire to touch either another wire, or an earthed component such as the bodyshell. A short-circuit fault will normally cause the relevant circuit fuse to blow.

Finding an open-circuit

9 To check for an open-circuit, connect one lead of a circuit tester or voltmeter to either the negative battery terminal or a known good earth.

10 Connect the other lead to a connector in the circuit being tested, preferably nearest to the battery or fuse.

11 Switch on the circuit, bearing in mind that some circuits are live only when the ignition switch is moved to a particular position.

12 If voltage is present (indicated either by the tester bulb lighting or a voltmeter reading, as applicable), this means that the section of the circuit between the relevant connector and the battery is problem-free.

13 Continue to check the remainder of the circuit in the same fashion.

14 When a point is reached at which no voltage is present, the problem must lie between that point and the previous test point with voltage. Most problems can be traced to a broken, corroded or loose connection.

Finding a short-circuit

15 To check for a short-circuit, first disconnect the load(s) from the circuit (loads are the components which draw current from a circuit, such as bulbs, motors, heating elements, etc).

16 Remove the relevant fuse from the circuit, and connect a circuit tester or voltmeter to the fuse connections.

17 Switch on the circuit, bearing in mind that some circuits are live only when the ignition switch is moved to a particular position.

18 If voltage is present (indicated either by the tester bulb lighting or a voltmeter reading, as applicable), this means that there is a short-circuit.

19 If no voltage is present, but the fuse still blows with the load(s) connected, this indicates an internal fault in the load(s).

Finding an earth fault

20 The battery negative terminal is connected to earth - the metal of the engine/transmission unit and the car body - and most systems are wired so that they only receive a positive feed, the current returning via the metal of the car body. This means that the component mounting and the body form part of that circuit. Loose or corroded mountings can therefore cause a range of electrical faults, ranging from total failure of a circuit, to a puzzling partial fault. In particular, lights may shine dimly (especially when another circuit sharing the same earth point is in operation), motors (eg wiper motors or the radiator cooling fan motor) may run slowly, and the operation of one circuit may have an apparently-unrelated effect on another. Note that on many vehicles, earth straps are used between certain components, such as the engine/transmission and the body, usually where there is no metal-to-metal contact between components due to flexible rubber mountings, etc.

21 To check whether a component is properly earthed, disconnect the battery, and connect one lead of an ohmmeter to a known good earth point. Connect the other lead to the wire or earth connection being tested. The resistance reading should be zero; if not, check the connection as follows.

22 If an earth connection is thought to be faulty, dismantle the connection, and clean back to bare metal both the bodyshell and the wire terminal or the component earth connection mating surface. Be careful to remove all traces of dirt and corrosion, then use a knife to trim away any paint, so that a clean metal-to-metal joint is made. On reassembly, tighten the joint fasteners securely; if a wire terminal is being refitted, use serrated washers between the terminal and the bodyshell, to ensure a clean and secure connection. When the connection is remade, prevent the onset of corrosion in the future by applying a coat of petroleum jelly or silicone-based grease. Alternatively, (at regular intervals) spray on a proprietary ignition sealer, or a water-dispersant lubricant.

3.1a Release the fasteners and lift up the fuse/relay box cover . . .

3.1b . . . for access to the fuses and relays on early 440 and 460 models

3.2 Later models have the fusebox on the driver's side of the facia

3 Fuses and relays - general information

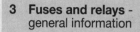

1 On early 440 and 460 models, the fuses and relays are located in a triangular fusebox, on the right-hand side of the bulkhead in the engine compartment. On later models, only the relays are located in the triangular box. Access is gained by unscrewing the two plastic knurled bolts and lifting the cover **(see illustrations)**.
2 On later 440 and 460 models, the fusebox is located under the dashboard on the driver's side. Tweezers are provided to remove the fuses **(see illustration)**. On fuel injection engines, additional fuses for the fuel pump and oxygen sensor are located behind the glove compartment.
3 On 480 models, the fuses are located in the passenger compartment, under the driver's side of the facia panel. Access is gained by removing the cover, and special tweezers are provided to remove the fuses. The cover incorporates a mirror to help locate the fuses. The relays are located in a triangular box, on the right-hand side of the bulkhead in the engine compartment. Access is gained by unscrewing the central screw and lifting the cover.
4 The fuse/relay circuits are shown on the inside of the cover **(see illustration)**.
5 To remove a fuse, use the tweezers provided to pull it directly out of the holder, then remove the fuse from the tweezers. The

wire within the fuse is clearly visible, and it will be broken if the fuse is blown.
6 Always renew a fuse with one of an identical rating; the fuse rating is stamped on top of the fuse. Never renew a fuse more than once without tracing the source of the trouble.
7 The various relays can be removed from their respective locations by carefully pulling them from the sockets **(see illustration)**.
8 If a system controlled by a relay becomes inoperative and the relay is suspect, operate the system; if the relay is functioning, it should be possible to hear it click as it is energised. If the relay proves satisfactory, the fault lies with the components or wiring of the system. If the relay is not being energised, then it is not receiving a main supply voltage or a switching voltage, or the relay is faulty.

4 Switches - removal and refitting

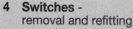

Ignition switch

Note: *The ignition lock barrel can be removed as described in Chapter 10, Section 21.*
1 Disconnect the battery negative terminal.
2 Remove the lower surround from under the steering column, and disconnect the wiring plug from the ignition switch.
3 Unscrew and remove the small grub screw under the steering lock housing, then withdraw the switch.
4 Refitting is a reversal of the removal procedure.

Horn switch/push

5 Refer to Chapter 10, and remove the steering wheel. The horn contacts are located in the horn pad, which cannot be dismantled.
6 On models without an airbag, the slip ring may be removed from the top of the steering column by depressing the two lugs and prising it out with a screwdriver. To remove the sliding contacts, the steering column shrouds must be removed, the wiring disconnected, and the tabs bent outwards.
7 On models with an airbag, the horn contact is part of the airbag contact unit, which is removed as described in Section 23.

Steering column multi-function switches

8 Disconnect the battery negative terminal.
9 Centralise the front wheels in the straight-ahead position, then remove the steering wheel as described in Chapter 10.
10 Unscrew the two upper and one lower screw securing the surround to the steering column. Using a small screwdriver, press in the two tabs located on each side of the surround, then remove the lower surround.
11 Disconnect the wiring at the connector **(see illustration)**.
12 On models not fitted with steering wheel height adjustment, bend out the tabs and remove the switch holder and stalks from the top of the steering column **(see illustration)**. Remove the upper surround.
13 On models with steering wheel height adjustment, move the steering wheel to its lowest position. Remove the upper surround, then bend out the tabs and remove the switch

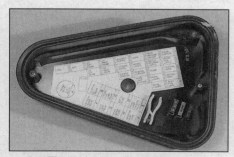

3.4 The fuse and relay locations are shown on the inside of the cover - also note the tweezers and spare fuses

3.7 Removing a relay from the fusebox

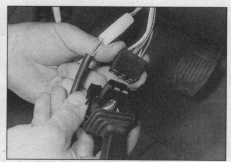

4.11 Disconnecting the wiring from the steering column multi-function switch

4.12 Removing the steering column multi-function switch (models without steering wheel height adjustment)

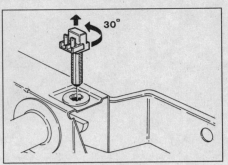

4.16 Brake stop-light switch removal

4.26a Removing the light switch assembly from the instrument panel surround

holder and stalks from the top of the steering column. Disconnect the wiring at the connector.

14 Refitting is a reversal of the removal procedure.

Brake stop-light switch

15 Remove the trim from under the steering column.

16 Turn the stop-light switch approximately 30° anti-clockwise, and pull it out of the pedal bracket **(see illustration)**.

17 Disconnect the wiring from the switch.

18 To refit the switch, first connect the wiring, then insert the switch in the pedal bracket, so that the switch pin is depressed by about 3.0 mm with the brake pedal in its rest position. Now turn the switch approximately 30° clockwise to lock it.

19 Switch on the ignition and depress the brake pedal slowly - the stop-lights should come on when the pedal has been depressed by a maximum of 20 mm.

Reversing light switch

20 Apply the handbrake, then jack up the front of the car and support on axle stands. Remove the splash guard from under the engine compartment.

21 Disconnect the wiring from the reversing light switch on the transmission.

22 Place a container beneath the transmission to catch any spilled oil.

23 Have ready a suitable plug to insert in the switch aperture. Unscrew the switch from the transmission, and plug the hole.

24 Check the sealing washer, and renew if necessary.

25 Refitting is a reversal of the removal procedure, but fit a new washer if necessary, and tighten the switch.

Light switch

440 and 460 models

26 Pull off the rotary knob, and unscrew the nut. Alternatively, the complete switch panel can be removed **(see illustrations)**.

27 Withdraw the switch, and disconnect the wiring.

480 models

28 Pull the complete switch out of its holder, and disconnect the wiring.

All models

29 Refitting is a reversal of the removal procedure.

Rear screen heating and rear foglight switch

440 and 460 models

30 Remove the light switch panel as described previously in this Section.

31 Disconnect the wiring, and remove the switch.

480 models

32 Pull the switch holder from the facia panel, and disconnect the wiring.

All models

33 Refitting is a reversal of the removal procedure.

Instrument panel dimmer switch

34 Using a small screwdriver, prise the

switch out of the facia (or from the steering column lower shroud) and disconnect the wiring.

35 Refitting is a reversal of the removal procedure.

Heater fan switch

440 and 460 models up to 1994, and 480 models

36 Using a small screwdriver, prise the switch out of the facia panel, then disconnect the wiring **(see illustration)**.

440 and 460 models, 1994 onwards

37 The heater fan switch is mounted on the rear of the heater control panel - remove the panel from the facia as described in Chapter 3 (there is no need to disconnect the heater control cables).

38 If not already done, disconnect the wiring plug from the heater fan switch.

39 Remove the fan switch mounting nuts, and withdraw the switch from the heater control panel.

All models

40 Refitting is a reversal of the removal procedure.

Door window and door mirror switches

440 and 460 models up to 1994, and 480 models

41 Remove the handle from the handbrake lever, with reference to Chapter 11, Section 35.

42 Prise the cover panel from the centre console using a small screwdriver **(see illustration)**.

4.26b Disconnecting the wiring from the rear of the light switch with the instrument panel surround removed

4.36 Removing the heater fan switch from the surround

4.42 Removing the door window switch panel from the centre console

4.44 The switch panel can be prised out of the door trim panel for access to the wiring plugs

43 Disconnect the wiring, and push the switch out of the cover panel.

440 and 460 models, 1994 onwards

44 Carefully prise the switch panel out of the door trim panel (see illustration).
45 Disconnect the wiring plug(s) from the switch as necessary, and remove it.

All models

46 Refitting is a reversal of the removal procedure.

Front foglight switch

440 and 460 models

47 Remove the light switch panel as described previously in this Section.
48 Disconnect the wiring, and remove the switch.

480 models

49 Carefully prise the switch panel from the top of the console by depressing the plastic tab.

4.61 Seat heating switch removal

4.68b . . . and withdraw it from the facia

4.55a Remove the hazard warning switch . . .

50 Press out the switch, and disconnect the wiring.

All models

51 Refitting is a reversal of the removal procedure.

Hazard warning switch

440 and 460 models up to 1994

52 Remove the screws and pull out the surround, then disconnect the wiring plugs.
53 Remove the information centre or the blanking plate.
54 Unscrew the four screws from the cover panel.
55 Withdraw the switch, and disconnect the wiring plug (see illustrations).

440 and 460 models, 1994 onwards

56 Refer to paragraphs 65 to 70. Note that it will also be necessary to prise out the seat belt warning light, using the method described.

4.68a Push the switch out from behind . . .

4.69 Disconnect the wiring plug from the switch

4.55b . . . and disconnect the wiring multi-plug

480 models

57 Remove the cover panel, together with the hazard warning switch.
58 Depress the plastic tabs, remove the switch from the cover panel, then disconnect the wiring.

All models

59 Refitting is a reversal of the removal procedure.

Seat heating switch

440 and 460 models up to 1994, and 480 models

60 Carefully prise the switch panel from the top of the console by depressing the plastic tab.
61 Press out the switch, and disconnect the wiring (see illustration).

440 and 460 models, 1994 onwards

62 Refer to paragraphs 65 to 70.

All models

63 Refitting is a reversal of the removal procedure.

Central locking switch

64 Refer to paragraphs 65 to 70.

Centrally-mounted facia switches

65 On 440 and 460 models from 1994 onwards, the redesigned facia layout saw some of the minor switches relocated to a central panel below the heater control panel.
66 These switches cannot be prised from their locations - prising will only remove the switch cover, and this effectively dismantles the switch, which is not desirable. The safest way to remove these switches is as follows.
67 First, prise off the blank switch cover at the right-hand side of the panel. If this reveals the back section of a false switch, use a pair of thin-nosed pliers to pull out the back half of the 'switch'.
68 Reach in through the aperture with a finger or hooked tool, and hook out the switch next to the blank just removed, pulling it towards you to withdraw it from the facia (see illustrations). If this is not the switch required, the wiring plug need not be disconnected.
69 Carry on prising out the switches in this way until the required switch is removed, and disconnect its wiring (see illustration).

12

4.71 Courtesy light switch removal

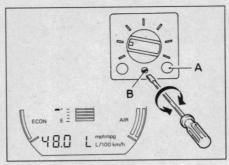

4.84 Information centre selector switch adjustment

A Button   B Set screw

4.87 Glovebox light switch removal

70 Refitting is a reversal of removal.

Courtesy light switch

71 Using a small screwdriver, prise the switch out of the body pillar **(see illustration)**. Make sure that the wiring is not disconnected as the switch is being removed, otherwise it will be very difficult to retrieve it.
72 If necessary, tape the wiring to the pillar to hold it, then disconnect it from the switch.
73 Refitting is a reversal of the removal procedure.

Tailgate switch

74 Remove the two bulbholders and the rear panel.
75 Unscrew the bolts from the striker plate.
76 Disconnect the wiring, and remove the striker plate together with the switch.
77 Refitting is a reversal of the removal procedure.

Central Electronic Module (CEM)

78 Open the bonnet, then remove the screw and the panel covering the CEM.
79 Unscrew the CEM mounting screws, disconnect the wiring, and remove the module.
80 Refitting is a reversal of the removal procedure.

Information centre selector switch

81 Using a small screwdriver, prise the switch out of the facia.
82 Disconnect the wiring, and remove the switch.
83 Refitting is a reversal of the removal procedure. If necessary, the selector switch may be calibrated as follows. Fill the fuel tank to maximum capacity.
84 Depress button (A) and switch on the ignition **(see illustration)**.
85 Using a small screwdriver on the set screw on the bottom of the switch, adjust the digital readout to 48 litres.
86 Switch off the ignition.

Glovebox light switch

87 Open the glovebox, and prise the switch out using a small screwdriver **(see illustration)**.
88 Refitting is a reversal of the removal procedure.

5 Bulbs (exterior lights) - renewal

General

1 Whenever a bulb is renewed, note the following points:
a) *Disconnect the battery negative lead before starting work (see Section 1).*
b) *Remember that if the light has just been in use, the bulb may be extremely hot.*
c) *Always check the bulb contacts and holder, ensuring that there is clean metal-to-metal contact between the bulb and its live(s) and earth. Clean off any corrosion or dirt before fitting a new bulb.*
d) *Wherever bayonet-type bulbs are fitted, ensure that the live contact(s) bear firmly against the bulb contact.*
e) *Always ensure that the new bulb is of the correct rating and that it is completely clean before fitting it; this applies particularly to headlight/foglight bulbs (see below).*

Headlight

440 and 460 models

2 With the bonnet open, remove the cover from the rear of the headlight by turning it anti-clockwise.
3 Ease the wiring plug from the rear of the bulb, using a rocking motion.
4 Release the spring clip, and pivot the clip clear **(see illustration)**.

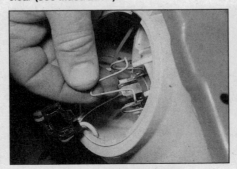

5.4 Release the spring clip . . .

5 Withdraw the bulb from its location in the headlight **(see illustration)**.

480 models

6 The headlights must first be set in their raised position, as follows. Switch on the ignition, then switch on the headlight main beam - this will cause the headlights to rise. Now release the bonnet, and switch off the ignition and main beam - the headlights should not retract.
7 Remove the screws, and withdraw the headlight surround.
8 Unscrew and remove the two upper and two lower screws from the surround, and remove the surround while supporting the headlight.
9 Withdraw the headlight, and disconnect the wiring plug. Remove the dust cap.
10 Release the spring clip using a screwdriver if it is tight, and pivot the clip down.
11 Withdraw the bulb from its location in the headlight.

All models

12 Fit the new bulb using a reversal of the removal procedure, but make sure that the arms on the bulb support are correctly located in the lens assembly.

> **HAYNES HiNT**
>
> *Take care not to touch the new bulb glass with your fingers, as this will lead to premature bulb failure - if touched, clean the bulb with methylated spirit.*

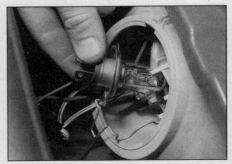

5.5 . . . and withdraw the headlight bulb

5.22 Front sidelight bulb removal on 440 and 460 models

5.31 Front direction indicator bulb renewal on 440 and 460 models (shown with light unit removed)

5.34 Remove the screw . . .

13 On 480 models, tighten the inner lower headlight surround screw first, followed by the outer screw and the upper screws.

14 On completion, lower the headlights by closing the bonnet.

Long-range headlights (480 models)

15 Remove the sidelight/indicator light cluster, with reference to paragraphs 24 to 28.

16 Depress the two clips, and tilt the headlight to remove it from the front panel.

17 Remove the rubber cap, and ease the wiring from behind the bulbholder.

18 Release the spring clip, and pivot it down.

19 Disconnect the wire attached to the bulb, then withdraw the bulb from its location in the headlight.

20 Fit the new bulb using a reversal of the removal procedure, but make sure that the tabs on the bulb support locate correctly in the lens assembly. Take care not to touch the new bulb glass with your fingers, as this will lead to premature bulb failure - if touched, clean the bulb with methylated spirit.

Front sidelight (440 and 460 models)

21 With the bonnet open, remove the cover from the rear of the headlight by turning it anti-clockwise.

22 Pull the sidelight bulbholder from the rear of the headlight, then remove the bulb by depressing it and turning it anti-clockwise **(see illustration)**.

23 If necessary, ease the wiring plug from the rear of the bulbholder, using a rocking motion.

Front sidelight/indicator light (480 models)

24 The headlights must first be set in their raised position, as follows. Switch on the ignition, then switch on the headlight main beam - this will cause the headlights to rise. Now release the bonnet, and switch off the ignition and main beam - the headlights should not retract.

25 Unscrew the sidelight/indicator light upper screw, located in the channel in front of the headlight.

26 Place some cloth or card on the front bumper, to avoid damage to the paintwork.

27 Insert a screwdriver between the rear of the indicator and the bumper, and depress the retaining spring. At the same time, give a sharp blow with the palm of the hand on the side of the indicator light - this will move the light cluster forwards.

28 Withdraw the light cluster and disconnect the wiring, then remove the relevant bulbholder by twisting it anti-clockwise.

29 Depress and twist the bulb to remove it from the bulbholder. If renewing the sidelight bulb, it is advisable to use only a genuine Volvo bulb, otherwise the headlight motors may fail to work - see Section 10.

30 Refitting is a reversal of the removal procedure, but align the pegs on the rear of the cluster with the holes in the front panel.

Front direction indicator (440 and 460 models)

31 Open the bonnet, and turn the indicator light bulbholder anti-clockwise to remove it from the light. An alternative method is to remove the indicator light completely first **(see illustration)**.

32 Depress and twist the bulb to remove it from the bulbholder.

33 Refitting is a reversal of the removal procedure.

Front direction indicator repeater

34 Remove the screw **(see illustration)**, and lift out the direction indicator repeater light from the front wing.

35 Separate the bulbholder from the housing, then remove the bulb by pulling it straight out **(see illustration)**.

36 Refitting is a reversal of the removal procedure.

Front foglight

37 Working under the front of the car, release the wire clip from the rear of the foglight, and remove the plastic cover **(see illustrations)**.

38 Unhook the legs of the wire clip, then swing the clip to one side to remove the bulb **(see illustrations)**. Unplug the wiring connector.

39 Refitting is a reversal of the removal procedure. Note that the rim of the bulb has a lug and cut-out, to ensure it will only fit the correct way round.

5.35 . . . and remove the front direction indicator repeater bulb and holder

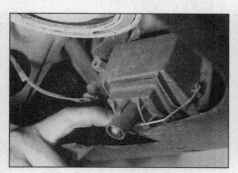

5.37a Release the wire clip . . .

5.37b . . . and remove the rear cover

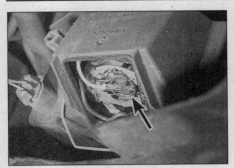

5.38a The bulb is held in place by a wire clip (arrowed), the ends of which can be unhooked . . .

5.38b . . . to remove the bulb - unplug the bulb wiring connector (arrowed)

5.40 Squeeze together the two plastic catches, and withdraw the bulbholder

Rear light cluster

440 and 460 models

40 Open the boot lid or tailgate, and remove the light cluster by squeezing the two plastic catches inwards (see illustration).

41 Depress and twist the relevant bulb anti-clockwise to remove it from the bulbholder (see illustration).

42 Refitting is a reversal of the removal procedure. Note that the tail/stop-light bulb is a double-filament type, and will only fit one way round in the bulbholder.

480 models

43 Open the tailgate, then open the storage cubby by turning the catch.

44 Remove the cover from over the rear light cluster, by pressing up the lower edge so that the upper edge can be released from the catches.

45 Depress the plastic tab in the corner, and lift out the rear light cluster.

46 Depress and twist the relevant bulb anti-clockwise to remove it from the bulbholder.

47 Refitting is a reversal of the removal procedure. Note that the tail/stop-light bulbs are double-filament type, and will only fit one way round in the bulbholder.

Number plate lights

48 On 440 and 460 models, prise the number plate light from the boot lid or tailgate, using a small screwdriver inserted in the slot on the left-hand side of the light (see illustration).

49 On 480 models, unscrew the two screws

and remove the lens from the light.

50 Release the festoon-type bulb from the spring contacts (see illustration).

51 Refitting is a reversal of the removal procedure, but check the tension of the spring contacts, and if necessary bend them so that they firmly contact the bulb end caps. Make sure that the half moon pattern on the light faces the number plate.

Rear foglight (480 models)

52 Unscrew the two screws, and remove the lens.

53 Depress and twist the bulb to remove it from the bulbholder.

54 Refitting is a reversal of the removal procedure.

High-level stop-light

440 models

55 Depress the grooved area on the cover, and remove the cover (see illustration).

56 Depress and twist the bulb anti-clockwise to remove it from the bulbholder.

57 Refitting is a reversal of the removal procedure. Press the cover until it snaps into place.

460 models without rear spoiler

58 Fold forwards the left-hand side of the rear seat for access to the high-level stop-light.

59 Prise off the cover using a small screwdriver in the lower hole.

60 Squeeze in the plastic tabs, and remove the bulbholder from the light.

5.41 Removing a bulb from the rear light cluster bulbholder on 440 and 460 models

61 Depress and twist the bulb anti-clockwise to remove it from the bulbholder.

62 Refitting is a reversal of the removal procedure. Hook the upper edge of the cover in the upper holes, then press in the lower edge until it snaps into position.

460 models with rear spoiler

63 Where the light is built into the spoiler, proceed as follows. Remove the screws and/or unclip the cover at the rear of the light unit.

64 Depress and twist the bulb anti-clockwise to remove it from the bulbholder.

65 Refitting is a reversal of the removal procedure.

480 models

66 Open the tailgate, then remove the cover from the tailgate wiper motor. On early models, press in the lower extensions and swivel the

5.48 Using a small screwdriver to prise out a rear number plate light

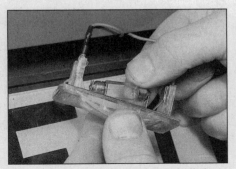

5.50 Releasing the festoon-type bulb from the rear number plate light spring contacts

5.55 High-level stop-light bulb with cover removed

6.2 Prise off the lens . . .

6.3 . . . for access to the interior light bulb

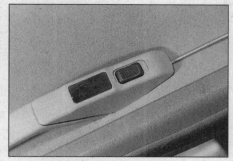

6.9 Removing the rear reading light

cover out of the upper hinge. On later models, remove the fasteners by pushing the central pins through with a narrow screwdriver, then swivel the cover out of the upper hinge.

67 Pull the light from its mounting.

68 Depress and twist the bulb anti-clockwise to remove it from the bulbholder.

69 Refitting is a reversal of the removal procedure. On later models, lock the fasteners by pushing in the pins until flush.

6 Bulbs (interior lights) - renewal

General

1 Whenever a bulb is renewed, note the following points:

a) *Disconnect the battery negative lead before starting work (see Section 1).*

b) *Remember that if the light has just been in use, the bulb may be extremely hot.*

c) *Always check the bulb contacts and holder, ensuring that there is clean metal-to-metal contact between the bulb and its live(s) and earth. Clean off any corrosion or dirt before fitting a new bulb.*

d) *Wherever bayonet-type bulbs are fitted, ensure that the live contact(s) bear firmly against the bulb contact.*

e) *Always ensure that the new bulb is of the correct rating and that it is completely clean before fitting it.*

Interior light

2 Prise off the lens by inserting a screwdriver in the slot and using a twisting action **(see illustration)**.

3 Release the festoon-type bulb from the spring contacts **(see illustration)**.

4 Refitting is a reversal of the removal procedure, but check the tension of the spring contacts, and if necessary bend them so that they firmly contact the bulb end caps.

Map reading light

5 Prise off the lens by inserting a screwdriver in the slot and using a twisting action.

6 Remove the screws, and slide out the bulbholder.

7 Release the festoon-type bulb from the spring contacts.

8 Refitting is a reversal of the removal procedure, but check the tension of the spring contacts, and if necessary bend them so that they firmly contact the bulb end caps.

Rear reading light

9 Squeeze the top and bottom of the light, and remove it from the base. Alternatively, use a small screwdriver **(see illustration)**.

10 Release the reflector, or turn it to one side **(see illustration)**.

11 Release the festoon-type bulb from the spring contacts.

12 Refitting is a reversal of the removal procedure, but check the tension of the spring contacts, and if necessary bend them so that they firmly contact the bulb end caps.

Glovebox light

13 Open the glovebox, then prise out the light using a small screwdriver **(see illustration)**.

14 Release the festoon-type bulb from the spring contacts.

15 Refitting is a reversal of the removal procedure, but check the tension of the spring contacts, and if necessary bend them so that they firmly contact the bulb end caps.

Luggage area and engine compartment lights

16 Prise the light from its location using a small screwdriver **(see illustration)**.

17 Release the festoon-type bulb from the spring contacts.

18 Refitting is a reversal of the removal procedure, but check the tension of the spring contacts, and if necessary bend them so that they firmly contact the bulb end caps.

Instrument panel warning lights and illumination

19 Remove the instrument panel, as described in Section 11.

20 Twist the bulbholder anti-clockwise through 90°, and remove it from the rear of the instrument panel **(see illustration)**.

21 Pull the wedge-type bulb from the bulbholder **(see illustration)**.

22 Refitting is a reversal of the removal procedure.

6.10 Releasing the reflector from the rear reading light

6.13 Glovebox light removal

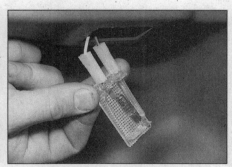

6.16 Luggage area light removal

6.20 Bulbholder removal from the instrument panel

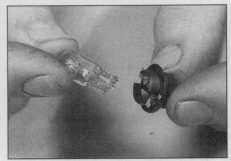

6.21 Removing the wedge-type bulb from the bulbholder

6.24 Removing the ignition switch illumination bulbholder

Ignition switch illumination

23 Remove the steering column lower shroud, with reference to Chapter 10.
24 Pull the bulbholder from the ignition switch/steering lock housing **(see illustration)**.
25 Pull the bulb from the bulbholder.
26 Refitting is a reversal of the removal procedure.

Heater control panel illumination

27 Refer to Chapter 3 and remove the heater control panel from the facia. Note that it should not be necessary to disconnect the heater control cables - use the panel removal procedure as a guide to gaining access to the bulbs.
28 The control panel bulbs are of the wedge-base type, and can be pulled from their holders.
29 Reassemble the control panel using a reversal of the removal procedure given in Chapter 3.

Clock illumination

30 Remove the clock, as described in Section 13.
31 Twist and turn the bulbholder, and remove it from the rear of the clock **(see illustration)**.
32 Pull the wedge-type bulb from the bulbholder.
33 Refitting is a reversal of the removal procedure.

Front seat belt warning light

440 and 460 models up to 1994, and 480 models

34 The seat belt warning light is located in the instrument panel, and is removed as described in paragraphs 19 to 22.

440 and 460 models from 1994 onwards

35 On later models, the warning light is located in the row of switches in the centre of the facia. To remove the warning light unit, remove the switches to the right of it, referring to Section 4, paragraphs 65 to 70.
36 Push the warning light unit out from behind, and disconnect the wiring plug.
37 Carefully unclip the front part of the unit for access to the wedge-type bulb, which can be pulled out.
38 Reassembly and refitting is a reversal of removal.

Rear seat belt warning light

39 Prise the warning light from the locker on the rear section of the centre console.
40 Disconnect the wiring, then remove the festoon-type bulb from the spring contacts **(see illustration)**.
41 Refitting is a reversal of the removal procedure.

Ashtray illumination light

42 Remove the ashtray from the centre console.
43 Pull the bulbholder from the rear of the ashtray **(see illustration)**.

44 Pull the wedge-type bulb from the bulbholder.
45 Refitting is a reversal of the removal procedure.

Switch illumination

46 Generally speaking, it will be necessary to dismantle any switch to gain access to its illumination bulb, and this carries a high risk of damage. If possible, it is preferable to obtain a complete switch assembly, perhaps from a vehicle breakers.
47 Before dismantling any switch, consult a Volvo dealer, and ensure that a new bulb is available.
48 Remove the switch in question with reference to Section 4.
49 Dismantling a switch generally involves separating the front section from the rear body of the switch, which (apart from the risk of damage) risks the loss of internal components, such as springs and contacts.
50 Switch illumination bulbs are usually of wedge-base type, which can be pulled out.
51 Reassemble the switch and refit using a reversal of the removal procedure.

7 Exterior light units - removal and refitting

1 Disconnect the battery negative lead before starting work (see Section 1).

6.31 Removing the bulbholder from the rear of the clock

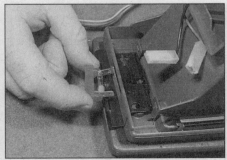

6.40 Removing the rear seat belt warning light

6.43 Removing the bulbholder from the rear of the ashtray

7.4 Headlight unit upper mounting bolts (arrowed)

7.5a Unhook the trim strip from the peg on the headlight . . .

7.5b . . . and disconnect it from the bottom of the headlight

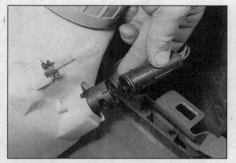

7.6 Disconnecting the wiring plug from the headlight unit housing

Headlight unit

440 and 460 models up to 1994

2 Remove the radiator grille (see Chapter 11).
3 Remove the direction indicator light, with reference to paragraphs 28 and 29.

7.8a Remove the securing bolts . . .

7.7a Removing the spring clips securing the headlight lens to the housing

4 Unscrew the two upper mounting bolts from the crossmember (see illustration).
5 Unhook and remove the trim strip from under the headlight (see illustrations).
6 Withdraw the headlight, and disconnect the wiring plug (see illustration).

7.8b . . . and take off the radiator cover panel

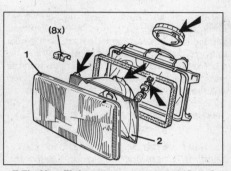

7.7b Headlight components on 440 and 460 models

1 Lens   2 Reflector

7 If necessary, the headlight may be dismantled by first removing the bulbs as described in Section 5. To remove the lens, prise off the spring clips (see illustrations). The reflector may be removed from the housing by turning the two adjustment screw holders one-third of a turn. The wiring harness can also be removed at this stage.

440 and 460 models, 1994 onwards

8 Remove the five securing bolts, and take off the radiator cover panel (see illustrations).
9 Remove the direction indicator light, with reference to paragraphs 31 to 33.
10 On models with headlight wipers, pull off the washer hose, then unscrew the wiper arm retaining nut and remove the wiper arm (see illustrations).

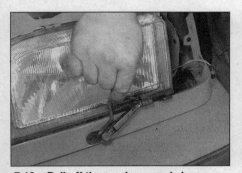

7.10a Pull off the washer supply hose . . .

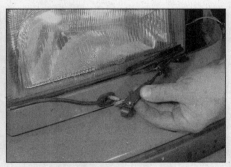

7.10b . . . unscrew the wiper arm retaining nut . . .

7.10c . . . and pull off the wiper arm

12

7.11 Removing the headlight trim strip

7.12a Remove the headlight lower mounting bolts (arrowed) . . .

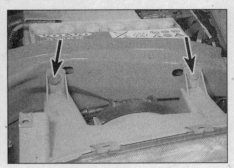

7.12b . . . the upper mounting bolts . . .

11 Unhook and remove the trim strip from under the headlight. On models with headlight wipers, feed the washer hose through the hole in the trim strip **(see illustration)**.

12 Remove the five headlight securing bolts (two above and below, one to the inside), and pull the headlight forwards **(see illustrations)**. Disconnect the wiring, and remove the headlight from the car.

480 models

13 Raise the headlights either as described in Section 5, paragraph 6, or by turning the wheel on the headlight motor.

14 If working on the left-hand headlight unit, remove the battery completely.

15 Unscrew the two screws from the top of the headlight surround, and remove the surround.

16 Unscrew the headlight pod upper and side mounting screws, and remove the pod.

17 Prise out the retaining clip, and disconnect the vibration damper from the headlight.

18 From the front crossmember, unscrew the two upper mounting nuts and lower mounting bolt.

19 Unscrew the side mounting bolt from the inner wing.

20 Withdraw the headlight unit, and disconnect the wiring at the two connectors.

21 If necessary, the headlight may be dismantled as follows. Disconnect the operating rod from the ball and socket.

22 Unscrew the mounting bolts, and disconnect the motor from the rod.

All models

23 Refitting is a reversal of the removal procedure. Where the headlight has been dismantled, clean the reflector with a soft, dry cloth before assembling. On completion, have the headlight alignment checked and if necessary adjusted.

Long-range headlights (480 models)

24 Remove the sidelight/direction indicator unit, as described in Section 5.

25 Depress the two side tabs, and withdraw the long range headlight. Disconnect the wiring at the connector.

26 Refitting is a reversal of the removal procedure.

Front sidelight/indicator light (480 models)

27 Refer to the procedure for the renewal of the front sidelight/indicator light bulb in Section 5.

7.12c . . . and the inner mounting bolt, then remove the headlight and disconnect the wiring

Front direction indicator (440 and 460 models)

Models up to 1994

28 With the bonnet open, release the spring securing the front direction indicator to the rear of the headlight **(see illustration)**.

29 Withdraw the light forwards from the headlight, and disconnect the wiring **(see illustrations)**.

30 Refitting is a reversal of the removal procedure. Make sure that the light is located over the plastic guides located on the headlight.

Models from 1994 onwards

31 With the bonnet open, reach in behind the light unit and squeeze together the two plastic retaining tabs.

32 Keeping the tabs pressed together, pull the light unit forwards **(see illustration)**.

7.28 Spring securing the front direction indicator to the rear of the headlight

7.29a Withdrawing the front direction indicator light forwards from the plastic guides on the headlight

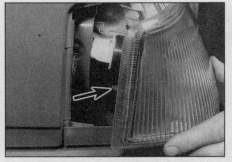

7.29b Front direction indicator light wiring plug and rear location peg (arrowed)

7.32 Squeeze together the retaining tabs, and withdraw the light unit

7.33 Either disconnect the wiring connector, or twist off the bulbholder, to remove the light unit

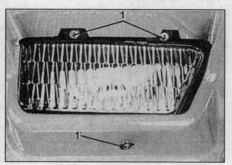

7.36 Front foglight location in the front spoiler

1 Mounting screws

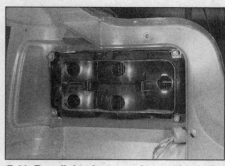

7.41 Rear light cluster and mounting bolts

33 Either twist and remove the bulbholder, or unplug the wiring connector, from the rear of the light, and remove it from the car **(see illustration)**.
34 Refitting is a reversal of the removal procedure.

Front direction indicator repeater

35 Refer to the procedure for the renewal of the front direction indicator repeater bulb in Section 5.

Front foglight

36 Remove the screws securing the front foglight to the front spoiler **(see illustration)**. On later models, there are two screws (under plastic covers) below the light unit - one is the beam adjuster, the other secures the light unit.
37 On 480 models, take care not to damage the ambient air temperature sensor, and also unscrew the light mounting bolts from the rear of the spoiler.
38 Withdraw the light from the rear of the spoiler, and disconnect the wiring. For better access to the rear of the spoiler, the car may be jacked up and supported on axle stands.
39 Refitting is a reversal of the removal procedure.

Rear light cluster

40 Remove the bulbholder, with reference to Section 5.
41 Unscrew the four mounting bolts/nuts, and remove the light unit from the rear of the car **(see illustration)**.

42 Refitting is a reversal of the removal procedure.

Number plate lights

43 Refer to renewal of the number plate light bulb in Section 5.

Rear foglight (480 models)

44 Refer to renewal of the rear foglight bulb in Section 5. The light body is also retained by the lens screws.

8 Headlight dim-dip system - general information

In addition to the normal Volvo day-running lights, a headlight dim-dip system is fitted to most models. The system is intended to prevent the car from being driven on sidelights or parking lights alone. When the sidelights or parking lights are switched on, as soon as the ignition is also switched on, the dipped-beam headlights come on, at one-sixth of their normal brightness (hence the term dim-dip lighting). Normal dipped beam is of course available, as soon as the dashboard switch is turned to the main lighting position.

9 Headlight beam alignment - general information

1 It is advisable to have the headlight beam alignment checked and if necessary adjusted by a Volvo dealer, using optical beam-setting equipment. Correct alignment of the headlight beams is most important, not only to ensure good vision for the driver, but also to protect other drivers from being dazzled.
2 In an emergency (such as after an accident), the headlights may be adjusted by turning the adjustment knobs or screws.
3 On 440 and 460 models, the adjustment knobs are located on the rear of the headlight - turn the upper knob to adjust the beam horizontally, and the lower knob to adjust the beam vertically **(see illustration)**.

4 On 480 models, two adjustment screws are located on the corners of the headlights **(see illustration)**.

10 Headlight motor (480 models) - removal and refitting

1 Disconnect the battery negative lead before starting work (see Section 1).
2 Before assuming that the headlight motor has failed, refer to Sections 2 and 3, and check for a blown fuse, inoperative relay, or wiring faults.
3 The headlight motor system is quite complex electrically, and there are a couple of common reasons why the motors can fail to work:
 a) First, the headlight motors are designed not to operate with the bonnet open; there is a microswitch in the bonnet lock itself. It is worth checking the wiring to the switch, and (as far as possible) verifying that the switch has not stuck in the 'bonnet open' position, causing the lights to fail even when the bonnet is closed.
 b) Second, and more common, is the failure of the motor circuit due to the fitment of non-standard sidelight bulbs. Although pattern bulbs will fit and work correctly, genuine Volvo sidelight bulbs have an offset pin which serves to complete the headlight motor circuit.
4 The headlight may also apparently fail due to a seized linkage. Try the effect of some

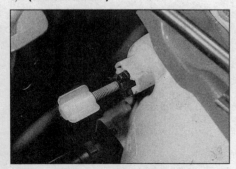

9.3 Headlight beam alignment adjustment knob

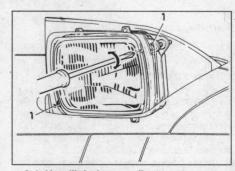

9.4 Headlight beam adjustment screw locations (1) on 480 models

12

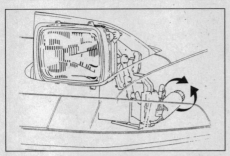

10.10 The headlight can be raised (or lowered) using the manual adjustment wheel

11.5 Instrument panel mounting screws

11.6 Speedometer cable connecting collar (arrowed) on the rear of the instrument panel

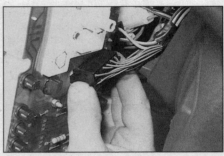

11.7 Disconnecting the wiring multi-plugs from the rear of the instrument panel

lubricant applied to the linkage joints, but be sure to only use a lubricant suitable for plastic/nylon parts (eg silicone-based), where these are employed.

5 To gain access to the motor, refer to Sections 5 and 7, and remove the headlight and front direction indicator/sidelight on the side concerned.

6 If the left-hand motor is being worked on, unscrew the four bolts and remove the battery tray. On the right-hand side, it may be helpful to unbolt the cooling system expansion tank, and move it as far as possible without disconnecting the hoses.

7 Remove the bolts securing the operating linkage and frame to the inner wing.

8 Disconnect the wiring plug from the motor, and withdraw the motor and linkage from the car.

9 It is not clear at the time of writing whether the motor is available separately from the operating linkage - before attempting to separate the motor, check on parts availability with your Volvo dealer.

10 Refitting is a reversal of removal. If a new motor/linkage is being fitted, set it to the 'head-light raised' position, either by connecting the motor and switching on the headlights, or by turning the wheel on the headlight motor **(see illustration)**.

11 On completion, have the headlight alignment checked and if necessary adjusted.

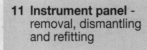

11 Instrument panel - removal, dismantling and refitting

Removal

1 Disconnect the battery negative lead.

440 and 460 models

2 Remove the steering wheel, as described in Chapter 10.

3 Remove the screws located over the instrument panel and below the side switches, and remove the instrument panel surround. Disconnect the wiring plugs from the rear of the surround.

4 Disconnect the speedometer cable from the transmission, with reference to Section 15.

5 Unscrew the two mounting screws located

on the right-hand side of the instrument panel **(see illustration)**, then pull out the panel and unclip it from the left-hand side.

6 Disconnect the speedometer cable by squeezing the plastic collar to release the clip **(see illustration)**.

7 Disconnect the wiring multi-plugs **(see illustration)** - noting their positions for correct refitting - and withdraw the instrument panel from the facia.

480 models

8 Remove the light switch, with reference to Section 4.

9 Remove the multi-switch assembly from the right-hand side of the instrument panel, with reference to Section 4.

10 Remove the heater blower switch, with reference to Section 4.

11 Remove the clock, with reference to Section 13.

12 Adjust the steering wheel to its lowest position.

13 Unscrew and remove the eight screws securing the instrument panel surround to the facia. Prise out the screw covers where applicable.

14 Unscrew the two mounting screws located on the right-hand side of the

instrument panel, then pull out the panel and unclip it from the left-hand side.

15 Disconnect the wiring multi-plugs - noting their position for correct refitting - and withdraw the instrument panel from the facia.

Dismantling

16 The various components of the instrument panel are as shown **(see illustrations)**, and dismantling is straightforward. Take care, however, not to break the plastic housings, and do not overtighten the screws and nuts.

Refitting

17 Refitting is a reversal of the removal procedure.

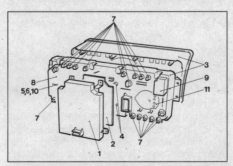

11.16a Instrument panel components on models with an information centre

1 Rear cover	7 Warning lights
2 ECU	8 Printed circuit board
3 Case and front cover	9 Voltage stabiliser
4 Speedometer	10 Information centre
5 Fuel gauge	11 Tachometer (rev. counter)
6 Temperature gauge	

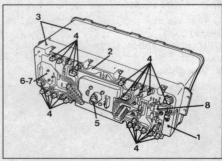

11.16b Instrument panel components on models without an information centre

1 Voltage stabiliser	5 Speedometer
2 Printed circuit board	6 Fuel gauge
3 Case and front cover	7 Temperature gauge
4 Warning lights	8 Tachometer (rev. counter)

13.1 Prising the clock from the facia panel

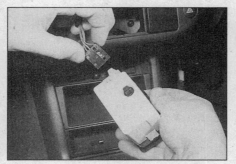

13.2 Disconnecting the wiring from the rear of the clock

14.5 Horn and mounting bracket - mounting nut arrowed

12 Cigar lighter and housing - removal and refitting

Removal

1 Remove the front ashtray from the centre console.

2 Remove the screws from the bottom of the cigar lighter housing (or on later models, the single screw at the top), and withdraw the housing from the centre console.

3 Pull out the ashtray illumination bulb, and disconnect the wiring from the cigar lighter.

4 Press the cigar lighter out of the housing.

Refitting

5 Refitting is a reversal of the removal procedure.

13 Clock - removal and refitting

Removal

1 Using a small screwdriver, prise the clock out of the facia (see illustration).

2 Disconnect the wiring plugs from the rear, and withdraw the clock (see illustration).

Refitting

3 Refitting is a reversal of the removal procedure.

14 Horn - removal and refitting

Removal

1 Apply the handbrake, then jack up the front of the car and support on axle stands.

2 Remove the engine compartment splash guard.

3 Remove the fuse supplying the horn from the fusebox.

4 Disconnect the wiring from the horn.

5 Unscrew the mounting nut, and remove the horn from the bracket (see illustration).

Refitting

6 Refitting is a reversal of the removal procedure.

15 Speedometer drive cable (440 and 460 models) - removal and refitting

Removal

1 With the bonnet open, clean the area around the speedometer cable location on the transmission.

2 Pull the speedometer cable retaining spring pin from the bracket on the rear of the transmission (see illustration).

3 Pull the speedometer cable from its location in the transmission (see illustration).

To prevent dust and dirt entering the transmission, blank off the hole with tape or a suitable plug.

4 Remove the instrument panel, with reference to Section 11.

5 Working in the engine compartment, pull the cable through the bulkhead, together with the rubber grommet.

Refitting

6 Refitting is a reversal of the removal procedure, but first examine the rubber O-ring on the transmission end of the cable, and renew it if necessary. Press the cable down as far as possible into the transmission before refitting the retaining pin.

16 Speedometer sensor (480 models) - removal and refitting

Removal

1 Apply the handbrake, then jack up the front of the car and support on axle stands.

2 The sensor is located on the right-hand side of the transmission, by the driveshaft inner joint (see illustrations). First disconnect the wiring connector, and clean the area around the sensor.

3 Unscrew the bolt, and remove the clamping bracket.

4 Withdraw the sensor through the hole in the transmission.

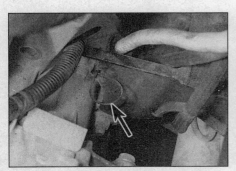

15.2 Pull out the retaining spring pin (arrowed) . . .

15.3 . . . and remove the speedometer cable from its location in the transmission

16.2a Speedometer sensor and wiring cable on 480 models

12

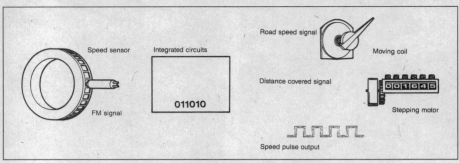

16.2b Speedometer sensor operation

17.4 Windscreen wiper motor with the cover removed

Refitting

5 Refitting is a reversal of the removal procedure, but first examine the rubber O-ring, and renew it if necessary.

17 Windscreen wiper motor and linkage - removal and refitting

Removal

1 Remove the wiper arms and blades, with reference to Chapter 1, Section 8.
2 Pull the sealing moulding from the bulkhead at the rear of the engine compartment, then carefully pull off the plastic cover.
3 Remove the cover from the relay box on the right-hand side of the bulkhead.
4 Pull the cover from the top of the windscreen wiper motor (see illustration).
5 Temporarily switch on the ignition, and operate the windscreen wipers so that the linkage is visible in the heater plenum chamber.
6 Remove the fuse supplying the windscreen wiper motor from the fusebox.
7 Disconnect the wiper motor wiring at the connector.
8 Unscrew the bolts from the wiper motor mounting bracket.
9 Remove the screws securing the wiper linkage spindle housings to the windscreen valance.
10 Disconnect the windscreen washer tubing.
11 Unscrew the motor mounting bolts, and

withdraw the motor and linkage from the heater plenum chamber.
12 If necessary, the assembly may be dismantled by disconnecting the control rods, unbolting the motor, and removing the nuts and rubbers from the bracket (see illustration).
13 Examine the parts for wear and damage, and renew them as necessary.

Refitting

14 Refitting is a reversal of the removal procedure.

18 Tailgate wiper motor and linkage - removal and refitting

Removal

1 Remove the fuse supplying the tailgate wiper motor from the fusebox.
2 Remove the wiper blade and arm, with reference to Chapter 1, Section 8.
3 Open the tailgate, and carefully prise out the inner trim panel for access to the motor (see illustration).
4 Disconnect the wiring plug from the motor.
5 Unscrew the mounting bolts, and remove the wiper motor and linkage assembly from inside the tailgate.
6 If necessary, unbolt the motor from the bracket.

Refitting

7 Refitting is a reversal of the removal procedure.

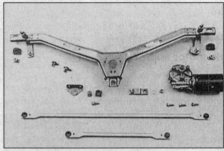

17.12 Windscreen wiper motor and linkage components

19 Washer system components - removal and refitting

Note: Before assuming that a washer jet is defective, try cleaning the nozzle with a suitable pin. A pin inserted into the jet nozzle can also be used to adjust the aim of the washer jets. If cleaning with a pin does not cure a non-working washer jet, it will have to be removed as described below for more thorough cleaning. Once the jet has been removed, it may be worth operating the washers prior to refitting the jet, in order to flush debris out of the washer supply hoses.

Windscreen washer jet

1 Pull the jet, together with its rubber seal, out of the scuttle (see illustration).
2 Disconnect the plastic tubing from the jet (see illustration). To prevent the tubing from

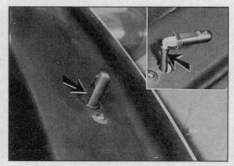

18.3 Tailgate wiper motor with the inner trim panel removed

19.1 Pulling the windscreen washer jet out of the scuttle

19.2 Windscreen washer jet removal

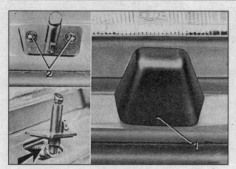

19.5 Headlight washer jet removal

1 Cap   *2 Mounting screws*

19.10 Headlight washer jet tubing clips (arrowed)

20.2 Removing the plastic covers from each side of the radio

dropping into the plenum chamber, stick it onto the scuttle with adhesive tape.

3 Refitting is a reversal of the removal procedure.

Headlight washer jet

440 and 460 models up to 1994, and 480 models

4 Depress the front base of the jet cap using a screwdriver, then lift it off.

5 Unscrew the mounting screws, and remove the jet from the valance **(see illustration)**.

6 Loosen the clip, and disconnect the tubing from the jet.

7 Refitting is a reversal of the removal procedure. Press on the cap until it snaps into position.

440 and 460 models from 1994 onwards

8 On later models with headlight wash/wipe, the washer jets are incorporated into the wiper arms. If necessary, the wiper arms can be removed as described in Section 7, paragraph 10.

Headlight washer jet tubing T-piece

9 On 440 and 460 models up to 1994, remove the radiator grille, with reference to Chapter 11.

10 Loosen the clips, and disconnect the three plastic tubes from the T-piece **(see illustration)**.

11 Refitting is a reversal of the removal procedure.

Tailgate washer jet

12 Remove the tailgate wiper motor and bracket, as described in Section 18.

13 Remove the washer jet from the rubber grommet in the tailgate.

14 Disconnect the plastic tubing from the jet.

15 Refitting is a reversal of the removal procedure.

Washer pump

16 The washer pumps are located on the reservoir on the front right-hand corner of the engine compartment. First disconnect the wiring plug.

17 Disconnect the plastic tubing, and pull the washer pump out of the reservoir. Be prepared for some loss of water by positioning a suitable container beneath the reservoir.

18 Refitting is a reversal of the removal procedure, but check the rubber grommet, and renew it if necessary.

20 Radio/cassette player - removal and refitting

Removal

1 If the radio has a security code, make sure this is known before disconnecting the battery. Disconnect the battery negative lead.

2 Prise the plastic covers from each side of the radio, where applicable **(see illustration)**.

3 In order to release the radio retaining clips, two U-shaped rods must be inserted into the special holes on each side of the radio. If possible, it is preferable to obtain purpose-made rods from an audio specialist, as these have cut-outs which snap firmly into the clips so that the radio can be pulled out **(see illustration)**.

4 Withdraw the radio sufficiently to disconnect the feed, earth, aerial and speaker leads **(see illustration)**.

Refitting

5 Refitting is a reversal of the removal procedure.

21 Speakers - removal and refitting

Removal

Front door speaker

1 Remove the front door inner trim panel, as described in Chapter 11.

2 With the wiring disconnected, remove the speaker from the trim panel **(see illustration)**.

Rear speaker - 440 and 480 models

3 Remove the side trim panel from the luggage area, with reference to Chapter 11.

4 Disconnect the wiring, and remove the speaker from the side panel.

20.3 Using the special U-shaped rods to remove the radio

20.4 Removing the radio from the facia

21.2 Speaker location in the front door trim panel

Rear speaker - 460 models

5 Either fold down the relevant half of the rear seat backrest, or gain access to the speaker from inside the boot.

6 Disconnect the wiring, and remove the speaker from the side panel.

Refitting

7 Refitting is a reversal of the removal procedure.

22 Airbag system - general information and precautions

⚠️ *Warning: Before carrying out any operations on the airbag system, disconnect the battery negative lead, position the lead away from the battery terminals, and wait at least 10 minutes before proceeding. This is to allow the electrical charge in the standby power unit to dissipate safely, preventing the airbag from firing accidentally. It is also advisable to disconnect the orange wiring plug under the steering column before removing the airbag module from the steering wheel. When operations are complete, make sure no one is inside the vehicle when the battery is reconnected.*

Note that the airbag must not be subjected to temperatures in excess of 90°C (194°F). When the airbag is removed, ensure that it is stored the correct way up to prevent possible inflation.

Do not allow any solvents or cleaning agents to contact the airbag module. It must be cleaned using only a damp cloth.

The airbag module and control unit are both sensitive to impact. If either is dropped or damaged, they should be renewed.

Disconnect the airbag control unit wiring plugs below the steering column and below the ashtray before using arc-welding equipment on the vehicle.

Do not connect any electrical test equipment to the airbag wiring, and do not splice other electrical feeds off the airbag harness.

A driver's airbag was fitted as standard to all models from October 1993 onwards. Models fitted with a driver's side airbag have SRS stamped on the airbag unit, which is fitted to the centre of the steering wheel.

The airbag system comprises the airbag unit (complete with gas generator), an impact sensor/control unit, a standby power unit, and a warning light in the instrument panel. Where pyrotechnic type seat belt tensioners are fitted (see Chapter 11, Section 32), these are also linked to the airbag system **(see illustration)**.

The airbag system is triggered in the event of a heavy frontal impact above a predetermined force; side or rear impacts are unlikely to trigger the airbag. The airbag is

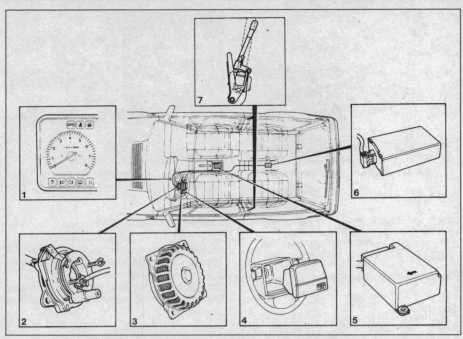

22.2 Airbag and Supplementary Restraint System component locations

1 *SRS warning light*
2 *Airbag module contact unit*
3 *Airbag module gas generator*
4 *Airbag module*
5 *Impact sensor/control unit*
6 *Standby power unit*
7 *Seat belt tensioners (pyrotechnic type)*

inflated within milliseconds, and forms a safety cushion between the driver and the steering wheel. This prevents contact between the upper body and the wheel, and therefore greatly reduces the risk of injury. The airbag then deflates almost immediately.

Every time the ignition is switched on, the airbag control unit performs a self-test. If all is well, the airbag (SRS) warning light will be illuminated for a maximum of 10 seconds, and will go out either after this time or when the engine is started.

If the warning light fails to come on, remains illuminated after the initial 10-second period, flashes, or comes on at any time when the vehicle is being driven, there is a fault in the airbag system. The vehicle should then be taken to a Volvo dealer for examination at the earliest possible opportunity. A diagnostic

connector plug is located in the storage locker in the centre console, into which a dedicated Volvo tester can be plugged - **do not** plug any DIY test equipment into this connector.

23 Airbag system components - removal and refitting

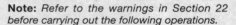

Note: *Refer to the warnings in Section 22 before carrying out the following operations.*

Driver's airbag

Removal

1 Disconnect the battery negative terminal, and wait at least 10 minutes before proceeding.

2 Remove the steering column lower shroud, and disconnect the orange wiring plug for the airbag system.

3 Using an Allen key, slacken and remove the two retaining screws from the rear of the steering wheel, rotating the wheel as necessary to gain access to the screws **(see illustration)**.

4 Return the steering wheel to the straight-ahead position, then carefully lift the airbag module away from the steering wheel and disconnect the wiring connector from the rear of the unit **(see illustration)**. Note that the airbag must not be knocked or dropped, and should be stored the correct way up with its padded surface uppermost.

23.3 Remove the two Allen screws from the rear of the steering wheel

23.4 Withdraw the airbag module from the steering wheel, and disconnect the wiring plug (arrowed)

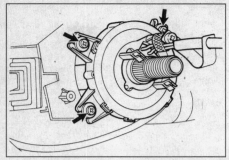

23.12 Airbag contact unit retaining screws (arrowed)

Refitting

5 Make sure that the steering wheel is in the straight-ahead position. Reconnect the wiring connector and seat the airbag unit in the steering wheel, ensuring that the wire does not become trapped. Fit the new retaining screws, and tighten them securely.
6 Reconnect the orange wiring plug under the steering column, and refit the column lower shroud.
7 Making sure that no-one is inside the car, reconnect the battery negative lead.
8 Finally, switch on the ignition, and check that the SRS warning light performs as normal - see Section 22.

Airbag contact unit

Removal

9 Remove the airbag unit as described above, and the steering wheel as described in Chapter 10.
10 Unscrew the two upper and one lower screw securing the surround to the steering column. Using a small screwdriver, press in the two tabs located on each side of the surround, then remove the lower surround.
11 Carefully cut the cable-tie securing the contact unit wiring to the ignition switch.
12 Undo the three retaining screws and remove the contact unit from the steering column **(see illustration)**. Disconnect the horn wiring connector.

Refitting

13 The contact unit should have been retained in its 'zero' position by the locking screw in the plastic strip.
14 If the contact unit has been turned from its 'zero' position, it will be necessary to reset it before fitting. Turn the contact reel as far as possible clockwise, to its stop - do not use excessive force. Now turn the reel anti-clockwise by approximately three full turns, and lock it in position using the locking screw shown in Chapter 10.
15 Fit the unit to the steering column and

securely tighten its retaining screws. Reconnect the horn wiring connector.
16 Secure the contact unit wiring to the ignition switch, using a new cable-tie. Refit the steering column shrouds.
17 Refit the steering wheel as described in Chapter 10, and the airbag unit as described above.

Impact sensor/control unit

Removal

18 The impact sensor/control unit is fitted in the centre of the car, under the storage locker in the centre console.
19 Disconnect the battery negative terminal, and wait at least 10 minutes before proceeding.
20 Remove the steering column lower shroud, and disconnect the orange wiring plug for the airbag system.
21 Remove the ashtray/storage locker at the front of the centre console (see Chapter 11, Section 35), then locate and disconnect the yellow wiring plug for the airbag system.
22 Referring to Chapter 11, Section 35, remove the rear section of the centre console.
23 Unscrew and remove the mounting bolts from the impact sensor, noting the earth lead under one of them.
24 Disconnect the wiring connector, and remove the impact sensor from the vehicle.

Refitting

25 When refitting, note the arrow on the impact sensor, which must point in the direction of travel (ie forwards).
26 Refit the impact sensor, ensuring that the earth lead is secured as before removal, and tighten the bolts securely.
27 Further refitting is a reversal of removal, ensuring that the airbag wiring connections are securely made.
28 Finally, switch on the ignition, and check that the SRS warning light performs as normal - see Section 22.

24 Anti-theft systems - general information

Note: *This information is applicable only to the anti-theft immobiliser and alarm systems fitted by Volvo as standard equipment.*

Immobiliser

1 Certain models from January 1995 onwards are equipped with an electronic immobiliser as standard, which is automatically activated (after a preset period) once the ignition is switched off. The immobiliser will activate prior to the completion of the preset period, if the driver's door is opened, or if the doors are locked using the remote locking keyfob.
2 The immobiliser can only be deactivated using the remote keyfob - for this reason, check and replace the batteries in the keyfob regularly!
3 The immobiliser is incorporated into the central locking system module, and cuts the ignition, starter and fuel pump circuits, preventing the engine from being started.
4 Any problems or work involving the immobiliser system should be entrusted to a Volvo dealer, as dedicated electronic equipment is required to diagnose faults.

Alarm

5 In addition to the immobiliser, some models from January 1995 onwards may be equipped with an anti-theft alarm.
6 Like the immobiliser, the alarm is operated using the remote locking keyfob, and is linked to the central locking system module.
7 Besides the normal alarm features, the system features ultrasonic protection for the vehicle interior, and a back-up battery.
8 Any problems or work involving the alarm system should be entrusted to a Volvo dealer, as dedicated electronic equipment is required to diagnose faults. If the alarm LED flashes very rapidly (four times a second), this indicates a fault in the system.

Key to wiring diagrams

Not all items are fitted to all models

1.0	**CEM**
2.0	**Fusebox**
3.0	**Relay box, positions**
3.01	Inhibitor relay, headlights
3.02	Relay, foglights (1987)
3.03	Ignition relay (terminal 15)
3.04	Relay, terminal 75
3.05	Relay, air conditioning
3.06	Relay, double acting - headlight motors
3.07	Changeover relay, rear foglights (not UK)
3.02	Relay, foglights (1988 on)
3.09	ABS pump relay
3.10	ABS power relay
3.11	Bulb failure detector, front bulbs
3.12	Inhibitor relay, foglights (not UK)
3.13	Headlight relay
3.14	Inhibitor relay, headlight dim-dip system (UK only)
3.15	Relay, auxiliary water pump (B18E and F engines)
3.16	Relay, auxiliary water pump (B18FT engine)
3.17	Interior light time-delay relay
3.18	Headlight washer relay
3.19	Windscreen wiper intermittent wipe relay
3.20	Rear wiper intermittent wipe relay
3.21	Sunroof relay
3.22	Relay, auxiliary water pump (B18EP/FP engines)
3.23	Time-delay relay, ventilation (B18KP engine)
3.24	Fan motor relay (B18KP engine)
3.25	Heater blower relay
	Earth rail, junction box
3.27	Rear foglights inhibitor relay
	Earth rail, junction box
3.28	Relay, central locking system
3.29	Relay, speed warning
4.0	**Instrument panel**
4.01	Warning light, hazard warning lights
4.02	Warning light, seat belts
4.03	Warning light, 'door open'
4.04	Warning light, direction indicator, left
4.05	Warning light, direction indicator, right
4.06	Warning light, bulb failure system
4.07	Warning light, washer fluid level
4.09	Tachometer (rev. counter)
4.10	Clock
4.11	Electronic speedometer
4.12	Fuel gauge
4.13	Warning light, fuel reserve (low fuel level)
4.14	Warning light, parking lights
4.15	Warning light, foglights
4.16	Warning light, rear foglight
4.17	Warning light, heated rear window
4.18	Warning light, headlight main beam/flash
4.19	Warning light, ABS
4.20	Warning light, handbrake on
4.21	Warning light, brake fluid level
4.22	Warning light, battery charge (alternator)
4.23	Warning light, oil pressure
4.24	Coolant temperature gauge
4.25	Warning light, coolant temperature
4.26	Ambient air temperature sensor (Electronic Information Centre)
4.28	Warning light, engine oil level
4.29	Oil temperature display (Electronic Information Centre)
4.30	Voltage regulator
4.31	MFU (Multi-function unit)
4.32	Electronic Information Centre (LCD panel)

4.33	LCD illumination, Electronic Information Centre
4.34	Instrument panel lighting
4.35	15/30 Power relay, instrument lighting
4.50	Channel selector switch, Electronic Information Centre
4.51	Warning light, rear seat belts
4.52	Warning light, choke on
4.53	Hall transmitter
4.54	MIL indication
4.55	Warning lamp, SRS5
5.0	**VEM (Ventilation electronic module) - heater control unit**
5.01	Recirculation switch, heating
5.02	ON/OFF switch, heating
5.03	Demister switch, heating
5.04	FLOOR air distribution switch, heating
5.05	Vent air distribution switch, heating
5.06	B/L air distribution switch, heating
5.07	AC switch (air conditioning)
5.08	AC MAX switch, air conditioning
5.10	Air valve, FLOOR/demisting
5.11	Air valve, B/L on
5.12	Air valve, B/L off
5.13	Air valve, recirculation
5.14	Heater panel illumination
5.15	On/off relay, VEM
5.16	Relay, position 4
5.17	AC relay
A	**Engine compartment wiring harness**
A1	Battery
A2	Alternator (and integral voltage regulator)
A3	Starter motor
A4	Horn unit (second of two)
A5	Radiator cooling fan
A7	Horn unit (first of two)
A8	Switch, engine compartment light
A9	Engine compartment light
A10	Windscreen washer pump
A11	Tailgate washer pump
A12	Electronic control unit (ECU)
A13	RH headlight, dipped beam
A14	RH headlight, main beam
A15	RH auxiliary driving light
A16	RH day-running light
A17	RH parking light
A18	RH direction indicator
A19	RH foglight
A20	Motor, RH headlight housing
A21	Headlight washer pump
A22	Ambient air temperature sensor
A23	LH headlight, dipped beam
A24	LH headlight, main beam
A26	LH day-running light
A27	LH parking light
A28	LH direction indicator
A29	LH foglight
A30	Motor, LH headlight housing
A31	Evaporator thermal switch, air conditioning
A32	Distributor
A33	Spark plugs
A34	Thermal switch, cooling fan, air conditioning
A35	Pressure switch (high/low), air conditioning
A36	Compressor clutch, air conditioning
A37	Coolant hose thermal switch (heater blower)
A38	Oil pressure switch, LL
A39	Coolant temperature sensor (for gauge)

A40	Oil level transmitter
A41	Float, brake fluid level monitoring
A42	Float, washer fluid level monitoring
A43	Engine oil temperature transmitter
A44	Speedometer sensor (final drive)
A45	Reversing lights switch
A46	Windscreen wiper motor
A47	Switch, bonnet lock
A48	Oil pressure sensor, HL
A49	Dim-dip headlight relay (UK only)
A50	Auxiliary water pump (B18F/FT engines)
A51	Thermistor, crankcase ventilation heating (B18F/FT engines)
A52	ECU, electronic ignition and boost pressure (B18FT engine)
A52.1	Diagnostic test point for A52
A53	Output stage and ignition coil (B18FT engine)
A54	Turbo boost pressure regulating valve (B18FT engine)
A55	Temperature sensor, turbocharger (B18FT engine)
A56	Injector cooling fan (B18FT engine)
A57	Temperature sensor, injector cooling (B18FT engine)
A58	Oil level/temperature sensor
A59	Oil temperature, ignition
A60	Carburettor pre-heating
A61	Fuel cut-off
A62	Starter inhibitor switch, automatic transmission
A63	Diagnostic test point, B18U/EP/FP, B20U/F
A64	Air valve (B18KP engine)
A65	Temperature sensor, air valve
A66	Thermal switch, cooling fan
A67	Catalytic converter protection device
A68	Three-way valve, air conditioning
A69	Valve, ignition adjustment, air conditioning
A70	Tachometric relay, air conditioning
A71	Cooling fan, carburettor
B	**Fuel system wiring harness**
B1	ECU, fuel injection system
B2	Control relay, fuel injection system
B3	Injectors
B4	Engine speed sensor, flywheel
B5	Inlet air temperature sensor, fuel injection system
B6	Coolant temperature sensor, fuel injection system
B7	CO setting potentiometer
B8	Air pressure sensor, fuel injection system
B9	Throttle butterfly switch (B18E/B18F engines)
B10	Knock sensor
B11	Idle speed regulating valve
B11.1	Diagnostic test point for B11 (B18F/FT engine)
B12	Fuel pump relay
B13	EGR modulation valve
B14	Air mass meter (B18F/FT engines)
B15	Oxygen sensor (B18F/FT engines)
B15.1	Diagnostic test point for B15
B16	Coolant temperature sensor, fuel injection system and auxiliary water pump, or ignition unit (B18FT engine)
B18	Throttle butterfly switch and throttle position sensor (B18FT engine)
B19	Fuse (next to B2) for oxygen sensor
B20	Fuse (next to B12) for fuel pump

B22	EVAP system (B18FP engine)
B23	Test pin, earth
B24	Safety switch, air conditioning
C	**Central wiring harness**
C1	Rheostat, dashboard lighting
C3	Hazard warning lights switch
C4	Direction indicators switch
C5	Main beam/dipped beam switch
C6	Rear wiper switch
C7	Rear washer switch
C8	Windscreen wash/wipe switch
C9	Ignition/starter switch
C10	Horn switch
C11	Heated rear window switch
C13	Clock
C14	Lighting switch
C16	Rear foglight switch
C18	Foglight switch
C21	RH front wing side repeater bulb
C22	LH front wing side repeater bulb
C24	Radio aerial lead
C25	Radio
C26	Radio illumination
C27	Ignition switch illumination
C28	Hazard warning light switch illumination
C29	Instrument panel (central) illumination
C30	Glovebox light switch
C31	Glovebox light
C32	Oil pressure gauge
C33	Voltmeter
C34	Lighting switch illumination
C35	Lights-on warning buzzer
C36	Direction indicator flasher unit
C37	Choke switch
C38	Heated front seat switch illumination
C39	LED, car alarm
D	**Centre console wiring harness**
D1	Switch lighting, centre console
D2	Driver's seat heating switch
D3	Driver's seat heating switch bulb
D4	Passenger seat heating switch
D5	Passenger seat heating switch bulb
D6	Switch, auxiliary driving lights
D7	Driver's door mirror switch
D8	Driver's door electric window switch
D9	Passenger door electric window switch
D10	Passenger door mirror switch
D11	Cigar lighter
D12	Cigar lighter illumination
D13	Driver's seat belt contact switch
D14	Driver's seat heating element and thermostat
D15	Passenger seat heating element and thermostat
D16	Passenger seat contact switch for seat heating/seat belt
D17	Passenger seat belt contact switch
D18	Handbrake switch
D19	Fuel gauge sender (fuel tank)
D20	Fuel pump, fuel injection system
D21	Ashtray illumination
D22	Driver's seat belt lock illumination
D23	Passenger seat belt lock illumination
D24	Automatic transmission selector illumination
D25	Central locking motor

D26	Rear electric window switch, on console
D27	Rear electric window switch, on door
D28	Interlock, rear electric window
D29	Rear electric window motor
D30	Rear electric window switch, on console, left
D31	Rear electric window switch, on door, left
D32	Motor, rear electric window, left
E	**Heating system wiring harness**
E1	Heater fan motor
E2	Heater fan series resistors
E3	Heater fan switch
E4	Heater fan switch illumination
E5	Relay, blower speed 1, air conditioning
E6	Relay, blower motor, AC MAX
E7	Air conditioning compressor time delay relay
E8	Air conditioning relay
E10	Lighting, heater control panel
E11	Cooling fan relay, air conditioning, position 2
E12	Pressure switch, air conditioning, 22 bar
F	**Driver's door wiring harness**
F1	Door mirror heating element (driver's)
F2	Electric window motor (driver's)
F3	Door lock switch, driver's door
F4	Central locking switch
F5	Door mirror motors (driver's)
F6	Keyhole illumination switch (driver's)
F7	Keyhole light
F8	Courtesy light switch (driver's)
F10	Loudspeaker (woofer)
F11	Loudspeaker (tweeter)
F12	Door lock switch, central locking system
G	**Passenger door wiring harness**
G1	Door mirror heating element (passenger's)
G2	Electric window motor (passenger's)
G3	Door lock switch, passenger's door
G4	Central locking switch
G5	Door mirror motors (passenger's)
G6	Courtesy light switch (passenger's)
G10	Loudspeaker (woofer)
G11	Loudspeaker (tweeter)
H	**Rear wiring harness**
H1	Direction indicator bulb, right rear
H2	Tail light filament, right
H3	Tail light filament, right
H4	Brake light, right
H5	Brake light, right
H6	Reversing light bulb, right
H7	Number plate light bulb, right
H8	Rear foglight bulb, right
H9	Brake lights switch
H10	Bulb failure detector, rear lights
H11	Direction indicator bulb, left rear
H12	Tail light filament, left
H13	Tail light filament, left
H14	Brake light, left
H15	Brake light, left
H16	Reversing light bulb, left
H17	Number plate light bulb, left
H18	Rear foglight bulb, left
H19	Full-throttle switch
H20	Boot light
H21	Boot light switch

H23	Switch, tailgate lock
H24	Radio aerial motor
H25	Radio aerial
H27	RH rear sidelight bulb
H28	LH rear sidelight bulb
H29	Radio aerial motor relay
H30	Central locking motor
H31	Loudspeaker, rear left
H32	Loudspeaker, rear right
J	**Tailgate wiring harness**
J1	Heating element, rear window
J2	Rear window wiper motor
J3	High-level brake light
K	**Interior light wiring harness**
K1	Rear passenger reading lamp, left
K2	Interior light switch
K3	Interior light bulb
K4	Switch, LH reading lamp
K5	LH reading lamp
K6	Switch, RH reading lamp
K7	RH reading lamp
K8	Rear passenger reading lamp, right
K9	Courtesy light switch, left
K10	Courtesy light switch, right
L	**Auxiliary systems wiring harness - ABS**
L1	Electronic control unit, ABS
L2	Pressure switch
L3	Pump motor
L4	Test plug, ABS pump
L5	Fluid level warning indicator/warning light
L6	Warning light switch
L7	Diagnostic plug
L8	Wheel sensor, rear right
L9	Wheel sensor, front left
L10	Wheel sensor, rear left
L11	Wheel sensor, front right
L12	Main valve
L13	Inlet valve, front left
L14	Inlet valve, rear
L15	Outlet valve, front right
L16	Outlet valve, front left
L17	Outlet valve, rear
L18	Inlet valve, front right
L19	Diode
L20	Diode
L21	ABS pump relay
L22	ABS power supply relay
L23	Combined relay
L24	Brake pedal sensor
L25	Resistor
M	**Sunroof wiring harness**
M1	Sunroof switch
M2	Roof open/closed microswitch
M3	Sunroof motor
M4	Sunroof relay unit
N	**SRS wiring harness - airbag and seat belt pre-tensioners**
N1	Electronic control unit
N2	Power supply and voltage converter
N3	Seat belt pre-tensioner, left
N4	Seat belt pre-tensioner, right
N5	Airbag, steering wheel module
N6	Diagnostic tester, airbag and seat belt pre-tensioners
N7	Diagnostic tester, seat belt pre-tensioners

Wire colour codes

Bl	Blue	Gr	Grey	P	Pink	W	White
Br	Brown	L	Lilac	R	Red	Y	Yellow
Gn	Green	Or	Orange	SB	Black		

All earth wiring is brown (Br), unless otherwise stated

12

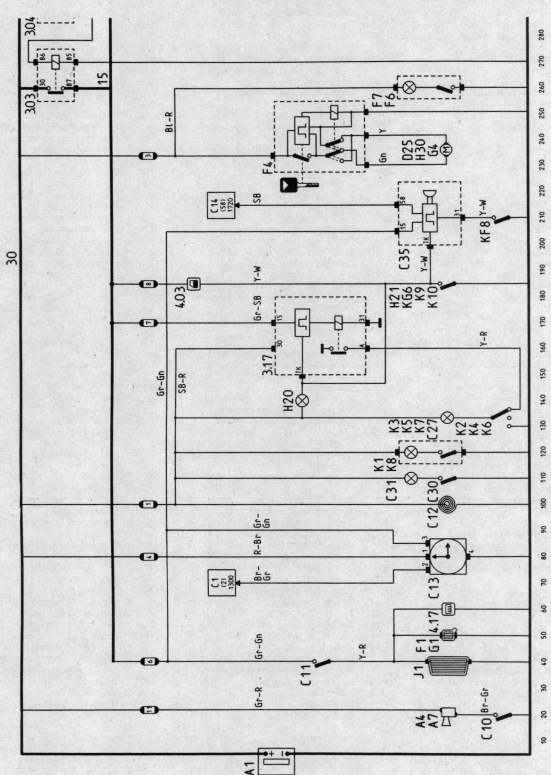

Typical wiring diagram - 440 and 460 models up to 1991

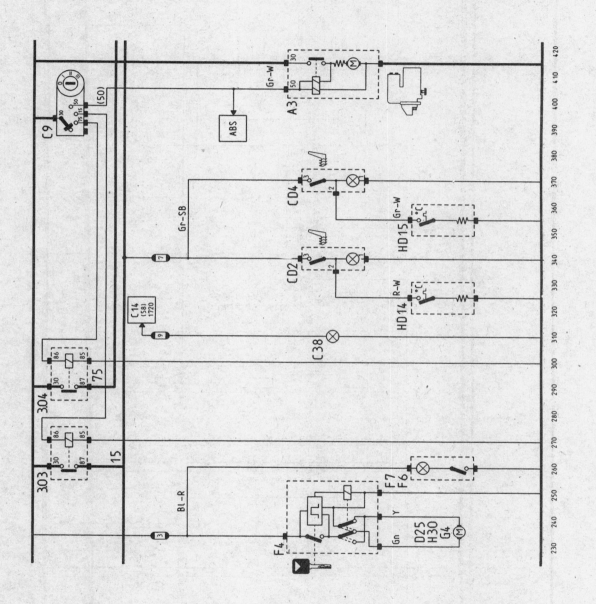

Typical wiring diagram - 440 and 460 models up to 1991 (continued)

12

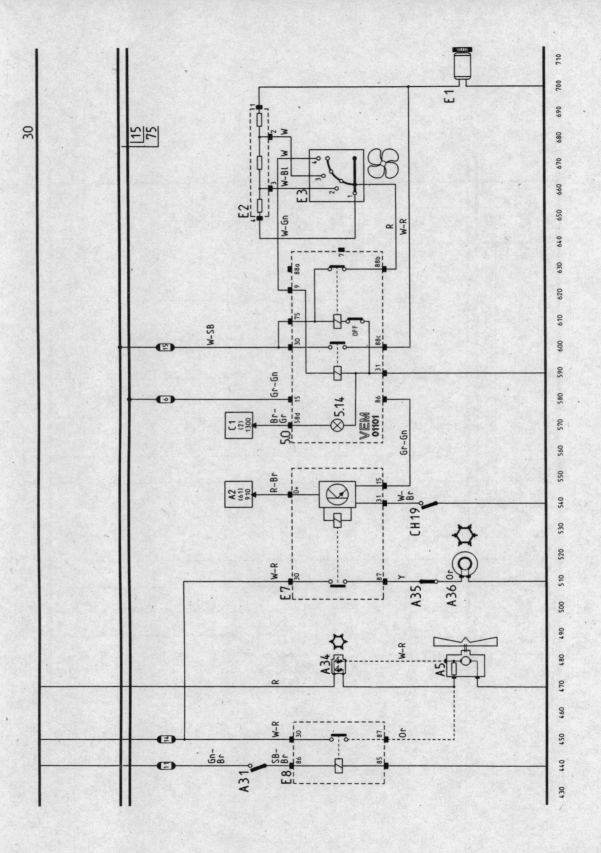

Typical wiring diagram - 440 and 460 models up to 1991 (continued)

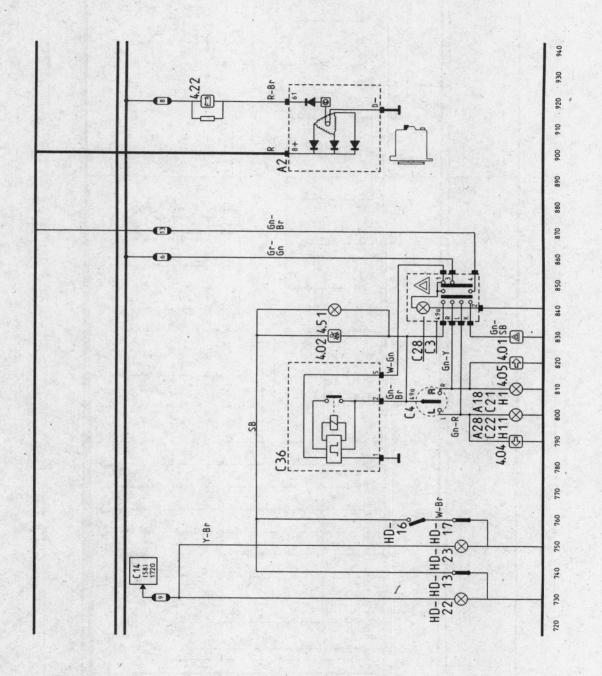

Typical wiring diagram - 440 and 460 models up to 1991 (continued)

12

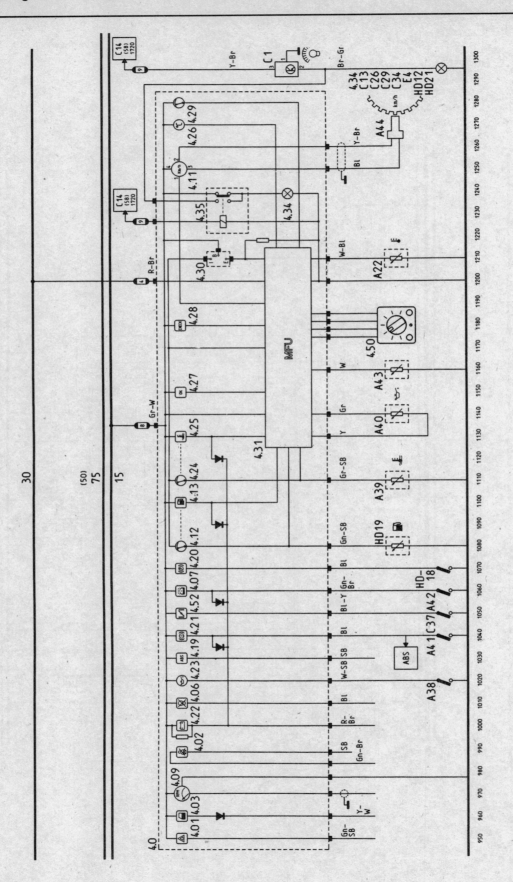

Typical wiring diagram - 440 and 460 models up to 1991 (continued)

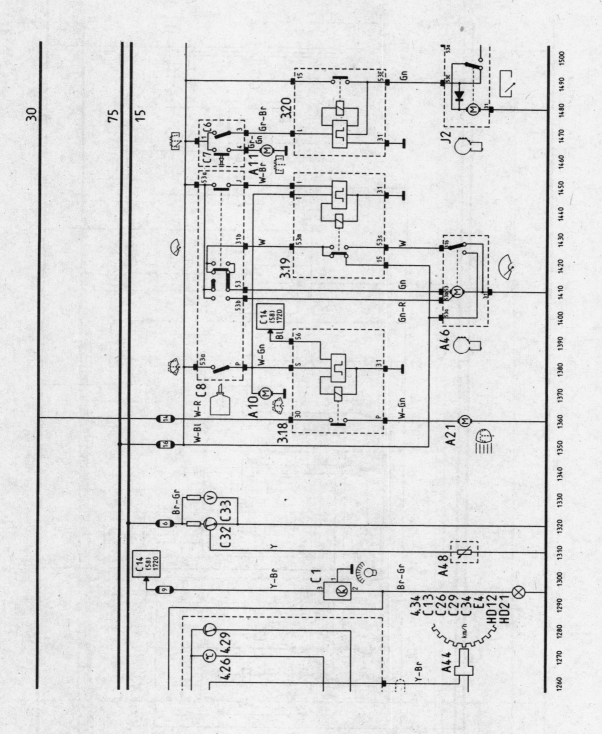

Typical wiring diagram - 440 and 460 models up to 1991 (continued)

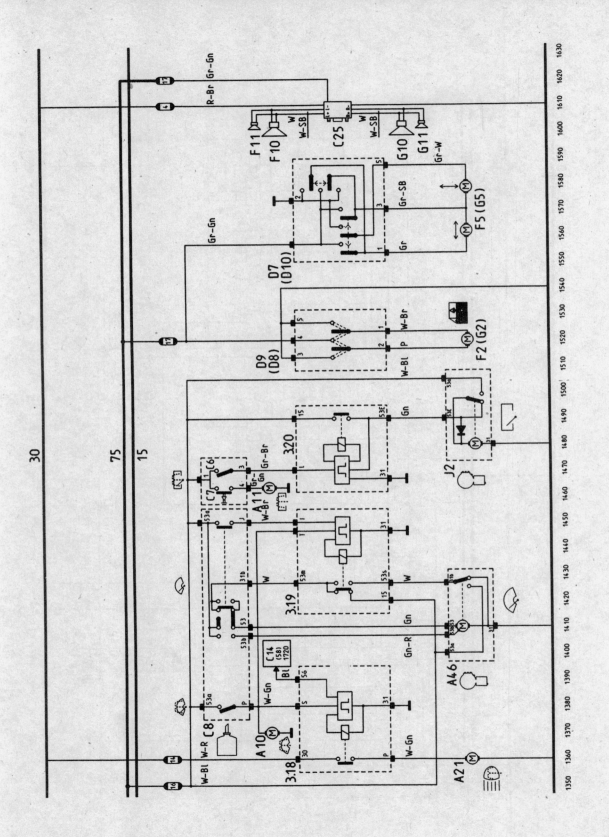

Typical wiring diagram - 440 and 460 models up to 1991 (continued)

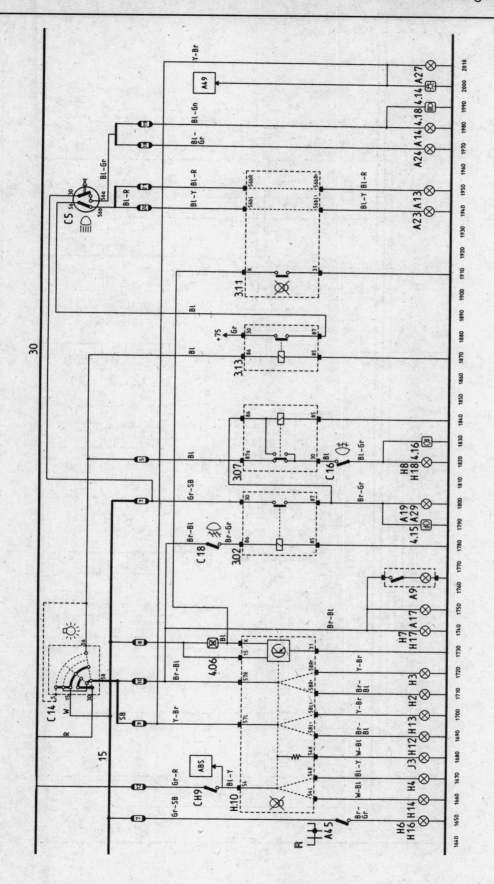

Typical wiring diagram - 440 and 460 models up to 1991 (continued)

12

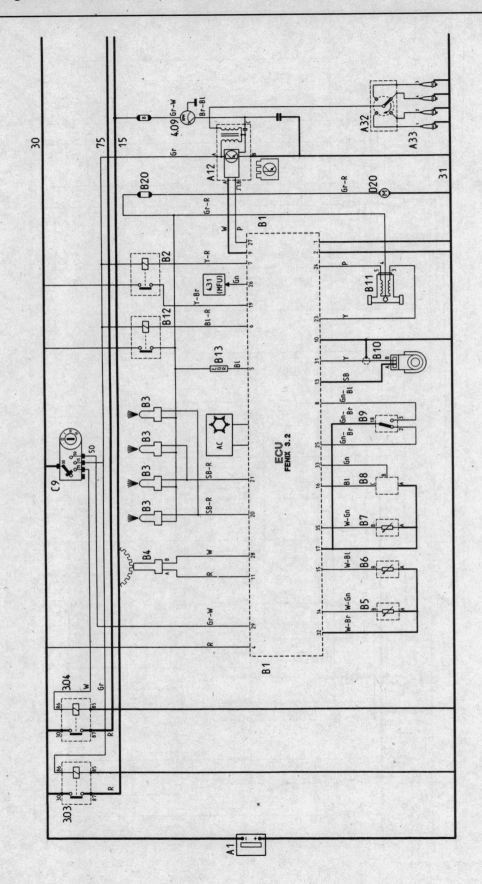

Wiring diagram for B18E engine - 440 and 460 models up to 1991

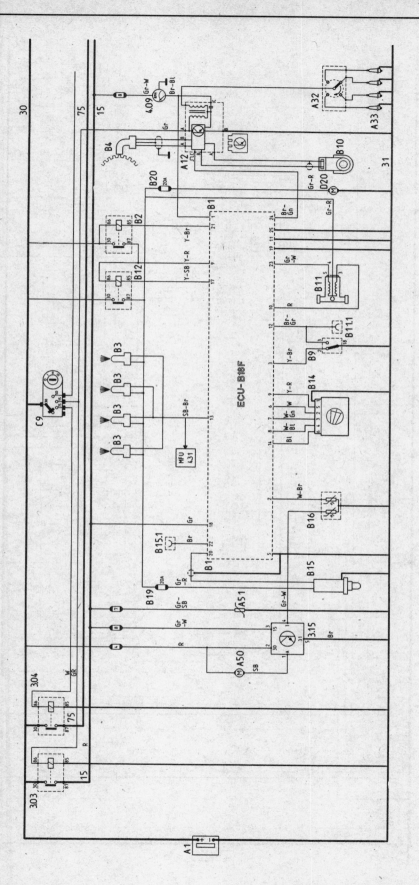

Wiring diagram for B18F engine - 440 and 460 models up to 1991

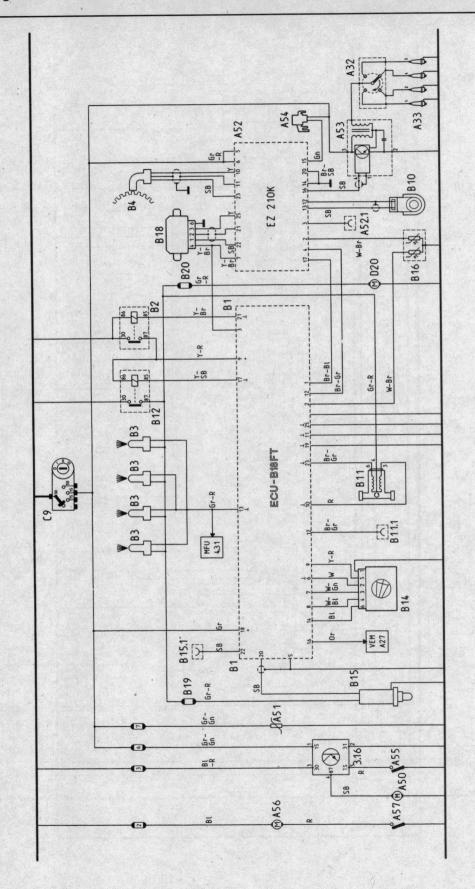

Wiring diagram for B18FT engine - 440 and 460 models up to 1991

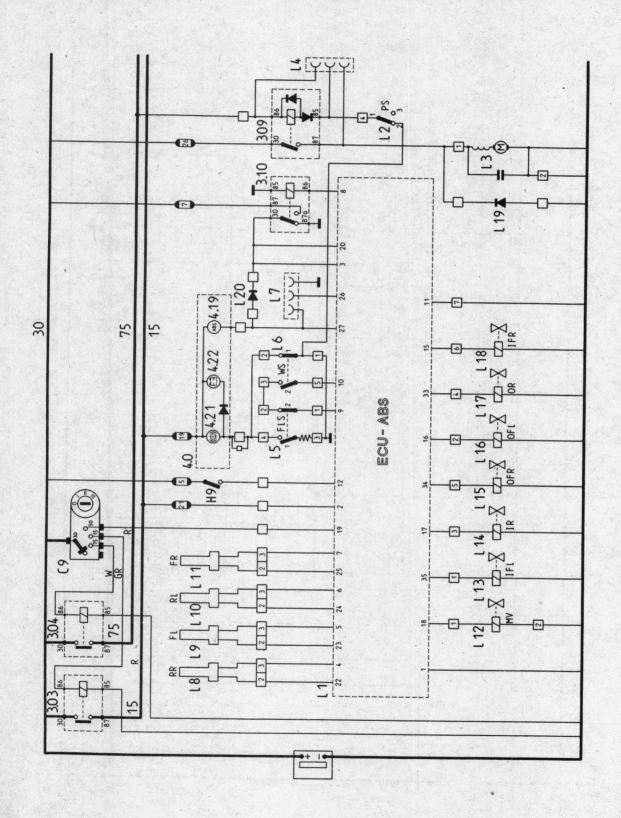

Wiring diagram for anti-lock braking system (ABS) - 440 and 460 models up to 1991

12

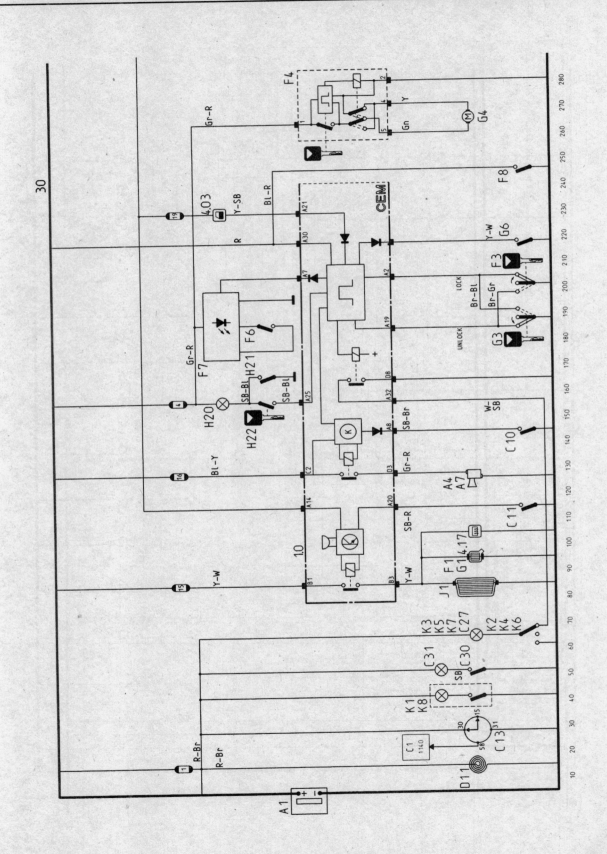

Typical wiring diagram - 480 models up to 1991

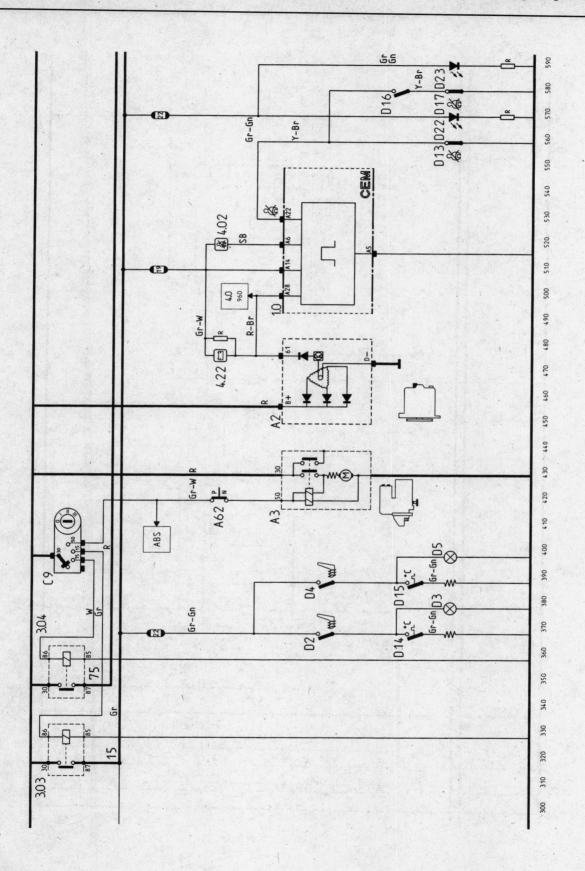

Typical wiring diagram - 480 models up to 1991 (continued)

12

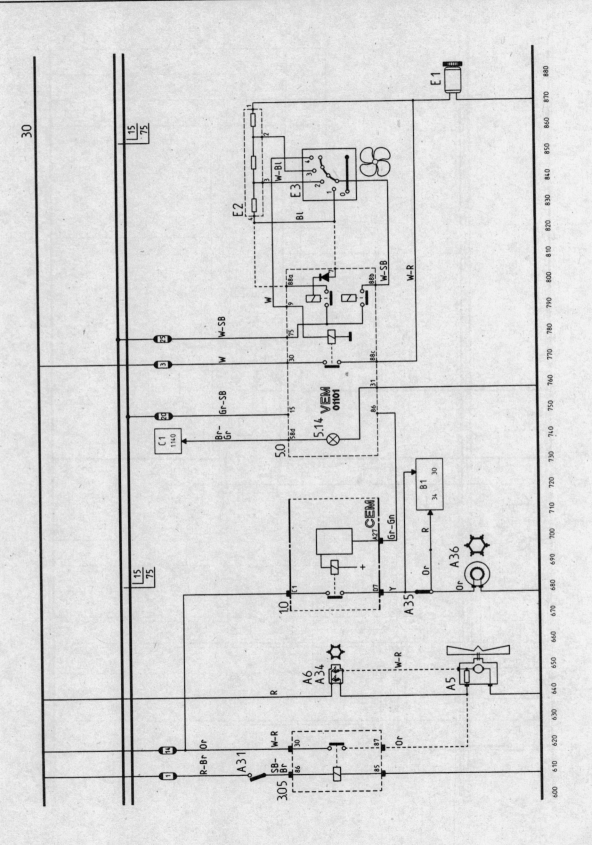

Typical wiring diagram - 480 models up to 1991 (continued)

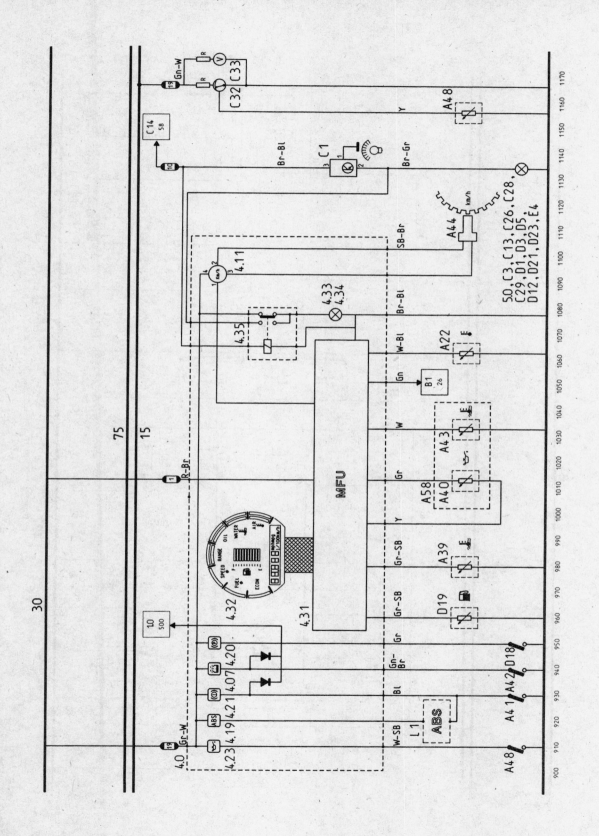

Typical wiring diagram - 480 models up to 1991 (continued)

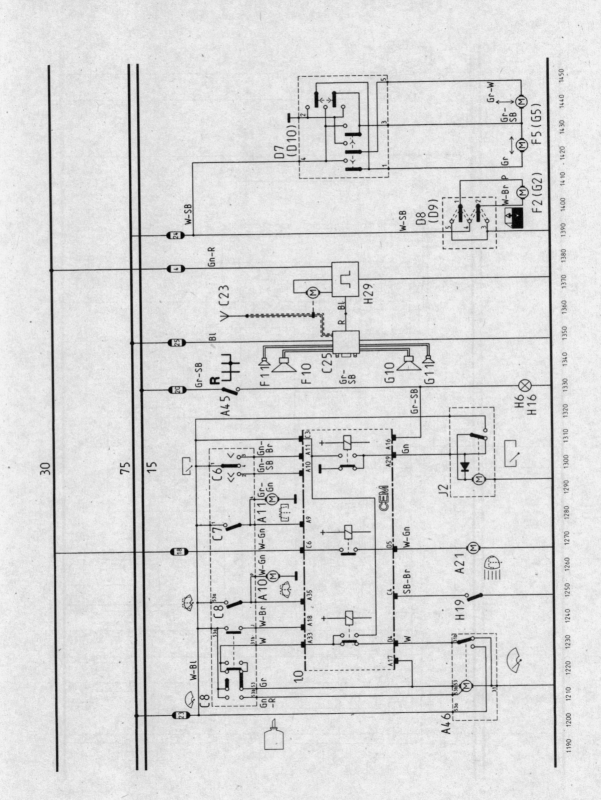

Typical wiring diagram - 480 models up to 1991 (continued)

Typical wiring diagram - 480 models up to 1991 (continued)

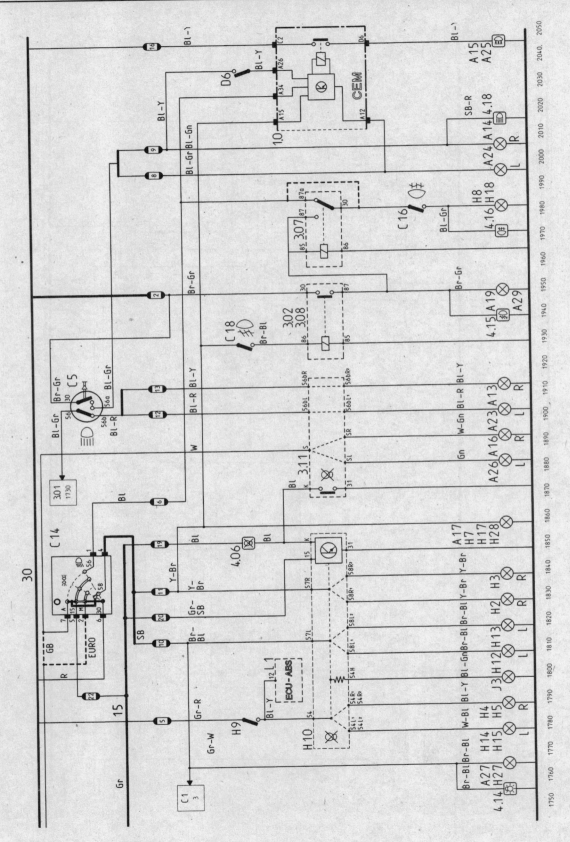

Typical wiring diagram - 480 models up to 1991 (continued)

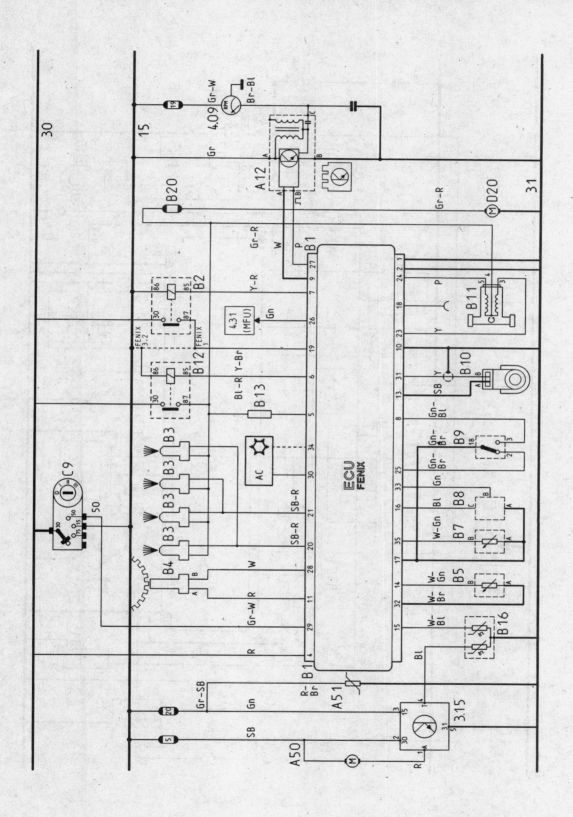

Wiring diagram for B18E engine - 480 models up to 1991

12

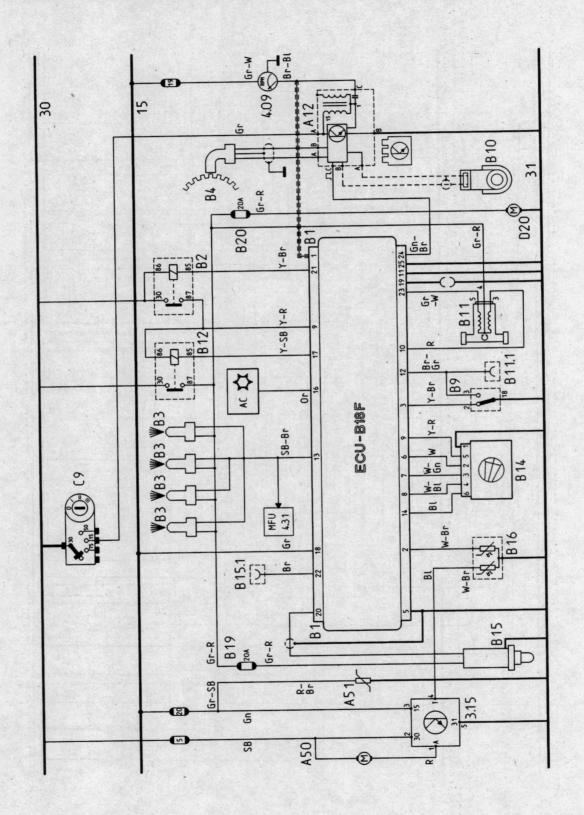

Wiring diagram for B18F engine - 480 models up to 1991

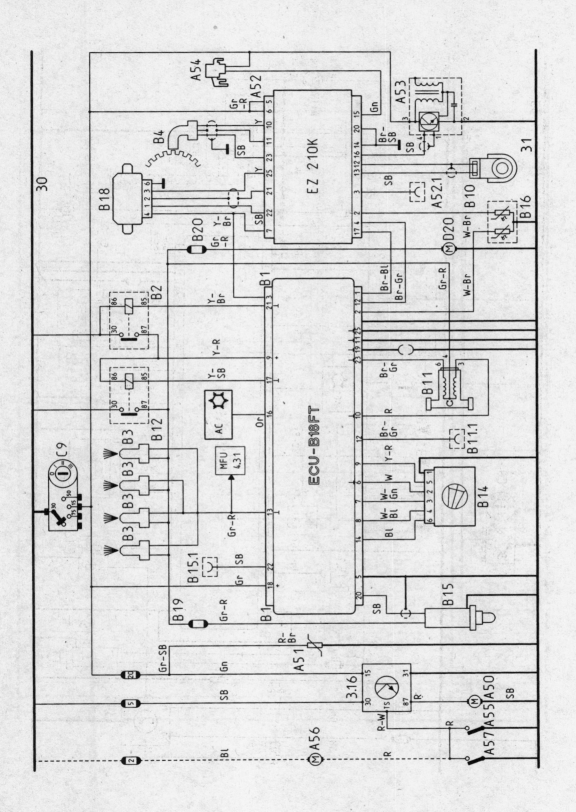

Wiring diagram for B18FT engine - 480 models up to 1991

12

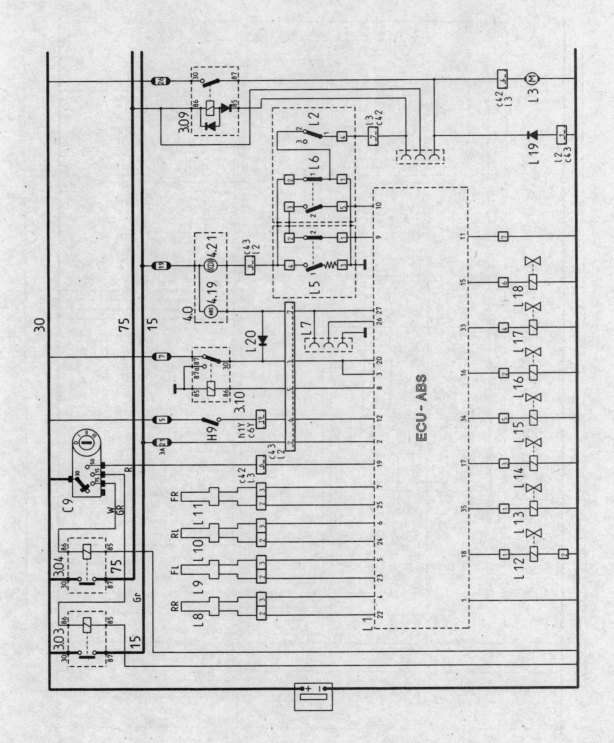

Wiring diagram for anti-lock braking system (ABS) - 480 models up to 1991

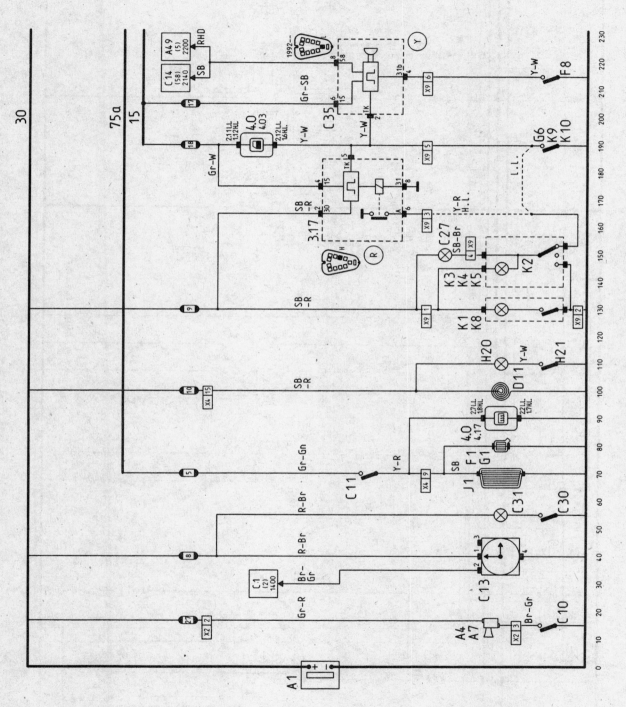

Typical wiring diagram - 440 and 460 models from 1992

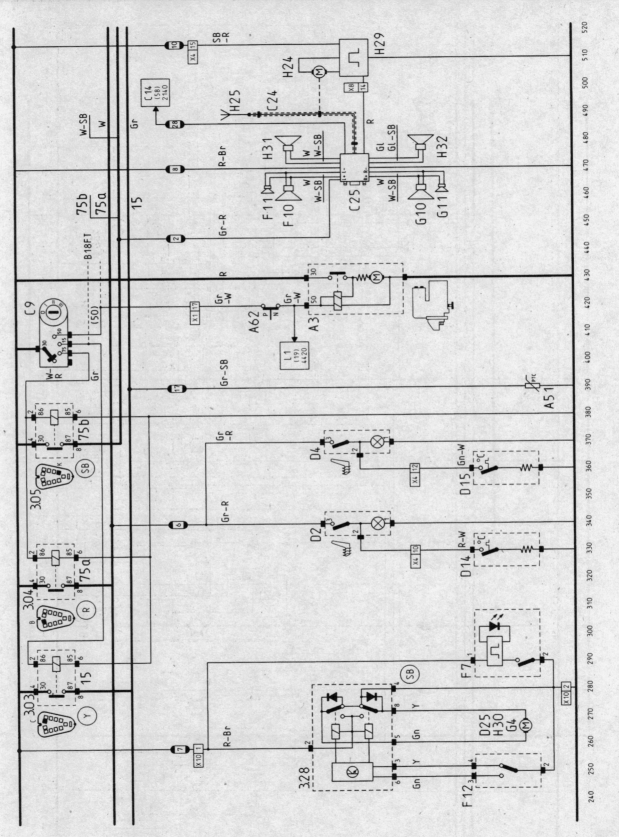

Typical wiring diagram - 440 and 460 models from 1992 (continued)

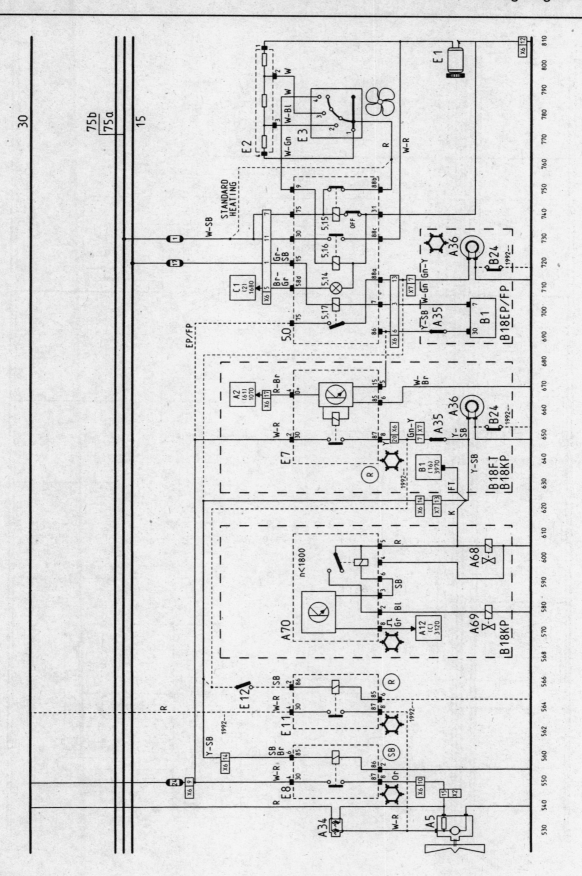

Typical wiring diagram - 440 and 460 models from 1992 (continued)

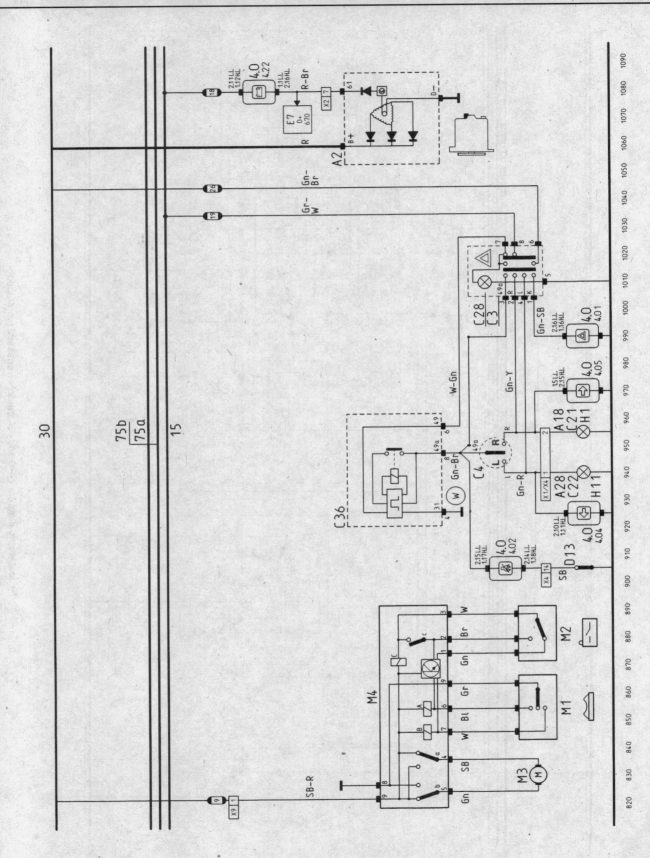

Typical wiring diagram - 440 and 460 models from 1992 (continued)

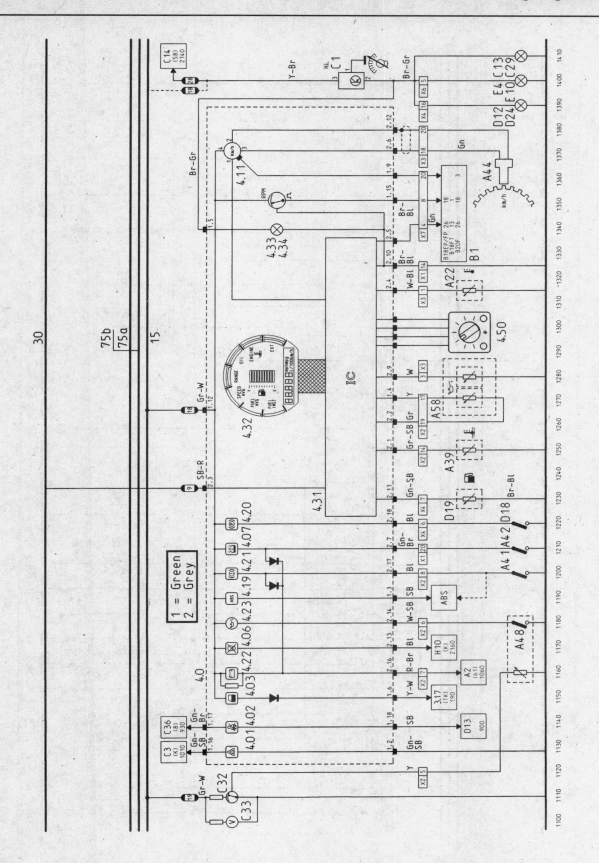

Typical wiring diagram - 440 and 460 models from 1992 (continued)

Typical wiring diagram - 440 and 460 models from 1992 (continued)

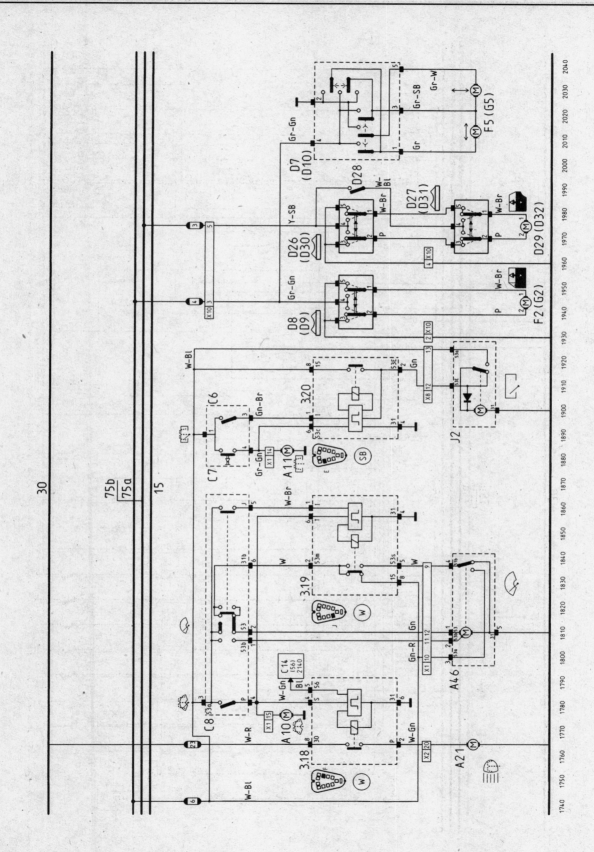

Typical wiring diagram - 440 and 460 models from 1992 (continued)

12

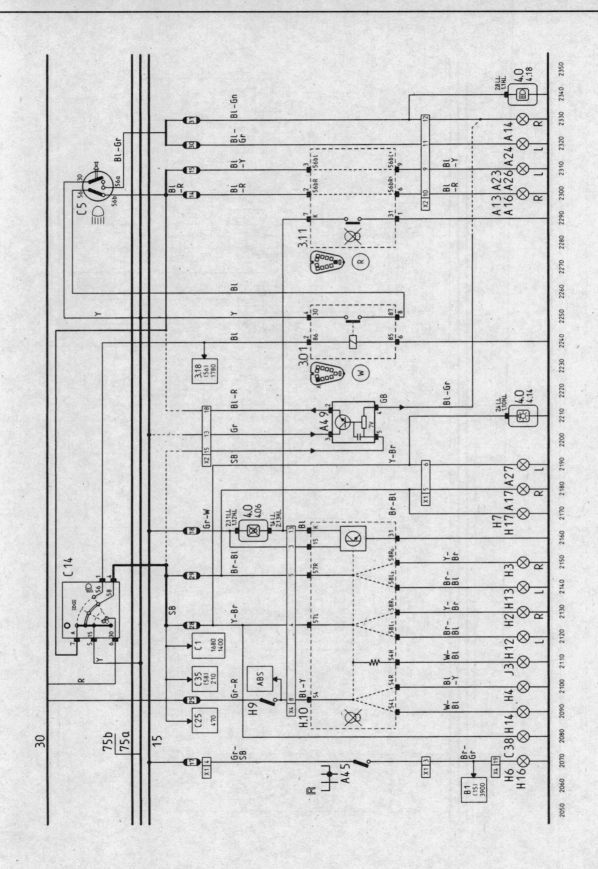

Typical wiring diagram - 440 and 460 models from 1992 (continued)

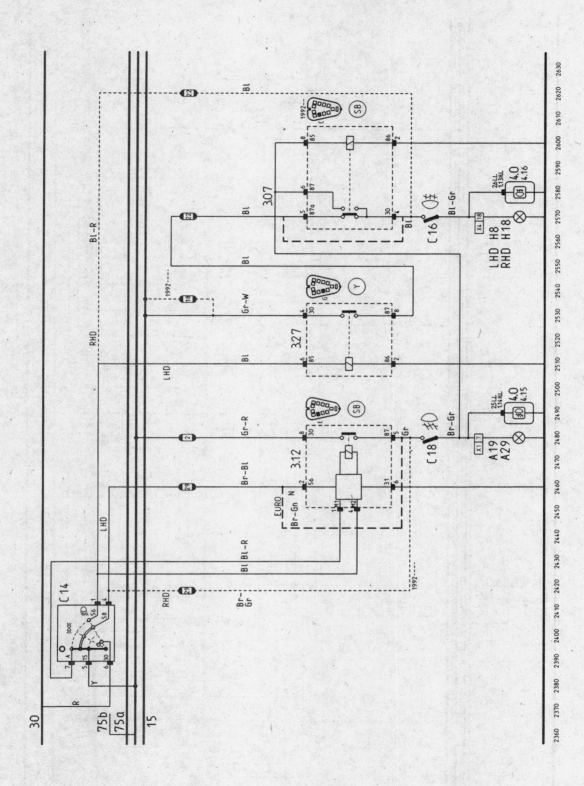

Typical wiring diagram - 440 and 460 models from 1992 (continued)

12

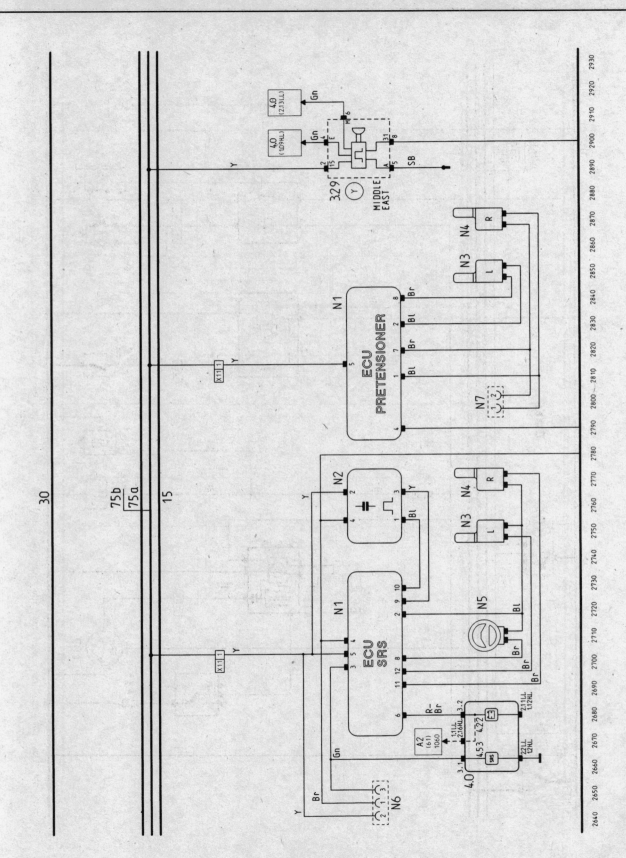

Typical wiring diagram - 440 and 460 models from 1992 (continued)

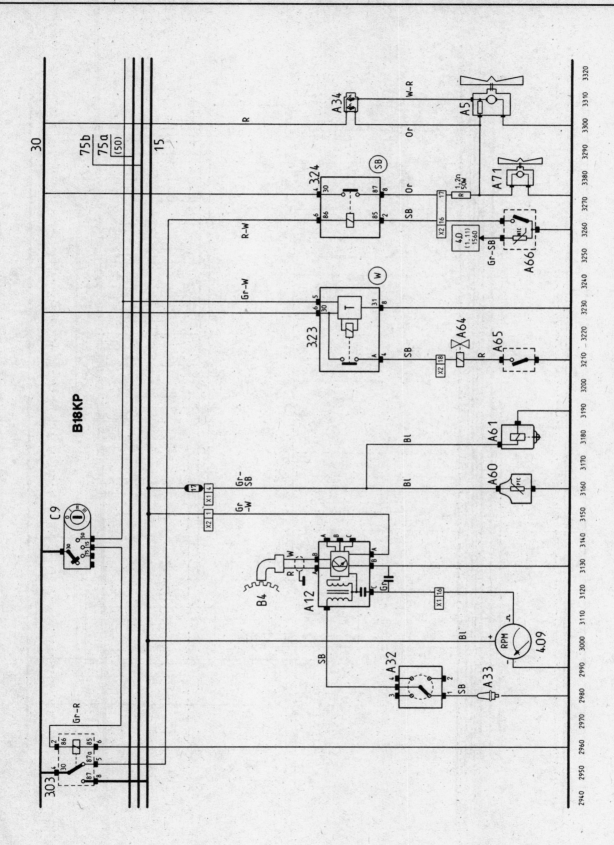

Wiring diagram for B18KP engine - 440 and 460 models from 1992

12

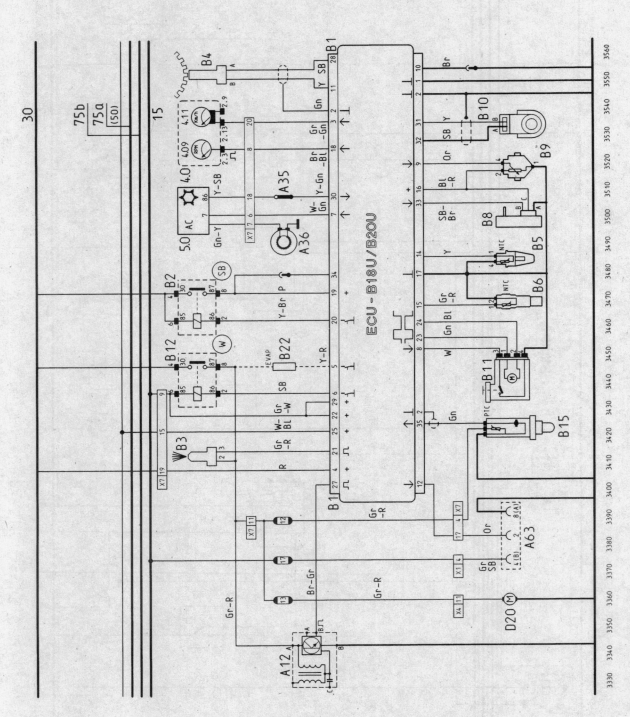

Wiring diagram for B18U / B20U engine - 440 and 460 models from 1992

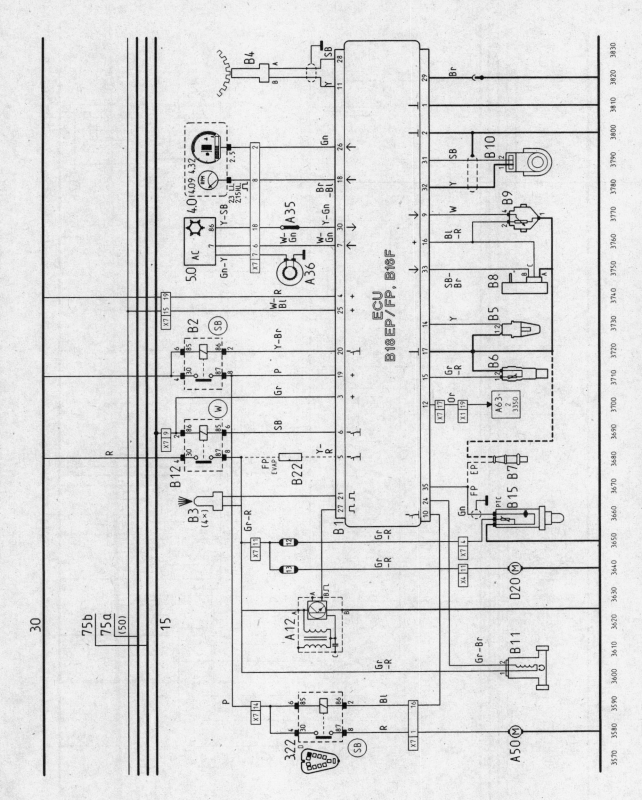

Wiring diagram for B18EP / FP engine – 440 and 460 models from 1992

12

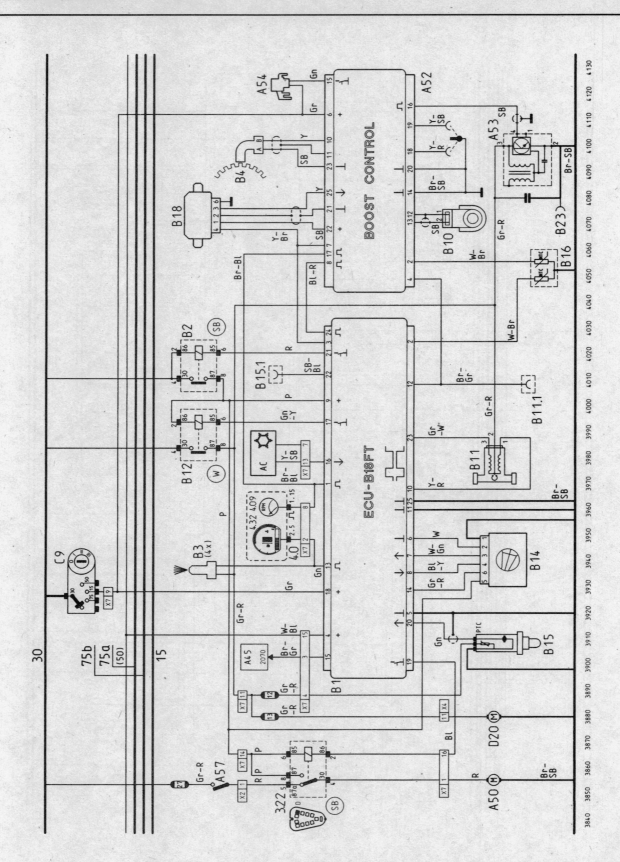

Wiring diagram for B18FT engine - 440 and 460 models from 1992

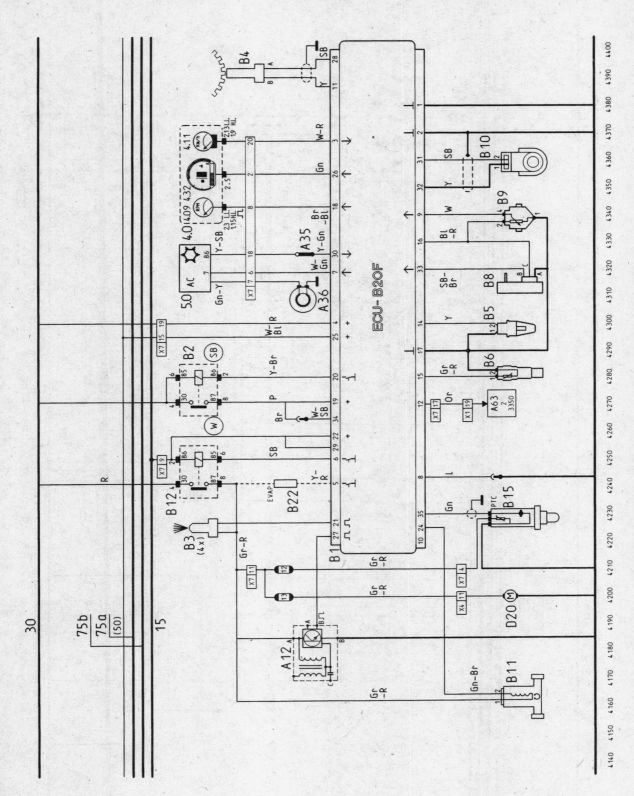

Wiring diagram for B20F engine - 440 and 460 models from 1992

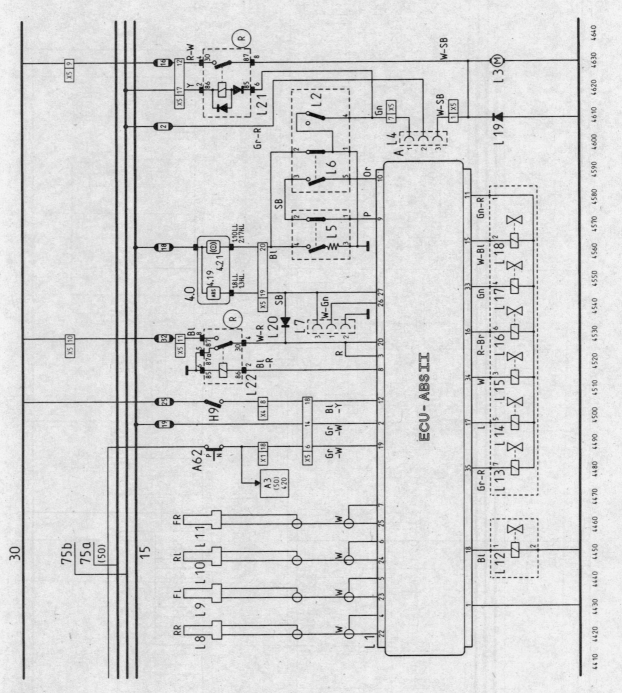

Wiring diagram for anti-lock braking system (ABS) Mk II - 440 and 460 models from 1992

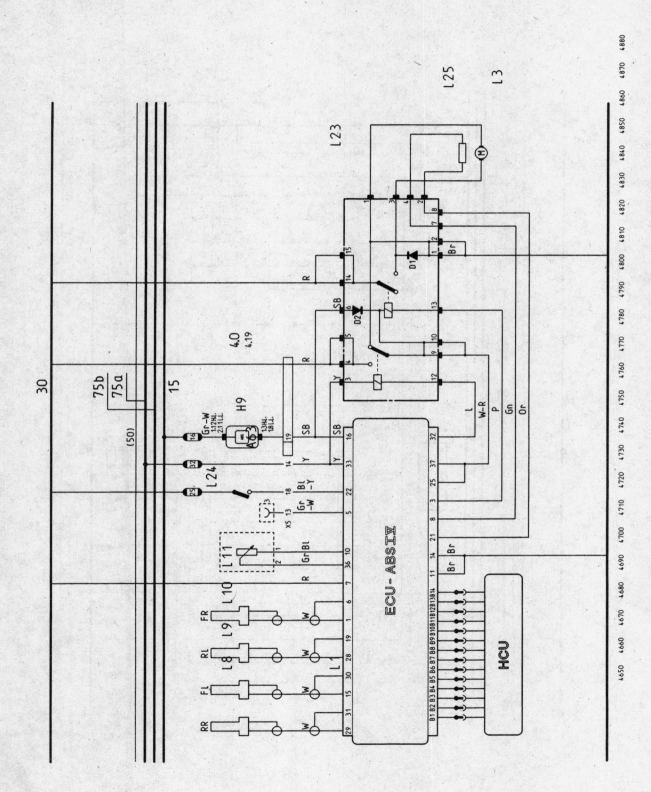

Wiring diagram for anti-lock braking system (ABS) Mk IV - 440 and 460 models from 1992

12

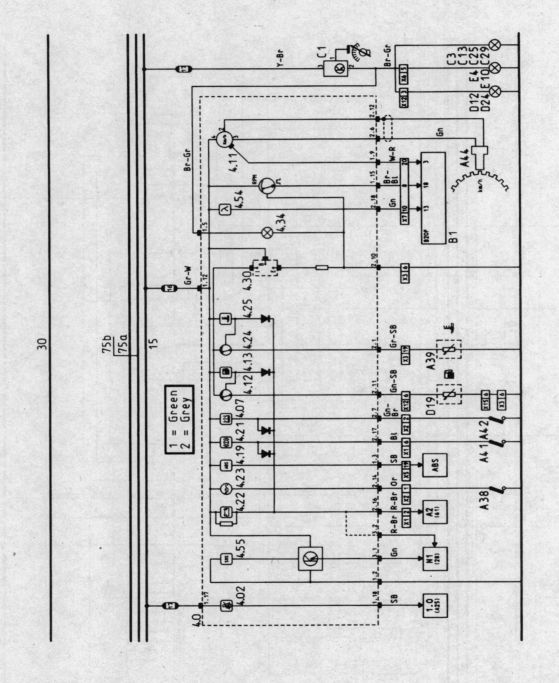

Supplementary wiring diagram (480 models from 1992) - Instrument panel

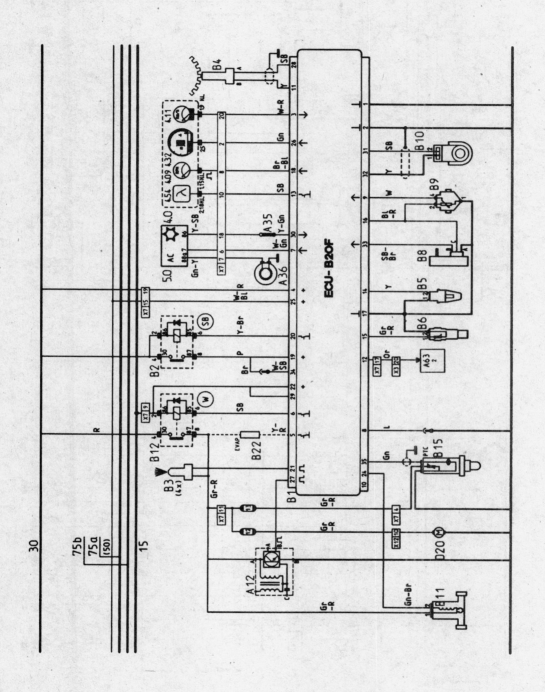

Supplementary wiring diagram (480 models from 1992) – B20F Fuel injection

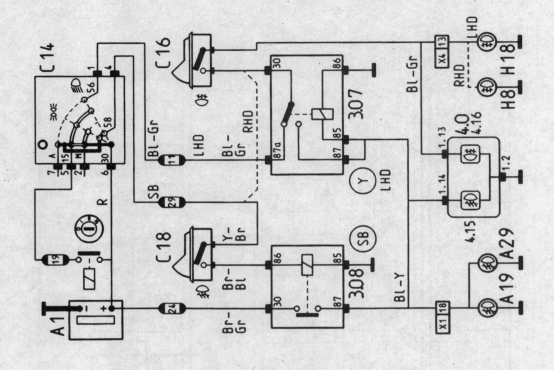

Supplementary wiring diagram (480 models from 1992) – Front and rear foglights

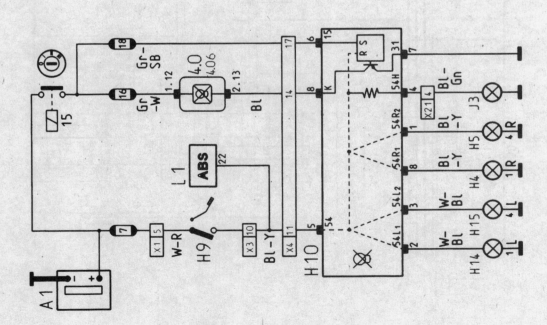

Supplementary wiring diagram (480 models from 1992) – Brake lights with bulb failure detector

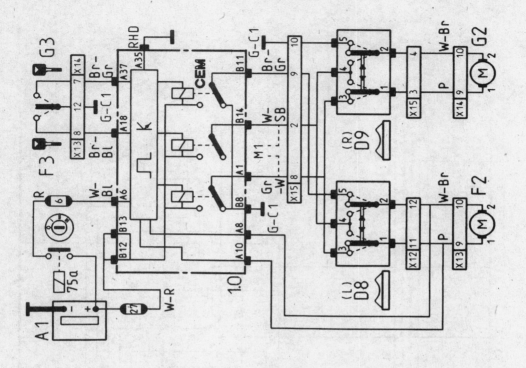

Supplementary wiring diagram (480 models from 1992) - Electric windows

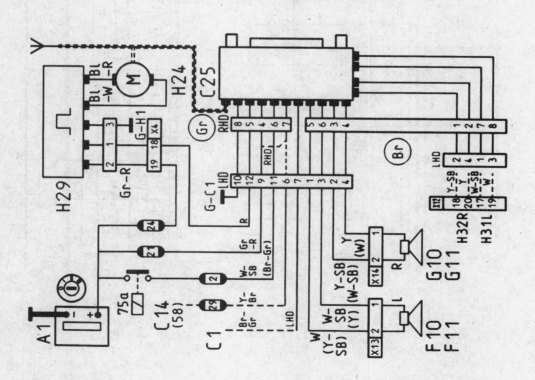

Supplementary wiring diagram (480 models from 1992) - Radio

12

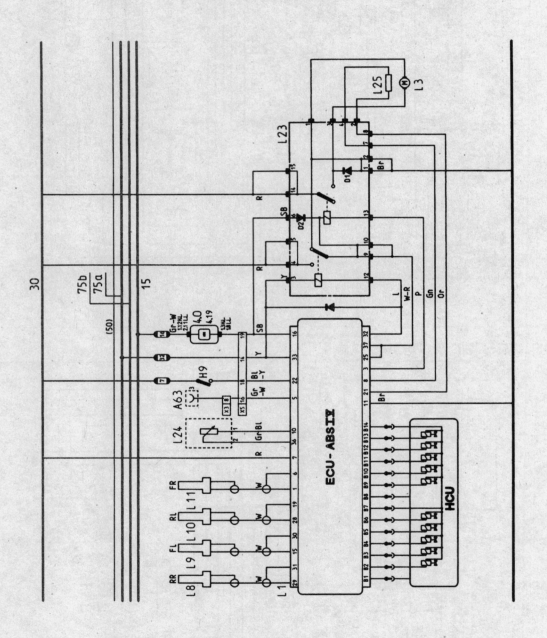

Supplementary wiring diagram (480 models from 1992) – Anti-lock Braking System (ABS) Mk IV

Dimensions and weights

Note: *All figures are approximate, and may vary according to model. Refer to manufacturer's data for exact figures.*

Dimensions

Overall length:
440	4312 mm
460	4405 mm
480	4258 mm

Overall width:
440 and 460	1690 mm
480	1710 mm

Overall height:
440 and 460	1390 mm
480	1320 mm

Weights (typical)

Kerb weight:
440	1003 to 1069 kg
460	997 to 1036 kg
480	1008 to 1078 kg

Maximum gross vehicle weight:
440 and 460 (carburettor)	1510 kg
440 and 460 (injection and turbo)	1580 kg
480	1355 to 1460 kg

Maximum roof rack load	75 kg

Maximum towing weight:
Braked trailer:	
440 and 460	1200 kg
480 (up to 1990)	900 kg
480 (from 1991)	1000 kg
Unbraked trailer	50% of braked trailer weight

Conversion factors

Length (distance)

Inches (in)	x 25.4	= Millimetres (mm)	x 0.0394	= Inches (in)
Feet (ft)	x 0.305	= Metres (m)	x 3.281	= Feet (ft)
Miles	x 1.609	= Kilometres (km)	x 0.621	= Miles

Volume (capacity)

Cubic inches (cu in; in³)	x 16.387	= Cubic centimetres (cc; cm³)	x 0.061	= Cubic inches (cu in; in³)
Imperial pints (Imp pt)	x 0.568	= Litres (l)	x 1.76	= Imperial pints (Imp pt)
Imperial quarts (Imp qt)	x 1.137	= Litres (l)	x 0.88	= Imperial quarts (Imp qt)
Imperial quarts (Imp qt)	x 1.201	= US quarts (US qt)	x 0.833	= Imperial quarts (Imp qt)
US quarts (US qt)	x 0.946	= Litres (l)	x 1.057	= US quarts (US qt)
Imperial gallons (Imp gal)	x 4.546	= Litres (l)	x 0.22	= Imperial gallons (Imp gal)
Imperial gallons (Imp gal)	x 1.201	= US gallons (US gal)	x 0.833	= Imperial gallons (Imp gal)
US gallons (US gal)	x 3.785	= Litres (l)	x 0.264	= US gallons (US gal)

Mass (weight)

Ounces (oz)	x 28.35	= Grams (g)	x 0.035	= Ounces (oz)
Pounds (lb)	x 0.454	= Kilograms (kg)	x 2.205	= Pounds (lb)

Force

Ounces-force (ozf; oz)	x 0.278	= Newtons (N)	x 3.6	= Ounces-force (ozf; oz)
Pounds-force (lbf; lb)	x 4.448	= Newtons (N)	x 0.225	= Pounds-force (lbf; lb)
Newtons (N)	x 0.1	= Kilograms-force (kgf; kg)	x 9.81	= Newtons (N)

Pressure

Pounds-force per square inch (psi; lbf/in²; lb/in²)	x 0.070	= Kilograms-force per square centimetre (kgf/cm²; kg/cm²)	x 14.223	= Pounds-force per square inch (psi; lbf/in²; lb/in²)
Pounds-force per square inch (psi; lbf/in²; lb/in²)	x 0.068	= Atmospheres (atm)	x 14.696	= Pounds-force per square inch (psi; lbf/in²; lb/in²)
Pounds-force per square inch (psi; lbf/in²; lb/in²)	x 0.069	= Bars	x 14.5	= Pounds-force per square inch (psi; lbf/in²; lb/in²)
Pounds-force per square inch (psi; lbf/in²; lb/in²)	x 6.895	= Kilopascals (kPa)	x 0.145	= Pounds-force per square inch (psi; lbf/in²; lb/in²)
Kilopascals (kPa)	x 0.01	= Kilograms-force per square centimetre (kgf/cm²; kg/cm²)	x 98.1	= Kilopascals (kPa)
Millibar (mbar)	x 100	= Pascals (Pa)	x 0.01	= Millibar (mbar)
Millibar (mbar)	x 0.0145	= Pounds-force per square inch (psi; lbf/in²; lb/in²)	x 68.947	= Millibar (mbar)
Millibar (mbar)	x 0.75	= Millimetres of mercury (mmHg)	x 1.333	= Millibar (mbar)
Millibar (mbar)	x 0.401	= Inches of water (inH₂O)	x 2.491	= Millibar (mbar)
Millimetres of mercury (mmHg)	x 0.535	= Inches of water (inH₂O)	x 1.868	= Millimetres of mercury (mmHg)
Inches of water (inH₂O)	x 0.036	= Pounds-force per square inch (psi; lbf/in²; lb/in²)	x 27.68	= Inches of water (inH₂O)

Torque (moment of force)

Pounds-force inches (lbf in; lb in)	x 1.152	= Kilograms-force centimetre (kgf cm; kg cm)	x 0.868	= Pounds-force inches (lbf in; lb in)
Pounds-force inches (lbf in; lb in)	x 0.113	= Newton metres (Nm)	x 8.85	= Pounds-force inches (lbf in; lb in)
Pounds-force inches (lbf in; lb in)	x 0.083	= Pounds-force feet (lbf ft; lb ft)	x 12	= Pounds-force inches (lbf in; lb in)
Pounds-force feet (lbf ft; lb ft)	x 0.138	= Kilograms-force metres (kgf m; kg m)	x 7.233	= Pounds-force feet (lbf ft; lb ft)
Pounds-force feet (lbf ft; lb ft)	x 1.356	= Newton metres (Nm)	x 0.738	= Pounds-force feet (lbf ft; lb ft)
Newton metres (Nm)	x 0.102	= Kilograms-force metres (kgf m; kg m)	x 9.804	= Newton metres (Nm)

Power

Horsepower (hp)	x 745.7	= Watts (W)	x 0.0013	= Horsepower (hp)

Velocity (speed)

Miles per hour (miles/hr; mph)	x 1.609	= Kilometres per hour (km/hr; kph)	x 0.621	= Miles per hour (miles/hr; mph)

Fuel consumption*

Miles per gallon, Imperial (mpg)	x 0.354	= Kilometres per litre (km/l)	x 2.825	= Miles per gallon, Imperial (mpg)
Miles per gallon, US (mpg)	x 0.425	= Kilometres per litre (km/l)	x 2.352	= Miles per gallon, US (mpg)

Temperature

Degrees Fahrenheit = (°C x 1.8) + 32   Degrees Celsius (Degrees Centigrade; °C) = (°F - 32) x 0.56

It is common practice to convert from miles per gallon (mpg) to litres/100 kilometres (l/100km), where mpg x l/100 km = 282

Spare parts are available from many sources, including maker's appointed garages, accessory shops, and motor factors. To be sure of obtaining the correct parts, it may sometimes be necessary to quote the vehicle identification number. If possible, it can also be useful to take the old parts along for positive identification. Items such as starter motors and alternators may be available under a service exchange scheme - any parts returned should always be clean.

Our advice regarding spare part sources is as follows.

Officially-appointed garages

This is the best source of parts which are peculiar to your car, and are not otherwise generally available (eg, badges, interior trim, certain body panels, etc). It is also the only place at which you should buy parts if the vehicle is still under warranty.

Accessory shops

These are very good places to buy materials and components needed for the maintenance of your car (oil, air and fuel filters, spark plugs, light bulbs, drivebelts, oils and greases, brake pads, touch-up paint, etc). Parts like this sold by a reputable shop are of the same standard as those used by the car manufacturer.

Motor factors

Good factors will stock all the more important components which wear out comparatively quickly and can sometimes supply individual components needed for the overhaul of a larger assembly. They may also handle work such as cylinder block reboring, crankshaft regrinding and balancing, etc.

Tyre and exhaust specialists

These outlets may be independent or members of a local or national chain. They frequently offer competitive prices when compared with a main dealer or local garage, but it will pay to obtain several quotes before making a decision. Also ask what 'extras' may be added to the quote - for instance, fitting a new valve and balancing the wheel are both often charged on top of the price of a new tyre.

Other sources

Beware of parts or materials obtained from market stalls, car boot sales or similar outlets. Such items are not invariably sub-standard, but there is little chance of compensation if they do prove unsatisfactory. In the case of safety-critical components such as brake pads, there is the risk not only of financial loss, but also of an accident causing injury or death.

Second-hand components or assemblies obtained from a car breaker can be a good buy in some circumstances, but this sort of purchase is best made by the experienced DIY mechanic.

Vehicle identification

Modifications are a continuing and unpublicised process in vehicle manufacture, quite apart from major model changes. Spare parts manuals and lists are compiled upon a numerical basis, the individual vehicle identification numbers being essential to correct identification of the component concerned.

When ordering spare parts, always give as much information as possible. Quote the car model, year of manufacture, body and engine numbers as appropriate.

The *vehicle identification plate* is located on the engine compartment front crossmember, either on the right-hand side or in the middle (see illustration). The paint code number is incorporated on the plate.

The *chassis number* is located in the plenum chamber beneath the windscreen on the right-hand side of the bulkhead.

The *engine number* is located on a plate on the front face of the cylinder block, next to the oil level dipstick tube (see illustration).

Vehicle identification plate

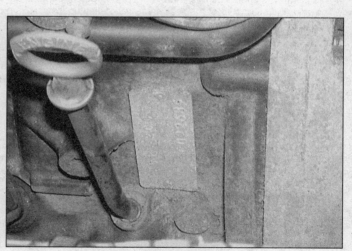

Engine number plate location

Whenever servicing, repair or overhaul work is carried out on the car or its components, observe the following procedures and instructions. This will assist in carrying out the operation efficiently and to a professional standard of workmanship.

Joint mating faces and gaskets

When separating components at their mating faces, never insert screwdrivers or similar implements into the joint between the faces in order to prise them apart. This can cause severe damage which results in oil leaks, coolant leaks, etc upon reassembly. Separation is usually achieved by tapping along the joint with a soft-faced hammer in order to break the seal. However, note that this method may not be suitable where dowels are used for component location.

Where a gasket is used between the mating faces of two components, a new one must be fitted on reassembly; fit it dry unless otherwise stated in the repair procedure. Make sure that the mating faces are clean and dry, with all traces of old gasket removed. When cleaning a joint face, use a tool which is unlikely to score or damage the face, and remove any burrs or nicks with an oilstone or fine file.

Make sure that tapped holes are cleaned with a pipe cleaner, and keep them free of jointing compound, if this is being used, unless specifically instructed otherwise.

Ensure that all orifices, channels or pipes are clear, and blow through them, preferably using compressed air.

Oil seals

Oil seals can be removed by levering them out with a wide flat-bladed screwdriver or similar implement. Alternatively, a number of self-tapping screws may be screwed into the seal, and these used as a purchase for pliers or some similar device in order to pull the seal free.

Whenever an oil seal is removed from its working location, either individually or as part of an assembly, it should be renewed.

The very fine sealing lip of the seal is easily damaged, and will not seal if the surface it contacts is not completely clean and free from scratches, nicks or grooves. If the original sealing surface of the component cannot be restored, and the manufacturer has not made provision for slight relocation of the seal relative to the sealing surface, the component should be renewed.

Protect the lips of the seal from any surface which may damage them in the course of fitting. Use tape or a conical sleeve where possible. Lubricate the seal lips with oil before fitting and, on dual-lipped seals, fill the space between the lips with grease.

Unless otherwise stated, oil seals must be fitted with their sealing lips toward the lubricant to be sealed.

Use a tubular drift or block of wood of the appropriate size to install the seal and, if the seal housing is shouldered, drive the seal down to the shoulder. If the seal housing is unshouldered, the seal should be fitted with its face flush with the housing top face (unless otherwise instructed).

Screw threads and fastenings

Seized nuts, bolts and screws are quite a common occurrence where corrosion has set in, and the use of penetrating oil or releasing fluid will often overcome this problem if the offending item is soaked for a while before attempting to release it. The use of an impact driver may also provide a means of releasing such stubborn fastening devices, when used in conjunction with the appropriate screwdriver bit or socket. If none of these methods works, it may be necessary to resort to the careful application of heat, or the use of a hacksaw or nut splitter device.

Studs are usually removed by locking two nuts together on the threaded part, and then using a spanner on the lower nut to unscrew the stud. Studs or bolts which have broken off below the surface of the component in which they are mounted can sometimes be removed using a stud extractor. Always ensure that a blind tapped hole is completely free from oil, grease, water or other fluid before installing the bolt or stud. Failure to do this could cause the housing to crack due to the hydraulic action of the bolt or stud as it is screwed in.

When tightening a castellated nut to accept a split pin, tighten the nut to the specified torque, where applicable, and then tighten further to the next split pin hole. Never slacken the nut to align the split pin hole, unless stated in the repair procedure.

When checking or retightening a nut or bolt to a specified torque setting, slacken the nut or bolt by a quarter of a turn, and then retighten to the specified setting. However, this should not be attempted where angular tightening has been used.

For some screw fastenings, notably cylinder head bolts or nuts, torque wrench settings are no longer specified for the latter stages of tightening, "angle-tightening" being called up instead. Typically, a fairly low torque wrench setting will be applied to the bolts/nuts in the correct sequence, followed by one or more stages of tightening through specified angles.

Locknuts, locktabs and washers

Any fastening which will rotate against a component or housing during tightening should always have a washer between it and the relevant component or housing.

Spring or split washers should always be renewed when they are used to lock a critical component such as a big-end bearing retaining bolt or nut. Locktabs which are folded over to retain a nut or bolt should always be renewed.

Self-locking nuts can be re-used in non-critical areas, providing resistance can be felt when the locking portion passes over the bolt or stud thread. However, it should be noted that self-locking stiffnuts tend to lose their effectiveness after long periods of use, and should then be renewed as a matter of course.

Split pins must always be replaced with new ones of the correct size for the hole.

When thread-locking compound is found on the threads of a fastener which is to be re-used, it should be cleaned off with a wire brush and solvent, and fresh compound applied on reassembly.

Special tools

Some repair procedures in this manual entail the use of special tools such as a press, two or three-legged pullers, spring compressors, etc. Wherever possible, suitable readily-available alternatives to the manufacturer's special tools are described, and are shown in use. In some instances, where no alternative is possible, it has been necessary to resort to the use of a manufacturer's tool, and this has been done for reasons of safety as well as the efficient completion of the repair operation. Unless you are highly-skilled and have a thorough understanding of the procedures described, never attempt to bypass the use of any special tool when the procedure described specifies its use. Not only is there a very great risk of personal injury, but expensive damage could be caused to the components involved.

Environmental considerations

When disposing of used engine oil, brake fluid, antifreeze, etc, give due consideration to any detrimental environmental effects. Do not, for instance, pour any of the above liquids down drains into the general sewage system, or onto the ground to soak away. Many local council refuse tips provide a facility for waste oil disposal, as do some garages. If none of these facilities are available, consult your local Environmental Health Department, or the National Rivers Authority, for further advice.

With the universal tightening-up of legislation regarding the emission of environmentally-harmful substances from motor vehicles, most vehicles have tamperproof devices fitted to the main adjustment points of the fuel system. These devices are primarily designed to prevent unqualified persons from adjusting the fuel/air mixture, with the chance of a consequent increase in toxic emissions. If such devices are found during servicing or overhaul, they should, wherever possible, be renewed or refitted in accordance with the manufacturer's requirements or current legislation.

OIL CARE
FOLLOW THE CODE
OIL BANK LINE
0800 66 33 66

Note: It is antisocial and illegal to dump oil down the drain. To find the location of your local oil recycling bank, call this number free.

The jack supplied with the vehicle tool kit should only be used for changing the roadwheels - see *Wheel changing* at the front of this book. When carrying out any other kind of work, raise the vehicle using a hydraulic (or trolley) jack, and always supplement the jack with axle stands positioned under the vehicle jacking points.

When using a hydraulic jack or axle stands, always position the jack head or axle stand head under one of the relevant jacking points **(see illustration)**.

If the front of the car is to be raised, apply the handbrake, chock the rear wheels then position the jack head under a stout wooden beam placed transversely across the underside of the car and in contact with the front subframe side rails; the beam should not touch the exhaust front pipe or the gearbox. Lower the beam onto axle stands, or position axle stands beneath the front jacking points.

To raise the rear of the car, chock the front wheels then jack up each side in turn with the jack head positioned under the rear jacking points, just forward of the rear wheels. As each side is raised, support it securely on axle stands before raising the other side. *Do not under any circumstances jack up the rear of the car under the rear axle.*

To raise the side of the car, chock the wheels opposite the side to be raised then place a block of wood under the side sill, and locate it centrally under the front door. Place the jack head in contact with the block, and raise the car. Shape the wooden blocks as necessary to avoid damaging the sill edges, and lower the car onto axle stands positioned under the jacking points. Never work under, around or near a raised car unless it is adequately supported in at least two places with axle stands or suitable sturdy blocks. *Never use makeshift piles of narrow wooden blocks or house bricks, as they can easily topple (or in the case of house bricks, disintegrate under the weight of the car).*

Do not jack the vehicle under any other part of the sill, sump, floor pan, or any of the steering or suspension components. With the vehicle raised, an axle stand should be positioned beneath the vehicle jack location point on the sill.

Never work under, around, or near a raised vehicle, unless it is adequately supported on stands.

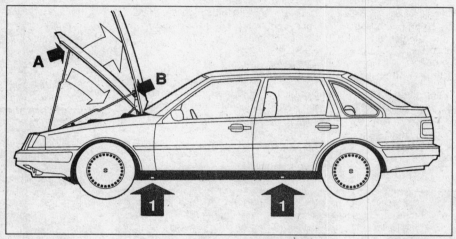

Jacking points (1) on the side sills

A   *Normal opening position of the bonnet*   B   *Service opening position of the bonnet*

Radio/cassette unit anti-theft system - precaution

The radio/cassette unit fitted by Volvo may be equipped with a built-in security code, to deter thieves. If the power source to the unit is cut, the anti-theft system will activate. Even if the power source is immediately reconnected, the unit will not function until the correct security code has been entered. Therefore, if you do not know the correct code, DO NOT disconnect the battery negative lead, or remove the radio/cassette unit from the vehicle. The exact procedure for reprogramming a unit which has been disconnected from its power supply varies from model to model. Consult the radio booklet which should have been supplied with the vehicle for specific details.

Introduction

A selection of good tools is a fundamental requirement for anyone contemplating the maintenance and repair of a motor vehicle. For the owner who does not possess any, their purchase will prove a considerable expense, offsetting some of the savings made by doing-it-yourself. However, provided that the tools purchased meet the relevant national safety standards and are of good quality, they will last for many years and prove an extremely worthwhile investment.

To help the average owner to decide which tools are needed to carry out the various tasks detailed in this manual, we have compiled three lists of tools under the following headings: *Maintenance and minor repair, Repair and overhaul,* and *Special.* Newcomers to practical mechanics should start off with the *Maintenance and minor repair* tool kit, and confine themselves to the simpler jobs around the vehicle. Then, as confidence and experience grow, more difficult tasks can be undertaken, with extra tools being purchased as, and when, they are needed. In this way, a *Maintenance and minor repair* tool kit can be built up into a *Repair and overhaul* tool kit over a considerable period of time, without any major cash outlays. The experienced do-it-yourselfer will have a tool kit good enough for most repair and overhaul procedures, and will add tools from the *Special* category when it is felt that the expense is justified by the amount of use to which these tools will be put.

Maintenance and minor repair tool kit

The tools given in this list should be considered as a minimum requirement if routine maintenance, servicing and minor repair operations are to be undertaken. We recommend the purchase of combination spanners (ring one end, open-ended the other); although more expensive than open-ended ones, they do give the advantages of both types of spanner.

☐ *Combination spanners:*
  Metric - 8 to 19 mm inclusive
☐ *Adjustable spanner - 35 mm jaw (approx.)*
☐ *Spark plug spanner (with rubber insert) - petrol models*
☐ *Spark plug gap adjustment tool - petrol models*
☐ *Set of feeler gauges*
☐ *Brake bleed nipple spanner*
☐ *Screwdrivers:*
  Flat blade - 100 mm long x 6 mm dia
  Cross blade - 100 mm long x 6 mm dia
  Torx - various sizes (not all vehicles)
☐ *Combination pliers*
☐ *Hacksaw (junior)*
☐ *Tyre pump*
☐ *Tyre pressure gauge*
☐ *Oil can*
☐ *Oil filter removal tool*
☐ *Fine emery cloth*
☐ *Wire brush (small)*
☐ *Funnel (medium size)*
☐ *Sump drain plug key (not all vehicles)*

Repair and overhaul tool kit

These tools are virtually essential for anyone undertaking any major repairs to a motor vehicle, and are additional to those given in the *Maintenance and minor repair* list. Included in this list is a comprehensive set of sockets. Although these are expensive, they will be found invaluable as they are so versatile - particularly if various drives are included in the set. We recommend the half-inch square-drive type, as this can be used with most proprietary torque wrenches.

The tools in this list will sometimes need to be supplemented by tools from the *Special* list:

☐ *Sockets (or box spanners) to cover range in previous list (including Torx sockets)*
☐ *Reversible ratchet drive (for use with sockets)*
☐ *Extension piece, 250 mm (for use with sockets)*
☐ *Universal joint (for use with sockets)*
☐ *Flexible handle or sliding T "breaker bar" (for use with sockets)*
☐ *Torque wrench (for use with sockets)*
☐ *Self-locking grips*
☐ *Ball pein hammer*
☐ *Soft-faced mallet (plastic or rubber)*
☐ *Screwdrivers:*
  Flat blade - long & sturdy, short (chubby), and narrow (electrician's) types
  Cross blade – long & sturdy, and short (chubby) types
☐ *Pliers:*
  Long-nosed
  Side cutters (electrician's)
  Circlip (internal and external)
☐ *Cold chisel - 25 mm*
☐ *Scriber*
☐ *Scraper*
☐ *Centre-punch*
☐ *Pin punch*
☐ *Hacksaw*
☐ *Brake hose clamp*
☐ *Brake/clutch bleeding kit*
☐ *Selection of twist drills*
☐ *Steel rule/straight-edge*
☐ *Allen keys (inc. splined/Torx type)*
☐ *Selection of files*
☐ *Wire brush*
☐ *Axle stands*
☐ *Jack (strong trolley or hydraulic type)*
☐ *Light with extension lead*
☐ *Universal electrical multi-meter*

Sockets and reversible ratchet drive

Brake bleeding kit

Torx key, socket and bit

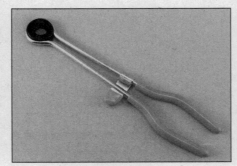

Hose clamp

Angular-tightening gauge

Special tools

The tools in this list are those which are not used regularly, are expensive to buy, or which need to be used in accordance with their manufacturers' instructions. Unless relatively difficult mechanical jobs are undertaken frequently, it will not be economic to buy many of these tools. Where this is the case, you could consider clubbing together with friends (or joining a motorists' club) to make a joint purchase, or borrowing the tools against a deposit from a local garage or tool hire specialist. It is worth noting that many of the larger DIY superstores now carry a large range of special tools for hire at modest rates.

The following list contains only those tools and instruments freely available to the public, and not those special tools produced by the vehicle manufacturer specifically for its dealer network. You will find occasional references to these manufacturers' special tools in the text of this manual. Generally, an alternative method of doing the job without the vehicle manufacturers' special tool is given. However, sometimes there is no alternative to using them. Where this is the case and the relevant tool cannot be bought or borrowed, you will have to entrust the work to a dealer.

☐ Angular-tightening gauge
☐ Valve spring compressor
☐ Valve grinding tool
☐ Piston ring compressor
☐ Piston ring removal/installation tool
☐ Cylinder bore hone
☐ Balljoint separator
☐ Coil spring compressors (where applicable)
☐ Two/three-legged hub and bearing puller
☐ Impact screwdriver
☐ Micrometer and/or vernier calipers
☐ Dial gauge
☐ Stroboscopic timing light
☐ Dwell angle meter/tachometer
☐ Fault code reader
☐ Cylinder compression gauge
☐ Hand-operated vacuum pump and gauge
☐ Clutch plate alignment set
☐ Brake shoe steady spring cup removal tool
☐ Bush and bearing removal/installation set
☐ Stud extractors
☐ Tap and die set
☐ Lifting tackle
☐ Trolley jack

Buying tools

Reputable motor accessory shops and superstores often offer excellent quality tools at discount prices, so it pays to shop around.

Remember, you don't have to buy the most expensive items on the shelf, but it is always advisable to steer clear of the very cheap tools. Beware of 'bargains' offered on market stalls or at car boot sales. There are plenty of good tools around at reasonable prices, but always aim to purchase items which meet the relevant national safety standards. If in doubt, ask the proprietor or manager of the shop for advice before making a purchase.

Care and maintenance of tools

Having purchased a reasonable tool kit, it is necessary to keep the tools in a clean and serviceable condition. After use, always wipe off any dirt, grease and metal particles using a clean, dry cloth, before putting the tools away. Never leave them lying around after they have been used. A simple tool rack on the garage or workshop wall for items such as screwdrivers and pliers is a good idea. Store all normal spanners and sockets in a metal box. Any measuring instruments, gauges, meters, etc, must be carefully stored where they cannot be damaged or become rusty.

Take a little care when tools are used. Hammer heads inevitably become marked, and screwdrivers lose the keen edge on their blades from time to time. A little timely attention with emery cloth or a file will soon restore items like this to a good finish.

Working facilities

Not to be forgotten when discussing tools is the workshop itself. If anything more than routine maintenance is to be carried out, a suitable working area becomes essential.

It is appreciated that many an owner-mechanic is forced by circumstances to remove an engine or similar item without the benefit of a garage or workshop. Having done this, any repairs should always be done under the cover of a roof.

Wherever possible, any dismantling should be done on a clean, flat workbench or table at a suitable working height.

Any workbench needs a vice; one with a jaw opening of 100 mm is suitable for most jobs. As mentioned previously, some clean dry storage space is also required for tools, as well as for any lubricants, cleaning fluids, touch-up paints etc, which become necessary.

Another item which may be required, and which has a much more general usage, is an electric drill with a chuck capacity of at least 8 mm. This, together with a good range of twist drills, is virtually essential for fitting accessories.

Last, but not least, always keep a supply of old newspapers and clean, lint-free rags available, and try to keep any working area as clean as possible.

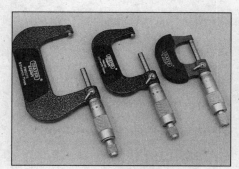
Micrometers

Dial test indicator ("dial gauge")

Strap wrench

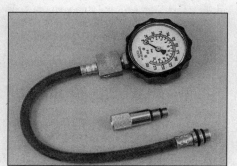
Compression tester

Fault code reader

This is a guide to getting your vehicle through the MOT test. Obviously it will not be possible to examine the vehicle to the same standard as the professional MOT tester. However, working through the following checks will enable you to identify any problem areas before submitting the vehicle for the test.

Where a testable component is in borderline condition, the tester has discretion in deciding whether to pass or fail it. The basis of such discretion is whether the tester would be happy for a close relative or friend to use the vehicle with the component in that condition. If the vehicle presented is clean and evidently well cared for, the tester may be more inclined to pass a borderline component than if the vehicle is scruffy and apparently neglected.

It has only been possible to summarise the test requirements here, based on the regulations in force at the time of printing. Test standards are becoming increasingly stringent, although there are some exemptions for older vehicles. For full details obtain a copy of the Haynes publication Pass the MOT! (available from stockists of Haynes manuals).

An assistant will be needed to help carry out some of these checks.

The checks have been sub-divided into four categories, as follows:

1 Checks carried out **FROM THE DRIVER'S SEAT**

2 Checks carried out **WITH THE VEHICLE ON THE GROUND**

3 Checks carried out **WITH THE VEHICLE RAISED AND THE WHEELS FREE TO TURN**

4 Checks carried out on **YOUR VEHICLE'S EXHAUST EMISSION SYSTEM**

---

1 Checks carried out **FROM THE DRIVER'S SEAT**

Handbrake

☐ Test the operation of the handbrake. Excessive travel (too many clicks) indicates incorrect brake or cable adjustment.

☐ Check that the handbrake cannot be released by tapping the lever sideways. Check the security of the lever mountings.

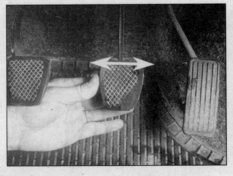

Footbrake

☐ Depress the brake pedal and check that it does not creep down to the floor, indicating a master cylinder fault. Release the pedal, wait a few seconds, then depress it again. If the pedal travels nearly to the floor before firm resistance is felt, brake adjustment or repair is necessary. If the pedal feels spongy, there is air in the hydraulic system which must be removed by bleeding.

☐ Check that the brake pedal is secure and in good condition. Check also for signs of fluid leaks on the pedal, floor or carpets, which would indicate failed seals in the brake master cylinder.

☐ Check the servo unit (when applicable) by operating the brake pedal several times, then keeping the pedal depressed and starting the engine. As the engine starts, the pedal will move down slightly. If not, the vacuum hose or the servo itself may be faulty.

Steering wheel and column

☐ Examine the steering wheel for fractures or looseness of the hub, spokes or rim.

☐ Move the steering wheel from side to side and then up and down. Check that the steering wheel is not loose on the column, indicating wear or a loose retaining nut. Continue moving the steering wheel as before, but also turn it slightly from left to right.

☐ Check that the steering wheel is not loose on the column, and that there is no abnormal

movement of the steering wheel, indicating wear in the column support bearings or couplings.

Windscreen and mirrors

☐ The windscreen must be free of cracks or other significant damage within the driver's field of view. (Small stone chips are acceptable.) Rear view mirrors must be secure, intact, and capable of being adjusted.

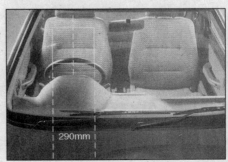

290mm

Seat belts and seats

Note: *The following checks are applicable to all seat belts, front and rear.*

☐ Examine the webbing of all the belts (including rear belts if fitted) for cuts, serious fraying or deterioration. Fasten and unfasten each belt to check the buckles. If applicable, check the retracting mechanism. Check the security of all seat belt mountings accessible from inside the vehicle.

☐ The front seats themselves must be securely attached and the backrests must lock in the upright position.

Doors

☐ Both front doors must be able to be opened and closed from outside and inside, and must latch securely when closed.

2 Checks carried out WITH THE VEHICLE ON THE GROUND

Vehicle identification

☐ Number plates must be in good condition, secure and legible, with letters and numbers correctly spaced – spacing at (A) should be twice that at (B).

☐ The VIN plate and/or homologation plate must be legible.

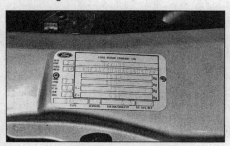

Electrical equipment

☐ Switch on the ignition and check the operation of the horn.

☐ Check the windscreen washers and wipers, examining the wiper blades; renew damaged or perished blades. Also check the operation of the stop-lights.

☐ Check the operation of the sidelights and number plate lights. The lenses and reflectors must be secure, clean and undamaged.

☐ Check the operation and alignment of the headlights. The headlight reflectors must not be tarnished and the lenses must be undamaged.

☐ Switch on the ignition and check the operation of the direction indicators (including the instrument panel tell-tale) and the hazard warning lights. Operation of the sidelights and stop-lights must not affect the indicators - if it does, the cause is usually a bad earth at the rear light cluster.

☐ Check the operation of the rear foglight(s), including the warning light on the instrument panel or in the switch.

Footbrake

☐ Examine the master cylinder, brake pipes and servo unit for leaks, loose mountings, corrosion or other damage.

☐ The fluid reservoir must be secure and the fluid level must be between the upper (**A**) and lower (**B**) markings.

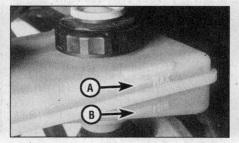

☐ Inspect both front brake flexible hoses for cracks or deterioration of the rubber. Turn the steering from lock to lock, and ensure that the hoses do not contact the wheel, tyre, or any part of the steering or suspension mechanism. With the brake pedal firmly depressed, check the hoses for bulges or leaks under pressure.

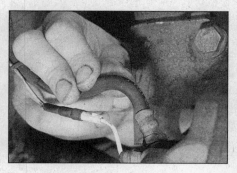

Steering and suspension

☐ Have your assistant turn the steering wheel from side to side slightly, up to the point where the steering gear just begins to transmit this movement to the roadwheels. Check for excessive free play between the steering wheel and the steering gear, indicating wear or insecurity of the steering column joints, the column-to-steering gear coupling, or the steering gear itself.

☐ Have your assistant turn the steering wheel more vigorously in each direction, so that the roadwheels just begin to turn. As this is done, examine all the steering joints, linkages, fittings and attachments. Renew any component that shows signs of wear or damage. On vehicles with power steering, check the security and condition of the steering pump, drivebelt and hoses.

☐ Check that the vehicle is standing level, and at approximately the correct ride height.

Shock absorbers

☐ Depress each corner of the vehicle in turn, then release it. The vehicle should rise and then settle in its normal position. If the vehicle continues to rise and fall, the shock absorber is defective. A shock absorber which has seized will also cause the vehicle to fail.

Exhaust system

☐ Start the engine. With your assistant holding a rag over the tailpipe, check the entire system for leaks. Repair or renew leaking sections.

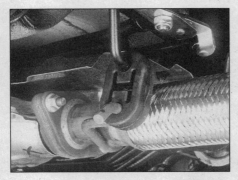

3 Checks carried out **WITH THE VEHICLE RAISED AND THE WHEELS FREE TO TURN**

Jack up the front and rear of the vehicle, and securely support it on axle stands. Position the stands clear of the suspension assemblies. Ensure that the wheels are clear of the ground and that the steering can be turned from lock to lock.

Steering mechanism

☐ Have your assistant turn the steering from lock to lock. Check that the steering turns smoothly, and that no part of the steering mechanism, including a wheel or tyre, fouls any brake hose or pipe or any part of the body structure.
☐ Examine the steering rack rubber gaiters for damage or insecurity of the retaining clips. If power steering is fitted, check for signs of damage or leakage of the fluid hoses, pipes or connections. Also check for excessive stiffness or binding of the steering, a missing split pin or locking device, or severe corrosion of the body structure within 30 cm of any steering component attachment point.

Front and rear suspension and wheel bearings

☐ Starting at the front right-hand side, grasp the roadwheel at the 3 o'clock and 9 o'clock positions and shake it vigorously. Check for free play or insecurity at the wheel bearings, suspension balljoints, or suspension mountings, pivots and attachments.
☐ Now grasp the wheel at the 12 o'clock and 6 o'clock positions and repeat the previous inspection. Spin the wheel, and check for roughness or tightness of the front wheel bearing.

☐ If excess free play is suspected at a component pivot point, this can be confirmed by using a large screwdriver or similar tool and levering between the mounting and the component attachment. This will confirm whether the wear is in the pivot bush, its retaining bolt, or in the mounting itself (the bolt holes can often become elongated).

☐ Carry out all the above checks at the other front wheel, and then at both rear wheels.

Springs and shock absorbers

☐ Examine the suspension struts (when applicable) for serious fluid leakage, corrosion, or damage to the casing. Also check the security of the mounting points.
☐ If coil springs are fitted, check that the spring ends locate in their seats, and that the spring is not corroded, cracked or broken.
☐ If leaf springs are fitted, check that all leaves are intact, that the axle is securely attached to each spring, and that there is no deterioration of the spring eye mountings, bushes, and shackles.

☐ The same general checks apply to vehicles fitted with other suspension types, such as torsion bars, hydraulic displacer units, etc. Ensure that all mountings and attachments are secure, that there are no signs of excessive wear, corrosion or damage, and (on hydraulic types) that there are no fluid leaks or damaged pipes.
☐ Inspect the shock absorbers for signs of serious fluid leakage. Check for wear of the mounting bushes or attachments, or damage to the body of the unit.

Driveshafts (fwd vehicles only)

☐ Rotate each front wheel in turn and inspect the constant velocity joint gaiters for splits or damage. Also check that each driveshaft is straight and undamaged.

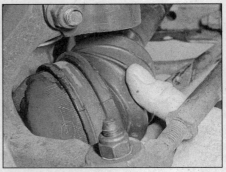

Braking system

☐ If possible without dismantling, check brake pad wear and disc condition. Ensure that the friction lining material has not worn excessively, (A) and that the discs are not fractured, pitted, scored or badly worn (B).

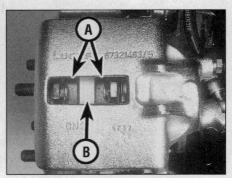

☐ Examine all the rigid brake pipes underneath the vehicle, and the flexible hose(s) at the rear. Look for corrosion, chafing or insecurity of the pipes, and for signs of bulging under pressure, chafing, splits or deterioration of the flexible hoses.
☐ Look for signs of fluid leaks at the brake calipers or on the brake backplates. Repair or renew leaking components.
☐ Slowly spin each wheel, while your assistant depresses and releases the footbrake. Ensure that each brake is operating and does not bind when the pedal is released.

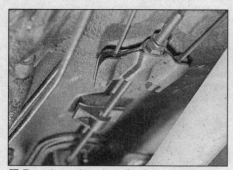

□ Examine the handbrake mechanism, checking for frayed or broken cables, excessive corrosion, or wear or insecurity of the linkage. Check that the mechanism works on each relevant wheel, and releases fully, without binding.

□ It is not possible to test brake efficiency without special equipment, but a road test can be carried out later to check that the vehicle pulls up in a straight line.

Fuel and exhaust systems

□ Inspect the fuel tank (including the filler cap), fuel pipes, hoses and unions. All components must be secure and free from leaks.

□ Examine the exhaust system over its entire length, checking for any damaged, broken or missing mountings, security of the retaining clamps and rust or corrosion.

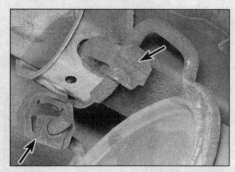

Wheels and tyres

□ Examine the sidewalls and tread area of each tyre in turn. Check for cuts, tears, lumps, bulges, separation of the tread, and exposure of the ply or cord due to wear or damage. Check that the tyre bead is correctly seated on the wheel rim, that the valve is sound and

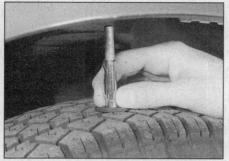

properly seated, and that the wheel is not distorted or damaged.

□ Check that the tyres are of the correct size for the vehicle, that they are of the same size and type on each axle, and that the pressures are correct.

□ Check the tyre tread depth. The legal minimum at the time of writing is 1.6 mm over at least three-quarters of the tread width. Abnormal tread wear may indicate incorrect front wheel alignment.

Body corrosion

□ Check the condition of the entire vehicle structure for signs of corrosion in load-bearing areas. (These include chassis box sections, side sills, cross-members, pillars, and all suspension, steering, braking system and seat belt mountings and anchorages.) Any corrosion which has seriously reduced the thickness of a load-bearing area is likely to cause the vehicle to fail. In this case professional repairs are likely to be needed.

□ Damage or corrosion which causes sharp or otherwise dangerous edges to be exposed will also cause the vehicle to fail.

4 Checks carried out on YOUR VEHICLE'S EXHAUST EMISSION SYSTEM

Petrol models

□ Have the engine at normal operating temperature, and make sure that it is in good tune (ignition system in good order, air filter element clean, etc).

□ Before any measurements are carried out, raise the engine speed to around 2500 rpm, and hold it at this speed for 20 seconds.

Allow the engine speed to return to idle, and watch for smoke emissions from the exhaust tailpipe. If the idle speed is obviously much too high, or if dense blue or clearly-visible black smoke comes from the tailpipe for more than 5 seconds, the vehicle will fail. As a rule of thumb, blue smoke signifies oil being burnt (engine wear) while black smoke signifies unburnt fuel (dirty air cleaner element, or other carburettor or fuel system fault).

□ An exhaust gas analyser capable of measuring carbon monoxide (CO) and hydrocarbons (HC) is now needed. If such an instrument cannot be hired or borrowed, a local garage may agree to perform the check for a small fee.

CO emissions (mixture)

□ At the time of writing, the maximum CO level at idle is 3.5% for vehicles first used after August 1986 and 4.5% for older vehicles. From January 1996 a much tighter limit (around 0.5%) applies to catalyst-equipped vehicles first used from August 1992. If the CO level cannot be reduced far enough to pass the test (and the fuel and ignition systems are otherwise in good condition) then the carburettor is badly worn, or there is some problem in the fuel injection system or catalytic converter (as applicable).

HC emissions

□ With the CO emissions within limits, HC emissions must be no more than 1200 ppm (parts per million). If the vehicle fails this test at idle, it can be re-tested at around 2000 rpm; if the HC level is then 1200 ppm or less, this counts as a pass.

□ Excessive HC emissions can be caused by oil being burnt, but they are more likely to be due to unburnt fuel.

Diesel models

□ The only emission test applicable to Diesel engines is the measuring of exhaust smoke density. The test involves accelerating the engine several times to its maximum unloaded speed.

Note: *It is of the utmost importance that the engine timing belt is in good condition before the test is carried out.*

□ Excessive smoke can be caused by a dirty air cleaner element. Otherwise, professional advice may be needed to find the cause.

Fault finding

Engine

- ☐ Engine fails to rotate when attempting to start
- ☐ Engine rotates but will not start
- ☐ Engine difficult to start when cold
- ☐ Engine difficult to start when hot
- ☐ Starter motor noisy or excessively rough in engagement
- ☐ Engine starts, but stops immediately
- ☐ Engine idles erratically
- ☐ Engine misfires at idle speed
- ☐ Engine misfires throughout the driving speed range
- ☐ Engine hesitates on acceleration
- ☐ Engine stalls
- ☐ Engine lacks power
- ☐ Engine backfires
- ☐ Oil pressure warning light illuminated with engine running
- ☐ Engine runs-on after switching off
- ☐ Engine noises

Cooling system

- ☐ Overheating
- ☐ Overcooling
- ☐ External coolant leakage
- ☐ Internal coolant leakage
- ☐ Corrosion

Fuel and exhaust systems

- ☐ Excessive fuel consumption
- ☐ Fuel leakage and/or fuel odour
- ☐ Excessive noise or fumes from exhaust system

Clutch

- ☐ Pedal travels to floor - no pressure or very little resistance
- ☐ Clutch fails to disengage (unable to select gears)
- ☐ Clutch slips (engine speed increases with no increase in vehicle speed)
- ☐ Judder as clutch is engaged
- ☐ Noise when depressing or releasing clutch pedal

Manual gearbox

- ☐ Noisy in neutral with engine running
- ☐ Noisy in one particular gear
- ☐ Difficulty engaging gears
- ☐ Jumps out of gear
- ☐ Vibration
- ☐ Lubricant leaks

Automatic transmission

- ☐ Fluid leakage
- ☐ Transmission fluid brown, or has burned smell
- ☐ General gear selection problems
- ☐ Transmission will not downshift (kickdown) with accelerator fully depressed
- ☐ Engine will not start in any gear, or starts in gears other than Park or Neutral
- ☐ Transmission slips, shifts roughly, is noisy or has no drive in forward or reverse gears

Braking system

- ☐ Vehicle pulls to one side under braking
- ☐ Noise (grinding or high-pitched squeal) when brakes applied
- ☐ Excessive brake pedal travel
- ☐ Brake pedal feels spongy when depressed
- ☐ Excessive brake pedal effort required to stop vehicle
- ☐ Judder felt through brake pedal or steering wheel when braking
- ☐ Brakes binding
- ☐ Rear wheels locking under normal braking

Driveshafts

- ☐ Clicking or knocking noise on turns (at slow speed on full-lock)
- ☐ Vibration when accelerating or decelerating

Suspension and steering

- ☐ Vehicle pulls to one side
- ☐ Wheel wobble and vibration
- ☐ Excessive pitching during braking, and/or excessive roll when cornering
- ☐ Wandering or general instability
- ☐ Excessively-stiff steering
- ☐ Excessive play in steering
- ☐ Lack of power assistance (where applicable)
- ☐ Tyre wear excessive

Electrical system

- ☐ Battery will not hold a charge for more than a few days
- ☐ Lights inoperative
- ☐ Ignition/no-charge warning light remains illuminated with engine running
- ☐ Ignition/no-charge warning light fails to come on
- ☐ Instrument readings inaccurate or erratic
- ☐ Horn inoperative or unsatisfactory in operation
- ☐ Windscreen/tailgate wipers inoperative, or unsatisfactory in operation
- ☐ Windscreen/tailgate washers inoperative, or unsatisfactory in operation
- ☐ Central locking system inoperative, or unsatisfactory in operation
- ☐ Electric windows inoperative, or unsatisfactory in operation

Introduction

The vehicle owner who does his or her own maintenance according to the recommended service schedules should not have to use this section of the manual very often. Modern component reliability is such that, provided those items subject to wear or deterioration are inspected or renewed at the specified intervals, sudden failure is comparatively rare. Faults do not usually just happen as a result of sudden failure, but develop over a period of time. Major mechanical failures in particular are usually preceded by characteristic symptoms over hundreds or even thousands of miles. Those components which do occasionally fail without warning are often small and easily carried in the vehicle.

With any fault finding, the first step is to decide where to begin investigations. Sometimes this is obvious, but on other occasions a little detective work will be necessary. The owner who makes half a dozen haphazard adjustments or replacements may be successful in curing a fault (or its symptoms), but will be none the wiser if the fault recurs and ultimately may have spent more time and money than was necessary. A calm and logical approach will be found to be more satisfactory in the long run.

Always take into account any warning signs or abnormalities that may have been noticed in the period preceding the fault - power loss, high or low gauge readings, unusual smells, etc - and remember that failure of components such as fuses or spark plugs may only be pointers to some underlying fault.

The pages which follow provide an easy reference guide to the more common problems which may occur during the operation of the vehicle. These problems and their possible causes are grouped under headings denoting various components or systems, such as Engine, Cooling system, etc. The Chapter and/or Section which deals with the problem is also shown in brackets. Whatever the fault, certain basic principles apply. These are as follows:

Verify the fault. This is simply a matter of being sure that you know what the symptoms are before starting work. This is particularly important if you are investigating a fault for someone else who may not have described it very accurately.

Don't overlook the obvious. For example, if the vehicle won't start, is there petrol in the tank? (Don't take anyone else's word on this particular point, and don't trust the fuel gauge either!) If an electrical fault is indicated, look for loose or broken wires before digging out the test gear.

Cure the disease, not the symptom. Substituting a flat battery with a fully-charged one will get you off the hard shoulder, but if the underlying cause is not attended to, the new battery will go the same way.

Similarly, changing oil-fouled spark plugs for a new set will get you moving again, but remember that the reason for the fouling (if it wasn't simply an incorrect grade of plug) will have to be established and corrected.

Don't take anything for granted. Particularly, don't forget that a new component may itself be defective (especially if it's been rattling around in the boot for months), and don't leave components out of a fault diagnosis sequence just because they are new or recently fitted. When you do finally diagnose a difficult fault, you'll probably realise that all the evidence was there from the start.

Engine

Engine fails to rotate when attempting to start

☐ Battery terminal connections loose or corroded (*Weekly checks*).
☐ Battery discharged or faulty (Chapter 5A).
☐ Broken, loose or disconnected wiring in the starting circuit (Chapter 5A or 12).
☐ Defective starter solenoid or switch (Chapter 5A).
☐ Defective starter motor (Chapter 5A).
☐ Flywheel ring gear or starter motor pinion teeth loose or broken (Chapter 2A or 5A).
☐ Engine earth strap broken or disconnected (Chapter 12).
☐ Automatic transmission not in Park/Neutral position, or starter inhibitor switch faulty (Chapter 7B).

Engine rotates but will not start

☐ Fuel tank empty.
☐ Battery discharged (engine rotates slowly) (Chapter 5A).
☐ Battery terminal connections loose or corroded (*Weekly checks*).
☐ Ignition components damp or damaged (Chapter 1 or 5B).
☐ Ignition flywheel sensor dirty, damaged, or wiring damaged (Chapter 5B).
☐ Broken, loose or disconnected wiring in the ignition circuit (Chapter 1, 5B, or 12).
☐ Worn, faulty or incorrectly-gapped spark plugs (Chapter 1).
☐ Immobiliser fault (Chapter 12).
☐ Choke mechanism sticking, incorrectly adjusted, or faulty (Chapter 4A).
☐ Fuel injection system or fuel pump fault (Chapter 4B).
☐ Major mechanical failure (eg camshaft drive) (Chapter 2A).

Engine difficult to start when cold

☐ Battery discharged (Chapter 5A).
☐ Battery terminal connections loose or corroded (*Weekly checks*).
☐ Worn, faulty or incorrectly-gapped spark plugs (Chapter 1).
☐ Choke mechanism sticking, incorrectly adjusted, or faulty (Chapter 4A).
☐ Fuel injection system fault, possibly temperature sensor(s) (Chapter 4B).
☐ Other ignition system fault (Chapters 1 and 5B).
☐ Low cylinder compressions (Chapter 2A).

Engine difficult to start when hot

☐ Air filter element dirty or clogged (Chapter 1).
☐ Choke mechanism sticking, incorrectly adjusted, or faulty (Chapter 4A).
☐ Carburettor float chamber flooding (Chapter 4A).
☐ Fuel injection system fault, possibly temperature sensor(s) (Chapter 4B).
☐ Low cylinder compressions (Chapter 2A).

Starter motor noisy or excessively rough in engagement

☐ Flywheel ring gear or starter motor pinion teeth loose or broken (Chapter 2A or 5A).
☐ Starter motor mounting bolts loose or missing (Chapter 5A).
☐ Starter motor internal components worn or damaged (Chapter 5A).

Engine starts, but stops immediately

☐ Insufficient fuel reaching carburettor (Chapter 4A).
☐ Blocked carburettor jet(s) or internal passages (Chapter 4A).
☐ Fuel injection system or fuel pump fault (Chapter 4B).
☐ Loose or faulty electrical connections in the ignition circuit (Chapter 1, 5B, or 12).
☐ Vacuum leak at the carburettor, single point injector unit, fuel injection throttle housing or inlet manifold (Chapter 4A or 4B).

Engine idles erratically

☐ Incorrectly-adjusted idle speed and/or mixture settings (Chapter 1).
☐ Air filter element clogged (Chapter 1).
☐ Vacuum leak at the carburettor, single point injector unit, fuel injection throttle housing, inlet manifold or associated hoses (Chapter 4A or 4B).
☐ Fuel injection system fault (Chapter 4B).
☐ Fuel injector(s) partially blocked (Chapter 4B).
☐ Worn, faulty or incorrectly-gapped spark plugs (Chapter 1).
☐ Incorrectly-adjusted valve clearances (Chapter 1).
☐ Uneven or low cylinder compressions (Chapter 2A).
☐ Camshaft lobes worn (Chapter 2A).
☐ Timing belt incorrectly tensioned (Chapter 2A).

Engine misfires at idle speed

☐ Worn, faulty or incorrectly-gapped spark plugs (Chapter 1).
☐ Faulty spark plug HT leads (Chapter 1).
☐ Incorrectly-adjusted idle mixture settings (Chapter 1).
☐ Incorrect ignition timing (Chapter 5B).
☐ Ignition flywheel sensor dirty, damaged, or wiring damaged (Chapter 5B).
☐ Vacuum leak at the carburettor, single point injector unit, fuel injection throttle housing, inlet manifold or associated hoses (Chapter 4A or 4B).
☐ Fuel injection system fault (Chapter 4B).
☐ Fuel injector(s) partially blocked (Chapter 4B).
☐ Distributor cap cracked, or tracking internally (Chapter 1).
☐ Incorrectly-adjusted valve clearances (Chapter 1).
☐ Uneven or low cylinder compressions (Chapter 2A).
☐ Disconnected, leaking or perished crankcase ventilation hoses (Chapter 1 or 4C).

Engine (continued)

Engine misfires throughout the driving speed range

- [ ] Blocked carburettor jet(s) or internal passages (Chapter 4A).
- [ ] Carburettor worn or incorrectly adjusted (Chapter 1 or 4A).
- [ ] Fuel injection system fault (Chapter 4B).
- [ ] Fuel injector(s) partially blocked (Chapter 4B).
- [ ] Fuel filter choked (Chapter 1).
- [ ] Fuel pump faulty or delivery pressure low (Chapter 4A or 4B).
- [ ] Fuel tank vent blocked or fuel pipes restricted (Chapter 4A or 4B).
- [ ] Vacuum leak at the carburettor, single point injector unit, fuel injection throttle housing, inlet manifold or associated hoses (Chapter 4A or 4B).
- [ ] Worn, faulty or incorrectly-gapped spark plugs (Chapter 1).
- [ ] Faulty spark plug HT leads (Chapter 1).
- [ ] Distributor cap cracked or tracking internally (Chapter 1).
- [ ] Faulty ignition coil (Chapter 5B).
- [ ] Ignition flywheel sensor dirty, damaged, or wiring damaged (Chapter 5B).
- [ ] Poor earth connection in engine compartment (Chapter 1 or 12).
- [ ] Uneven or low cylinder compressions (Chapter 2A).

Engine hesitates on acceleration

- [ ] Worn, faulty or incorrectly-gapped spark plugs (Chapter 1).
- [ ] Carburettor accelerator pump faulty (Chapter 4A).
- [ ] Blocked carburettor jets or internal passages (Chapter 4A).
- [ ] Vacuum leak at the carburettor, inlet manifold or associated hoses (Chapter 4A).
- [ ] Carburettor worn or incorrectly adjusted (Chapter 1 or 4A).
- [ ] Fuel injection system fault (Chapter 4B).
- [ ] Fuel injector(s) partially blocked (Chapter 4B).
- [ ] Poor earth connection in engine compartment (Chapter 1 or 12).

Engine stalls

- [ ] Incorrectly-adjusted idle speed and/or mixture settings (Chapter 1).
- [ ] Blocked carburettor jet(s) or internal passages (Chapter 4A).
- [ ] Vacuum leak at the carburettor, single point injector unit, fuel injection throttle housing, inlet manifold or associated hoses (Chapter 4A or 4B).
- [ ] Fuel filter choked (Chapter 1).
- [ ] Fuel pump faulty or delivery pressure low (Chapter 4A or 4B).
- [ ] Fuel tank vent blocked or fuel pipes restricted (Chapter 4A or 4B).
- [ ] Fuel injector(s) partially blocked (Chapter 4B).
- [ ] Fuel injection system fault (Chapter 4B).

Engine lacks power

- [ ] Incorrect ignition timing (Chapter 5B).
- [ ] Carburettor worn or incorrectly adjusted (Chapter 1 or 4A).
- [ ] Timing belt incorrectly fitted or tensioned (Chapter 2A).
- [ ] Fuel filter choked (Chapter 1).
- [ ] Fuel pump faulty or delivery pressure low (Chapter 4A or 4B).
- [ ] Fuel injector(s) partially blocked (Chapter 4B).
- [ ] Uneven or low cylinder compressions (Chapter 2A).
- [ ] Worn, faulty or incorrectly-gapped spark plugs (Chapter 1).
- [ ] Vacuum leak at the carburettor, single point injector unit, fuel injection throttle housing, inlet manifold or associated hoses (Chapter 4A or 4B).
- [ ] Brakes binding (Chapter 9).
- [ ] Clutch slipping (Chapter 6).
- [ ] Automatic transmission fluid level incorrect (Chapter 1).

Engine backfires

- [ ] Ignition timing incorrect (Chapter 5B).
- [ ] Spark plug HT leads connected in wrong order (Chapter 1 or 5B).
- [ ] Ignition flywheel sensor dirty, damaged, or wiring damaged (Chapter 5B).
- [ ] Timing belt incorrectly fitted or tensioned (Chapter 2A).
- [ ] Carburettor worn or incorrectly adjusted (Chapter 1 or 4A).
- [ ] Vacuum leak at the carburettor, single point injector unit, fuel injection throttle housing, inlet manifold or associated hoses (Chapter 4A or 4B).

Oil pressure warning light illuminated with engine running

- [ ] Low oil level or incorrect oil grade (Weekly checks).
- [ ] Faulty oil pressure transmitter (sender) unit or wiring (Chapter 12).
- [ ] Worn engine bearings and/or oil pump (Chapter 2B).
- [ ] High engine operating temperature (Chapter 3).
- [ ] Oil pump pressure relief valve defective (Chapter 2A).
- [ ] Oil pump pick-up strainer clogged (Chapter 2A).

Engine runs-on after switching off

- [ ] Idle speed excessively high (Chapter 1).
- [ ] Idle mixture too weak (Chapter 1).
- [ ] Faulty carburettor anti-run-on solenoid (Chapter 4A).
- [ ] Excessive carbon build-up in engine - de-coke required (Chapter 2B).
- [ ] High engine operating temperature (Chapter 3).

Engine noises

Pre-ignition (pinking) or knocking during acceleration or under load

- [ ] Ignition timing incorrect (Chapter 5B).
- [ ] Incorrect grade of fuel (Chapter 4A or 4B).
- [ ] Vacuum leak at the carburettor, single point injector unit, fuel injection throttle housing, inlet manifold or associated hoses (Chapter 4A or 4B).
- [ ] Excessive carbon build-up in engine - de-coke required (Chapter 2B).
- [ ] Worn or damaged distributor or other ignition system component (Chapter 1 or 5B).
- [ ] Carburettor worn or incorrectly adjusted (Chapter 1 or 4A).

Whistling or wheezing noises

- [ ] Leaking inlet manifold, single point injector unit, fuel injection throttle housing, or carburettor gasket (Chapter 4A or 4B).
- [ ] Leaking exhaust manifold gasket or pipe-to-manifold joint (Chapter 1).
- [ ] Leaking vacuum hose (Chapter 4C, 5B or 9).
- [ ] Blowing cylinder head gasket (Chapter 2A).

Tapping or rattling noises

- [ ] Incorrect valve clearances (Chapter 1).
- [ ] Worn valve gear or camshaft (Chapter 2).
- [ ] Ancillary component fault (water pump, alternator, etc) (Chapter 3 or 5A).

Knocking or thumping noises

- [ ] Worn big-end bearings (regular heavy knocking, perhaps less under load) (Chapter 2B).
- [ ] Worn main bearings (rumbling and knocking, perhaps worsening under load) (Chapter 2B).
- [ ] Piston slap, due to worn pistons/bores (most noticeable when cold) (Chapter 2B).
- [ ] Ancillary component fault (alternator, water pump, etc) (Chapter 3 or 5A).

Cooling system

Overheating

- ☐ Insufficient coolant in system (*Weekly checks*).
- ☐ Thermostat faulty (Chapter 3).
- ☐ Radiator core blocked or grille restricted (Chapter 3).
- ☐ Electric cooling fan or thermoswitch faulty (Chapter 3).
- ☐ Pressure cap faulty (Chapter 1 or 3).
- ☐ Water pump drivebelt worn, or incorrectly adjusted (Chapter 1).
- ☐ Ignition timing incorrect (Chapter 5B).
- ☐ Inaccurate temperature gauge sender unit (Chapter 3).
- ☐ Air-lock in cooling system (Chapter 1).

Overcooling

- ☐ Thermostat faulty (Chapter 3).
- ☐ Inaccurate temperature gauge sender unit (Chapter 3).

External coolant leakage

- ☐ Deteriorated or damaged hoses or hose clips (Chapter 1).
- ☐ Radiator core or heater matrix leaking (Chapter 3).
- ☐ Pressure cap faulty (Chapters 1 and 3).
- ☐ Water pump seal leaking (Chapter 3).
- ☐ Boiling due to overheating (Chapter 3).
- ☐ Cylinder head or engine block core plug leaking (Chapter 2A or 2B).

Internal coolant leakage

- ☐ Leaking cylinder head gasket - water in oil, or oil in coolant (Chapter 2A).
- ☐ Cracked cylinder head or cylinder bore (Chapter 2A or 2B).

Corrosion

- ☐ Infrequent draining and flushing (Chapter 1).
- ☐ Incorrect antifreeze mixture or inappropriate type (Chapter 1).

Fuel and exhaust systems

Excessive fuel consumption

- ☐ Air filter element dirty or clogged (Chapter 1).
- ☐ Carburettor worn or incorrectly adjusted (Chapter 1 or 4A).
- ☐ Choke cable incorrectly adjusted or choke sticking (Chapter 4A).
- ☐ Fuel injection system fault (Chapter 4B).
- ☐ Ignition timing incorrect (Chapter 5B).
- ☐ Brakes binding (Chapter 1 or 9).
- ☐ Tyres under-inflated (*Weekly checks*).

Fuel leakage and/or fuel odour

- ☐ Damaged or corroded fuel tank, pipes or connections (Chapter 1, 4A or 4B).
- ☐ Carburettor float chamber flooding (Chapter 4A).
- ☐ Fuel injection system seals leaking - most obvious at operating pressure (Chapter 4B).

Excessive noise or fumes from exhaust system

- ☐ Leaking exhaust system or manifold joints (Chapter 1 or 4C).
- ☐ Leaking, corroded or damaged silencers or pipe (Chapter 1 or 4C).
- ☐ Broken mountings causing body or suspension contact (Chapter 1 or 4C).

Clutch

Pedal travels to floor - no pressure or very little resistance

- ☐ Broken clutch cable (Chapter 6).
- ☐ Incorrect clutch adjustment (Chapter 1).
- ☐ Broken clutch release bearing or fork (Chapter 6).
- ☐ Broken diaphragm spring in clutch pressure plate (Chapter 6).

Clutch fails to disengage (unable to select gears)

- ☐ Incorrect clutch adjustment (Chapter 1).
- ☐ Clutch disc sticking on gearbox input shaft splines (Chapter 6).
- ☐ Clutch disc sticking to flywheel or pressure plate (Chapter 6).
- ☐ Faulty pressure plate assembly (Chapter 6).
- ☐ Clutch release mechanism worn or incorrectly assembled (Chapter 6).

Noise when depressing or releasing clutch pedal

- ☐ Worn clutch release bearing (Chapter 6).
- ☐ Worn or dry clutch pedal bushes (Chapter 6).
- ☐ Faulty pressure plate assembly (Chapter 6).
- ☐ Pressure plate diaphragm spring broken (Chapter 6).
- ☐ Broken clutch disc cushioning springs (Chapter 6).

Clutch slips (engine speed increases with no increase in vehicle speed)

- ☐ Incorrect clutch adjustment (Chapter 1).
- ☐ Clutch disc linings excessively worn (Chapter 6).
- ☐ Clutch disc linings contaminated with oil or grease (Chapter 6).
- ☐ Faulty pressure plate or weak diaphragm spring (Chapter 6).

Judder as clutch is engaged

- ☐ Clutch disc linings contaminated with oil or grease (Chapter 6).
- ☐ Clutch disc linings excessively worn (Chapter 6).
- ☐ Clutch cable sticking or frayed (Chapter 6).
- ☐ Faulty or distorted pressure plate or diaphragm spring (Chapter 6).
- ☐ Worn or loose engine or gearbox mountings (Chapter 2A).
- ☐ Clutch disc hub or gearbox input shaft splines worn (Chapter 6).

Manual gearbox

Noisy in neutral with engine running

☐ Input shaft bearings worn (noise apparent with clutch pedal released but not when depressed) (Chapter 7A).*
☐ Clutch release bearing worn (noise apparent with clutch pedal depressed, possibly less when released) (Chapter 6).

Noisy in one particular gear

☐ Worn, damaged or chipped gear teeth (Chapter 7A).*

Difficulty engaging gears

☐ Clutch fault/incorrect adjustment (Chapter 6).
☐ Worn or damaged gear linkage (Chapter 7A).
☐ Incorrectly-adjusted gear linkage (Chapter 7A).
☐ Worn synchroniser units (Chapter 7A).*

Jumps out of gear

☐ Worn or damaged gear linkage (Chapter 7A).
☐ Incorrectly-adjusted gear linkage (Chapter 7A).
☐ Worn synchroniser units (Chapter 7A).*
☐ Worn selector forks (Chapter 7A).*

Vibration

☐ Lack of oil (Chapter 1).
☐ Worn bearings (Chapter 7A).*

Lubricant leaks

☐ Leaking differential output oil seal (Chapter 7A).
☐ Leaking housing joint (Chapter 7A).*
☐ Leaking input shaft oil seal (Chapter 7A).*

Although the corrective action necessary to remedy the symptoms described is beyond the scope of the home mechanic, the above information should be helpful in isolating the cause of the condition so that the owner can communicate clearly with a professional mechanic.

Automatic transmission

Note: *Due to the complexity of the automatic transmission, it is difficult for the home mechanic to properly diagnose and service this unit. For problems other than the following, the vehicle should be taken to a dealer service department or automatic transmission specialist.*

Fluid leakage

☐ Automatic transmission fluid is usually dark red in colour. Fluid leaks should not be confused with engine oil, which can easily be blown onto the transmission by airflow.
☐ To determine the source of a leak, first remove all built-up dirt and grime from the transmission housing and surrounding areas, using a degreasing agent or by steam-cleaning. Drive the vehicle at low speed so the airflow will not blow the leak far from its source. Raise and support the vehicle, and determine where the leak is coming from. The following are common areas of leakage:

a) *Fluid pan (Chapters 1 and 7B).*
b) *Dipstick tube (Chapters 1 and 7B).*
c) *Transmission to fluid cooler fluid pipes/unions (Chapter 7B).*

Transmission fluid brown, or has burned smell

☐ Transmission fluid level low, or fluid in need of renewal (Chapter 1).

General gear selection problems

☐ Chapter 7B deals with checking and adjusting the selector linkage on automatic transmissions. The following are common problems which may be caused by a poorly-adjusted linkage:

a) *Engine starting in gears other than Park or Neutral.*

b) *Indicator on gear selector lever pointing to a gear other than the one actually being used.*
c) *Vehicle moves when in Park or Neutral.*
d) *Poor gearshift quality or erratic gear changes.*
e) *Refer to Chapter 7B for the selector linkage adjustment procedure.*

Transmission will not downshift (kickdown) with accelerator pedal fully depressed

☐ Low transmission fluid level (Chapter 1).
☐ Incorrect selector mechanism adjustment (Chapter 7B).

Engine will not start in any gear, or starts in gears other than Park or Neutral

☐ Incorrect starter/inhibitor switch adjustment (Chapter 7B).
☐ Incorrect selector mechanism adjustment (Chapter 7B).

Transmission slips, shifts roughly, is noisy, or has no drive in forward or reverse gears

☐ There are many probable causes for the above problems, but the home mechanic should be concerned with only one possibility - fluid level.
☐ Before taking the vehicle to a dealer or transmission specialist, check the fluid level and condition of the fluid as described in Chapter 1.
☐ Correct the fluid level as necessary, or change the fluid and filter if needed. If the problem persists, professional help will be necessary.

Driveshafts

Clicking or knocking noise on turns (at slow speed on full-lock)

☐ Lack of constant velocity joint lubricant (Chapter 8).
☐ Worn outer constant velocity joint (Chapter 8).

Vibration when accelerating or decelerating

☐ Worn inner constant velocity joint (Chapter 8).
☐ Bent or distorted driveshaft (Chapter 8).

Braking system

Note: *Before assuming that a brake problem exists, make sure that the tyres are in good condition and correctly inflated, that the front wheel alignment is correct and that the vehicle is not unevenly loaded. Apart from checking the condition of all pipe and hose connections, any faults occurring with the anti-lock braking system (ABS) should be referred to a Volvo dealer for diagnosis.*

Poor brake performance

- ☐ Air in hydraulic system - bleed the brakes (Chapter 9).
- ☐ Brake fluid contaminated - change fluid (Chapter 9).
- ☐ Seized or partially-seized brake caliper piston(s) (Chapter 9).
- ☐ Brake pads incorrectly fitted (Chapter 1 or 9).
- ☐ Incorrect grade of brake pads fitted (Chapter 1 or 9).
- ☐ Brake pads glazed - replace (Chapter 9).
- ☐ Automatic adjustment mechanism on rear brake shoes seized (Chapter 9).
- ☐ Brake pads or linings contaminated with oil or brake fluid (Chapter 1 or 9).

Vehicle pulls to one side under braking

- ☐ Worn, defective, damaged or contaminated front or rear brake pads/shoes on one side (Chapter 1).
- ☐ Seized or partially-seized front or rear brake caliper/wheel cylinder piston (Chapter 9).
- ☐ A mixture of brake pad/shoe lining materials fitted between sides (Chapter 1).
- ☐ Brake caliper mounting bolts loose (Chapter 9).
- ☐ Rear drum brake backplate mounting bolts loose (Chapter 9).
- ☐ Worn or damaged steering or suspension components (Chapter 10).

Noise (grinding or high-pitched squeal) when brakes applied

- ☐ Brake pad or shoe friction lining material worn down to metal backing (Chapter 1).
- ☐ Excessive corrosion of brake disc or drum - may be apparent after the vehicle has been standing for some time (Chapter 1).
- ☐ Foreign object (stone chipping, etc) trapped between brake disc and splash shield (Chapter 1).

Excessive brake pedal travel

- ☐ Inoperative rear drum brake self-adjust mechanism (Chapter 1).
- ☐ Faulty master cylinder (Chapter 9).
- ☐ Air in hydraulic system (Chapter 9).

Brake pedal feels spongy when depressed

- ☐ Air in hydraulic system (Chapter 9).
- ☐ Deteriorated flexible rubber brake hoses (Chapter 1 or 9).
- ☐ Master cylinder mounting nuts loose (Chapter 9).
- ☐ Faulty master cylinder (Chapter 9).

Excessive brake pedal effort required to stop vehicle

- ☐ Faulty vacuum servo unit (Chapter 9).
- ☐ Faulty brake servo vacuum hose (Chapter 9).
- ☐ Primary or secondary hydraulic circuit failure (Chapter 9).
- ☐ Seized brake caliper or wheel cylinder piston(s) (Chapter 9).
- ☐ Brake pads or brake shoes incorrectly fitted (Chapter 9).
- ☐ Incorrect grade of brake pads or brake shoes fitted (Chapter 9).
- ☐ Brake pads or brake shoe linings contaminated (Chapter 1).

Judder felt through brake pedal or steering wheel when braking

- ☐ Excessive run-out or distortion of discs or drums (Chapter 9).
- ☐ Brake pad or brake shoe linings worn (Chapter 1).
- ☐ Brake caliper or rear drum brake backplate mounting bolts loose (Chapter 9).
- ☐ Wear in suspension or steering components or mountings (Chapter 10).

Brakes binding

- ☐ Seized brake caliper or wheel cylinder piston(s) (Chapter 9).
- ☐ Incorrectly-adjusted handbrake mechanism or linkage (Chapter 1).
- ☐ Faulty master cylinder (Chapter 9).

Rear wheels locking under normal braking

- ☐ Rear brake shoe linings contaminated (Chapter 1).
- ☐ Faulty brake pressure regulating valve (Chapter 9).

Suspension and steering systems

Note: *Before diagnosing suspension or steering faults, be sure that the trouble is not due to incorrect tyre pressures, mixtures of tyre types or binding brakes.*

Vehicle pulls to one side

- ☐ Defective tyre (*Weekly checks*).
- ☐ Excessive wear in suspension or steering components (Chapter 10).
- ☐ Incorrect front wheel alignment (Chapter 10).
- ☐ Accident damage to steering or suspension components (Chapter 10).

Wheel wobble and vibration

- ☐ Front roadwheels out of balance (vibration felt mainly through the steering wheel) (Chapter 10).
- ☐ Rear roadwheels out of balance (vibration felt throughout the vehicle) (Chapter 10).
- ☐ Roadwheels damaged or distorted (Chapter 10).
- ☐ Faulty or damaged tyre (*Weekly checks*).
- ☐ Worn steering or suspension joints, bushes or components (Chapter 10).
- ☐ Wheel bolts loose (Chapter 1).

Excessive pitching during braking, and/or excessive roll when cornering

- ☐ Defective shock absorbers (Chapter 10).
- ☐ Broken or weak coil spring and/or suspension component (Chapter 10).
- ☐ Worn or damaged anti-roll bar or mountings (Chapter 10).

Wandering or general instability

- ☐ Incorrect front wheel alignment (Chapter 10).
- ☐ Worn steering or suspension joints, bushes or components (Chapter 10).
- ☐ Roadwheels out of balance (Chapter 10).
- ☐ Faulty or damaged tyre (*Weekly checks*).
- ☐ Wheel bolts loose (Chapter 1).
- ☐ Defective shock absorbers (Chapter 10).

Excessively-stiff steering

- ☐ Lack of steering gear lubricant (Chapter 10).
- ☐ Seized tie-rod end balljoint or suspension balljoint (Chapter 10).
- ☐ Broken or incorrectly-adjusted power steering pump drivebelt - where applicable (Chapter 1).
- ☐ Incorrect front wheel alignment (Chapter 10).
- ☐ Steering rack or column bent or damaged (Chapter 10).

Suspension and steering systems (continued)

Excessive play in steering

- [ ] Worn steering column universal joint(s) or intermediate coupling (Chapter 10).
- [ ] Worn steering tie-rod end balljoints (Chapter 10).
- [ ] Worn rack-and-pinion steering gear (Chapter 10).
- [ ] Worn steering or suspension joints, bushes or components (Chapter 10).

Lack of power assistance

- [ ] Broken or incorrectly-adjusted power steering pump drivebelt (Chapter 1).
- [ ] Incorrect power steering fluid level (Weekly checks).
- [ ] Restriction in power steering fluid hoses (Chapter 10).
- [ ] Faulty power steering pump (Chapter 10).
- [ ] Faulty rack-and-pinion steering gear (Chapter 10).

Tyre wear excessive

Tyres worn unevenly

- [ ] Tyres out of balance (Weekly checks).
- [ ] Damaged wheel rim (Weekly checks).
- [ ] Worn shock absorbers (Chapter 10).
- [ ] Faulty tyre (Weekly checks).

Tyres worn on inside or outside edges

- [ ] Tyres under-inflated (wear on both edges) (Weekly checks).
- [ ] Incorrect camber or castor angles (wear on one edge only) (Chapter 10).
- [ ] Worn steering or suspension joints, bushes or components (Chapter 10).
- [ ] Excessively-hard cornering.
- [ ] Accident damage.

Tyre treads exhibit feathered edges

- [ ] Incorrect toe setting (Chapter 10).

Tyres worn in centre of tread

- [ ] Tyres over-inflated (Weekly checks).

Tyres worn on inside and outside edges

- [ ] Tyres under-inflated (Chapter 1).

Electrical system

Note: For problems associated with the starting system, refer to the faults listed under Engine earlier in this Section.

Battery will not hold a charge more than a few days

- [ ] Battery defective internally (Chapter 5A).
- [ ] Battery electrolyte level low (Chapter 1).
- [ ] Battery terminal connections loose or corroded (Weekly checks).
- [ ] Alternator drivebelt worn or incorrectly adjusted (Chapter 1).
- [ ] Alternator not charging at correct output (Chapter 5A).
- [ ] Alternator or voltage regulator faulty (Chapter 5A).
- [ ] Short-circuit causing continual battery drain (Chapter 12).

Lights inoperative

- [ ] Bulb blown (Weekly checks or Chapter 12).
- [ ] Corrosion of bulb or bulbholder contacts (Chapter 12).
- [ ] Blown fuse (Weekly checks or Chapter 12).
- [ ] Faulty relay (Chapter 12).
- [ ] Broken, loose, or disconnected wiring (Chapter 12).
- [ ] Faulty switch (Chapter 12).

480 models - headlight motors inoperative

- [ ] Pattern (non-Volvo) sidelight bulbs fitted (Chapter 12).
- [ ] Bonnet lock microswitch faulty (Chapter 12).
- [ ] Headlight operating linkage seized (Chapter 12).

Ignition warning light remains illuminated with engine running

- [ ] Alternator drivebelt broken, worn, or incorrectly adjusted (Chapter 1).
- [ ] Alternator brushes worn, sticking, or dirty (Chapter 5A).
- [ ] Alternator brush springs weak or broken (Chapter 5A).
- [ ] Internal fault in alternator or voltage regulator (Chapter 5A).
- [ ] Broken, disconnected, or loose wiring in charging circuit (Chapter 5A or 12).

Ignition warning light fails to come on

- [ ] Warning light bulb blown (Chapter 12).
- [ ] Broken or disconnected wiring in warning light circuit (Chapter 5A or 12).
- [ ] Alternator faulty (Chapter 5A).

Instrument readings inaccurate or erratic

Instrument readings increase with engine speed

- [ ] Faulty instrument panel voltage stabiliser (Chapter 12).

Fuel or temperature gauge give no reading

- [ ] Faulty gauge sender unit (Chapter 3, 4A or 4B).
- [ ] Wiring open-circuit (Chapter 12).
- [ ] Faulty gauge (Chapter 12).

Fuel or temperature gauges give continuous maximum reading

- [ ] Faulty gauge sender unit (Chapter 3, 4A or 4B).
- [ ] Wiring short-circuit (Chapter 12).
- [ ] Faulty gauge (Chapter 12).

Horn inoperative or unsatisfactory in operation

Horn operates all the time

- [ ] Horn push either earthed or stuck down (Chapter 12).
- [ ] Horn cable to horn push earthed (Chapter 12).

Horn fails to operate

- [ ] Blown fuse (Weekly checks or Chapter 12).
- [ ] Cable or cable connections loose, broken or disconnected (Chapter 12).
- [ ] Faulty horn (Chapter 12).

Horn emits intermittent or unsatisfactory sound

- [ ] Cable connections loose (Chapter 12).
- [ ] Horn mountings loose (Chapter 12).
- [ ] Faulty horn (Chapter 12).

Wipers inoperative, or unsatisfactory in operation

Wipers fail to operate, or operate very slowly

- [ ] Wiper blades stuck to screen, or linkage seized or binding (Chapter 12).
- [ ] Blown fuse (Chapter 12).
- [ ] Cable or cable connections loose, broken or disconnected (Chapter 12).
- [ ] Faulty relay (Chapter 12).
- [ ] Faulty wiper motor (Chapter 12).

Wiper blades sweep too large/too small an area of glass

- [ ] Wiper arms incorrectly positioned on spindles (Chapter 1).
- [ ] Excessive wear of wiper linkage (Chapter 12).
- [ ] Wiper motor or linkage mountings loose or insecure (Chapter 12).

Wiper blades fail to clean the glass effectively

- [ ] Wiper blade rubbers worn or perished (*Weekly checks*).
- [ ] Wiper arm tension springs broken, or arm pivots seized (Chapter 1).
- [ ] Insufficient windscreen washer additive to adequately remove road film (*Weekly checks*).

Windscreen/tailgate washers inoperative, or unsatisfactory in operation

One or more washer jets inoperative

- [ ] Blocked washer jet (Chapter 12).
- [ ] Disconnected, kinked or restricted fluid hose (Chapter 12).
- [ ] Insufficient fluid in washer reservoir (*Weekly checks*).

Washer pump fails to operate

- [ ] Broken or disconnected wiring or connections (Chapter 12).
- [ ] Blown fuse (*Weekly checks* or Chapter 12).
- [ ] Faulty washer switch (Chapter 12).
- [ ] Faulty washer pump (Chapter 12).

Washer pump runs for some time before fluid is emitted

- [ ] Faulty one-way valve in fluid supply hose (Chapter 12).

Electric windows inoperative, or unsatisfactory in operation

Window glass will only move in one direction

- [ ] Faulty switch (Chapter 12).

Window glass slow to move

- [ ] Incorrectly-adjusted door glass guide channels (Chapter 11).
- [ ] Regulator seized or damaged, or in need of lubrication (Chapter 11).
- [ ] Door internal components or trim fouling regulator (Chapter 11).
- [ ] Faulty motor (Chapter 11).

Window glass fails to move

- [ ] Incorrectly-adjusted door glass guide channels (Chapter 11).
- [ ] Blown fuse (*Weekly checks* or Chapter 12).
- [ ] Faulty relay (Chapter 12).
- [ ] Broken or disconnected wiring or connections (Chapter 12).
- [ ] Faulty motor (Chapter 11).

Central locking system inoperative, or unsatisfactory in operation

Complete system failure

- [ ] Blown fuse (*Weekly checks* or Chapter 12).
- [ ] Faulty relay (Chapter 12).
- [ ] Broken or disconnected wiring or connections (Chapter 12).

Latch locks but will not unlock, or unlocks but will not lock

- [ ] Faulty microswitch/master switch (Chapter 11).
- [ ] Broken or disconnected latch operating rods or levers (Chapter 11).
- [ ] Faulty relay (Chapter 12).

One solenoid/motor fails to operate

- [ ] Broken or disconnected wiring or connections (Chapter 12).
- [ ] Faulty solenoid/motor (Chapter 11).
- [ ] Broken, binding or disconnected latch operating rods or levers (Chapter 11).
- [ ] Fault in door latch (Chapter 11).

A

ABS (Anti-lock brake system) A system, usually electronically controlled, that senses incipient wheel lockup during braking and relieves hydraulic pressure at wheels that are about to skid.

Air bag An inflatable bag hidden in the steering wheel (driver's side) or the dash or glovebox (passenger side). In a head-on collision, the bags inflate, preventing the driver and front passenger from being thrown forward into the steering wheel or windscreen.

Air cleaner A metal or plastic housing, containing a filter element, which removes dust and dirt from the air being drawn into the engine.

Air filter element The actual filter in an air cleaner system, usually manufactured from pleated paper and requiring renewal at regular intervals.

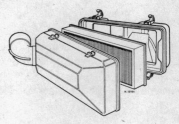

Air filter

Allen key A hexagonal wrench which fits into a recessed hexagonal hole.

Alligator clip A long-nosed spring-loaded metal clip with meshing teeth. Used to make temporary electrical connections.

Alternator A component in the electrical system which converts mechanical energy from a drivebelt into electrical energy to charge the battery and to operate the starting system, ignition system and electrical accessories.

Alternator (exploded view)

Ampere (amp) A unit of measurement for the flow of electric current. One amp is the amount of current produced by one volt acting through a resistance of one ohm.

Anaerobic sealer A substance used to prevent bolts and screws from loosening. Anaerobic means that it does not require oxygen for activation. The Loctite brand is widely used.

Antifreeze A substance (usually ethylene glycol) mixed with water, and added to a vehicle's cooling system, to prevent freezing of the coolant in winter. Antifreeze also contains chemicals to inhibit corrosion and the formation of rust and other deposits that

would tend to clog the radiator and coolant passages and reduce cooling efficiency.

Anti-seize compound A coating that reduces the risk of seizing on fasteners that are subjected to high temperatures, such as exhaust manifold bolts and nuts.

Anti-seize compound

Asbestos A natural fibrous mineral with great heat resistance, commonly used in the composition of brake friction materials. Asbestos is a health hazard and the dust created by brake systems should never be inhaled or ingested.

Axle A shaft on which a wheel revolves, or which revolves with a wheel. Also, a solid beam that connects the two wheels at one end of the vehicle. An axle which also transmits power to the wheels is known as a live axle.

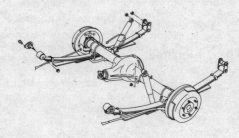

Axle assembly

Axleshaft A single rotating shaft, on either side of the differential, which delivers power from the final drive assembly to the drive wheels. Also called a driveshaft or a halfshaft.

B

Ball bearing An anti-friction bearing consisting of a hardened inner and outer race with hardened steel balls between two races.

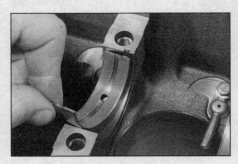

Bearing

Bearing The curved surface on a shaft or in a bore, or the part assembled into either, that permits relative motion between them with minimum wear and friction.

Big-end bearing The bearing in the end of the connecting rod that's attached to the crankshaft.

Bleed nipple A valve on a brake wheel cylinder, caliper or other hydraulic component that is opened to purge the hydraulic system of air. Also called a bleed screw.

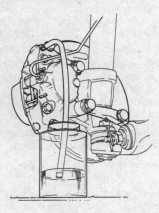

Brake bleeding

Brake bleeding Procedure for removing air from lines of a hydraulic brake system.

Brake disc The component of a disc brake that rotates with the wheels.

Brake drum The component of a drum brake that rotates with the wheels.

Brake linings The friction material which contacts the brake disc or drum to retard the vehicle's speed. The linings are bonded or riveted to the brake pads or shoes.

Brake pads The replaceable friction pads that pinch the brake disc when the brakes are applied. Brake pads consist of a friction material bonded or riveted to a rigid backing plate.

Brake shoe The crescent-shaped carrier to which the brake linings are mounted and which forces the lining against the rotating drum during braking.

Braking systems For more information on braking systems, consult the *Haynes Automotive Brake Manual*.

Breaker bar A long socket wrench handle providing greater leverage.

Bulkhead The insulated partition between the engine and the passenger compartment.

C

Caliper The non-rotating part of a disc-brake assembly that straddles the disc and carries the brake pads. The caliper also contains the hydraulic components that cause the pads to pinch the disc when the brakes are applied. A caliper is also a measuring tool that can be set to measure inside or outside dimensions of an object.

Camshaft A rotating shaft on which a series of cam lobes operate the valve mechanisms. The camshaft may be driven by gears, by sprockets and chain or by sprockets and a belt.

Canister A container in an evaporative emission control system; contains activated charcoal granules to trap vapours from the fuel system.

Canister

Carburettor A device which mixes fuel with air in the proper proportions to provide a desired power output from a spark ignition internal combustion engine.

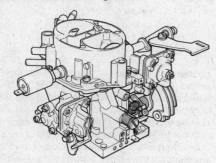

Carburettor

Castellated Resembling the parapets along the top of a castle wall. For example, a castellated balljoint stud nut.

Castellated nut

Castor In wheel alignment, the backward or forward tilt of the steering axis. Castor is positive when the steering axis is inclined rearward at the top.

Catalytic converter A silencer-like device in the exhaust system which converts certain pollutants in the exhaust gases into less harmful substances.

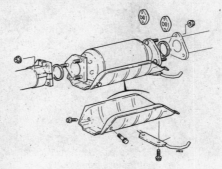

Catalytic converter

Circlip A ring-shaped clip used to prevent endwise movement of cylindrical parts and shafts. An internal circlip is installed in a groove in a housing; an external circlip fits into a groove on the outside of a cylindrical piece such as a shaft.

Clearance The amount of space between two parts. For example, between a piston and a cylinder, between a bearing and a journal, etc.

Coil spring A spiral of elastic steel found in various sizes throughout a vehicle, for example as a springing medium in the suspension and in the valve train.

Compression Reduction in volume, and increase in pressure and temperature, of a gas, caused by squeezing it into a smaller space.

Compression ratio The relationship between cylinder volume when the piston is at top dead centre and cylinder volume when the piston is at bottom dead centre.

Constant velocity (CV) joint A type of universal joint that cancels out vibrations caused by driving power being transmitted through an angle.

Core plug A disc or cup-shaped metal device inserted in a hole in a casting through which core was removed when the casting was formed. Also known as a freeze plug or expansion plug.

Crankcase The lower part of the engine block in which the crankshaft rotates.

Crankshaft The main rotating member, or shaft, running the length of the crankcase, with offset "throws" to which the connecting rods are attached.

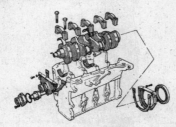

Crankshaft assembly

Crocodile clip See Alligator clip

D

Diagnostic code Code numbers obtained by accessing the diagnostic mode of an engine management computer. This code can be used to determine the area in the system where a malfunction may be located.

Disc brake A brake design incorporating a rotating disc onto which brake pads are squeezed. The resulting friction converts the energy of a moving vehicle into heat.

Double-overhead cam (DOHC) An engine that uses two overhead camshafts, usually one for the intake valves and one for the exhaust valves.

Drivebelt(s) The belt(s) used to drive accessories such as the alternator, water pump, power steering pump, air conditioning compressor, etc. off the crankshaft pulley.

Accessory drivebelts

Driveshaft Any shaft used to transmit motion. Commonly used when referring to the axleshafts on a front wheel drive vehicle.

Driveshaft

Drum brake A type of brake using a drum-shaped metal cylinder attached to the inner surface of the wheel. When the brake pedal is pressed, curved brake shoes with friction linings press against the inside of the drum to slow or stop the vehicle.

Drum brake assembly

E

EGR valve A valve used to introduce exhaust gases into the intake air stream.

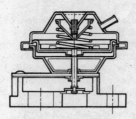

EGR valve

Electronic control unit (ECU) A computer which controls (for instance) ignition and fuel injection systems, or an anti-lock braking system. For more information refer to the *Haynes Automotive Electrical and Electronic Systems Manual.*

Electronic Fuel Injection (EFI) A computer controlled fuel system that distributes fuel through an injector located in each intake port of the engine.

Emergency brake A braking system, independent of the main hydraulic system, that can be used to slow or stop the vehicle if the primary brakes fail, or to hold the vehicle stationary even though the brake pedal isn't depressed. It usually consists of a hand lever that actuates either front or rear brakes mechanically through a series of cables and linkages. Also known as a handbrake or parking brake.

Endfloat The amount of lengthwise movement between two parts. As applied to a crankshaft, the distance that the crankshaft can move forward and back in the cylinder block.

Engine management system (EMS) A computer controlled system which manages the fuel injection and the ignition systems in an integrated fashion.

Exhaust manifold A part with several passages through which exhaust gases leave the engine combustion chambers and enter the exhaust pipe.

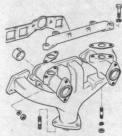

Exhaust manifold

F

Fan clutch A viscous (fluid) drive coupling device which permits variable engine fan speeds in relation to engine speeds.

Feeler blade A thin strip or blade of hardened steel, ground to an exact thickness, used to check or measure clearances between parts.

Feeler blade

Firing order The order in which the engine cylinders fire, or deliver their power strokes, beginning with the number one cylinder.

Flywheel A heavy spinning wheel in which energy is absorbed and stored by means of momentum. On cars, the flywheel is attached to the crankshaft to smooth out firing impulses.

Free play The amount of travel before any action takes place. The "looseness" in a linkage, or an assembly of parts, between the initial application of force and actual movement. For example, the distance the brake pedal moves before the pistons in the master cylinder are actuated.

Fuse An electrical device which protects a circuit against accidental overload. The typical fuse contains a soft piece of metal which is calibrated to melt at a predetermined current flow (expressed as amps) and break the circuit.

Fusible link A circuit protection device consisting of a conductor surrounded by heat-resistant insulation. The conductor is smaller than the wire it protects, so it acts as the weakest link in the circuit. Unlike a blown fuse, a failed fusible link must frequently be cut from the wire for replacement.

G

Gap The distance the spark must travel in jumping from the centre electrode to the side

Adjusting spark plug gap

electrode in a spark plug. Also refers to the spacing between the points in a contact breaker assembly in a conventional points-type ignition, or to the distance between the reluctor or rotor and the pickup coil in an electronic ignition.

Gasket Any thin, soft material - usually cork, cardboard, asbestos or soft metal - installed between two metal surfaces to ensure a good seal. For instance, the cylinder head gasket seals the joint between the block and the cylinder head.

Gasket

Gauge An instrument panel display used to monitor engine conditions. A gauge with a movable pointer on a dial or a fixed scale is an analogue gauge. A gauge with a numerical readout is called a digital gauge.

H

Halfshaft A rotating shaft that transmits power from the final drive unit to a drive wheel, usually when referring to a live rear axle.

Harmonic balancer A device designed to reduce torsion or twisting vibration in the crankshaft. May be incorporated in the crankshaft pulley. Also known as a vibration damper.

Hone An abrasive tool for correcting small irregularities or differences in diameter in an engine cylinder, brake cylinder, etc.

Hydraulic tappet A tappet that utilises hydraulic pressure from the engine's lubrication system to maintain zero clearance (constant contact with both camshaft and valve stem). Automatically adjusts to variation in valve stem length. Hydraulic tappets also reduce valve noise.

I

Ignition timing The moment at which the spark plug fires, usually expressed in the number of crankshaft degrees before the piston reaches the top of its stroke.

Inlet manifold A tube or housing with passages through which flows the air-fuel mixture (carburettor vehicles and vehicles with throttle body injection) or air only (port fuel-injected vehicles) to the port openings in the cylinder head.

J

Jump start Starting the engine of a vehicle with a discharged or weak battery by attaching jump leads from the weak battery to a charged or helper battery.

L

Load Sensing Proportioning Valve (LSPV) A brake hydraulic system control valve that works like a proportioning valve, but also takes into consideration the amount of weight carried by the rear axle.

Locknut A nut used to lock an adjustment nut, or other threaded component, in place. For example, a locknut is employed to keep the adjusting nut on the rocker arm in position.

Lockwasher A form of washer designed to prevent an attaching nut from working loose.

M

MacPherson strut A type of front suspension system devised by Earle MacPherson at Ford of England. In its original form, a simple lateral link with the anti-roll bar creates the lower control arm. A long strut - an integral coil spring and shock absorber - is mounted between the body and the steering knuckle. Many modern so-called MacPherson strut systems use a conventional lower A-arm and don't rely on the anti-roll bar for location.

Multimeter An electrical test instrument with the capability to measure voltage, current and resistance.

N

NOx Oxides of Nitrogen. A common toxic pollutant emitted by petrol and diesel engines at higher temperatures.

O

Ohm The unit of electrical resistance. One volt applied to a resistance of one ohm will produce a current of one amp.

Ohmmeter An instrument for measuring electrical resistance.

O-ring A type of sealing ring made of a special rubber-like material; in use, the O-ring is compressed into a groove to provide the sealing action.

O-ring

Overhead cam (ohc) engine An engine with the camshaft(s) located on top of the cylinder head(s).

Overhead valve (ohv) engine An engine with the valves located in the cylinder head, but with the camshaft located in the engine block.

Oxygen sensor A device installed in the engine exhaust manifold, which senses the oxygen content in the exhaust and converts this information into an electric current. Also called a Lambda sensor.

P

Phillips screw A type of screw head having a cross instead of a slot for a corresponding type of screwdriver.

Plastigage A thin strip of plastic thread, available in different sizes, used for measuring clearances. For example, a strip of Plastigage is laid across a bearing journal. The parts are assembled and dismantled; the width of the crushed strip indicates the clearance between journal and bearing.

Plastigage

Propeller shaft The long hollow tube with universal joints at both ends that carries power from the transmission to the differential on front-engined rear wheel drive vehicles.

Proportioning valve A hydraulic control valve which limits the amount of pressure to the rear brakes during panic stops to prevent wheel lock-up.

R

Rack-and-pinion steering A steering system with a pinion gear on the end of the steering shaft that mates with a rack (think of a geared wheel opened up and laid flat). When the steering wheel is turned, the pinion turns, moving the rack to the left or right. This movement is transmitted through the track rods to the steering arms at the wheels.

Radiator A liquid-to-air heat transfer device designed to reduce the temperature of the coolant in an internal combustion engine cooling system.

Refrigerant Any substance used as a heat transfer agent in an air-conditioning system. R-12 has been the principle refrigerant for many years; recently, however, manufacturers have begun using R-134a, a non-CFC substance that is considered less harmful to the ozone in the upper atmosphere.

Rocker arm A lever arm that rocks on a shaft or pivots on a stud. In an overhead valve engine, the rocker arm converts the upward movement of the pushrod into a downward movement to open a valve.

Rotor In a distributor, the rotating device inside the cap that connects the centre electrode and the outer terminals as it turns, distributing the high voltage from the coil secondary winding to the proper spark plug. Also, that part of an alternator which rotates inside the stator. Also, the rotating assembly of a turbocharger, including the compressor wheel, shaft and turbine wheel.

Runout The amount of wobble (in-and-out movement) of a gear or wheel as it's rotated. The amount a shaft rotates "out-of-true." The out-of-round condition of a rotating part.

S

Sealant A liquid or paste used to prevent leakage at a joint. Sometimes used in conjunction with a gasket.

Sealed beam lamp An older headlight design which integrates the reflector, lens and filaments into a hermetically-sealed one-piece unit. When a filament burns out or the lens cracks, the entire unit is simply replaced.

Serpentine drivebelt A single, long, wide accessory drivebelt that's used on some newer vehicles to drive all the accessories, instead of a series of smaller, shorter belts. Serpentine drivebelts are usually tensioned by an automatic tensioner.

Serpentine drivebelt

Shim Thin spacer, commonly used to adjust the clearance or relative positions between two parts. For example, shims inserted into or under bucket tappets control valve clearances. Clearance is adjusted by changing the thickness of the shim.

Slide hammer A special puller that screws into or hooks onto a component such as a shaft or bearing; a heavy sliding handle on the shaft bottoms against the end of the shaft to knock the component free.

Sprocket A tooth or projection on the periphery of a wheel, shaped to engage with a chain or drivebelt. Commonly used to refer to the sprocket wheel itself.

Starter inhibitor switch On vehicles with an automatic transmission, a switch that prevents starting if the vehicle is not in Neutral or Park.

Strut See MacPherson strut.

T

Tappet A cylindrical component which transmits motion from the cam to the valve stem, either directly or via a pushrod and rocker arm. Also called a cam follower.

Thermostat A heat-controlled valve that regulates the flow of coolant between the cylinder block and the radiator, so maintaining optimum engine operating temperature. A thermostat is also used in some air cleaners in which the temperature is regulated.

Thrust bearing The bearing in the clutch assembly that is moved in to the release levers by clutch pedal action to disengage the clutch. Also referred to as a release bearing.

Timing belt A toothed belt which drives the camshaft. Serious engine damage may result if it breaks in service.

Timing chain A chain which drives the camshaft.

Toe-in The amount the front wheels are closer together at the front than at the rear. On rear wheel drive vehicles, a slight amount of toe-in is usually specified to keep the front wheels running parallel on the road by offsetting other forces that tend to spread the wheels apart.

Toe-out The amount the front wheels are closer together at the rear than at the front. On front wheel drive vehicles, a slight amount of toe-out is usually specified.

Tools For full information on choosing and using tools, refer to the *Haynes Automotive Tools Manual*.

Tracer A stripe of a second colour applied to a wire insulator to distinguish that wire from another one with the same colour insulator.

Tune-up A process of accurate and careful adjustments and parts replacement to obtain the best possible engine performance.

Turbocharger A centrifugal device, driven by exhaust gases, that pressurises the intake air. Normally used to increase the power output from a given engine displacement, but can also be used primarily to reduce exhaust emissions (as on VW's "Umwelt" Diesel engine).

U

Universal joint or U-joint A double-pivoted connection for transmitting power from a driving to a driven shaft through an angle. A U-joint consists of two Y-shaped yokes and a cross-shaped member called the spider.

V

Valve A device through which the flow of liquid, gas, vacuum, or loose material in bulk may be started, stopped, or regulated by a movable part that opens, shuts, or partially obstructs one or more ports or passageways. A valve is also the movable part of such a device.

Valve clearance The clearance between the valve tip (the end of the valve stem) and the rocker arm or tappet. The valve clearance is measured when the valve is closed.

Vernier caliper A precision measuring instrument that measures inside and outside dimensions. Not quite as accurate as a micrometer, but more convenient.

Viscosity The thickness of a liquid or its resistance to flow.

Volt A unit for expressing electrical "pressure" in a circuit. One volt that will produce a current of one ampere through a resistance of one ohm.

W

Welding Various processes used to join metal items by heating the areas to be joined to a molten state and fusing them together. For more information refer to the *Haynes Automotive Welding Manual*.

Wiring diagram A drawing portraying the components and wires in a vehicle's electrical system, using standardised symbols. For more information refer to the *Haynes Automotive Electrical and Electronic Systems Manual*.

Note: *References throughout this index are in the form* **"Chapter number" • "Page number"**

Haynes Manuals – The Complete List

ALFA ROMEO
Title	Book No.
Alfa Romeo Alfasud/Sprint (74 - 88) up to F	0292
Alfa Romeo Alfetta (73 - 87) up to E	0531

AUDI
Title	Book No.
Audi 80 (72 - Feb 79) up to T	0207
Audi 80, 90 (79 - Oct 86) up to D & Coupe (81 - Nov 88) up to F	0605
Audi 80, 90 (Oct 86 - 90) D to H & Coupe (Nov 88 - 90) F to H	1491
Audi 100 (Oct 82 - 90) up to H & 200 (Feb 84 - Oct 89) A to G	0907
Audi 100 & A6 Petrol & Diesel (May 91 - May 97) H to P	3504
Audi A4 (95 - Feb 00) M to V	3575

AUSTIN
Title	Book No.
Austin A35 & A40 (56 - 67) *	0118
Austin Allegro 1100, 1300, 1.0, 1.1 & 1.3 (73 - 82)*	0164
Austin Healey 100/6 & 3000 (56 - 68) *	0049
Austin/MG/Rover Maestro 1.3 & 1.6 (83 - May 95) up to M	0922
Austin/MG Metro (80 - May 90) up to G	0718
Austin/Rover Montego 1.3 & 1.6 (84 - 94) A to L	1066
Austin/MG/Rover Montego 2.0 (84 - 95) A to M	1067
Mini (59 - 69) up to H	0527
Mini (69 - Oct 96) up to P	0646
Austin/Rover 2.0 litre Diesel Engine (86 - 93) C to L	1857

BEDFORD
Title	Book No.
Bedford CF (69 - 87) up to E	0163
Bedford/Vauxhall Rascal & Suzuki Supercarry (86 - Oct 94) C to M	3015

BMW
Title	Book No.
BMW 1500, 1502, 1600, 1602, 2000 & 2002 (59 - 77)*	0240
BMW 316, 320 & 320i (4-cyl) (75 - Feb 83) up to Y	0276
BMW 320, 320i, 323i & 325i (6-cyl) (Oct 77 - Sept 87) up to E	0815
BMW 3-Series (Apr 91 - 96) H to N	3210
BMW 3- & 5-Series (sohc) (81 - 91) up to J	1948
BMW 520i & 525e (Oct 81 - June 88) up to E	1560
BMW 525, 528 & 528i (73 - Sept 81) up to X	0632

CITROËN
Title	Book No.
Citroën 2CV, Ami & Dyane (67 - 90) up to H	0196
Citroën AX Petrol & Diesel (87 - 97) D to P	3014
Citroën BX (83 - 94) A to L	0908
Citroën C15 Van Petrol & Diesel (89 - Oct 98) F to S	3509
Citroën CX (75 - 88) up to F	0528
Citroën Saxo Petrol & Diesel (96 - 01) N to X	3506
Citroën Visa (79 - 88) up to F	0620
Citroën Xantia Petrol & Diesel (93 - 98) K to S	3082
Citroën XM Petrol & Diesel (89 - 00) G to X	3451
Citroën Xsara Petrol & Diesel (97 - Sept 00) R to W	3751
Citroën ZX Diesel (91 - 98) J to S	1922
Citroën ZX Petrol (91 - 98) H to S	1881
Citroën 1.7 & 1.9 litre Diesel Engine (84 - 96) A to N	1379

FIAT
Title	Book No.
Fiat 126 (73 - 87) *	0305
Fiat 500 (57 - 73) up to M	0090
Fiat Bravo & Brava (95 - 00) N to W	3572
Fiat Cinquecento (93 - 98) K to R	3501
Fiat Panda (81 - 95) up to M	0793
Fiat Punto Petrol & Diesel (94 - Oct 99) L to V	3251
Fiat Regata (84 - 88) A to F	1167
Fiat Tipo (88 - 91) E to J	1625
Fiat Uno (83 - 95) up to M	0923
Fiat X1/9 (74 - 89) up to G	0273

FORD
Title	Book No.
Ford Anglia (59 - 68) *	0001
Ford Capri II (& III) 1.6 & 2.0 (74 - 87) up to E	0283
Ford Capri II (& III) 2.8 & 3.0 (74 - 87) up to E	1309
Ford Cortina Mk III 1300 & 1600 (70 - 76) *	0070
Ford Cortina Mk IV (& V) 1.6 & 2.0 (76 - 83) *	0343
Ford Cortina Mk IV (& V) 2.3 V6 (77 - 83) *	0426
Ford Escort Mk I 1100 & 1300 (68 - 74) *	0171
Ford Escort Mk I Mexico, RS 1600 & RS 2000 (70 - 74)*	0139
Ford Escort Mk II Mexico, RS 1800 & RS 2000 (75 - 80)*	0735
Ford Escort (75 - Aug 80) *	0280
Ford Escort (Sept 80 - Sept 90) up to H	0686
Ford Escort & Orion (Sept 90 - 00) H to X	1737
Ford Fiesta (76 - Aug 83) up to Y	0334
Ford Fiesta (Aug 83 - Feb 89) A to F	1030
Ford Fiesta (Feb 89 - Oct 95) F to N	1595
Ford Fiesta (Oct 95 - 01) N-reg. onwards	3397
Ford Focus (98 - 01) S to Y	3759
Ford Granada (Sept 77 - Feb 85) up to B	0481
Ford Granada & Scorpio (Mar 85 - 94) B to M	1245
Ford Ka (96 - 02) P-reg. onwards	3570
Ford Mondeo Petrol (93 - 99) K to T	1923
Ford Mondeo Diesel (93 - 96) L to N	3465
Ford Orion (83 - Sept 90) up to H	1009
Ford Sierra 4 cyl. (82 - 93) up to K	0903
Ford Sierra V6 (82 - 91) up to J	0904
Ford Transit Petrol (Mk 2) (78 - Jan 86) up to C	0719
Ford Transit Petrol (Mk 3) (Feb 86 - 89) C to G	1468
Ford Transit Diesel (Feb 86 - 99) C to T	3019
Ford 1.6 & 1.8 litre Diesel Engine (84 - 96) A to N	1172
Ford 2.1, 2.3 & 2.5 litre Diesel Engine (77 - 90) up to H	1606

FREIGHT ROVER
Title	Book No.
Freight Rover Sherpa (74 - 87) up to E	0463

HILLMAN
Title	Book No.
Hillman Avenger (70 - 82) up to Y	0037
Hillman Imp (63 - 76) *	0022

HONDA
Title	Book No.
Honda Accord (76 - Feb 84) up to A	0351
Honda Civic (Feb 84 - Oct 87) A to E	1226
Honda Civic (Nov 91 - 96) J to N	3199

HYUNDAI
Title	Book No.
Hyundai Pony (85 - 94) C to M	3398

JAGUAR
Title	Book No.
Jaguar E Type (61 - 72) up to L	0140
Jaguar MkI & II, 240 & 340 (55 - 69) *	0098
Jaguar XJ6, XJ & Sovereign; Daimler Sovereign (68 - Oct 86) up to D	0242
Jaguar XJ6 & Sovereign (Oct 86 - Sept 94) D to M	3261
Jaguar XJ12, XJS & Sovereign; Daimler Double Six (72 - 88) up to F	0478

JEEP
Title	Book No.
Jeep Cherokee Petrol (93 - 96) K to N	1943

LADA
Title	Book No.
Lada 1200, 1300, 1500 & 1600 (74 - 91) up to J	0413
Lada Samara (87 - 91) D to J	1610

LAND ROVER
Title	Book No.
Land Rover 90, 110 & Defender Diesel (83 - 95) up to N	3017
Land Rover Discovery Petrol & Diesel (89 - 98) G to S	3016
Land Rover Series IIA & III Diesel (58 - 85) up to C	0529
Land Rover Series II, IIA & III Petrol (58 - 85) up to C	0314

MAZDA
Title	Book No.
Mazda 323 (Mar 81 - Oct 89) up to G	1608
Mazda 323 (Oct 89 - 98) G to R	3455
Mazda 626 (May 83 - Sept 87) up to E	0929
Mazda B-1600, B-1800 & B-2000 Pick-up (72 - 88) up to F	0267
Mazda RX-7 (79 - 85) *	0460

MERCEDES-BENZ
Title	Book No.
Mercedes-Benz 190, 190E & 190D Petrol & Diesel (83 - 93) A to L	3450
Mercedes-Benz 200, 240, 300 Diesel (Oct 76 - 85) up to C	1114
Mercedes-Benz 250 & 280 (68 - 72) up to L	0346
Mercedes-Benz 250 & 280 (123 Series) (Oct 76 - 84) up to B	0677
Mercedes-Benz 124 Series (85 - Aug 93) C to K	3253
Mercedes-Benz C-Class Petrol & Diesel (93 - Aug 00) L to W	3511

MG
Title	Book No.
MGA (55 - 62) *	0475
MGB (62 - 80) up to W	0111
MG Midget & AH Sprite (58 - 80) up to W	0265

MITSUBISHI
Title	Book No.
Mitsubishi Shogun & L200 Pick-Ups (83 - 94) up to M	1944

MORRIS
Title	Book No.
Morris Ital 1.3 (80 - 84) up to B	0705
Morris Minor 1000 (56 - 71) up to K	0024

NISSAN
Title	Book No.
Nissan Bluebird (May 84 - Mar 86) A to C	1223
Nissan Bluebird (Mar 86 - 90) C to H	1473
Nissan Cherry (Sept 82 - 86) up to D	1031
Nissan Micra (83 - Jan 93) up to K	0931
Nissan Micra (93 - 99) K to T	3254
Nissan Primera (90 - Aug 99) H to T	1851
Nissan Stanza (82 - 86) up to D	0824
Nissan Sunny (May 82 - Oct 86) up to D	0895
Nissan Sunny (Oct 86 - Mar 91) D to H	1378
Nissan Sunny (Apr 91 - 95) H to N	3219

OPEL
Title	Book No.
Opel Ascona & Manta (B Series) (Sept 75 - 88) up to F	0316
Opel Ascona (81 - 88) (Not available in UK see Vauxhall Cavalier 0812)	3215
Opel Astra (Oct 91 - Feb 98) (Not available in UK see Vauxhall Astra 1832)	3156
Opel Astra & Zafira Diesel (Feb 98 - Sept 00) (See Astra & Zafira Diesel Book No. 3797)	
Opel Astra & Zafira Petrol (Feb 98 - Sept 00) (See Vauxhall/Opel Astra & Zafira Petrol Book No. 3758)	
Opel Calibra (90 - 98) (See Vauxhall/Opel Calibra Book No. 3502)	
Opel Corsa (83 - Mar 93) (Not available in UK see Vauxhall Nova 0909)	3160
Opel Corsa (Mar 93 - 97) (Not available in UK see Vauxhall Corsa 1985)	3159
Opel Frontera Petrol & Diesel (91 - 98) (See Vauxhall/Opel Frontera Book No. 3454)	
Opel Kadett (Nov 79 - Oct 84) up to B	0634
Opel Kadett (Oct 84 - Oct 91) (Not available in UK see Vauxhall Astra & Belmont 1136)	3196
Opel Omega & Senator (86 - 94) (Not available in UK see Vauxhall Carlton & Senator 1469)	3157
Opel Omega (94 - 99) (See Vauxhall/Opel Omega Book No. 3510)	
Opel Rekord (Feb 78 - Oct 86) up to D	0543
Opel Vectra (Oct 88 - Oct 95) (Not available in UK see Vauxhall Cavalier 1570)	3158
Opel Vectra Petrol & Diesel (95 - 98) (Not available in UK see Vauxhall Vectra 3396)	3523

PEUGEOT
Title	Book No.
Peugeot 106 Petrol & Diesel (91 - 01) J to X	1882
Peugeot 205 Petrol (83 - 97) A to P	0932
Peugeot 206 Petrol and Diesel (98 - 01) S to X	3757
Peugeot 305 (78 - 89) up to G	0538

* Classic reprint

Title	Book No.
Peugeot 306 Petrol & Diesel (93 - 99) K to T	3073
Peugeot 309 (86 - 93) C to K	1266
Peugeot 405 Petrol (88 - 97) E to P	1559
Peugeot 405 Diesel (88 - 97) E to P	3198
Peugeot 406 Petrol & Diesel (96 - 97) N to R	3394
Peugeot 505 (79 - 89) up to G	0762
Peugeot 1.7/1.8 & 1.9 litre Diesel Engine (82 - 96) up to N	0950
Peugeot 2.0, 2.1, 2.3 & 2.5 litre Diesel Engines (74 - 90) up to H	1607

PORSCHE

Title	Book No.
Porsche 911 (65 - 85) up to C	0264
Porsche 924 & 924 Turbo (76 - 85) up to C	0397

PROTON

Title	Book No.
Proton (89 - 97) F to P	3255

RANGE ROVER

Title	Book No.
Range Rover V8 (70 - Oct 92) up to K	0606

RELIANT

Title	Book No.
Reliant Robin & Kitten (73 - 83) up to A	0436

RENAULT

Title	Book No.
Renault 4 (61 - 86) *	0072
Renault 5 (Feb 85 - 96) B to N	1219
Renault 9 & 11 (82 - 89) up to F	0822
Renault 18 (79 - 86) up to D	0598
Renault 19 Petrol (89 - 94) F to M	1646
Renault 19 Diesel (89 - 96) F to N	1946
Renault 21 (86 - 94) C to M	1397
Renault 25 (84 - 92) B to K	1228
Renault Clio Petrol (91 - May 98) H to R	1853
Renault Clio Diesel (91 - June 96) H to N	3031
Renault Clio Petrol & Diesel (May 98 - May 01) R to Y	3906
Renault Espace Petrol & Diesel (85 - 96) C to N	3197
Renault Fuego (80 - 86) *	0764
Renault Laguna Petrol & Diesel (94 - 00) L to W	3252
Renault Mégane & Scénic Petrol & Diesel (96 - 98) N to R	3395
Renault Mégane & Scénic (Apr 99 - 02) T-reg onwards	3916

ROVER

Title	Book No.
Rover 213 & 216 (84 - 89) A to G	1116
Rover 214 & 414 (89 - 96) G to N	1689
Rover 216 & 416 (89 - 96) G to N	1830
Rover 211, 214, 216, 218 & 220 Petrol & Diesel (Dec 95 - 98) N to R	3399
Rover 414, 416 & 420 Petrol & Diesel (May 95 - 98) M to R	3453
Rover 618, 620 & 623 (93 - 97) K to P	3257
Rover 820, 825 & 827 (86 - 95) D to N	1380
Rover 3500 (76 - 87) up to E	0365
Rover Metro, 111 & 114 (May 90 - 98) G to S	1711

SAAB

Title	Book No.
Saab 90, 99 & 900 (79 - Oct 93) up to L	0765
Saab 95 & 96 (66 - 76) *	0198
Saab 99 (69 - 79) *	0247
Saab 900 (Oct 93 - 98) L to R	3512
Saab 9000 (4-cyl) (85 - 98) C to S	1686

SEAT

Title	Book No.
Seat Ibiza & Cordoba Petrol & Diesel (Oct 93 - Oct 99) L to V	3571
Seat Ibiza & Malaga (85 - 92) B to K	1609

SKODA

Title	Book No.
Skoda Estelle (77 - 89) up to G	0604
Skoda Favorit (89 - 96) F to N	1801
Skoda Felicia Petrol & Diesel (95 - 01) M to X	3505

SUBARU

Title	Book No.
Subaru 1600 & 1800 (Nov 79 - 90) up to H	0995

SUNBEAM

Title	Book No.
Sunbeam Alpine, Rapier & H120 (67 - 76) *	0051

SUZUKI

Title	Book No.
Suzuki SJ Series, Samurai & Vitara (4-cyl) (82 - 97) up to P	1942
Suzuki Supercarry & Bedford/Vauxhall Rascal (86 - Oct 94) C to M	3015

TALBOT

Title	Book No.
Talbot Alpine, Solara, Minx & Rapier (75 - 86) up to D	0337
Talbot Horizon (78 - 86) up to D	0473
Talbot Samba (82 - 86) up to D	0823

TOYOTA

Title	Book No.
Toyota Carina E (May 92 - 97) J to P	3256
Toyota Corolla (Sept 83 - Sept 87) A to E	1024
Toyota Corolla (80 - 85) up to C	0683
Toyota Corolla (Sept 87 - Aug 92) E to K	1683
Toyota Corolla (Aug 92 - 97) K to P	3259
Toyota Hi-Ace & Hi-Lux (69 - Oct 83) up to A	0304

TRIUMPH

Title	Book No.
Triumph Acclaim (81 - 84) *	0792
Triumph GT6 & Vitesse (62 - 74) *	0112
Triumph Herald (59 - 71) *	0010
Triumph Spitfire (62 - 81) up to X	0113
Triumph Stag (70 - 78) up to T	0441
Triumph TR2, TR3, TR3A, TR4 & TR4A (52 - 67)*	0028
Triumph TR5 & 6 (67 - 75) *	0031
Triumph TR7 (75 - 82) *	0322

VAUXHALL

Title	Book No.
Vauxhall Astra (80 - Oct 84) up to B	0635
Vauxhall Astra & Belmont (Oct 84 - Oct 91) B to J	1136
Vauxhall Astra (Oct 91 - Feb 98) J to R	1832
Vauxhall/Opel Astra & Zafira Diesel (Feb 98 - Sept 00) R to W	3797
Vauxhall/Opel Astra & Zafira Petrol (Feb 98 - Sept 00) R to W	3758
Vauxhall/Opel Calibra (90 - 98) G to S	3502
Vauxhall Carlton (Oct 78 - Oct 86) up to D	0480
Vauxhall Carlton & Senator (Nov 86 - 94) D to L	1469
Vauxhall Cavalier 1300 (77 - July 81) *	0461
Vauxhall Cavalier 1600, 1900 & 2000 (75 - July 81) up to W	0315
Vauxhall Cavalier (81 - Oct 88) up to F	0812
Vauxhall Cavalier (Oct 88 - 95) F to N	1570
Vauxhall Chevette (75 - 84) up to B	0285
Vauxhall Corsa (Mar 93 - 97) K to R	1985
Vauxhall/Opel Corsa (Apr 97 - Oct 00) P to X	3921
Vauxhall/Opel Frontera Petrol & Diesel (91 - Sept 98) J to S	3454
Vauxhall Nova (83 - 93) up to K	0909
Vauxhall/Opel Omega (94 - 99) L to T	3510
Vauxhall Vectra Petrol & Diesel (95 - 98) N to R	3396
Vauxhall/Opel 1.5, 1.6 & 1.7 litre Diesel Engine (82 - 96) up to N	1222

VOLKSWAGEN

Title	Book No.
Volkswagen 411 & 412 (68 - 75) *	0091
Volkswagen Beetle 1200 (54 - 77) up to S	0036
Volkswagen Beetle 1300 & 1500 (65 - 75) up to P	0039
Volkswagen Beetle 1302 & 1302S (70 - 72) up to L	0110
Volkswagen Beetle 1303, 1303S & GT (72 - 75) up to P	0159
Volkswagen Beetle Petrol & Diesel (Apr 99 - 01) T reg onwards	3798
Volkswagen Golf & Bora Petrol & Diesel (April 98 - 00) R to X	3727

Title	Book No.
Volkswagen Golf & Jetta Mk 1 1.1 & 1.3 (74 - 84) up to A	0716
Volkswagen Golf, Jetta & Scirocco Mk 1 1.5, 1.6 & 1.8 (74 - 84) up to A	0726
Volkswagen Golf & Jetta Mk 1 Diesel (78 - 84) up to A	0451
Volkswagen Golf & Jetta Mk 2 (Mar 84 - Feb 92) A to J	1081
Volkswagen Golf & Vento Petrol & Diesel (Feb 92 - 96) J to N	3097
Volkswagen LT vans & light trucks (76 - 87) up to E	0637
Volkswagen Passat & Santana (Sept 81 - May 88) up to E	0814
Volkswagen Passat Petrol & Diesel (May 88 - 96) E to P	3498
Volkswagen Passat 4-cyl Petrol & Diesel (Dec 96 - Nov 00) P to X	3917
Volkswagen Polo & Derby (76 - Jan 82) up to X	0335
Volkswagen Polo (82 - Oct 90) up to H	0813
Volkswagen Polo (Nov 90 - Aug 94) H to L	3245
Volkswagen Polo Hatchback Petrol & Diesel (94 - 99) M to S	3500
Volkswagen Scirocco (82 - 90) up to H	1224
Volkswagen Transporter 1600 (68 - 79) up to V	0082
Volkswagen Transporter 1700, 1800 & 2000 (72 - 79) up to V	0226
Volkswagen Transporter (air-cooled) (79 - 82) up to Y	0638
Volkswagen Transporter (water-cooled) (82 - 90) up to H	3452
Volkswagen Type 3 (63 - 73) *	0084

VOLVO

Title	Book No.
Volvo 120 & 130 Series (& P1800) (61 - 73) *	0203
Volvo 142, 144 & 145 (66 - 74) up to N	0129
Volvo 240 Series (74 - 93) up to K	0270
Volvo 262, 264 & 260/265 (75 - 85) *	0400
Volvo 340, 343, 345 & 360 (76 - 91) up to J	0715
Volvo 440, 460 & 480 (87 - 97) D to P	1691
Volvo 740 & 760 (82 - 91) up to J	1258
Volvo 850 (92 - 96) J to P	3260
Volvo 940 (90 - 96) H to N	3249
Volvo S40 & V40 (96 - 99) N to V	3569
Volvo S70, V70 & C70 (96 - 99) P to V	3573

AUTOMOTIVE TECHBOOKS

Title	Book No.
Automotive Air Conditioning Systems	3740
Automotive Brake Manual	3050
Automotive Carburettor Manual	3288
Automotive Diagnostic Fault Codes Manual	3472
Automotive Diesel Engine Service Guide	3286
Automotive Electrical and Electronic Systems Manual	3049
Automotive Engine Management and Fuel Injection Systems Manual	3344
Automotive Gearbox Overhaul Manual	3473
Automotive Service Summaries Manual	3475
Automotive Timing Belts Manual – Austin/Rover	3549
Automotive Timing Belts Manual – Ford	3474
Automotive Timing Belts Manual – Peugeot/Citroën	3568
Automotive Timing Belts Manual – Vauxhall/Opel	3577
Automotive Welding Manual	3053
In-Car Entertainment Manual (3rd Edition)	3363

* Classic reprint

CL13.4/02

Preserving Our Motoring Heritage

< The Model J Duesenberg Derham Tourster. Only eight of these magnificent cars were ever built – this is the only example to be found outside the United States of America

Almost every car you've ever loved, loathed or desired is gathered under one roof at the Haynes Motor Museum. Over 300 immaculately presented cars and motorbikes represent every aspect of our motoring heritage, from elegant reminders of bygone days, such as the superb Model J Duesenberg to curiosities like the bug-eyed BMW Isetta. There are also many old friends and flames. Perhaps you remember the 1959 Ford Popular that you did your courting in? The magnificent 'Red Collection' is a spectacle of classic sports cars including AC, Alfa Romeo, Austin Healey, Ferrari, Lamborghini, Maserati, MG, Riley, Porsche and Triumph.

A Perfect Day Out

Each and every vehicle at the Haynes Motor Museum has played its part in the history and culture of Motoring. Today, they make a wonderful spectacle and a great day out for all the family. Bring the kids, bring Mum and Dad, but above all bring your camera to capture those golden memories for ever. You will also find an impressive array of motoring memorabilia, a comfortable 70 seat video cinema and one of the most extensive transport book shops in Britain. The Pit Stop Cafe serves everything from a cup of tea to wholesome, home-made meals or, if you prefer, you can enjoy the large picnic area nestled in the beautiful rural surroundings of Somerset.

> John Haynes O.B.E., Founder and Chairman of the museum at the wheel of a Haynes Light 12.

< Graham Hill's Lola Cosworth Formula 1 car next to a 1934 Riley Sports.

The Museum is situated on the A359 Yeovil to Frome road at Sparkford, just off the A303 in Somerset. It is about 40 miles south of Bristol, and 25 minutes drive from the M5 intersection at Taunton.
Open 9.30am - 5.30pm (10.00am - 4.00pm Winter) 7 days a week, *except Christmas Day, Boxing Day and New Years Day*
Special rates available for schools, coach parties and outings Charitable Trust No. 292048